RICHARD J. E. KEREKES
McGILL UNIVERSITY
DEPT. CHEM. ENG.

CHEMICAL REACTION ENGINEERING

CHEMICAL REACTION ENGINEERING

AN INTRODUCTION TO THE DESIGN OF CHEMICAL REACTORS

OCTAVE LEVENSPIEL
DEPARTMENT OF CHEMICAL ENGINEERING
ILLINOIS INSTITUTE OF TECHNOLOGY

JOHN WILEY AND SONS, INC.
New York · London · Sydney

FOURTH PRINTING, JULY, 1966

Library of Congress Catalog Card Number: 62-15185

Printed in the United States of America

PREFACE

Chemical reaction engineering is the branch of engineering that is concerned with the exploitation of chemical reactions on a commercial scale for purposes other than the production of power. Here the goal is the successful design of chemical reactors, and this is achieved by knowing what a reactor can produce and by knowing how this product can be controlled to suit requirements. Chemical reaction engineering, probably more than any other single activity, sets chemical engineering apart as a distinct branch of the engineering profession.

The primary problem facing the engineer in chemical reaction engineering is to decide which of the many possible design alternatives is the most favorable. This is brought out in this text by treating the major reactor types side by side, giving particular attention to their performance capabilities. This procedure should help develop a strong intuitive sense for good design which can then guide and reinforce the formal methods presented for optimization.

This is a teaching book; thus simple ideas are introduced first and are then extended to the more complex. However, emphasis is placed on developing a strategy of design common to all systems, both homogeneous and heterogeneous, rather than presenting distinct approaches and complex applications.

This is an introductory book. The pace is leisurely, and occasionally time is taken to discuss why certain assumptions are made, why an alternative approach is not taken, and to indicate the limitations of the treatment when applied to real situations. These discussions lead to a grasp of the physical situation—an awareness of the controlling factors involved—which should always accompany the manipulation of formulas. Only when we recognize the limitations of our methods do we have enough understanding to extend these methods judiciously to new, more complicated, and untried situations.

Problems in this book are intended to contribute materially to the learning process. Some are simple, some complement the text material, and others challenge the brave soul to venture beyond. Light relief is provided by a sprinkling of unconventional problems which serve to show that the methods employed are flexible and can be used in quite unrelated situations.

This book treats some of the latest and most promising lines of thought previously available only in the technical journals. Though some of these concepts are rather sophisticated, the level of treatment should be suitable for presentation at the undergraduate level.

In recent years a single course in chemical reaction engineering has appeared in more and more undergraduate curricula. At Illinois Institute of Technology Chapters 1–8, 11, and 14 are covered in a one-semester course at the senior level; the rest of the topics are considered in a follow-up course at the graduate level.

When it is widely recognized that the principles of chemical reaction engineering can be presented in understandable fashion at the undergraduate level, this subject will take its proper place in the chemical engineering curriculum, probably as an undergraduate one-year course following physical chemistry and complementing unit operations under whatever name the latter may be taught.

I should like to express appreciation to R. J. Adler, G. A. Lessells, S. Szepe, C. Y. Wen, and R. Zeleny for their helpful comments on individual chapters; to R. F. Bukacek, L. T. Fan, and E. Wollaston for using the preliminary notes of this book in class and for detailing to me the results of their experiences; to K. M. Watson for introducing me to, and for championing, the term *space time*, which I use throughout the book; to D. Kunii for reorienting my ideas on the subject of Chapter 12 and for subsequently reviewing this chapter; and to K. B. Bischoff, G. F. Froment, and R. L. Steinberger for their critical (and often disturbing) appraisals and for their encouraging interest throughout this writing project.

Finally I should like to acknowledge a very special debt to my wife Mary Jo who so graciously undertook what must have been the seemingly endless chores associated with the preparation of this book.

OCTAVE LEVENSPIEL

July 1962
Chicago, Illinois

CONTENTS

NOTATION

Symbols and constants which are defined and used locally are not included here. British units are given to illustrate the dimensions of the various symbols.

a interfacial contact area per unit volume of tower in fluid-fluid systems, ft^{-1}; Ch. 13 only

$a, b, \ldots, r, s, \ldots$
stoichiometric coefficients for reacting substances A, B, . . . , R, S, . . .

A, B, . . .
reactants

C_A concentration of reactant A, $moles/ft^3$

C_{Ac} concentration of A at the unreacted core, $moles/ft^3$

C_{Ae} equilibrium concentration of A, $moles/ft^3$

C_{Ag} concentration of A in the gas stream, $moles/ft^3$

C_{As} concentration of A at the surface of the catalyst or reacting particle, $moles/ft^3$

C_{pA} molar specific heat, Btu/(mole A)(°F)

C curve
dimensionless tracer response to an idealized pulse input; see Eq. 9.2

$\mathbf{C_p}$ specific heat of fluid stream per mole of key reactant, usually A, Btu/(mole key)(°F)

$\mathbf{C_p}'$ mean specific heat of unreacted feed stream per mole of key reactant, Btu/(mole of key)(°F)

$\mathbf{C_p}''$ mean specific heat of product stream if key reactant is completely converted, Btu/(mole key)(°F)

∇C_p difference in specific heats, defined in Eq. 8.5, Btu/°F for the reaction as written

D dispersion or axial dispersion coefficient, ft^2/hr; see Eq. 9.22

$\mathscr{D}$ diffusion coefficient, ft^2/hr; see p. 262

$ei(\alpha)$ equals $-Ei(-\alpha)$, exponential integral, defined in Eq. 10.9
E activation energy; see Eq. 2.32; for units see footnote, p. 23
$-Ei(-\alpha)$
equals $ei(\alpha)$, exponential integral, defined in Eq. 10.9
$\mathbf{E}$ exit age distribution function, dimensionless; see p. 245
$\mathbf{E}(t)$ equals $\mathbf{E}/\bar{t}$, exit age distribution function, hr^{-1}; see Eq. 9.8
$\mathscr{E}$ effectiveness factor, defined in Eqs. 13.13 and 14.11, dimensionless

f fugacity, atm; Ch. 8 only
f volume fraction of phase in which reaction is occurring; Ch. 13 only
f_g volume fraction of gas in gas-liquid system; Ch. 13 only
f_l volume fraction of liquid in gas-liquid system; Ch. 13 only
F volumetric feed rate of solids, or mass feed rate for negligible density change of solid, ft^3/hr or lb/hr; Ch. 12 only
F_A molar flow rate of substance A, moles/hr
$F(R_i)$ feed rate of solids of size R_i, ft^3/hr or lb/hr; Ch. 12 only
ΔF° standard free energy of the reaction, Btu for the stoichiometry as written; see Eq. 8.9 or Eq. 1.2
F curve
dimensionless tracer response to a step input, fraction of tracer in exit stream; see p. 247

G equals $G'p_U/\pi$, upward molar flow rate of inerts in the gas phase per unit cross section of tower, moles/(hr)(ft^2)
G' upward molar flow rate of all gas per unit cross section of tower, moles/(hr)(ft^2)

h height of absorption column, ft.
H phase distribution coefficient; for gas-liquid systems $H = p/C$, (atm)(ft^3)/mole, Henry's law constant
$\mathbf{H}'$ enthalpy of unreacted feed stream per mole of entering key reactant, usually A, Btu/mole key
$\mathbf{H}''$ enthalpy of product stream if key component is completely reacted, Btu/mole key
ΔH_r heat of reaction at temperature T, Btu for the stoichiometry as written; see Eq. 1.1 or 8.1
$\Delta \mathbf{H}_r$ heat of reaction per mole of entering key reactant, Btu/mole key

i any participant, reactant or product, in the reaction; Ch. 13 only
$\mathbf{I}$ internal age distribution function, dimensionless; see p. 244
$\mathbf{I}(t)$ equals $\mathbf{I}/\bar{t}$, internal age distribution function, hr^{-1}; see Eq. 9.8

j number of equal-sized backmix reactors or ideal stirred tanks in series

k reaction rate constant, $(\text{ft}^3/\text{mole})^{1-n}/\text{hr}$; see Eq. 2.6
k_g mass transfer coefficient, ft/hr; see Eq. 12.4. In Ch. 13 k_g refers specifically to the gas phase, moles/(hr)(ft^2)(atm); see Eq. 13.2
k_l mass transfer coefficient in liquid phase, ft/hr; see Eq. 13.2
k_s reaction rate constant based on unit surface, ft/hr; see Eq. 14.5
K equilibrium constant for a reaction for the stoichiometry as written, dimensionless; see Eq. 1.2 or Eq. 8.9
K_f, K_p, K_y, K_C
see Eq. 8.10

l length
L length of reactor
L equals $L'C_U/C_T$, downward molar flow rate of inerts in the liquid phase per unit cross section of tower, moles/(hr)(ft^2); Ch. 14 only
L' downward molar flow rate of all liquid per unit cross section of tower, moles/(hr)(ft^2)

m equals $\sqrt{k/\mathscr{D}}$, ft^{-1}; Chs. 13 and 14 only
M_k kth moment about the origin; see p. 251
M_k' kth moment about the mean; see p. 251

n order of reaction; see Eq. 2.5
N moles

p_A partial pressure of component A, atm
p_A^* partial pressure of A in gas which would be in equilibrium with C_A in liquid; hence $p_A^* = H_A C_A$, atm

Q heat transfer rate to reacting system, Btu/hr
Q flux of material, moles/(hr)(ft^2); Chs. 11 and 12 only
$\mathbf{Q}$ heat transfer to reacting system per mole of key feed component, Btu/mole key

r radial position within a particle
r_A equals $\dfrac{1}{V}\dfrac{dN_A}{dt}$, rate of reaction based on volume of fluid, moles A formed/(hr)(ft^3); see Eq. 1.3
r_A' equals $\dfrac{1}{V_r}\dfrac{dN_A}{dt}$, rate of reaction based on volume of reactor if this is different from volume of fluid, moles A formed/(hr)(ft^3); see Eq. 1.4

r_A'' equals $\frac{1}{S}\frac{dN_A}{dt}$, rate of reaction based on unit surface, moles A formed/(hr)(ft^2); see Eq. 1.5

r_A''' equals $\frac{1}{W}\frac{dN_A}{dt}$, rate of reaction based on unit mass of catalyst, moles A formed/(hr)(lb catalyst); see Eq. 1.6

r_c radius of unreacted core

R radius of particle

R the ideal gas law constant,
= 1.98 Btu/(lb mole)(°R)
= 1.98 cal/(gm mole)(°K)
= 0.730 (ft^3)(atm)/(lb mole)(°R)
= 0.08206 (liter) (atm)/(gm mole)(°K),

R, S, . . . products of reaction

s space velocity, hr^{-1}; see Eq. 5.5

S surface, ft^2

S_{in} interior surface of porous particle, ft^2

S_{ex} exterior surface of particle, ft^2

t time

$\bar{t}$ equals V/v, reactor holding time or mean residence time of fluid in a flow reactor, hr

$\bar{t}(R_i)$ mean residence time in reactor of particles of size R_i, hr

T temperature

U inert or carrier material in a phase

v volumetric flow rate, ft^3/hr

V volume, ft^3

V_r equals V/ϵ, reactor volume, if different from volume occupied by reacting fluid

W mass, lb

$W(R_i)$ mass of solids of size R_i in the reactor, lb

X_A fraction of reactant A converted into product; see Eqs. 3.9, 3.10, and 3.64

$\mathbf{X}_A$ equals C_A/C_U, moles A/mole inert in liquid

$\mathbf{Y}_A$ equals p_A/p_U, moles A/mole inert in gas

Z equals l/L, fractional length through a reactor

$\mathbf{Y}_A$ equals p_A/π, see p. 208, p. 412

GREEK SYMBOLS

$\delta(t)$ Dirac delta function, an idealized pulse occurring at time t, defined as follows:

$$\left.\begin{aligned}\delta(t) &= \infty \text{ at } t = 0\\ &= 0 \text{ elsewhere}\end{aligned}\right\} \text{such that} \int_{-\infty}^{\infty} \delta(t)\, dt = 1$$

With this definition: $\int_{-\infty}^{\infty} f(t)\,\delta(t)\,dt = f(0)$

ϵ porosity or fraction voids in a packed bed or fluidized bed

ε_A fractional change in volume on reaction; see Eqs. 3.62 to 3.65

θ equals $t/\bar{t}$, reduced time, dimensionless; see Eq. 9.1

κ elutriation velocity constant, defined in Eq. 12.57, hr^{-1}

μ mean of a distribution function, defined in Eq. 9.9

π total pressure, atm.

ρ molar density, $moles/ft^3$

σ^2 equals $\sigma_t^2/\bar{t}^2$, variance of a tracer curve or distribution function in θ units, dimensionless; see Eqs. 9.11, 9.12, and 9.15

σ_t^2 variance in time units, hr^2

τ space time, hr; see Eq. 5.5

$\boldsymbol{\tau}$ time for complete reaction of a single solid particle, hr

$\boldsymbol{\tau}(R_i)$ time for complete conversion of particles of size R_i, hr

φ instantaneous fractional yield; see Eq. 7.7

$\varphi(M/N)$

instantaneous fractional yield of M with respect to N, moles M formed per mole N formed or reacted away; see p. 165

Φ over-all fractional yield; see Eq. 7.9

$\Phi(M/N)$

over-all fractional yield of M with respect to N, moles M formed per mole N formed or reacted away; see Eq. 7.9

SUBSCRIPTS

f leaving or final condition

i entering

T total moles in liquid phase; Ch. 13 only

U carrier or inert component in a phase; Ch. 13 only

0 entering or reference

1

INTRODUCTION

Every industrial chemical process is designed to produce economically a desired product from a variety of starting materials through a succession of treatment steps. Figure 1 shows a typical situation. The raw materials undergo a number of physical treatment steps to put them in the form in which they can be reacted chemically. They then pass through the reactor. The products of the reaction must then undergo further physical treatment —separations, purifications, etc.—for the final desired product to be obtained.

Design of equipment for the physical treatment steps is studied in the unit operations. In this book we are concerned with the chemical treatment step of a process. Economically this may be an inconsequential unit, say a simple mixing tank. More often than not, however, the chemical treatment step is the heart of the process, the thing that makes or breaks the process economically.

Design of the reactor is no routine matter, and a great variety of designs can be proposed for a process. In searching for optimum design it is not just the cost of reactor that must be minimized. One design may have low reactor cost, but the materials leaving the unit may be such that their treatment requires much higher cost than alternative designs. Hence, in proper design the economics of the over-all process must be considered.

Now in the design of the reactor unit we must use information, knowledge, and experience from a variety of areas—thermodynamics,

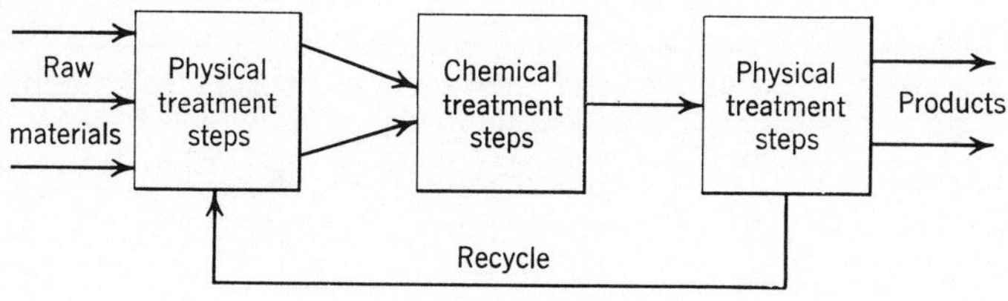

Fig. 1. Typical chemical process.

chemical kinetics, fluid mechanics, heat transfer, mass transfer, and economics. Chemical reaction engineering is the syntheses of all these factors with the aim of properly designing a chemical reactor.

The design of chemical reactors is probably the one area of interest in engineering that is unique to chemical engineering, and it is probably this function more than anything else which justifies the existence of chemical engineering as a distinct branch of engineering.

In chemical reactor design there are two questions which must be answered:

1. What changes can we expect to occur?
2. How fast will they take place?

The first question concerns thermodynamics, the second the various rate processes—chemical kinetics, heat transfer, etc. Tying these all together and trying to determine how these processes are interrelated can be an extremely difficult problem; hence in any study we should start with the simplest of situations and build up our analysis by considering additional factors until we are able to handle the more difficult problems. This is what we shall attempt to do.

Let us first of all briefly take an over-all view of the subject, some of it being review, some new. Discussion on thermodynamics and chemical kinetics will set the stage for an outline of the way we cover the subject.

Thermodynamics

Thermodynamics gives two important pieces of information needed in design, the heat liberated or absorbed during reaction and the maximum possible extent of reaction.

Chemical reactions are invariably accompanied by the liberation or absorption of heat, the magnitude of which must be known for proper design. Consider the reaction

$$aA \rightarrow rR + sS, \qquad \Delta H_r \begin{cases} \text{positive, endothermic} \\ \text{negative, exothermic} \end{cases} \tag{1}$$

The heat of reaction at temperature T is the heat transferred *from* surroundings *to* the reacting system when a moles of A disappear to form r moles of R and s moles of S, with the system measured at the same temperature and pressure before and after reaction. With heats of reaction known or estimable from thermochemical data, the magnitude of the heat effects during reaction can be calculated.

Thermodynamics also allows calculation of the equilibrium constant K from the standard free energies $F°$, of the reacting materials. Thus for the reaction just given

$$\Delta F° = rF°_R + sF°_S - aF°_A = -RT \ln K \tag{2}$$

With the equilibrium constant known, the expected maximum attainable yield of the products of reaction can be estimated.

Chemical kinetics

Under appropriate conditions materials may be transformed into new and different materials which constitute different chemical species. If this occurs only by rearrangment or redistribution of the constituent atoms to form new molecules, we say that a chemical reaction has occurred. Chemistry is concerned with the study of such reactions. It studies the mode and mechanism of such reactions, the relative ease of their occurrence, the physical and energy changes involved and products obtained from the given materials, and, finally, the rate of attainment of these end products.

It is the last-mentioned area of interest, chemical kinetics, which is of primary concern to us. Chemical kinetics is simply the study of the factors that influence the rate of reaction and the explanations for the rate of reaction. Its study is important for a number of reasons:

1. For physical chemists it is the tool for gaining insight into the nature of reacting systems, for understanding how chemical bonds are made and broken, and for estimating their energies and stability.

2. For the organic chemist the value of chemical kinetics is greater still because the mode of reaction of compounds provides clues to their structure. Thus relative strengths of chemical bonds and molecular structure of compounds can be investigated by this tool.

3. In addition, it is the basis for important theories in combustion and dissolution and provides a method to study heat and mass transfer and suggests methods for tackling rate phenomena in other fields of study.

4. For the chemical engineer the kinetics of a reaction must be known if he is to make a satisfactory design for equipment in which these reactions are to be effected on a technical scale. Of course, if the reaction is rapid enough so that the system is essentially at equilibrium, design is very much simplified. Kinetic information is not needed, and thermodynamic information alone is sufficient for design.

Now our approach to chemical kinetics, the way we express kinetic laws, depends in large part on the type of reaction we are dealing with, and it may be well to consider next the classification of chemical reactions.

Classification of reactions

There are many ways of classifying chemical reactions. In chemical reaction engineering probably the most useful scheme is the breakdown according to the number and types of phases involved, the big division being between the *homogeneous* and *heterogeneous* systems. A reaction is homogeneous if it takes place in one phase alone. A reaction is heterogeneous if it requires the presence of at least two phases to proceed at the rate that it does. It is immaterial whether the reaction takes place in one, two, or more phases, or at an interface, or whether the reactants and products are distributed among the phases or are all contained within a single phase. All that counts is that at least two phases are necessary for the reaction to proceed as it does.

Table I. Classification of chemical reactions useful in reactor design

	Noncatalytic	Catalytic
Homogeneous	Most gas-phase reactions	Most liquid-phase reactions
	Fast reactions such as burning of a flame	Reactions in colloidal systems
Heterogeneous	Burning of coal Roasting of ores Attack of solids by acids Gas-liquid absorption with reaction	Ammonia synthesis Oxidation of ammonia to produce nitric acid Catalytic cracking of petroleum hydrocarbons Methanol synthesis

Sometimes this classification is not clear-cut as with the large class of biological reactions, the enzyme-substrate reactions. Here the enzyme acts as a catalyst in the manufacture of proteins. Now enzymes themselves are highly complicated large-molecular-weight proteins of colloidal size, 10 to 100 mμ. Hence enzyme-containing solutions are midway between homogeneous and heterogeneous systems. Though such systems are sometimes called microheterogeneous systems, we do not consider them as a separate class, for as far as their kinetics is concerned, they are treated either as homogeneous or heterogeneous systems depending on the circumstances. Other examples for which the distinction between homogeneous and heterogeneous systems is not sharp are the very rapid chemical reactions, such as the burning of a gas flame. Here large nonhomogeneity in composition and temperature may exist. Strictly speaking, then, we do not have a single phase, for a phase implies uniform temperature, pressure, and composition throughout. Thus we conclude that only in the context of a given situation can we decide how the reaction is the most usefully classified.

Cutting across this classification is the catalytic reaction whose rate is altered by the presence in the reacting mixture of materials that are neither reactants nor products. These foreign materials, called catalysts, need not be present in large amounts. Catalysts act somehow as go-betweens, either hindering or accelerating the reaction process while being modified relatively slowly if at all.

Table 1 shows the classification of chemical reactions according to our scheme with a few examples of typical reactions of each type.

Variables affecting the rate of reaction

Many variables may affect the rate of a chemical reaction. In homogeneous systems the temperature, pressure, and composition are obvious variables. In heterogeneous systems, because more than one phase is involved, the problem becomes more complex. Material may have to move from phase to phase during reaction; hence the rate of mass transfer can become important. For example, in the burning of a coal briquette the diffusion of oxygen through the gas film surrounding the particle, and through the ash layer at the surface of the particle, can play an important role in limiting the rate of reaction. In addition, the rate of heat transfer may also become important. Consider, for example, an exothermic reaction taking place at the interior surface of a porous catalyst pellet. Here reactants must diffuse into and products out of the pellet. In addition, however, heat is released at the various locations within the catalyst pellet. If the reaction is rapid and the heat is not removed rapidly enough, severe nonuniform temperature distribution can occur within the pellet itself, which in turn will result in differing point rates of reaction. These heat and mass transfer effects become increasingly important the faster the rate of reaction, and in very fast reactions, such as burning flames, they become controlling. Thus heat and mass transfer may play important roles in determining the rates of heterogeneous reactions.

In all cases considered, if the reaction involves a number of steps in series, it is the slowest step of the series that exerts the greatest influence and can be said to control. A big problem is to find out which variables affect each of these steps and to what degree. Only when we can determine the magnitude of each factor do we have a clear picture of the effect of these variables on the rate of reaction. Furthermore, only when we have this information do we have confidence in the ability of extrapolations of small-scale laboratory kinetic data to predict the performance of large-scale industrial equipment.

Definition of reaction rate

We next ask how we should define the rate of reaction so that it is as meaningful and useful and as broad in application as possible. To answer this, let us adopt a number of definitions of rate of reaction, all interrelated and all intensive rather than extensive measures. But first we must select one component for consideration and define the rate in terms of this component. Thus let us consider the rate of change of component i involved in the chemical reaction. If the rate of change in the number of moles of this component is dN_i/dt, the rate in the various areas of kinetics is defined as follows. Based on unit volume of reacting fluid,

$$r_i = \frac{1}{V}\frac{dN_i}{dt} = \frac{\text{moles } i \text{ formed}}{\text{(unit volume of fluid)(time)}} \tag{3}$$

Based on unit volume of reactor, if different from the rate based on unit volume of fluid,

$$r_i' = \frac{1}{V_r}\frac{dN_i}{dt} = \frac{\text{moles } i \text{ formed}}{\text{(unit volume of reactor)(time)}} \tag{4}$$

Based on unit interfacial surface in two-fluid systems or based on unit surface of solid in gas-solid systems,

$$r_i'' = \frac{1}{S}\frac{dN_i}{dt} = \frac{\text{moles } i \text{ formed}}{\text{(unit surface)(time)}} \tag{5}$$

Based on unit mass of solid in fluid-solid systems,

$$r_i''' = \frac{1}{W}\frac{dN_i}{dt} = \frac{\text{moles } i \text{ formed}}{\text{(unit mass of solid)(time)}} \tag{6}$$

In homogeneous systems the volume of fluid in the reactor is nearly always identical to the volume of reactor. In this frequently encountered system no distinction is made between V and V_r, and Eqs. 3 and 4 are used interchangeably. Packed- and fluidized-bed reactors for homogeneous reactions are the only exception to this rule. In heterogeneous systems all these definitions of reaction rate are encountered. The choice of the form of the rate equation used in any given situation is governed by the ease of its use, and occasionally we may even find it more convenient to define the reaction rate in a way altogether different from those presented here.

The rate of reaction is a function of the variables of the system

$$r_i = f\text{(system variables)}$$

The form of this functional relationship remains the same, no matter how we choose to define the rate of reaction. It is only the constants of proportionality and their dimensions that change when we switch from one defining rate equation to another.

The following example illustrates the interrelation of the various forms of rate equations.

Example 1

Chemical A is being converted into chemical R in a vessel packed with non-porous, spherical catalyst beads. The specific surface area of the catalyst is 60 ft^2/ft^3 of packed bed, its bulk density is 180 lb/ft^3 of packed bed, and the porosity of the bed $\epsilon = 0.40$. The stoichiometric equation is

$$A \rightarrow 2R$$

and the rate of disappearance of A based on unit mass of catalyst is proportional to the concentration of A present in the gas. Thus in English units, using hours, we find from experiment

$$-r_A''' = -\frac{1}{W}\frac{dN_A}{dt} = 0.1\, C_A$$

The negative sign shows that the rate of change of A is negative, or that A disappears.

(*a*) Write out rate equation given, showing the units of the various terms.
(*b*) Find r_A', the rate based on unit volume of reactor, Eq. 4.
(*c*) Find r_A, the rate based on unit volume of fluid, Eq. 3.
(*d*) Find r_A'', the rate based on the unit surface of catalyst, Eq. 5.

Solution. (*a*) Noting that C_A = moles A/ ft^3 voids, we obtain, with Eq. 6,

$$-r_A''' = -\frac{1}{W}\frac{dN_A}{dt} = \frac{\text{moles A}}{(\text{lb solid})(\text{hr})} = \left(0.1\frac{\text{ft}^3\text{ voids}}{(\text{lb solid})(\text{hr})}\right)\left(C_A\frac{\text{moles A}}{\text{ft}^3\text{ voids}}\right)$$

(*b*) Catalyst mass per reactor volume W/V_r = 180 lb solid/ft^3 reactor. Therefore, based on unit volume of reactor,

$$-r_A' = -\frac{1}{V_r}\frac{dN_A}{dt} = \frac{\text{moles A}}{(\text{ft}^3\text{ reactor})(\text{hr})} = -\frac{W}{V_r}\cdot\frac{1}{W}\frac{dN_A}{dt} = -\frac{W}{V_r}r_A'''$$

$$= \left(180\frac{\text{lb solid}}{\text{ft}^3\text{ reactor}}\right)\left(0.1\frac{\text{ft}^3\text{ voids}}{(\text{lb solid})(\text{hr})}\right)\left(C_A\frac{\text{moles A}}{\text{ft}^3\text{ voids}}\right)$$

$$= \left(18\frac{\text{ft}^3\text{ voids}}{(\text{ft}^3\text{ reactor})(\text{hr})}\right)\left(C_A\frac{\text{moles A}}{\text{ft}^3\text{ voids}}\right)$$

(*c*) The porosity V/V_r = 0.4 ft^3 voids/ft^3 reactor. Therefore based on unit volume of fluid

$$-r_A = -\frac{1}{V}\frac{dN_A}{dt} = \frac{\text{moles A}}{(\text{ft}^3\text{ voids})(\text{hr})} = -\frac{V_r}{V}\frac{1}{V_r}\frac{dN_A}{dt} = -\frac{V_r}{V}r_A'$$

$$= \left(\frac{1}{0.4}\frac{\text{ft}^3\text{ reactor}}{\text{ft}^3\text{ voids}}\right)\left(18\frac{\text{ft}^3\text{ voids}}{(\text{ft}^3\text{ reactor})(\text{hr})}\right)\left(C_A\frac{\text{moles A}}{\text{ft}^3\text{ voids}}\right)$$

$$= \left(\frac{45}{\text{hr}}\right)\left(C_A\frac{\text{moles A}}{\text{ft}^3\text{ voids}}\right)$$

(*d*) Catalyst surface per reactor volume S/V_r = 60 ft^2 surface/ft^3 reactor.

Therefore based on unit surface of reactor

$$-r_A'' = -\frac{1}{S}\frac{dN_A}{dt} = \frac{\text{moles A}}{(\text{ft}^3\text{ surface})(\text{hr})} = -\frac{V_r}{S}\frac{1}{V_r}\frac{dN_A}{dt} = -\frac{V_r}{S}r_A'$$

$$= \left(\frac{1}{60}\frac{\text{ft}^3\text{ reactor}}{\text{ft}^2\text{ surface}}\right)\left(18\frac{\text{ft}^3\text{ voids}}{(\text{ft}^3\text{ reactor})(\text{hr})}\right)\left(C_A\frac{\text{moles A}}{\text{ft}^3\text{ voids}}\right)$$

$$= \left(0.3\frac{\text{ft}^3\text{ voids}}{(\text{ft}^2\text{ surface})(\text{hr})}\right)\left(C_A\frac{\text{moles A}}{\text{ft}^3\text{ voids}}\right)$$

Note: In parts *b* and *c* the constants 18 and 45 have the same dimensions and are different only because the volumes on which the rates are defined vary. This shows that to avoid confusion we should specify which of the volumes V or V_r is being considered. Distinctions such as these are necessary in the study of heterogeneous systems.

Over-all plan

Our over-all plan is to start with homogeneous systems (Chapters 2 to 10) to see how rate expressions are suggested from theory (Chapter 2), how they are determined experimentally (Chapter 3), and how they are applied to design of batch and flow chemical reactors involving ideal flow (Chapters 4 to 8) and the nonideal flow of real reactors (Chapters 9 and 10). The additional complications of design for heterogeneous systems are then introduced (Chapter 11), and the specific problems of noncatalytic fluid solid systems, two fluid systems, and solid catalyzed fluid systems are then considered in turn (Chapters 12 to 14).

RELATED READINGS

T. E. Corrigan, *Chem. Eng.*, **61,** 230 (July 1954).

2

KINETICS OF HOMOGENEOUS REACTIONS

In homogeneous reactions all reacting materials are found within a single phase, be it gas, liquid, or solid. In addition, if the reaction is catalytic, the catalyst must also be present within the same phase as the reactants and products. Though there are a number of ways of defining the rate of reaction, only one such measure is used in homogeneous systems. This is the intensive measure of rate based on unit volume of reacting fluid or system. Thus the rate of reaction of any reaction component A is defined as

$$r_A = \frac{1}{V}\frac{dN_A}{dt} = \frac{1}{V}\frac{d(C_A V)}{dt} = \frac{\begin{pmatrix}\text{moles of A which}\\ \text{appear by reaction}\end{pmatrix}}{(\text{unit volume})(\text{unit time})} \tag{1}$$

By this definition, if A appears as product, the rate is positive; if it is a reactant which is being consumed, the rate is negative.

Now we may expect that the variables which affect the progress of this class of reactions are the composition of the materials within the phase as well as the temperature and pressure of the system. Shape of container, surface properties of solid materials in contact with the phase in question, and the diffusional characteristic of the fluid should not affect the rate of homogeneous reaction. Thus we may write for the rate of reaction of component A

$$r_A = f(\text{temperature, pressure, composition})$$

These variables, pressure, temperature, and composition, are interdependent in that the pressure is fixed, given the temperature and composition of the phase.* Thus we may write without loss of generality

$$r_A = f\,(\text{temperature, composition})$$

In this chapter we are concerned with the various forms of this functional relationship and consider in turn the explanations on the basis of chemical theory for the composition dependency and temperature dependency of the rate expression, and finally we consider the question of predictability of rates of reaction.

CONCENTRATION-DEPENDENT TERM OF A RATE EQUATION

Before we can find the form of the concentration term in a rate expression, we must distinguish between a number of types of reactions. This distinction is based on the form and number of kinetic equations used to describe the progress of a chemical reaction. Since we are concerned with the concentration-dependent term of rate equations, we assume in the discussion to follow that the temperature of the system is kept constant.

Single and multiple reactions

First of all, when materials react to form products it is usually easy to decide after examining the stoichiometry, preferably at more than one temperature, whether we should consider a single reaction or a number of reactions to be occurring.

When a single stoichiometric equation and single rate equation are chosen to represent the progress of the reaction, we have a *single reaction*. When more than one stoichiometric equation is used to represent the observed changes, more than one kinetic expression is needed to follow the changes in composition of all components of the reaction and we have *multiple reactions*.

Multiple reactions may be classified as consecutive or series reactions,

$$A \longrightarrow R \longrightarrow S$$

parallel, competing, or side reactions,

$$\begin{matrix} A \longrightarrow R \\ A \longrightarrow S \end{matrix}, \qquad \begin{matrix} A \longrightarrow R \\ B \longrightarrow S \end{matrix}$$

* Strictly speaking, this interdependency only applies at equilibrium; however, for lack of any better supposition, we assume it also to be true for systems not at equilibrium which are not changing too rapidly.

and mixed reactions

$$A + B \longrightarrow R$$
$$R + B \longrightarrow S$$

The mixed reactions illustrated are parallel with respect to B and consecutive with respect to A, R, and S.

Elementary and nonelementary reactions

Consider a single reaction with stoichiometric equation

$$A + B \longrightarrow R$$

If we postulate that the mechanism which controls the rate of reaction involves the collision or interaction of a single molecule of A with a single molecule of B to give a product molecule, the number of collisions of molecules A and B is proportional to the rate of reaction. But the number of collisions at given temperature is proportional to the concentration of reactants in the mixture; hence the rate of disappearance of A is given by

$$-r_A = kC_AC_B$$

Such reactions, which are viewed to occur in a single step, are called *elementary reactions*, and in any such reaction the rate equation is suggested by a stoichiometric equation which represents the actual mode of action.

When there is no direct correspondence between stoichiometric equation and the rate expression, we have a *nonelementary reaction*. The classical example of a nonelementary reaction is that between hydrogen and bromine,

$$H_2 + Br_2 \rightarrow 2HBr$$

which has a rate expression*

$$r_{HBr} = \frac{k_1[H_2][Br_2]^{1/2}}{k_2 + [HBr]/[Br_2]}$$

Nonelementary reactions are explained by assuming that what we observe as a single reaction is in reality the over-all effect of a sequence of elementary reactions. The reason for observing only a single reaction rather than two or more elementary reactions is that the amount of intermediates formed is negligibly small and unmeasurable. Consideration of such explanations of nonelementary reactions follows later.

* To eliminate much writing, at various places in this chapter we use square brackets to indicate concentrations. Thus,

$$C_{HBr} = [HBr]$$

Kinetic view of equilibrium for elementary reactions

Consider the elementary reversible reactions

$$\mathrm{A} + \mathrm{B} \rightleftharpoons \mathrm{R} + \mathrm{S}, \qquad K_C,\ K$$

The rate of formation of R by the forward reaction is

$$\text{Rate of formation} = r_{\mathrm{R,\,forward}} = k_1 C_\mathrm{A} C_\mathrm{B}$$

and the rate of disappearance by the reverse reaction is

$$\text{Rate of disappearance} = -r_{\mathrm{R,\,backward}} = k_2 C_\mathrm{R} C_\mathrm{S}$$

At equilibrium with no net formation of R

$$r_{\mathrm{R,\,forward}} + r_{\mathrm{R,\,reverse}} = 0$$

or

$$\frac{k_1}{k_2} = \frac{C_\mathrm{R} C_\mathrm{S}}{C_\mathrm{A} C_\mathrm{B}} \tag{2}$$

Since for this reaction K_C is defined as*

$$K_C = \frac{C_\mathrm{R} C_\mathrm{S}}{C_\mathrm{A} C_\mathrm{B}} \tag{3}$$

at equilibrium we have

$$K_C = \frac{k_1}{k_2} = \frac{C_\mathrm{R} C_\mathrm{S}}{C_\mathrm{A} C_\mathrm{B}}$$

Since K_C and k_1/k_2, constants that are independent of concentration, are equal to each other at one concentration, the equilibrium concentration, they must be equal to each other at all concentrations. Now at nonequilibrium conditions Eqs. 2 and 3 do not hold. Thus

$$K_C = \frac{k_1}{k_2} \left[= \frac{C_\mathrm{R} C_\mathrm{S}}{C_\mathrm{A} C_\mathrm{B}} \right]_{\substack{\text{only at} \\ \text{equilibrium}}} \tag{4}$$

For nonelementary reactions we cannot make a generalization of this type; however, Denbigh (1955) does treat this situation showing the restrictions imposed by thermodynamics on the possible forms of the kinetic equation.

So kinetics views equilibrium as a dynamic but steady state with a constant interchange of reactant and product molecules, rather than as a static situation.

We can now view equilibrium in one of three ways.

---

* See any chemical engineering thermodynamics textbook or the brief thermodynamics review in Chapter 8.

1. From thermodynamics we say that equilibrium is attained, if for any possible change, the free energy of the system increases. Thus for any movement away from equilibrium,

$$(\Delta F)_{p,T} \geqslant 0$$

2. From statistical mechanics equilibrium is the state of the system consisting of the greatest number of equally likely molecular configurations which are macroscopically indistinguishable and can be considered to be identical. Thus from the gross point of view the state of the system that has the overwhelmingly great probability of occurring is called the equilibrium state.

3. Kinetically, the system is at equilibrium if the rates of change of all the forward and backward elementary reactions are equal.

These three criteria depend in turn on energy, probability, and rate considerations. Actually the thermodynamic and probabilistic views are enunciations of the same theorem in different languages. The kinetic point of view, however, has further implications, for it requires knowledge of the mechanism of reaction for systems not at equilibrium. Thus in terms of understanding what is occurring, the kinetic point of view is more illuminating.

Molecularity and order

The molecularity of an elementary reaction is the number of molecules involved in the rate-determining step of a reaction. Molecularity of reactions has been found to be one, two, and occasionally three. Needless to say, the molecularity refers only to an elementary reaction and can only be in whole numbers.

Often we find that the rate of progress of a reaction, involving say materials A, B, . . . , D, can be approximated by an expression of the following type:

$$r_A = kC_A{}^aC_B{}^b \cdots C_D{}^d, \qquad a + b + \cdots + d = n \tag{5}$$

where a, b, $\cdots$ are not necessarily related to the stoichiometric coefficients. We call the powers to which the concentrations are raised the order of the reaction. Thus the reaction is

ath order with respect to A
bth order with respect to B
and nth order over-all

Since the orders refer to the empirically found rate expression, they need not be whole numbers, but the molecularity of a reaction must be in terms of whole numbers since it refers to the actual mechanism of the elementary reaction.

Rate constant k

When a rate expression for a homogeneous chemical reaction is written in the form of Eq. 5, the units of the rate constant k for the nth-order reaction are

$$(\text{time})^{-1}\,(\text{concentration})^{1-n} \tag{6a}$$

which for a first-order reaction become simply

$$(\text{time})^{-1} \tag{6b}$$

Representation of a reaction rate

In expressing a rate equation we may use any measure equivalent to concentration, such as the partial pressures of the components. Thus

$$r_A = kp_A{}^a p_B{}^b \cdots p_D{}^d$$

Whatever measure we use leaves the order unchanged; however, it will affect the units of the rate constant k.

For brevity elementary reactions are often represented by an equation showing both the molecularity and the rate constant. Thus

$$2A \xrightarrow{k_1} 2R \tag{7}$$

represents a bimolecular irreversible reaction with second-order rate constant k_1 implying that the rate of reaction is

$$-r_A = r_R = k_1 C_A{}^2$$

It would not be proper to write Eq. 7 as

$$A \xrightarrow{k_1} R$$

for it would imply that the rate expression is

$$-r_A = r_R = k_1 C_A$$

Thus we must be careful to distinguish between a stoichiometric equation that may be multiplied by any constant and the equation that represents an elementary reaction.

We should note that writing the elementary reaction with the rate constant, as just shown, may not be sufficient to avoid ambiguity. At times it may be necessary to specify the component in the reaction to which the rate constant is referred. For example, consider the reaction

$$B + 2D \xrightarrow{k_2} 3T \tag{8}$$

If the rate is measured in terms of B, the rate equation is

$$-r_B = k_2' C_B C_D{}^2$$

But if it refers to D, the rate equation is

$$-r_D = k_2''C_BC_D^2$$

Or if it refers to the product T,

$$r_T = k_2'''C_BC_D^2$$

But from the stoichiometry

$$r_B = \tfrac{1}{2}r_D = -\tfrac{1}{3}r_T$$

Hence

$$k_2' = \tfrac{1}{2}k_2'' = \tfrac{1}{3}k_2'''$$

Which of these three primed k_2 values are we referring to in Eq. 8? We cannot tell. Hence, to avoid ambiguity when the elementary reaction involves different numbers of molecules of the various components, we must specify the component being considered.

To sum up, we must be careful to avoid ambiguity in expressing the rate in condensed form. To eliminate any possible confusion, write the stoichiometric equation followed by the complete rate expression giving the units of the rate constant.

Kinetic models for nonelementary reactions

To explain the kinetics of nonelementary reactions we assume that a sequence of elementary reactions is actually occurring but that we cannot measure or observe the intermediates formed because they are present only in very minute quantities. Thus we observe only the initial reactants and final products, or what appears to be a single reaction. For example, if the kinetics of the reaction

$$A_2 + B_2 \longrightarrow 2AB$$

indicates that the reaction is nonelementary, we may postulate a series of elementary steps to explain the kinetics such as

$$A_2 \rightleftharpoons 2A^*$$
$$A^* + B_2 \rightleftharpoons AB + B^*$$
$$A^* + B^* \rightleftharpoons AB$$

To test our postulational scheme, we must see whether the kinetic expression predicted by it corresponds to the experimentally found kinetic equation. The types of intermediates we may postulate are suggested by the chemistry of the materials. These may be grouped as follows.

Free radicals. Free atoms or larger fragments of stable molecules which contain one or more unpaired electrons are called free radicals. The unpaired electron is designated by a "dot" in the chemical symbol for the substance. Some free radicals are relatively stable such as triphenylmethyl,

$$(C_6H_5)_3C\cdot$$

but as a rule they are unstable and highly reactive, such as

$$CH_3\cdot,\ C_2H_5\cdot,\ I\cdot,\ H\cdot,\ CCl_3\cdot$$

Ions and polar substances. Electrically charged atoms, molecules, or fragments of molecules such as

$$N_3^-,\ Na^+,\ OH^-,\ H_3O^+,\ NH_4^+,\ CH_3OH_2^+,\ I^-$$

are called ions. These may act as active intermediates in reactions.

Molecules. Consider the consecutive reactions

$$A \rightarrow R \rightarrow S$$

Ordinarily these are treated as multiple reactions. If the product material R is highly reactive, however, its mean lifetime will be very small and its concentration in the reacting mixture can become unmeasurably small. In such a situation R is not observed and can be considered to be a reactive intermediate.

Transition complexes. The numerous collisions between reactant molecules result in a wide distribution of energies among the individual molecules. This can result in strained bonds, unstable forms of molecules, or unstable association of molecules which can then either decompose to give products or by further collisions return to molecules in the normal state. Such unstable forms are called transition complexes.

Postulated reaction schemes involving these intermediates can be of two types.

Nonchain reactions. In the nonchain reaction the intermediate is formed in the first reaction and then disappears as it reacts further to give the product. Thus

$$\text{Reactants} \rightarrow (\text{Intermediates})^*$$
$$(\text{Intermediates})^* \rightarrow \text{Products}$$

Chain reactions. In chain reactions the intermediate is formed in a first reaction, called the chain initiation step. It then reacts with the reactant to produce the product and more intermediate in the chain propagation step. Occasionally the intermediate is consumed in the chain termination step. Thus

Reactant → (Intermediate)*	Initiation
(Intermediate)* + Reactant → (Intermediate)* + Product	Propagation
(Intermediate)* → Product	Termination

The essential feature of the chain reaction is the propagation step. In this step the intermediate is not consumed but acts simply as a catalyst for the conversion of material. Thus each molecule of intermediate can catalyze a long chain of reactions before being finally destroyed.

The following are examples of mechanisms of various kinds.

1. *Free radicals, chain reaction mechanism.* The reaction

$$H_2 + Br_2 \rightarrow 2HBr$$

with experimental rate

$$r_{HBr} = \frac{k_1[H_2][Br_2]^{1/2}}{k_2 + [HBr]/[Br_2]}$$

can be explained by the following scheme:

$Br_2 \rightleftharpoons 2Br\cdot$	Initiation and termination
$Br\cdot + H_2 \rightleftharpoons HBr + H\cdot$	Propagation
$H\cdot + Br_2 \rightarrow HBr + Br\cdot$	Propagation

2. *Molecular intermediates, nonchain mechanism.* The general class of enzyme-catalyzed biological reactions

$$A + B \rightarrow AB$$

is viewed to proceed as follows:

$$A + \text{enzyme} \rightleftharpoons (A\cdot \text{enzyme})^*$$

$$(A\cdot \text{enzyme})^* + B \rightarrow AB + \text{enzyme}$$

In such reactions the concentration of intermediate may become more than negligible, in which case a special analysis is required; see Michaelis and Menten (1913).

3. *Ionic intermediates, catalyzed nonchain mechanism.* The kinetics of the acid-catalyzed hydration of the unsaturated hydrocarbon isobutene

$$\underset{\text{isobutene}}{CH_3\text{—}\overset{\overset{\displaystyle CH_3}{|}}{C}\text{=}CH_2} + H_2O \xrightleftharpoons{\text{dilute } HNO_3} \underset{\textit{tert}\text{-butyl alcohol}}{CH_3\text{—}\overset{\overset{\displaystyle CH_3}{|}}{C}OH\text{—}CH_3}$$

is consistent with a multistep mechanism involving formation of a number of intermediates, all polar. Thus in general

$$\begin{matrix}| \;\; | \\ -C{=}C- \end{matrix} + H^+ \underset{\text{fast}}{\overset{\text{fast}}{\rightleftharpoons}} \left[\begin{matrix} | \qquad | \\ -C{=\!=}C- \\ \diagdown\,{}^{+}\,\diagup \\ H \end{matrix}\right]^* \underset{\text{fast}}{\overset{\text{slow}}{\rightleftharpoons}} \left[\begin{matrix} | \qquad | \\ -C^+{-}C- \\ \quad\;\; | \\ \quad\;\; H \end{matrix}\right]^*$$

complex carbonium ion

$$\left[\begin{matrix} | \qquad | \\ -C^+{-}C- \\ \quad\;\; | \\ \quad\;\; H \end{matrix}\right]^* + H_2O \underset{\text{slow}}{\overset{\text{fast}}{\rightleftharpoons}}$$

$$\left[\begin{matrix} | \qquad\quad | \\ -C{-\!-\!-}C- \\ | \qquad\quad | \\ O^+ \qquad H \\ \diagup \;\; \diagdown \\ H \qquad H \end{matrix}\right]^* \overset{\text{fast}}{\rightleftharpoons} \begin{matrix} | \;\; | \\ -C{-}C- \\ | \;\; | \\ O \;\; H \\ | \\ H \end{matrix} + H^+$$

4. *Transition complex, nonchain mechanism.* The spontaneous decomposition of azomethane

$$(CH_3)_2N_2 \rightarrow C_2H_6 + N_2$$

exhibits under various conditions first-order, second-order, or intermediate kinetics. In general, the decomposition

$$A \rightarrow R + S$$

can be explained as follows:

Formation of unstable reactant $A + A \rightarrow A^* + A$
Return to stable form by collision $A^* + A \rightarrow A + A$
Spontaneous decomposition of unstable reactant $A^* \rightarrow R + S$

or more concisely

$$2A \rightleftharpoons A^* + A$$
$$A^* \rightarrow R + S$$

Azomethane decomposition is consistent with such a scheme.

5. *Transition complex, nonchain reaction.* The intermediate in the reaction

$$H_2 + I_2 \rightleftharpoons 2HI$$

with elementary second-order kinetics is an example of another type of transition complex, this one consisting of an association of molecules. Thus

$$\begin{matrix} H \\ | \\ H \end{matrix} + \begin{matrix} I \\ | \\ I \end{matrix} \rightleftharpoons \left[\begin{matrix} H\cdots I \\ \vdots \quad \vdots \\ H\cdots I \end{matrix}\right]^* \rightleftharpoons \begin{matrix} H{-}I \\ + \\ H{-}I \end{matrix}$$

This reaction is called a four-center-type reaction.

At first free radicals were hypothesized to give a rational explanation to observed kinetic occurrences without any direct evidence of their actual existence. In recent years, however, with the development of more sensitive experimental techniques such as high-resolution spectroscopic analyses and reaction freezing at very low temperatures, the existence of many free radicals has been directly verified. Today it is thought that such substances play a role in explaining many types of reactions. In general, free-radical reactions occur in the gas phase at high temperature. More often than not they occur by a chain mechanism and may be greatly affected by radiation and traces of impurities. Such impurities may inhibit the reaction by rapidly consuming the free radicals, whereas radiation may trigger the chain by helping to supply the small number of free radicals needed to start and sustain the reaction.

Ionic reactions occur mainly in aqueous solutions or other polar solvents. Their rates are often dependent on the nature of the solvent, and they are often catalyzed by bases or acids. Ionic reactions can also occur in the gas phase, but then only under the extremely energetic conditions of high temperature, electrical discharge, or X-ray irradiation.

Transition-type intermediates are considered to be the unstable intermediates "at the top of the energy hump" (see p. 25 and Fig. 1). There is no direct evidence for their existence; however, their use does explain observed data.

Intermediates consisting of rapidly decomposing molecules have real existence and have been observed to occur in a variety of reactions, both gas and liquid.

Testing kinetic models

Two problems make the search for the correct mechanism of reaction difficult. First, the reaction may proceed by more than one mechanism, say free radical and ionic, with the relative rates changing with the conditions of the reaction. Second, more than one mechanism can be consistent with given kinetic data. Resolving these problems is difficult and requires an extensive knowledge of the chemistry of the substances involved. Leaving these aside, let us see how to test the correspondence between a proposed mechanism and experimental kinetics. To test a hypothesized mechanism involving a sequence of elementary reactions, we must match the predicted rate expressions with experimental rate expressions. We rely on the following two rules. (1) If component i takes place in more than one reaction, its net rate of change is the sum total of the rates of change of that component in each of the elementary reactions, or

$$r_{i,\text{net}} = \sum_{\substack{\text{all elementary}\\ \text{reactions}}} r_i \tag{9}$$

(2) Because the intermediates are present in such small quantities, their rates of change in the system after a very short time can never be great; hence with negligible error these rates are taken to be zero. This is called the steady-state approximation. Such an approximation is needed if we are to solve the attendant mathematics, and our justification for its use is that the predicted results based on this assumption very often agree with experiment. The trial and error procedure involved in finding a mechanism is illustrated in the following example.

Example

The reaction

$$2A + B = A_2B \tag{10}$$

has been studied kinetically, and the rate of formation of product has been found to be well correlated by the following rate equation:

$$r_{A_2B} = \frac{0.72 C_A{}^2 C_B}{1 + 2C_A} = \frac{0.72[A]^2[B]}{1 + 2[A]} \tag{11}$$

What reaction mechanism is suggested by this rate expression if the chemistry of the reaction intimates that the intermediate probably consists of an association of reactant molecules and that a chain reaction does not occur?

Solution. If this were an elementary reaction, the rate would be given by

$$r_{A_2B} = kC_A{}^2C_B = k[A]^2[B] \tag{12}$$

As Eqs. 11 and 12 are not of the same type, we evidently have a nonelementary reaction occurring. Let us try various mechanisms or models and see which one gives a rate expression similar in form to the experimentally found expression. Let us start with simple two-step models and if unsuccessful work up to more complicated three-, four-, or five-step models.

Model 1. Hypothesize a two-step reversible scheme involving the formation of an intermediate substance $A_2{}^*$, not actually seen and hence thought to be present only in small amounts. Thus

$$\begin{aligned} 2A &\underset{k_2}{\overset{k_1}{\rightleftharpoons}} A_2{}^* \\ A_2{}^* + B &\underset{k_4}{\overset{k_3}{\rightleftharpoons}} A_2B \end{aligned} \tag{13}$$

which really involves four elementary reactions:

$$2A \xrightarrow{k_1} A_2{}^* \tag{14}$$

$$A_2{}^* \xrightarrow{k_2} 2A \tag{15}$$

$$A_2{}^* + B \xrightarrow{k_3} A_2B \tag{16}$$

$$A_2B \xrightarrow{k_4} A_2{}^* + B \tag{17}$$

Let the k values refer in each case to the any one of the components disappearing; thus k_1 refers to A, k_2 refers to A_2*, etc. Now let us write out the expression for r_{A_2B}, the rate of formation of A_2B. Since this component is involved in Eqs. 16 and 17, its over-all rate of change is the sum of the individual rates. Thus we have

$$r_{A_2B} = k_3[A_2^*][B] - k_4[A_2B] \tag{18}$$

All the terms in this equation except $[A_2^*]$ can be found. Unfortunately A_2^* is not observed experimentally; hence if it is present, it can only be present in extremely small nonmeasurable quantities. Thus we would like to replace it in terms of concentrations of materials that can be measured, such as A, B, or AB. This is done in the following manner. From the four elementary reactions which all involve A_2^* we find

$$r_{A_2^*} = \tfrac{1}{2}k_1[A]^2 - k_2[A_2^*] - k_3[A_2^*][B] + k_4[A_2B] \tag{19}$$

Because of its small concentration we may assume that $[A_2^*]$ reaches a steady or equilibrium state within a very short time; thus its rate of change is zero or

$$r_{A_2^*} = 0 \tag{20}$$

This is the steady-state approximation. From Eqs. 19 and 20 we find

$$[A_2^*] = \frac{\tfrac{1}{2}k_1[A]^2 + k_4[A_2B]}{k_2 + k_3[B]} \tag{21}$$

which when replaced into Eq. 18 gives the rate of formation of A_2B in terms of measurable quantities. Thus

$$r_{A_2B} = \frac{\tfrac{1}{2}k_1k_3[A]^2[B] - k_2k_4[A_2B]}{k_2 + k_3[B]} \tag{22}$$

In searching for a model consistent with observed kinetics we may, if we wish, restrict a more general model by arbitrarily selecting the magnitude of the various rate constants. Since Eq. 22 does not match Eq. 11, let us see if its simplified forms will. Thus, if k_2 is very small, this expression reduces to

$$r_{A_2B} = \tfrac{1}{2}k_1[A]^2 \tag{23}$$

a reaction which is second order with respect to A and independent of B. If k_4 is very small, r_{A_2B} reduces to

$$r_{A_2B} = \frac{(k_1k_3/2k_2)[A]^2[B]}{1 + (k_3/k_2)[B]} \tag{24}$$

Neither of these special forms, Eqs. 23 and 24, match the experimentally found rate, Eq. 11. Thus the hypothesized mechanism, Eq. 13, is incorrect.

Model 2. As our first model gave a rate, Eq. 24, somewhat similar to Eq. 11, let us try, for our second model, a mechanism somewhat similar to that of Model 1. Let us try the mechanism

$$\begin{aligned} A + B &\underset{k_2}{\overset{k_1}{\rightleftharpoons}} AB^* \\ AB^* + A &\underset{k_4}{\overset{k_3}{\rightleftharpoons}} A_2B \end{aligned} \tag{25}$$

Following a procedure analogous to that used for Model 1, we find the desired rate

$$r_{A_2B} = k_3[AB^*][A] - k_4[A_2B] \tag{26}$$

Next eliminate [AB*] in this expression. With the steady-state approximation we obtain

$$r_{AB^*} = 0 = k_1[A][B] - k_2[AB^*] - k_3[AB^*][A] + k_4[A_2B]$$

from which

$$[AB^*] = \frac{k_1[A][B] + k_4[A_2B]}{k_2 + k_3[A]} \tag{27}$$

Replacing Eq. 27 in Eq. 26 to eliminate the concentration of intermediate, we obtain

$$r_{A_2B} = \frac{k_1k_3[A]^2[B] - k_2k_4[A_2B]}{k_2 + k_3[A]} \tag{28}$$

Let us restrict this general model. With k_4 very small we obtain

$$r_{A_2B} = \frac{(k_1k_3/k_2)[A]^2[B]}{1 + (k_3/k_2)[A]} \tag{29}$$

Comparing Eqs. 11 and 29, we see that they are of the same form. Thus the reaction may be represented by the mechanism

$$\begin{aligned} A + B &\underset{k_2}{\overset{k_1}{\rightleftharpoons}} AB^* \\ AB^* + A &\overset{k_3}{\longrightarrow} A_2B \end{aligned} \tag{30}$$

The individual rate constants can only be determined if one more piece of information is known. From Eq. 4 we see that the equilibrium constant $K_C = k_1/k_2$ is just the information needed.

We were fortunate in this example to have represented our data by a form of equation which happened to match exactly that obtained from the theoretical mechanism. Often a number of equation types will fit a set of experimental data equally well, especially for somewhat scattered data. Hence to avoid rejecting the correct mechanism, it is advisable to test the fit of the various theoretically derived equations to the raw experimental data using statistical criteria whenever possible.

TEMPERATURE-DEPENDENT TERM OF A RATE EQUATION

Temperature dependency from Arrhenius' law

For many reactions and in particular elementary reactions the rate expression can be written as a product of a temperature-dependent term and a composition-dependent term, or

$$\begin{aligned} r_i &= f_1(\text{temperature}) \cdot f_2(\text{composition}) \\ &= k \cdot f_2(\text{composition}) \end{aligned} \tag{31}$$

For such reactions the temperature-dependent term, the reaction rate constant, has been found in practically all cases to be well represented by Arrhenius' law:

$$k = k_0 \, e^{-E/RT} \tag{32}$$

where k_0 is called the frequency factor and E is called the activation energy of the reaction.* This expression fits experimental data well over wide temperature ranges and is strongly suggested from various standpoints as being a reasonable first approximation to the true temperature dependency.

Temperature dependency from thermodynamics

The temperature dependency of the equilibrium constant of the elementary reversible reactions such as

$$A \underset{k_2}{\overset{k_1}{\rightleftharpoons}} R, \qquad \Delta H_r \tag{33}$$

is given by the van't Hoff equation, Eq. 8.15,

$$\frac{d(\ln K)}{dT} = \frac{\Delta H_r}{RT^2} \tag{34}$$

Because $K = K_C = [R]/[A] = k_1/k_2$ for this reaction, we can then rewrite the van't Hoff relationship as

$$\frac{d(\ln k_1)}{dT} - \frac{d(\ln k_2)}{dT} = \frac{\Delta H_r}{RT^2}$$

Though it does not necessarily follow, the fact that the difference in derivatives is equal to $\Delta H_r/RT^2$ suggests that each derivative alone is equal to a term of that form, or

$$\frac{d(\ln k_1)}{dT} = \frac{E_1}{RT^2} \quad \text{and} \quad \frac{d(\ln k_2)}{dT} = \frac{E_2}{RT^2} \tag{35}$$

* There seems to be a disagreement in the dimensions used to report the activation energy; some authors use calories, and others use calories per mole. On the one hand, calories per mole are clearly indicated by Eq. 32. In contrast to the dimensionally identical thermodynamic quantities $\Delta F°$ and ΔH_r, however, the numerical value of E does not depend on how we represent the reaction stoichiometry (number of moles used). Thus reporting calories per mole may be misinterpreted. To avoid this E is reported here simply as calories.

What moles are we referring to in the units of E? These are always the quantities associated with the molar representation of the rate-controlling step of the reaction. Numerically E can be found without knowing what this is; however, if E is to be compared with analogous quantities from thermodynamics, collision theory, or transition-state theory, this mechanism must be known and its stoichiometric representation must be used throughout.

This whole question can be avoided by using the ratio E/R throughout, since E and R always refer to the same number of moles.

where
$$E_1 - E_2 = \Delta H_r \tag{36}$$

In addition, if the energy terms are assumed to be temperature independent, Eq. 35 can be integrated to give Arrhenius' equation, Eq. 32.

Temperature dependency from collision theory

The collision rate of molecules in a gas can be found from the kinetic theory of gases. For the bimolecular collisions of like molecules A we have

$$\begin{aligned} Z_{AA} &= \boldsymbol{\sigma}_A{}^2\mathbf{n}_A{}^2\sqrt{\frac{4\pi\mathbf{k}T}{\mathbf{M}_A}} = \boldsymbol{\sigma}_A{}^2\frac{\mathbf{N}^2}{10^6}\sqrt{\frac{4\pi\mathbf{k}T}{\mathbf{M}_A}}C_A{}^2 \\ &= \frac{\text{number of collisions of A with A}}{(\text{sec})(\text{cc})} \end{aligned} \tag{37}$$

where $\boldsymbol{\sigma}$ = diameter of a molecule, cm
$\mathbf{M}$ = (molecular weight)/$\mathbf{N}$, mass of a molecule, gms
$\mathbf{N} = 6.023 \times 10^{23}$ molecules/gm mole, Avogadro's number
C_A = concentration of A, gm moles/liter
$\mathbf{n}_A = \mathbf{N}C_A/10^3$, number of molecules of A/cc
$\mathbf{k} = R/\mathbf{N} = 1.38 \times 10^{-16}$ erg/°K, Boltzmann constant

For the bimolecular collisions of unlike molecules in a mixture of A and B we have

$$\begin{aligned} Z_{AB} &= \left(\frac{\boldsymbol{\sigma}_A + \boldsymbol{\sigma}_B}{2}\right)^2\mathbf{n}_A\mathbf{n}_B\sqrt{8\pi\mathbf{k}T\left(\frac{1}{\mathbf{M}_A} + \frac{1}{\mathbf{M}_B}\right)} \\ &= \left(\frac{\boldsymbol{\sigma}_A + \boldsymbol{\sigma}_B}{2}\right)^2\frac{\mathbf{N}^2}{10^6}\sqrt{8\pi\mathbf{k}T\left(\frac{1}{\mathbf{M}_A} + \frac{1}{\mathbf{M}_B}\right)}C_AC_B \end{aligned} \tag{38}$$

If every collision between reactant molecules results in the transformation of reactants into product, these expressions give the rate of bimolecular reaction. The actual rate is usually much lower than that predicted, however, indicating that only a small fraction of all collisions between reactant molecules result in reaction. This suggests that only the more energetic and violent collisions between molecules lead to reaction, or more specifically, only those collisions that involve energies in excess of a given minimum energy E lead to reaction. From the Maxwell distribution law of molecular energies the fraction of all bimolecular collisions that involve energies in excess of this minimum energy is given approximately by

$$e^{-E/RT}$$

when $E \gg RT$. Since we are only considering energetic collisions, this assumption is reasonable. Thus the rate of reaction is given by

$$-r_A = -\frac{1}{V}\frac{dN_A}{dt} = kC_AC_B = \begin{pmatrix}\text{collision rate,}\\ \text{moles/(liter)(sec)}\end{pmatrix}\begin{pmatrix}\text{fraction of collisions}\\ \text{involving energies}\\ \text{in excess of } E\end{pmatrix}$$

$$= Z_{AB}\frac{1000}{\mathbf{N}}e^{-E/RT}$$

$$= \left(\frac{\boldsymbol{\sigma}_A + \boldsymbol{\sigma}_B}{2}\right)^2 \frac{\mathbf{N}}{10^3}\sqrt{8\pi\mathbf{k}T\left(\frac{1}{\mathbf{M}_A} + \frac{1}{\mathbf{M}_B}\right)}\, e^{-E/RT}\, C_AC_B \tag{39}$$

A similar expression can be found for the bimolecular collisions between like molecules. For both, in fact for all bimolecular reactions, we see from Eq. 39 that the temperature dependency of the rate constant is given by

$$k \propto T^{1/2}e^{-E/RT} \tag{40}$$

Temperature dependency from transition-state theory

A more detailed mechanism by which reactants are transformed into products is given by the transition-state theory. This pictures reactants combining to form unstable intermediates called activated complexes which then decompose spontaneously into products. It assumes in addition that an equilibrium exists between reactants and activated complex at all times and that the rate of decomposition of complex is the same for all reactions and is given by $\mathbf{k}T/\mathbf{h}$ where $\mathbf{k}$ is the Boltzmann constant and $\mathbf{h} = 6.63 \times 10^{-27}$ erg-sec is the Planck constant. Thus for the forward elementary reaction of a reversible reaction,

$$A + B \underset{k_2}{\overset{k_1}{\rightleftharpoons}} AB, \qquad \Delta H_r \tag{41}$$

we have the following conceptual scheme:

$$A + B \underset{k_4}{\overset{k_3}{\rightleftharpoons}} AB^* \xrightarrow{k_5} AB \tag{42}$$

with

$$K_C^* = \frac{k_3}{k_4} = \frac{[AB^*]}{[A][B]}$$

and

$$k_5 = \frac{\mathbf{k}T}{\mathbf{h}}$$

The observed rate of reaction is then

$$r_{\mathrm{AB}} = \begin{pmatrix}\text{concentration of} \\ \text{activated complex}\end{pmatrix}\begin{pmatrix}\text{rate of decomposition} \\ \text{of activated complex}\end{pmatrix}$$

$$= \frac{\mathbf{k}T}{\mathbf{h}}[\mathrm{AB}^*]$$

$$= \frac{\mathbf{k}T}{\mathbf{h}} K_C{}^* C_\mathrm{A} C_\mathrm{B} \tag{43}$$

By expressing the equilibrium constant of the activated complex in terms of the standard free energy,

$$\Delta F^* = \Delta H^* - T\,\Delta S^* = -RT \ln K_C{}^*$$

or

$$K_C{}^* = e^{-\Delta F^*/RT} = e^{-\Delta H^*/RT + \Delta S^*/R} \tag{44}$$

the rate of reaction becomes

$$r_{\mathrm{AB}} = \frac{\mathbf{k}T}{\mathbf{h}} e^{\Delta S^*/R} e^{-\Delta H^*/RT} C_\mathrm{A} C_\mathrm{B} \tag{45}$$

Theoretically both ΔS^* and ΔH^* vary very slowly with temperature. Hence, of the three terms that make up the rate constant in Eq. 45, the middle one $e^{\Delta S^*/R}$ is so much less temperature-sensitive than the other two terms that we may take it to be constant. Hence for the forward and reverse reactions of Eq. 41 we find approximately

$$k_1 \propto Te^{-\Delta H_1{}^*/RT}$$

$$k_2 \propto Te^{-\Delta H_2{}^*/RT} \tag{46}$$

where

$$\Delta H_1{}^* - \Delta H_2{}^* = \Delta H_r$$

We may next look for a relationship between ΔH^* and the Arrhenius activation energy E. Though none can be logically derived, still we can arbitrarily define one. This is generally done by using analogy arguments from thermodynamics. Thus we have for liquids and solids

$$E = \Delta H^* + RT \tag{47}$$

and for gases

$$E = \Delta H^* - (\text{molecularity} - 1)RT \tag{48}$$

With this definition the difference between E and ΔH^* is small and in the order of RT; hence we can predict from transition-state theory approximately that

$$k \propto Te^{-E/RT} \tag{49}$$

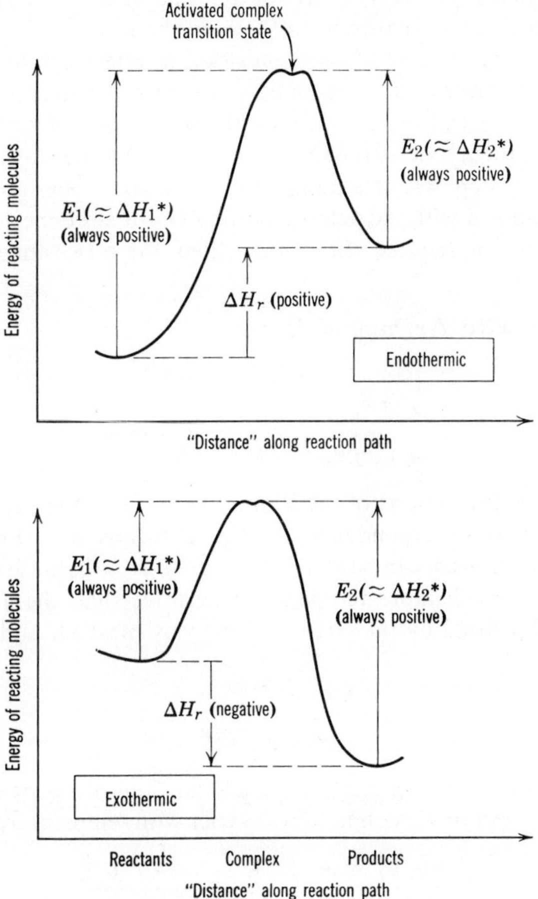

Fig. 1. Visualization of the energies involved in the transformation of reactants to products in an elementary reaction.

Figure 1 illustrates the energies involved in reactants and complexes in such a scheme.

It is interesting to note the divergence in approach between the collision and transition-state theories. Consider A and B colliding and forming an unstable intermediate which then decomposes into the product, or

$$A + B \rightarrow AB^* \rightarrow AB \tag{50}$$

Collision theory views the rate to be governed by the number of energetic collisions between reactants. What happens to the unstable intermediate is of no concern. It is simply assumed that this intermediate breaks down rapidly enough into products so as not to influence the rate of the over-all process. Transition-state theory on the other hand views the reaction rate to be governed by the rate of decomposition of intermediate. The rate of formation of intermediate is assumed to be so rapid that it is present in equilibrium concentrations at all times. How it is formed is of no concern. Thus collision theory views the first step of Eq. 50 to be slow and thus the rate-controlling step, whereas transition-state theory views the second step of Eq. 50 combined with the determination of complex concentration to be the rate-controlling factors. In a sense, then, these two theories complement each other.

Comparison with Arrhenius' law

The expression

$$\begin{aligned} k &\propto T^m e^{-E/RT} \\ &= k_0' T^m e^{-E/RT}, \end{aligned} \qquad 0 \leqslant m \leqslant 1 \tag{51}$$

summarizes the predictions of the simpler versions of the various theories for the temperature dependency of the rate constant. For the more complicated versions m can be as great as 3 or 4. Now because the exponential term is so much more temperature-sensitive than the T^m term, the variation of k caused by the latter is effectively masked, and we have in effect

$$\begin{aligned} k &\propto e^{-E/RT} \\ &= k_0 e^{-E/RT} \end{aligned} \tag{32}$$

We may show this another way. Taking logarithms of Eq. 51 and differentiating with respect to T, we find how k varies with temperature. This gives

$$\frac{d(\ln k)}{dT} = \frac{m}{T} + \frac{E}{RT^2} = \frac{mRT + E}{RT^2}$$

As $mRT \ll E$ for most reactions studied, we may ignore the mRT term and may write

$$\frac{d(\ln k)}{dT} = \frac{E}{RT^2}$$

or

$$k \propto e^{-E/RT} \tag{32}$$

Variables affecting the temperature dependency of reactions

A plot of ln k versus $1/T$ for any reaction should yield a straight line if Arrhenius' law is applicable. Figure 2 is a typical plot of this kind and is used to show the temperature dependency of reaction rates. From this figure and Tables 1 and 2 we may draw the following conclusions.

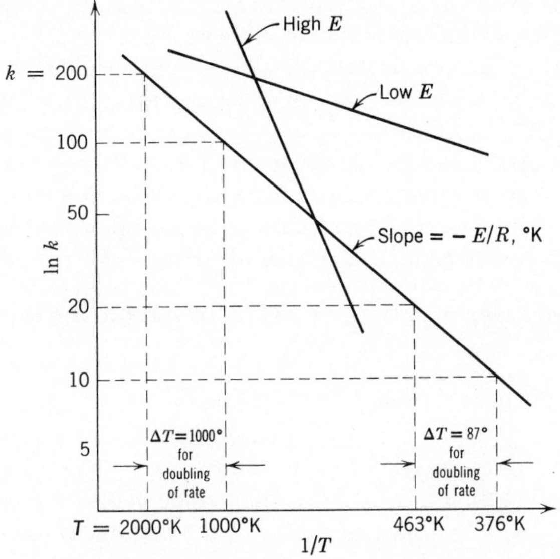

Fig. 2. Sketch showing temperature dependency of the reaction rate.

Table 1. Temperature rise needed to double the rate of reaction for activation energies and average temperatures shown; hence shows temperature sensitivity of reactions

	Activation Energy E		
Temperature	10,000 cal	40,000 cal	70,000 cal
0°C	11	3	2
400°C	70	17	9
1000°C	273	62	37
2000°C	1037	197	107

Table 2. Relative rates of reaction as a function of activation energy and temperature

	Activation Energy E		
Temperature	10,000 cal	40,000 cal	70,000 cal
0°C	10^{48}	10^{24}	1
400°C	7×10^{52}	10^{43}	2×10^{33}
1000°C	2×10^{54}	10^{49}	10^{44}
2000°C	10^{55}	10^{52}	2×10^{49}

1. Reactions with high activation energies are very temperature-sensitive; reactions with low activation energies are relatively temperature-insensitive.

2. A given reaction is much more temperature-sensitive at low temperature than at high temperature.

3. From the Arrhenius law the frequency factor k_0 does not affect the temperature sensitivity of a reaction. In an actual reaction there may be a slight temperature dependency of this term as predicted by Eq. 51; however, this is rather minor and can be ignored.

Rate of elementary reactions from collision and transition-state theory

Experimental values for rates of reaction are in most cases either in the order of magnitude of, or are below, those predicted by collision theory. Thus collision theory may be used to estimate the upper bound to the expected rate of reaction. The order of magnitude of the rates so predicted are given in Table 3, in which entries show the time required for 50% of

Table 3. Approximate time required for 50% of reactants to disappear by reaction

	Activation Energy E		
Temperature	10,000 cal	40,000 cal	70,000 cal
0°C	3×10^{-5}	3×10^{19}	3×10^{43}
400°C	10^{-9}	8×10^{2}	4×10^{9}
1000°C	2×10^{-11}	2×10^{-6}	30
2000°C	10^{-13}	9×10^{-11}	7×10^{-8}

$A + B \rightarrow$ products
$C_{A0} = C_{B0} = 0.5$ atm
Molecular weights: 100
Molecular diameters: $\sigma_A = \sigma_B = 3.35 \times 10^{-8}$ cm
Calculations are based on collision theory.
Time in seconds

the reactants A and B to disappear when equimolar quantities of gaseous A and B are being reacted in a container, the reaction being bimolecular and taking place at 1 atm. Once in a while a reaction is encountered with rates much higher than those predicted by collision theory. This is good evidence pointing to the occurrence of a complex reaction, frequently catalytic.

Occasionally, for the elementary reaction between simpler molecules enough information is available to allow prediction of the rates from transition-state theory. When available, these predictions usually agree more closely with experiment than do the predictions of collision theory.

SEARCHING FOR A MECHANISM

The more we know about what is occurring during reaction, what the reacting materials are, and how they react, the more assurance we have for proper design. This is the incentive to find out as much as we can about the factors influencing a reaction within the limitations of time and effort set by the economic optimization of the many factors involved in the industrial exploitation of a process.

There are three areas of investigation of a reaction, the *stoichiometry*, the *kinetics*, and the *mechanism*. In general, the stoichiometry is studied first, and when this is far enough along the kinetics is then investigated. With empirical rate expressions available, the mechanism is then looked into. In any investigative program considerable feedback of information occurs from area to area. For example, our ideas about the stoichiometry of the reaction may change on the basis of kinetic data obtained, and the form of the kinetic equations themselves may be suggested by mechanism studies. With this kind of interrelationship of the many factors, no straightforward experimental program can be formulated for the study of reactions. Thus it becomes a matter of shrewd scientific detective work, with carefully planned experimental programs especially designed to discriminate between rival hypotheses, which in turn have been suggested and formulated on the basis of all pertinent information available at that time.

Although we cannot delve into the many aspects of this problem, a number of clues which are often used in such experimentation can be mentioned.

1. Stoichiometry may suggest whether we have a single reaction or not.

2. Stoichiometry can suggest whether a single reaction is elementary or not because no elementary reactions with molecularity greater than three have been observed to date. As an example the reaction

$$N_2 + 3H_2 \rightarrow 2NH_3$$

is not elementary.

3. The correspondence or lack of correspondence between the stoichiometric equation and experimental kinetic expression can indicate whether we are dealing with an elementary reaction or not. This has been pointed out earlier.

4. A large difference in the order of magnitude between the experimentally found frequency factor of a reaction and that calculated from collision

theory or transition-state theory may suggest a nonelementary reaction; however, this is not necessarily true. For example, certain isomerizations have very low frequency factors and are still elementary.

5. Consider two alternate paths for a simple reversible reaction. If one of these paths is preferred for the forward reaction, the same path must also be preferred for the reverse reaction. This is called the principle of microscopic reversibility. Consider for example the forward reaction of

$$2NH_3 \rightleftharpoons N_2 + 3H_2$$

At first sight this could very well be an elementary bimolecular reaction with the two molecules of ammonia combining to yield directly the four product molecules. From this principle, however, the reverse reaction would then also have to be an elementary reaction involving the direct combination of three molecules of hydrogen with one of nitrogen. Since such a process is rejected as improbable, the bimolecular forward mechanism must also be rejected in favor of some other mechanism.

6. The principle of microreversibility leads us to the rule that changes involving bond rupture, molecular syntheses, or splitting are likely to occur one at a time, each then being an elementary step in the mechanism. From this point of view the simultaneous splitting of the complex into the four product molecules in the reaction

$$2NH_3 \rightarrow (NH_3)_2^* \rightarrow N_2 + 3H_2$$

is very unlikely. This rule does not apply to changes which involve a shift in electron density along a molecule. Changes of this type may take place in a cascade-like manner. For example, the transformation

$$\underset{\text{vinyl allyl ether}}{CH_2{=}CH{-}CH_2{-}O{-}CH{=}CH_2} \rightarrow \underset{n\text{-pentaldehyde-ene 4}}{CH_2{=}CH{-}CH_2{-}CH_2{-}CHO}$$

can be explained in terms of the following shifts in electron density:

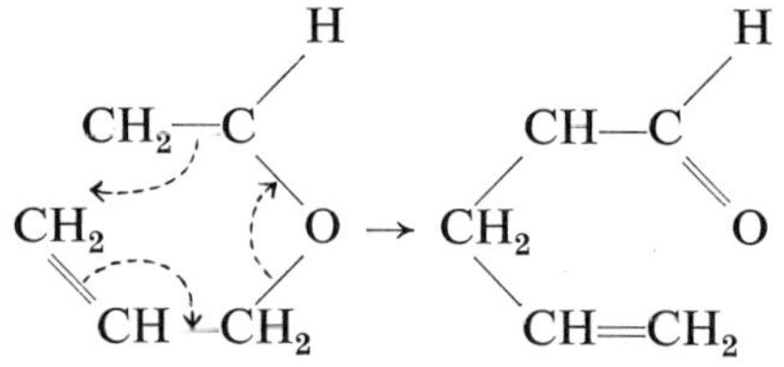

```
              H                       H
             /                       /
      CH2---C                  CH---C
                \             /      \\
 CH2             O   →    CH2          O
    \\          /            \
     CH ---- CH2               CH=CH2
```

or

```
              H                       H
             /                       /
      CH2===C                  CH---C
                \             /      \\
 CH2             O   →    CH2          O
    \\          /            \
     CH ---- CH2               CH=CH2
```

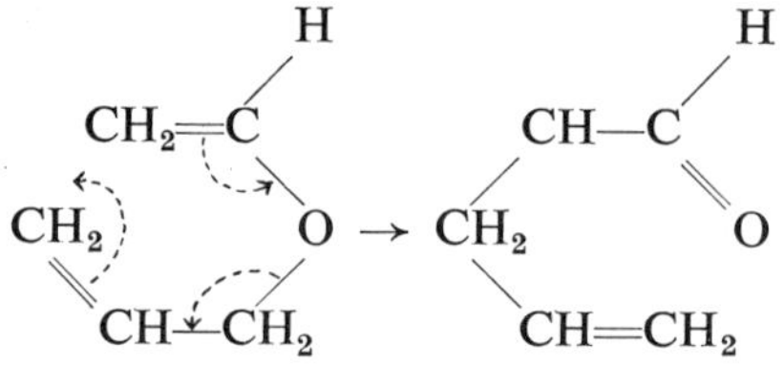

7. Comparing theoretical and experimental energies of activation can lend strong support to the mechanism chosen or can supply evidence for rejecting a mechanism. With the additional assumption that the frequency factor is constant (from collision theory it rarely varies by more than a factor of 50 for gas-phase reactions), comparison of activation energies may suggest which of two competing mechanisms provides the favored path for a reaction; with identical frequency factors the reaction with lower activation energy is the faster. Consider the hypothetical decomposition of A to R + S either directly or by means of a three-step mechanism, with activation energies and form of corresponding rate expressions all known. Thus

Mechanism I:

$$2A \rightarrow R + S \qquad E = 46 \text{ kcal}, \qquad r_R = kC_A^2$$

Mechanism II:

$$\begin{aligned} &\text{Step 1} \quad E_1 = 65 \text{ kcal} \\ &\text{Step 2} \quad E_2 = 6 \text{ kcal}, \qquad r_R = \frac{k_1 k_2^{1/2}}{k_3} C_A^2 \\ &\text{Step 3} \quad E_3 = 38 \text{ kcal} \end{aligned}$$

Experimentally the activation energy is found to be

$$E_{\text{expt}} = 28 \text{ kcal}$$

Let us see which mechanism is suggested by consideration of activation energies.

First, comparing the actual activation energy, $E = 28$ kcal, with that calculated for the elementary reaction, $E = 46$ kcal, we see that the actual rate is much more rapid than that predicted by the elementary reaction; hence another mechanism is probably favored. Note that in arriving at this conclusion we assume that the frequency factors are alike; hence the rate of reaction is taken to be a function of the activation energy alone.

Second, if the reaction takes place by means of the three-step mechanism, the observed temperature dependency is incorporated in the $k_1 k_2^{1/2}/k_3$ term. Thus from the Arrhenius-type relationship for each of the rate constants,

$$\Delta E_{\text{over-all}} = E_1 + \tfrac{1}{2}E_2 - E_3 = 65 + \tfrac{1}{2}(6) - 38 = 30 \text{ kcal}$$

The close correspondence of this calculated activation energy with the actual value, $E = 28$ kcal, provides evidence for the correctness of this mechanism. Unfortunately this procedure cannot be used for kinetic expressions such as Eq. 29.

When energies of activation are not available for the specific elementary reactions under consideration, we may be forced to estimate them by empirical rules and generalizations obtained from reactions of a similar kind, even though some of these rules may be of questionable reliability. Some of these rules are as follows [see Jungers et al. (1958)].

1. In the splitting or decomposition of a single molecule the activation energy is simply the energy of the bond which is ruptured. Thus the activation energy of the reaction

$$CH_3\text{—}CHO \rightarrow CH_3\cdot + CHO\cdot$$

is simply the energy of the carbon-carbon bond.

2. The activation energy for the reaction

$$A + BC \rightarrow AB + C, \qquad \text{exothermic}$$

is 5.5% of the B—C bond which is broken. For endothermic reaction the heat of reaction must be added to this value.

3. The activation energy for the exchange reaction

$$AB + CD \rightarrow AC + BD, \qquad \text{exothermic}$$

is 28% of the sum of the A—B and C—D bonds. For the reverse reaction which is endothermic, the heat of reaction must be added to this value.

4. The activation energy for the combination of free radicals is negligible. In terms of collision theory this means that every collision of free radicals is effective.

These rules suggest that the energy of rupturing bonds is an indication of the activation energy of the reaction. Thus it is useful to be able to estimate in turn the bond energies between atoms of various kinds. These

Table 4. R′—R″ bond dissociation energies

R″ \ R′	H	CH_3	C_2H_5	$CH_2{=}CH$	$CH{\equiv}C$	$n\text{-}C_3H_7$	$(CH_3)_2CH$	C_6H_5	$C_6H_5\text{—}CH_2$
H	103.24[a]	101	98	104?	121?	95	89?	104?	77.5
CH_3	101	83	82	90?	110?	79	74.5?	91?	63
C_2H_5	98	82	82	90?	109?	79	75?	91?	62
$CH_2{=}CH$	104?	90?	90?	101?	–	87?	85?	101?	–
C_6H_5	104?	91?	91?	101?	119?	88?	83?	103?	76.5?
Cl	102.2[a]	80	80	86?	–	77?	–	88?	–
Br	86.5[a]	66–67	65	–	–	–	–	–	50.5
OH	116[a]	90–91	90–93	–	–	92	~90	107?	73?
NH_2	102[a]	79	78	–	–	77?	–	94?	59
CHO	<78?[a]	71–75	71?	84?	–	71?	–	83?	–

Values selected from Szwarc (1950), and where not available ([a]) from Cottrell (1954). For additional values see these sources and Steacie (1954).

are influenced primarily by the two atoms involved and to a lesser extent by the nature of the molecule as a whole. Average values for various bond energies are shown in Table 4 and may be used for estimation purposes.

PREDICTABILITY OF REACTION RATE FROM THEORY

The rate expression in general involves two factors, the temperature-dependent and the concentration-dependent factors. Consider the prediction of these factors in turn.

Concentration-dependent term

There is no way at present to predict a priori the path of a reaction. Actually, if the reaction has a number of competing paths available, it will take the path that affords the smallest resistance, the fastest one available. Only a knowledge of the energies of all possible intermediates will allow prediction of the path to be taken and the corresponding rate expression. As such information is not available a priori, prediction of the form of the concentration term is not possible. Actually, the form of the experimentally found rate expression is often the clue used to investigate the energies of the intermediates of a reaction.

Temperature-dependent term

Assuming that we already know the mechanism of reaction, whether it is elementary or not, we may then proceed to the prediction of the frequency factor and activation energy terms of the rate constant.

Frequency factor predictions from either collision or transition-state theory may come within a factor of 100 of the correct value; however, in specific cases predictions may be much further off.

Though activation energies can be estimated from transition-state theory, reliability is poor, and it is probably best to estimate them from the experimental findings for reactions of similar compounds. For example, the activation energies of the following homologous series of reactions,

$$RI + C_2H_5ONa \xrightarrow{\text{ethanol}} C_6H_5OR + NaI$$

where R is

CH_3	C_7H_{15}	iso-C_3H_7	*sec*-C_4H_9
C_2H_5	C_8H_{17}	iso-C_4H_9	*sec*-C_6H_{13}
C_3H_7	$C_{16}H_{33}$	iso-C_5H_{11}	*sec*-C_8H_{17}
C_4H_9			*tert*-C_4H_9

all lie between 21.5 and 23.5 kcal.

Use of predicted values in design

The frequent order-of-magnitude predictions of the theories tend to confirm the correctness of their representations, help find the form and the energies of various intermediates, and give us a better understanding of chemical structure. However, theoretical predictions rarely match experiment by a factor of two. In addition, we can never tell beforehand whether the predicted rate will be in the order of magnitude of the experimentally found rate or will be off by a factor of 10^6. Therefore for engineering design this kind of information should not be relied on, and experimentally found rates should be used in all cases. Thus the theoretical studies may be used as a supplementary aid to suggest the temperature sensitivity of a given reaction from a similar type of reaction, to suggest the upper limits of reaction rate, etc. Final design invariably rests on experimentally found rates.

Experimental findings

Primary sources of kinetic data are conveniently found in *Chemical Abstracts*, either in the formula index for the materials being reacted or in the subject index under kinetics.

At present there is no complete compilation of kinetic data; probably the most comprehensive single source is found in

> "Tables of Chemical Kinetics: Homogeneous Reactions," National Bureau of Standards (U.S.), Circular 510, 1951, and Supplements.

Other secondary sources are textbooks on chemical kinetics and series devoted to reactions of a given type, as for example in the field of catalysis:

> *Advances in Catalysis*, Academic Press, New York, a volume published annually since 1948.
>
> *Catalysis*, P. H. Emmett, ed., Reinhold, New York, approximately one volume published annually since 1954.

RELATED READINGS

A. A. Frost and R. G. Pearson, *Kinetics and Mechanism*, second edition, John Wiley and Sons, New York, 1961.

J. C. Jungers et al., *Cinétique chimique appliquée*, Technip, Paris, 1958.

W. J. Moore, *Physical Chemistry*, Prentice-Hall, New York, 1950, Ch. 17.

E. W. R. Steacie, *Atomic and Free Radical Reactions*, Reinhold, New York, 1946.

REFERENCES

T. L. Cottrell, *The Strength of Chemical Bonds*, Butterworths, London, 1954.

K. G. Denbigh, *The Principles of Chemical Equilibrium*, Cambridge University Press, Cambridge, England, 1955, p. 442.

J. C. Jungers et al., *Cinétique chimique appliqueé*, Technip, Paris, 1958.

L. Michaelis and M. L. Menten, *Biochem. Z.*, **49,** 333 (1913). This treatment is discussed by K. J. Laidler, *Chemical Kinetics*, McGraw-Hill, New York, 1950, p. 304.
R. Ogg, *J. Chem. Phys.*, **15,** 337 (1947).
E. W. R. Steacie, *Atomic and Free Radical Reactions*, second edition, Reinhold, New York, 1954.
M. Szwarc, *Chem. Revs.*, **47,** 75 (1950).

PROBLEMS

1. A reaction has the stoichiometric equation 2A = R + S. What is the order of reaction?

2. Given the reaction $2NO_2 + \frac{1}{2}O_2 = N_2O_5$, what is the relation between the rates of formation and disappearance of the three components of the reaction?

3. A reaction with stoichiometric equation $\frac{1}{2}$A + B = R + S has the following rate expression

$$-r_A = -\frac{1}{V}\frac{dN_A}{dt} = 2C_A^{0.5}C_B$$

What is the rate expression for this reaction if the stoichiometric equation is written as A + 2B = 2R + 2S?

4. The rate constant for the low-pressure gas-phase hydroaffiliation of isometric inkahol at 0°C has been reported independently by two teams of investigators in the following ways:

Team I: $k = 1260 \times e^{-0.02}$ lb moles/(barrel)(50-min class period)(ft water)^2
Team II: $k = 4.2 \times 10^3$/(sec)(mm Hg)(atm)

The first study, having been made by the team of Lurch, Stagger, and Reel, can be considered to be absolutely reliable. On this basis

(*a*) What can you say about the rate constant found by the second team?
(*b*) What should the second team have found in their study using mm Hg for the units of concentration or pressure and seconds for the units of time?

5. Given the low-pressure gas-phase reaction A = R with rate

$$-r_A = -\frac{dC_A}{dt} = k_1 p_A^{2.2} - k_2 p_R^{0.5}$$

with p in atmospheres, C in lb moles/ft^3, t in hours, and $k_1 = 17.3$, $k_2 = 0.2$. The reaction takes place at 72°F and 1 atm pressure.

(*a*) What are the units of k_1 and k_2.
(*b*) With the rate equation in the following form

$$-\frac{dC_A}{dt} = k_1' C_A^{2.2} - k_2' C_R^{0.5}$$

find k_1' and k_2'.

6. Show that the following scheme

$$N_2O_5 \underset{k_2}{\overset{k_1}{\rightleftharpoons}} NO_2 + NO_3^* \xrightarrow{k_3} NO_2 + O_2 + NO^*$$
$$NO^* + NO_3^* \xrightarrow{k_4} 2NO_2$$

proposed by Ogg (1947) is consistent with, and can explain, the observed first-order decomposition of N_2O_5.

7. Under the influence of oxidizing agents, hypophosphorous acid is transformed into phosphorous acid:

$$H_3PO_2 \xrightarrow{\text{oxidizing agent}} H_3PO_3$$

The kinetics of this transformation present the following features. At low concentration of oxidizing agent

$$r_{H_3PO_3} = k[\text{oxidizing agent}][H_3PO_2]$$

At high concentration of oxidizing agent

$$r_{H_3PO_3} = k'[H^+][H_3PO_2]$$

To explain the observed kinetics, it has been postulated that with hydrogen ion as catalyst normal unreactive H_3PO_2 is transformed into an active form, the nature of which is unknown. This intermediate then reacts with the oxidizing agent to give H_3PO_3. Show that this scheme does explain the observed kinetics.

8. Present mechanisms consistent with the experimentally found rate equations for the following reactions:

(*a*) $2A + B = A_2B$

$$r_{A_2B} = k[A][B]$$

(*b*) $2D_2E = 2DE + D_2$

$$r_{D_2} = \frac{1960[D_2E]^2}{[DE] + 18[D_2E]}$$

9. The decomposition of A at 400°C for pressures between 1 and 10 atm follows a first-order rate law.

(*a*) Show that a mechanism similar to azomethane decomposition, pg. 18,

$$A + A \rightleftharpoons A^* + A$$
$$A^* \rightarrow R + S$$

is consistent with the observed kinetics.

Now many different mechanisms can be put forward to explain first-order kinetics. To claim that this mechanism is correct in the face of the other alternatives requires that we present additional strong evidence in favor of it.

(*b*) For this purpose what further experiments would you suggest we run and what results would you expect to find?

10. Chemicals A, B, and D combine to give R and S with stoichiometry A + B + D = R + S, and after the reaction has proceeded to a significant extent, the observed rate is

$$r_R = kC_AC_BC_D/C_R$$

(*a*) What is the order of the reaction?

The following two mechanisms involving formation of active intermediate have been proposed to explain the observed kinetics.

Mechanism I:
$$A + B \rightleftharpoons X^* + R$$
$$D + X^* \rightarrow S$$

Mechanism II:
$$A + D \rightleftharpoons Y^* + R$$
$$B + Y^* \rightarrow S$$

(*b*) Are these mechanisms consistent with the kinetic data?

(*c*) If neither is consistent, devise a scheme that is consistent with the kinetics. If only one is consistent, what line of investigation may strengthen the conviction that the mechanism selected is correct? If both are consistent, how would you be able to choose between them?

11. A_2B decomposes with stoichiometry $A_2B = AB + \frac{1}{2}A_2$. Much effort has been expended to discover the kinetics of this reaction, but the results are discouraging, and no concise rate equation can be made to fit the data. The following observations can be made from the data, however.

1. At the start of any experimental run the reaction seems to be of first order with respect to reactant.
2. When the reactant is just about gone, the data is well correlated by an equation which is second order with respect to reactant.
3. Introducing product AB into the feed leaves the rate unaffected.
4. Introducing product A_2 into the feed slows down the rate of reaction; however, no proportionality can be found between A_2 added or present in the solution versus the slowing down of the reaction.

With the hope that a theoretical treatment may suggest a satisfactory form of rate expression, the following mechanisms are explored.

Mechanism I:
$$2A_2B \rightleftharpoons (A_4B_2)^*$$
$$(A_4B_2)^* \rightleftharpoons A_2 + 2AB$$

Mechanism II:
$$A_2B \rightleftharpoons A^* + AB$$
$$A_2B + A^* \rightleftharpoons A_2 + AB$$

If the rate expression derived from any of these mechanisms is consistent with the qualitative observations, it should then be further tested qualitatively with the actual data.

(*a*) Are any of these mechanisms consistent with the qualitative experimental findings? If a mechanism is rejected, state on what basis you reject it?

(*b*) If neither of these mechanisms is satisfactory, can you devise one that is consistent with the experimental findings?

12. At 500°K the rate of a bimolecular reaction is ten times the rate at 400°K. Find E the activation energy of this reaction

(*a*) from Arrhenius' law,

(*b*) from collision theory.

(*c*) What is the percentage difference in rate of reaction at 600°K predicted by these two methods?

13. At 250°C the stoichiometry of the first-order gas-phase decomposition of A shows $A \rightarrow 0.96R + 0.04S$. We suspect that this stoichiometry is better explained by considering the competing decomposition paths

$$A \xrightarrow{k_1} R$$
$$A \xrightarrow{k_2} S$$

with $k_1/k_2 = 24$. Further experiments are planned for 300°C. What ratio of rate constants k_1/k_2 would we expect to find if this hypothesis of competing paths is correct?

14. Suppose that the decomposition of hydrocarbon A proceeds in the following manner, $R_1, R_2, \ldots$ being stable product molecules and $X_1, X_2, \ldots$ being free-radical intermediates.

Formation of free radical:

$$A \rightarrow X_1 + R_1, \qquad E_1 = 80 \tag{1}$$

Chain propagation steps:

$$X_1 + A \rightarrow X_2 + R_2, \qquad E_2 = 38 \tag{2}$$
$$X_2 \rightarrow X_1 + R_3, \qquad E_3 = 15 \tag{3}$$

With one of the following three chain termination steps:

$$X_1 + X_1 \rightarrow R_4, \qquad E_4 = 8 \tag{4}$$
$$X_1 + X_2 \rightarrow R_5, \qquad E_5 = 8 \tag{5}$$
$$X_2 + X_2 \rightarrow R_6, \qquad E_6 = 8 \tag{6}$$

With Eq. 4 as the chain termination step, the decomposition of A is given by the approximately 1.5-order rate equation:

$$-\frac{d[A]}{dt} = k_1[A](1 + k_2\sqrt{[A]/k_1k_4}) \approx k_2\sqrt{k_1/k_4}\,[A]^{3/2}$$

With Eq. 5 as the chain termination step, the decomposition of A is given by the first-order rate equation:

$$-\frac{d[A]}{dt} = k_1[A](1 + \sqrt{k_2k_3/2k_1k_5}) \approx \sqrt{k_1k_2k_3/2k_5}\,[A]$$

(*a*) What is the predicted rate equation and order of reaction if Eq. 6 is the chain termination step?

(*b*) Calculate the activation energy for each of these three mechanisms, Eqs. 1, 2, 3, 4, Eqs. 1, 2, 3, 5, and Eqs. 1, 2, 3, 6.

(*c*) Suppose we were considering three distinct sets of reactions:

Set 1 consisting of Eqs. 1, 2, 3, 4.

Set 2 consisting of Eqs. 1, 2, 3, 5.

Set 3 consisting of Eqs. 1, 2, 3, 6.

Which would you expect to be most rapid?

(*d*) Suppose we were considering the decomposition of a single material A in which all three chain termination mechanisms, Eqs. 4, 5, 6, occur competitively and concurrently. Which would you expect to predominate? Solve this by simply examining Eqs. 1 to 6.

(*e*) If your answers to parts *c* and *d* differ, resolve the paradox.

Note: Since E_1 is very large, k_1 is considered to be very much smaller than the other rate constants.

15. Thermal decomposition of hydrocarbons at elevated temperatures often yields mixtures of a wide variety of products. This is explained in terms of a free-radical mechanism with slow formation of radical in the initiation step followed by a variety of rapid chain propagation reactions.

With the following starting materials (*a*) CH_4, (*b*) C_2H_6, (*c*) C_3H_8, (*d*) $C_6H_5CH_3$, what is the most likely chain initiation step?

16. For the reaction

$$H\cdot + CH_4 \underset{k_2}{\overset{k_1}{\rightleftharpoons}} CH_3\cdot + H_2$$

the activation energies have been estimated to be

$$E_1 = 13 \text{ kcal}, \qquad E_2 = 9 \text{ kcal}$$

Estimate the strength of the C—H bond in methane.

17. *Chemical and Engineering News* [**38**, 48 (July 18, 1960)] reports a new and exciting process which uses free radicals for the conversion of radiation into other forms of energy. Essentially the scheme is as follows.

Diatomic gas such as hydrogen is split into free radicals by absorption of radiant energy. These radicals are then adsorbed by a highly porous material. Their recombination on demand releases large quantities of energy for use. The reconstituted molecules are then recycled for retreatment.

(*a*) In a home unit using such a process, how many pounds of atomic hydrogen must be recombined to supply heat for a bath?

(*b*) What must be the recirculation rate in pounds per hour to supply electricity for a television set (250 watts) and two 75-watt lamps.

Assume: For a bath 30 gal of water are to be heated from 40 to 120°F.
Conversion of heat to electricity is 4% efficient.
Heat of adsorption of hydrogen on the porous material is 5 kcal/gm mole.

Before engaging in the commercial operations to produce free radicals, see the additional comments in *Chemical and Engineering News*, **38**, 5 (Oct. 10, 1960); **38**, 5 (Oct. 17, 1960).

3

INTERPRETATION OF BATCH REACTOR DATA

A rate equation characterizes the rate of reaction. The form of the rate equation selected may be dictated by theoretical considerations of a given model or may simply be the result of an empirical curve-fitting procedure. In any case the value of the constants of the equation can only be found by experiment; predictive methods are at present unable to do the job.

The determination of the rate equation is usually a two-step procedure; first the concentration dependency is found at fixed temperature and then the temperature dependence of the rate constants is found, yielding the complete rate equation.

Equipment by which empirical information is obtained can be large or small and rather varied, but it can be divided into two types, the *batch* and *flow* reactors. The batch reactor is simply a container to hold the contents while they react. All that has to be determined is the extent of reaction at various times. As we shall see, an experimental batch reactor is usually operated isothermally and at constant volume because of the ease of interpretation of the results of such runs. The progress of a reaction in a batch reactor can be followed in one of a number of ways.

1. By following the concentration of a given component.
2. By following the change in some physical property of the system such as the electrical conductivity or refractive index.
3. By following the change in total pressure of a constant-volume system.
4. By following the change in volume of a constant-pressure system.

The batch reactor is a relatively simple device adaptable to small-scale laboratory setups. It needs but little auxiliary equipment or instrumentation. Thus it is the preferred device for obtaining homogeneous kinetic data. Most of this chapter is concerned with the batch reactor.

The flow reactor is used primarily in the study of the kinetics of heterogeneous reactions, though in a number of instances it is used to complement and offers advantages over the batch reactor in the study of homogeneous reactions. Reactions which are difficult to follow, reactions with complicated kinetics which yield a variety of products, very rapid reactions, and gas-phase reactions are examples of situations which may be more easily followed in flow reactors. Planning of experiments and interpretation of data obtained in flow reactors are considered in later chapters.

There are two procedures for analyzing experimental kinetic data, the *integral* and the *differential* methods. In the integral method of analysis we select a kinetic model with corresponding rate equation and, after appropriate integrations and mathematical manipulations, predict that a plot of the C versus t data on specific x versus y coordinates should yield a straight line. The data are plotted, and if a reasonably good straight line is obtained the mechanism is said to fit the data satisfactorily.

In the differential method of analysis we select a kinetic model and fit its corresponding rate expression to the data directly. However, since the rate expression is a differential equation, we must first find $\frac{1}{V}\frac{dN}{dt}$ from the data before the fitting procedure is attempted.

There are specific advantages and disadvantages to each of these methods. The integral method is easy to use and is recommended when testing specific mechanisms, when fitting relatively simple mechanisms, or when the data are so scattered that we cannot reliably find the derivatives needed in the differential method. The differential method may be more useful in more complicated situations but requires more accurate or larger amounts of data. The integral method requires that we hypothesize a mechanism of reaction; this is not necessary for the differential method, which may be used to find empirically the equation of best fit to a set of data.

In general, it is suggested that integral analysis be attempted first, and, if not successful, that the differential method be tried. For complicated cases special experimental methods involving partial solution of the problem or use of flow reactors coupled with differential analysis may have to be used.

CONSTANT-VOLUME BATCH REACTOR

When we mention the constant-volume batch reactor we are referring to the volume of the reactor actually taken up by the reaction mixture. Thus we are referring to a constant-density reaction. Most liquid-phase reactions as well as all gas-phase reactions occurring in a constant-volume bomb fall in this class.

In the constant-volume system the measure of the reaction rate becomes simply

$$r_i = \frac{1}{V}\frac{dN_i}{dt} = \frac{1}{V}\frac{d(C_iV)}{dt} = \frac{1}{V}\frac{C_i\,dV + V\,dC_i}{dt} = \frac{dC_i}{dt} \tag{1}$$

or for ideal gases

$$r_i = \frac{1}{RT}\frac{dp_i}{dt} \tag{2}$$

These measures of rate can be followed directly in most systems. Because of the ease of interpretation of such data, the constant-volume system is used whenever possible, even though the commercial exploitation of chemical reactions is usually effected in constant-pressure systems.

No matter how we choose to follow the progress of the reaction, Eqs. 1 and 2 show that eventually we must convert this measure into the concentration or partial pressure of one of the reactants or products if we are to follow the rate of reaction. A convenient and frequently used procedure is to follow the total pressure of the system. Let us next see how such data can be transformed into concentration or partial pressures of the individual reacting materials so that we may use Eq. 1 or 2 to find the reaction rate.

Analysis of total pressure data obtained in a constant-volume system. In isothermal gas-phase reactions where the number of moles of material change during reaction, following the total pressure π of the system, may be the easiest way to determine the progress of the reaction. We tabulate π versus t data, which must then be transformed into a C_i versus t tabulation. Let us derive a general expression with which to find the concentration of any component at any time, given the initial conditions of the system and the reaction stoichiometry. We should emphasize that if the precise stoichiometry is not known, the method cannot be used.

Write the general stoichiometric equation, and under each term indicate the number of moles of that component present:

$$a\text{A} + b\text{B} + \cdots = r\text{R} + s\text{S} + \cdots$$

At time 0:

$$N_{\text{A}0}, \quad N_{\text{B}0}, \quad N_{\text{R}0}, \quad N_{\text{S}0}, \qquad N_{\text{inert}}$$

At time t:

$$N_\text{A} = N_{\text{A}0} - ax, \quad N_\text{B} = N_{\text{B}0} - bx, \quad N_\text{R} = N_{\text{R}0} + rx,$$

$$N_\text{S} = N_{\text{S}0} + sx, \qquad N_{\text{inert}}$$

Initially the total number of moles present in the system is

$$N_0 = N_{A0} + N_{B0} + \cdots + N_{R0} + N_{S0} + \cdots + N_{\text{inert}}$$

but at time t it is

$$N = N_0 + x(r + s + \cdots - a - b - \cdots) = N_0 + x\,\Delta n$$

where

$$\Delta n = r + s + \cdots - a - b - \cdots$$

Assuming that the ideal gas law holds, we may write for any reactant, say A, in the system of volume V

$$C_A = \frac{p_A}{RT} = \frac{N_A}{V} = \frac{N_{A0} - ax}{V}$$

Combining these two expressions we obtain

$$C_A = \frac{N_{A0}}{V} - \frac{a}{\Delta n}\frac{N - N_0}{V}$$

or

$$p_A = C_ART = p_{A0} - \frac{a}{\Delta n}(\pi - \pi_0) \tag{3}$$

Equation 3 gives the concentration or partial pressure of reactant A as a function of the total pressure π at time t, initial partial pressure of A, C_{A0}, and initial total pressure of the system π_0.

Similarly for any product R we can find

$$p_R = C_RRT = p_{R0} + \frac{r}{\Delta n}(\pi - \pi_0) \tag{4}$$

Equations 3 and 4 are the desired relationships between total pressure of the system and the partial pressure of reacting materials.

Integral method of analysis of data

General procedure. The integral method of analysis always puts a specific rate equation to the test by integrating and comparing the predicted C versus t curve with the experimental C versus t data. Invariably this rate equation is suggested by a hypothetical mechanism or model. If the fit is unsatisfactory, the mechanism is rejected and another one suggested and tested. In contrast with the differential method, the integral method is not well suited to the finding of empirical equations of best fit to the data. The procedure may be summarized as follows.

1. A mechanism is hypothesized and its corresponding rate expression is found. This expression, written for the disappearance of reactant A in a constant-volume system, will be of the following form:

$$-r_A = -\frac{dC_A}{dt} = f(kC) \tag{5}$$

or in the more restricted case in which the concentration-dependent terms may be separated from the concentration-independent terms, we have

$$-r_A = -\frac{dC_A}{dt} = kf(C) \tag{6}$$

With either form we proceed as follows; however, it is easier to illustrate the procedure using Eq. 6.

2. Equation 6 is rearranged to give

$$-\frac{dC_A}{f(C_A)} = k\,dt$$

Now $f(C)$ only involves concentrations of materials, which may be expressed in terms of C_A. Thus the left-hand side may be integrated to give

$$-\int_{C_{A0}}^{C_A} \frac{dC_A}{f(C_A)} = F(C_A) = k\int_0^t dt = kt$$

3. From the experimentally found values of concentration of materials, determine the numerical value of $F(C_A)$ at various times. If the integral

$$-\int_{C_{A0}}^{C_A} \frac{dC_A}{f(C_A)}$$

is not easily evaluated, a graphical procedure may be used. The procedure involves finding the area under the $1/f(C_A)$ versus C_A curve to give $F(C_A)$ as shown in Fig. 1.

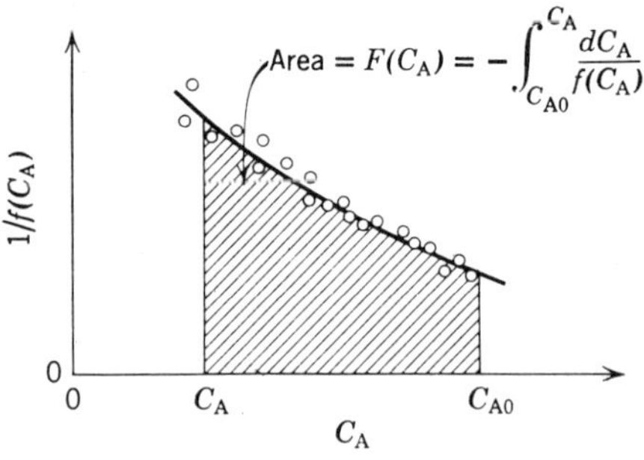

Fig. 1. Graphical integration of a rate equation.

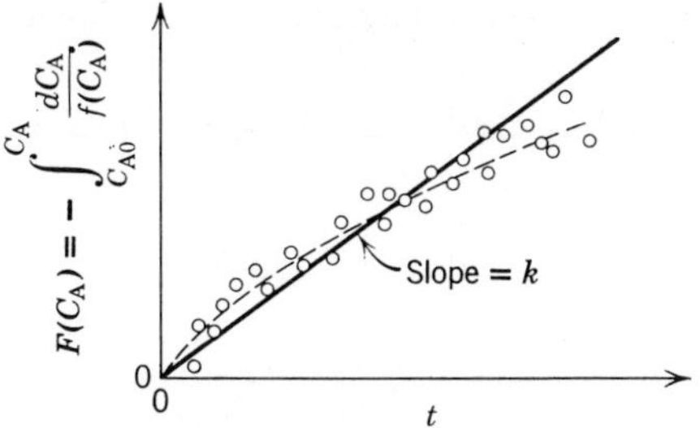

Fig. 2. Test of a rate equation by the integral method of analysis.

4. Plot $F(C_A)$ versus t and see whether this gives a straight line (Fig. 2). If so, then the mechanism selected is consistent with the data.

5. If the data do not seem to fall on a straight line, different mechanisms should be tried until a satisfactory fit is obtained.

The integral method is especially advantageous for fitting simple reaction types corresponding to elementary reactions. Therefore let us next examine a number of these forms.

Irreversible unimolecular-type first-order reactions. Consider the reaction

$$A \rightarrow \text{products}$$

Suppose we wish to test the first-order rate equation of the following type,

$$-\frac{dC_A}{dt} = kC_A \tag{7}$$

for this reaction. Separating and integrating we obtain

$$-\int_{C_{A0}}^{C_A} \frac{dC_A}{C_A} = k\int_0^t dt$$

or

$$-\ln\frac{C_A}{C_{A0}} = kt \tag{8}$$

which is the desired result.

Now the fractional conversion of a given reactant is defined as the fraction of reactant converted into product or

$$N_A = N_{A0}(1 - X_A) \tag{9}$$

Fractional conversion (or simply conversion) is a convenient variable often used in place of concentration in engineering work; therefore most of the results which follow will be presented in terms of both C_A and X_A.

Let us now see how Eq. 8 can be derived using conversions. First of all

$$C_A = \frac{N_A}{V} = \frac{N_{A0}(1 - X_A)}{V} = C_{A0}(1 - X_A)$$

and

$$-dC_A = C_{A0}\, dX_A \tag{10}$$

Hence Eq. 7 becomes

$$\frac{dX_A}{dt} = k(1 - X_A)$$

Integrating we obtain

$$\int_0^{X_A} \frac{dX_A}{1 - X_A} = k \int_0^t dt$$

or

$$-\ln(1 - X_A) = kt \tag{11}$$

a result equivalent to Eq. 8. A plot of $\ln(1 - X_A)$ or $\ln(C_A/C_{A0})$ versus t as shown in Fig. 3 gives a straight line through the origin for an equation of this type.

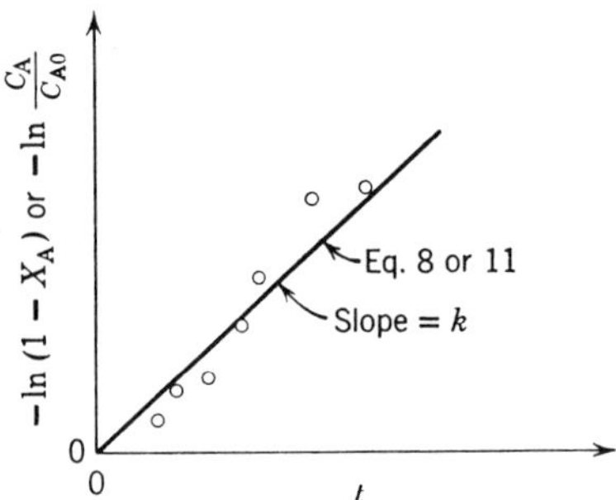

Fig. 3. Test for the first-order reaction, Eq. 7.

Caution: We should point out that equations such as

$$\frac{dC_A}{dt} = kC_A^{0.6}C_B^{0.4}$$

are considered first order but are not necessarily amenable to this kind of analysis. Hence not all first-order reactions can be treated by this method.

Irreversible bimolecular-type second-order reactions. Consider the reaction

$$A + B \rightarrow \text{products}$$

with corresponding rate equation

$$-r_A = -\frac{dC_A}{dt} = -\frac{dC_B}{dt} = kC_AC_B \tag{12}$$

Noting that the amounts of A and B which have disappeared at any time t

* Equation 64 presents a more general relationship between concentration and conversion for variable volume (or variable density) systems.

are $C_{A0}X_A = C_{B0}X_B$ for both A and B, we may write Eq. 12 in terms of X_A:

$$-r_A = C_{A0}\frac{dX_A}{dt} = k(C_{A0} - C_{A0}X_A)(C_{B0} - C_{A0}X_A)$$

Letting $M = C_{B0}/C_{A0}$ be the initial molar ratio of reactants, we obtain

$$-r_A = C_{A0}\frac{dX_A}{dt} = kC_{A0}^2(1 - X_A)(M - X_A)$$

which on separation and formal integration becomes

$$\int_0^{X_A}\frac{dX_A}{(1 - X_A)(M - X_A)} = C_{A0}k\int_0^t dt$$

After breakdown into partial fractions, integration, and rearrangement, the final result is

$$\ln\frac{1 - X_B}{1 - X_A} = \ln\frac{M - X_A}{M(1 - X_A)} = \ln\frac{C_BC_{A0}}{C_{B0}C_A} = \ln\frac{C_B}{MC_A}$$
$$= C_{A0}(M - 1)kt = (C_{B0} - C_{A0})kt, \quad M \neq 1 \qquad (13)$$

Figure 4 shows that a plot of $\ln(C_B/C_A)$ versus t yields a straight line of slope $k(C_{B0} - C_{A0})$ for a reaction following this second-order rate law.

If C_{B0} is much larger than C_{A0}, C_B remains approximately constant at all times, and Eq. 13 approaches Eq. 8 or 11 for the first-order reaction. Thus the second-order reaction becomes a pseudo first-order reaction.

Caution 1. In the special case where reactants are used in the stoichiometric ratio the integrated rate expression becomes indeterminate and

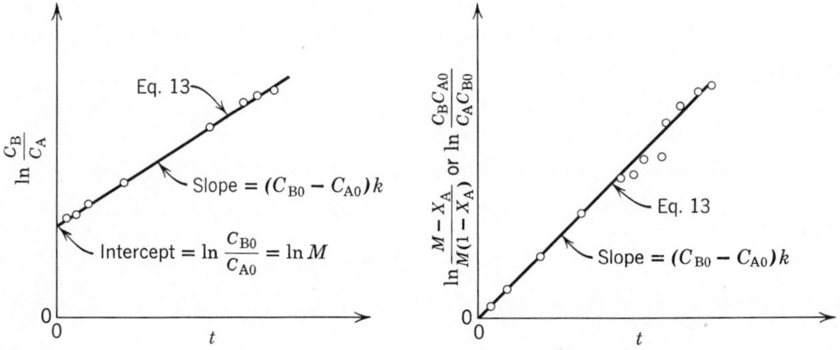

Fig. 4. Test for the bimolecular reaction A + B → products, $C_{A0} \neq C_{B0}$ or rate equation, Eq. 12.

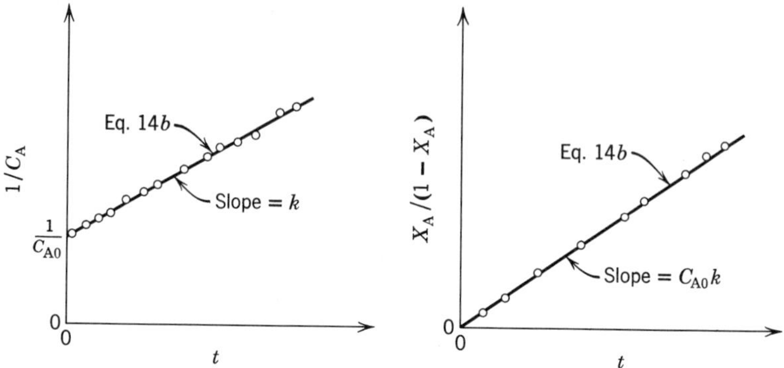

Fig. 5. Test for the bimolecular mechanisms,
A + B → products, $C_{A0} = C_{B0}$
2A → products
or rate equation, Eq. 14.

requires taking limits of quotients for evaluation. This difficulty is avoided if we go back to the original differential rate expression and solve it for this particular reactant ratio. Thus for the second-order reaction when the initial concentrations of reactants A and B are the same or for the reaction

$$2\text{A} \rightarrow \text{products}$$

the defining second-order differential equation becomes

$$-\frac{dC_\text{A}}{dt} = kC_\text{A}^2 = kC_{\text{A}0}^2(1 - X_\text{A})^2 \tag{14a}$$

which on integration yields

$$\frac{1}{C_\text{A}} - \frac{1}{C_{\text{A}0}} = \frac{1}{C_{\text{A}0}}\frac{X_\text{A}}{1 - X_\text{A}} = kt \tag{14b}$$

Thus the plot of $1/C_\text{A}$ versus t as shown in Fig. 5 is a straight line.

In practice we should choose reactant ratios either equal to or widely different from the stoichiometric ratios.

Caution 2. The integrated rate expression depends on the stoichiometry of the reaction as well as the kinetics. To illustrate, if the reaction

$$\text{A} + 2\text{B} \rightarrow \text{products} \tag{15a}$$

is first order with respect to both A and B, hence second order over-all, or

$$-\frac{dC_\text{A}}{dt} = kC_\text{A}C_\text{B} = kC_{\text{A}0}^2(1 - X_\text{A})(M - 2X_\text{A}) \tag{15b}$$

the integrated form is

$$\ln \frac{C_B C_{A0}}{C_{B0} C_A} = \ln \frac{M - 2X_A}{M(1 - X_A)} = C_{A0}(M - 2)kt, \qquad M \neq 2 \quad (15c)$$

With a stoichiometric reactant ratio the integrated form is

$$\frac{1}{C_A} - \frac{1}{C_{A0}} = \frac{1}{C_{A0}} \frac{X_A}{1 - X_A} = 2kt, \qquad M = 2 \qquad (15d)$$

These two comments hold for all reaction types.

Irreversible trimolecular-type third-order reactions. For the reaction

$$A + B + D \rightarrow \text{products}$$

let the rate equation be

$$-r_A = -\frac{dC_A}{dt} = kC_A C_B C_D \qquad (16)$$

or in terms of X_A

$$C_{A0} \frac{dX_A}{dt} = kC_{A0}^3(1 - X_A)\left(\frac{C_{B0}}{C_{A0}} - X_A\right)\left(\frac{C_{D0}}{C_{A0}} - X_A\right)$$

On separation of variables, breakdown into partial fractions, and integration, we obtain finally

$$\frac{1}{(C_{A0} - C_{B0})(C_{A0} - C_{D0})} \ln \frac{C_{A0}}{C_A} + \frac{1}{(C_{B0} - C_{D0})(C_{B0} - C_{A0})} \ln \frac{C_{B0}}{C_B}$$

$$+ \frac{1}{(C_{D0} - C_{A0})(C_{D0} - C_{B0})} \ln \frac{C_{D0}}{C_D} = kt \qquad (17)$$

Now if C_{D0} is much larger than C_{A0} and C_{B0}, the reaction becomes second order and Eq. 17 reduces to Eq. 13.

All trimolecular reactions found so far are of the form of Eq. 18 or 19. Thus we have

$$A + 2B \rightarrow \text{products} \qquad (18a)$$

with differential rate equation

$$-\frac{dC_A}{dt} = kC_A C_B^2 \qquad (18b)$$

or

$$\frac{dX_A}{dt} = kC_{A0}^2(1 - X_A)(M - 2X_A)^2 \tag{18c}$$

where $M = C_{B0}/C_{A0}$. On integration this gives

$$\frac{(2C_{A0} - C_{B0})(C_{B0} - C_B)}{C_{B0}C_B} + \ln\frac{C_{A0}C_B}{C_{B0}C_A} = (2C_{A0} - C_{B0})^2kt, \qquad M \neq 2 \tag{18d}$$

or

$$\frac{1}{C_A^2} - \frac{1}{C_{A0}^2} = 8kt, \qquad M = 2 \tag{18e}$$

For the reaction

$$A + B \rightarrow \text{products} \tag{19a}$$

with differential rate equation

$$-\frac{dC_A}{dt} = kC_AC_B^2 \tag{19b}$$

integration gives

$$\frac{(C_{A0} - C_{B0})(C_{B0} - C_B)}{C_{B0}C_B} + \ln\frac{C_{A0}C_B}{C_{B0}C_A} = (C_{A0} - C_{B0})^2kt, \quad M \neq 1 \tag{19c}$$

or

$$\frac{1}{C_A^2} - \frac{1}{C_{A0}^2} = 2kt, \qquad M = 1 \tag{19d}$$

Empirical rate equations of *n*th order. When the mechanism of reaction is not known, we often attempt to fit the data with an *n*th-order rate equation of the form

$$-r_A = -\frac{dC_A}{dt} = kC_A^n \tag{20}$$

which on separation and integration yields

$$C_A^{1-n} - C_{A0}^{1-n} = (n - 1)kt, \qquad n \neq 1 \tag{21}$$

or in terms of the fraction of A converted

$$C_{A0}^{1-n}[(1 - X_A)^{1-n} - 1] = (n - 1)kt \tag{22}$$

The order n cannot be found explicitly from either Eqs. 21 or 22, so a trial-and-error solution must be made. This is not too difficult a chore, however; we select a value for n and calculate k. The value of n which minimizes the variation in k is the desired value of n.

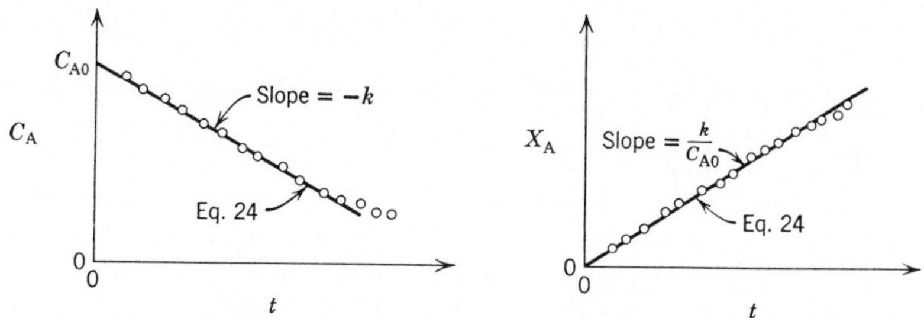

Fig. 6. Test for a zero-order reaction, or rate equation, Eq. 23.

Zero-order reactions. A reaction is zero order when the rate of conversion is independent of the concentration of materials; thus

$$-r_A = -\frac{dC_A}{dt} = k \tag{23}$$

Integrating we obtain directly

$$C_{A0} - C_A = C_{A0}X_A = kt \tag{24}$$

which means that the conversion is proportional to time, as shown in Fig. 6. Zero-order reactions are usually encountered in heterogeneous catalytic kinetics and are always an indication that a complex reaction is occurring involving a number of steps in succession. The bottleneck in the process, the step that determines the rate, is visualized as an equilibrium-type surface-dependent reaction which is relatively slow and independent of reactant concentration; hence the zero order. If the concentration of reactants is lowered sufficiently, however, the concentration-dependent steps in the series will also slow down until the point is reached where these steps become slower than the equilibrium step. They then become controlling, and the reaction order will start rising from zero.

Over-all order of irreversible reactions from the half-life $t_{1/2}$. Often for the irreversible reaction

$$\alpha A + \beta B + \cdots \rightarrow \text{products}$$

we may write

$$-r_A = -\frac{dC_A}{dt} = kC_A{}^a C_B{}^b \cdots$$

Now if the reactants are present in their stoichiometric ratios, they will remain at that ratio throughout the reaction. Thus for reactants A and B at any time $C_B/C_A = \beta/\alpha$. So we may write

$$-r_A = -\frac{dC_A}{dt} = kC_A{}^a\left(\frac{\beta}{\alpha}C_A\right)^b \cdots = k\left(\frac{\beta}{\alpha}\right)^b \cdots C_A^{a+b+\cdots}$$

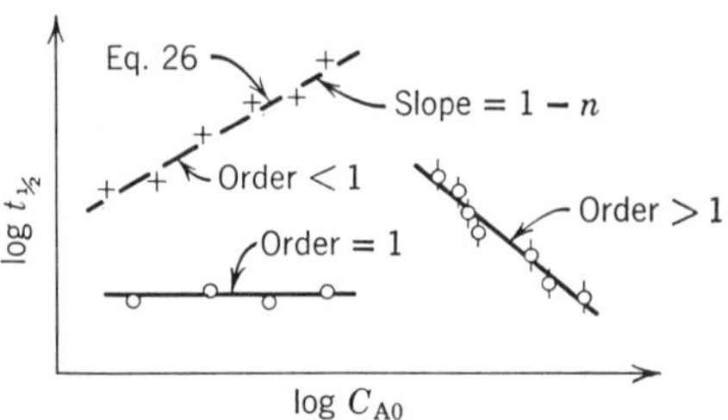

Fig. 7. Over-all order of reaction from a series of half-life experiments, each at a different initial-reactant concentration.

or

$$-\frac{dC_A}{dt} = k'C_A{}^n \tag{25}$$

which on integration for $n \neq 1$ gives

$$C_A^{1-n} - C_{A0}^{1-n} = k'(n-1)t$$

Defining the half-life of the reaction, $t_{1/2}$, as the time needed for the concentration of reactants to drop to one-half the original value, we obtain

$$t_{1/2} = \frac{2^{n-1}-1}{k(n-1)} C_{A0}^{1-n} \tag{26}$$

This expression shows that a plot of log $t_{1/2}$ versus log C_{A0} gives a straight line of slope $1 - n$ as shown in Fig. 7.

Numerous variations of this procedure are possible. For instance, by having all but one component, say A, in excess, we can find the order with respect to that one component. For this situation the general expression reduces to

$$\frac{dC_A}{dt} = k''C_A{}^a$$

where

$$k'' = k(C_{B0}^b \cdots)$$

This method can be extended to any fractional life data $t_{1/m}$ but cannot be used for reactions in which it is impossible to maintain stoichiometric ratios, such as autocatalytic reactions.

The half-life method requires making a series of runs, each at a different initial concentration, and shows that the fractional conversion in given time rises with increased concentration for orders greater than one, drops with increased concentration for orders less than one, and is independent of initial concentration for reactions of first order.

Irreversible reactions in parallel. Consider the simplest case, A decomposing or disappearing by two possible competing paths. both elementary reactions:

$$A \xrightarrow{k_1} R$$

$$A \xrightarrow{k_2} S$$

The rates of change of the three components are

$$-r_A = -\frac{dC_A}{dt} = k_1 C_A + k_2 C_A = (k_1 + k_2) C_A \tag{27}$$

$$r_R = \frac{dC_R}{dt} = k_1 C_A \tag{28}$$

$$r_S = \frac{dC_S}{dt} = k_2 C_A \tag{29}$$

This is the first time we have encountered a complex reaction. In such reactions following the concentration of a single component will not allow us to find the rate constants. Thus following C_A, C_R, or C_S alone will not give k_1 or k_2. At least two components must be followed. Then by simple material balance, noting that $C_A + C_R + C_S$ is constant, we can find the concentration of the third component.

Now the k values are found using all three differential rate equations. Equation 27 is of simple first order and can be integrated to give

$$-\ln \frac{C_A}{C_{A0}} = (k_1 + k_2) t \tag{30}$$

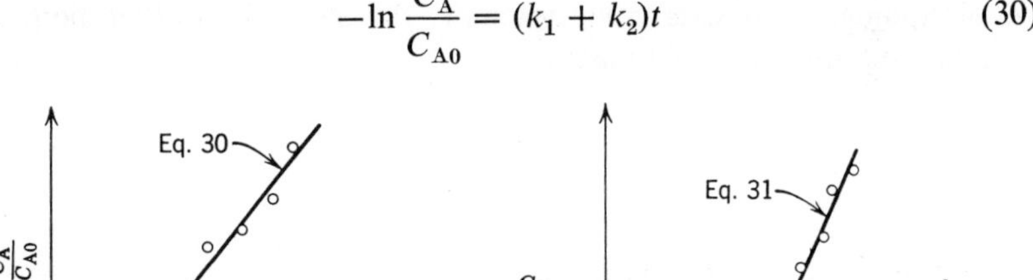

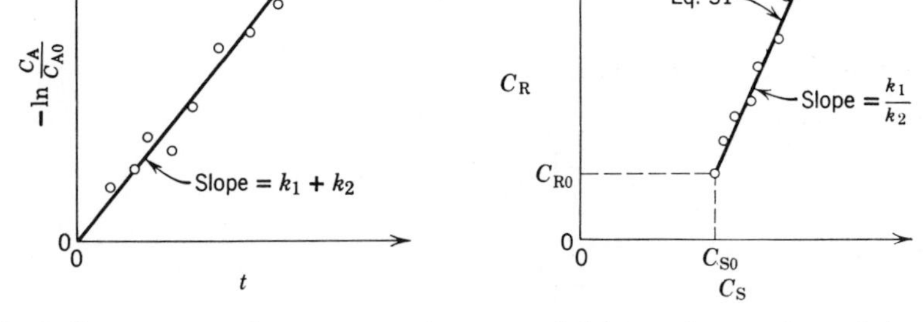

Fig. 8. Rate constants for two competing or parallel first-order reactions of the type $A \begin{smallmatrix} \nearrow R \\ \searrow S \end{smallmatrix}$ with rate equations, Eqs. 27, 28, and 29.

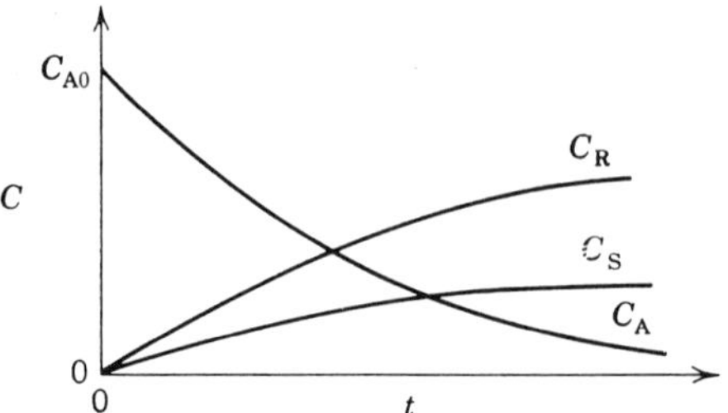

Fig. 9. Typical concentration-time curves for parallel reactions.

When plotted as in Fig. 8, the slope is $k_1 + k_2$. Now dividing Eq. 28 by Eq. 29 we obtain

$$\frac{r_R}{r_S} = \frac{dC_R}{dC_S} = \frac{k_1}{k_2}$$

which when integrated gives simply

$$\frac{C_R - C_{R0}}{C_S - C_{S0}} = \frac{k_1}{k_2} \tag{31}$$

This result is shown in Fig. 8. Thus the slope of a plot of C_R versus C_S gives the ratio k_1/k_2. Knowing k_1/k_2 as well as $k_1 + k_2$ gives k_1 and k_2. Typical concentration-time curves of the three components in a batch reactor for the reaction when $C_{R0} = C_{S0} = 0$ and $k_1 > k_2$ are shown in Fig. 9.

Homogeneous catalyzed reactions. Suppose the reaction rate for a homogeneous catalyzed system is the sum of rates of both the uncatalyzed and catalyzed reactions,

$$A \xrightarrow{k_1} R$$

$$A + C \xrightarrow{k_2} R + C$$

with corresponding reaction rates

$$-\left(\frac{dC_A}{dt}\right)_1 = k_1 C_A$$

$$-\left(\frac{dC_A}{dt}\right)_2 = k_2 C_A C_C$$

This means that the reaction would proceed even without a catalyst present and that the rate of catalyzed reaction is directly proportional to

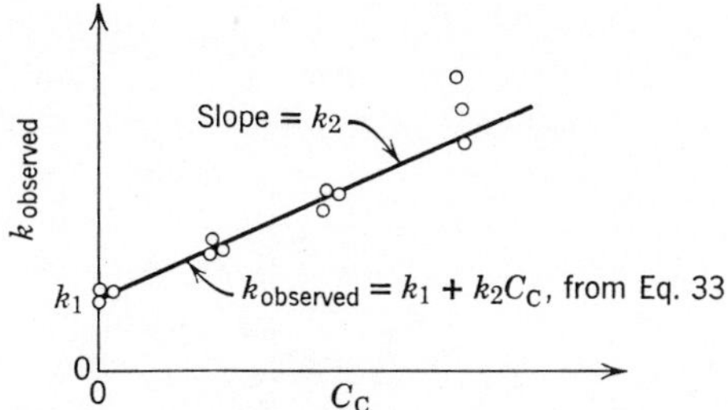

Fig. 10. Rate constants for a homogeneous catalyzed reaction from a series of runs with different catalyst concentrations.

the catalyst concentration. The over-all rate of disappearance of reactant A is

$$-\frac{dC_A}{dt} = k_1C_A + k_2C_AC_C = (k_1 + k_2C_C)C_A \tag{32}$$

On integration, noting that the catalyst concentration remains unchanged, we have

$$-\ln\frac{C_A}{C_{A0}} = -\ln(1 - X_A) = (k_1 + k_2C_C)t = k_{\text{observed}}t \tag{33}$$

Making a series of runs with varying catalyst concentration allows us to find k_1 and k_2. This is done by plotting the observed k value against the catalyst concentration as shown in Fig. 10. The slope of such a plot is k_2 and the intercept k_1.

Reactions in parallel are considered in more detail in Chapter 7.

Autocatalytic reactions. A reaction in which one of the products of reaction acts as a catalyst is called an autocatalytic reaction. The simplest such reaction is

$$A + R \rightarrow R + R$$

for which the rate equation is

$$-r_A = -\frac{dC_A}{dt} = kC_AC_R$$

Now the total number of moles of A and R remain unchanged as A is consumed. Thus at any time we may write

$$C_0 = C_A + C_R = C_{A0} + C_{R0} = \text{constant}$$

Thus the rate equation becomes

$$-r_A = -\frac{dC_A}{dt} = kC_A(C_0 - C_A) \tag{34}$$

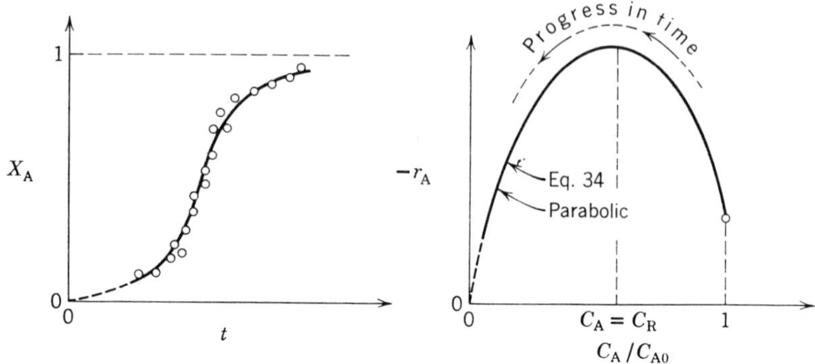

Fig. 11. Characteristic conversion-time and rate-concentration curves for autocatalytic reactions.

Rearranging and breaking into partial fractions, we obtain

$$-\frac{dC_A}{C_A(C_0 - C_A)} = -\frac{1}{C_0}\left(\frac{dC_A}{C_A} + \frac{dC_A}{C_0 - C_A}\right) = k\,dt$$

which on integration becomes

$$\ln \frac{C_{A0}(C_0 - C_A)}{C_A(C_0 - C_{A0})} = \ln \frac{C_{A0}C_R}{C_A C_{R0}} = C_0 kt = (C_{A0} + C_{R0})kt \qquad (35)$$

In terms of the initial-reactant ratio $M = C_{R0}/C_{A0}$ and fractional conversion of A we obtain

$$\ln \frac{M + X_A}{M(1 - X_A)} = C_{A0}(M + 1)kt = (C_{A0} + C_{R0})kt \qquad (36)$$

In an autocatalytic reaction some product R must be present if the reaction is to proceed at all. Starting with a very small concentration of R, we see qualitatively that the rate will rise as R is formed. At the other extreme, when A is just about used up the rate must drop to zero. This result is given in Fig. 11, which shows that the rate follows a parabola, the maximum occurring when the concentrations of A and R are equal.

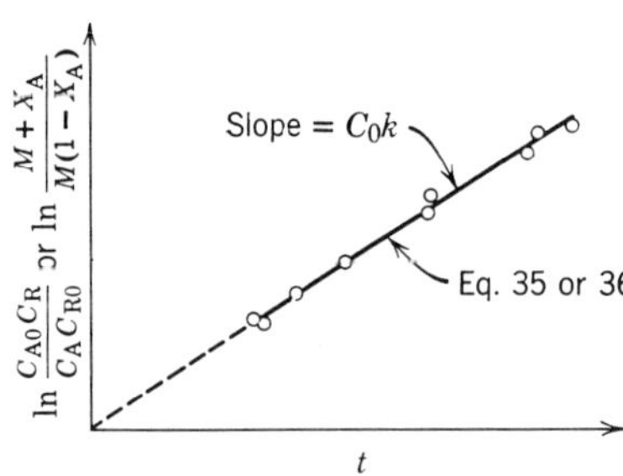

Fig. 12. Test of mechanism for autocatalytic reactions, or rate equation, Eq. 34.

To test for an autocatalytic reaction, plot the time and concentration coordinates of Eq. 35 or 36 as shown in Fig. 12 and see whether a straight line passing through zero results. Autocatalytic reactions are considered in more detail in Chapter 6.

Irreversible reactions in series. We at first consider consecutive unimolecular-type first-order reactions such as

$$A \xrightarrow{k_1} R \xrightarrow{k_2} S$$

whose rate equations for the three components are

$$\frac{dC_A}{dt} = -k_1 C_A \tag{37}$$

$$\frac{dC_R}{dt} = k_1 C_A - k_2 C_R \tag{38}$$

$$\frac{dC_S}{dt} = k_2 C_R \tag{39}$$

Let us start with a concentration C_{A0} of A, no R or S present, and see how the concentrations of the various materials vary. By integration of Eq. 37 we find the concentration of A to be

$$-\ln \frac{C_A}{C_{A0}} = k_1 t \qquad \text{or} \qquad C_A = C_{A0} e^{-k_1 t} \tag{40}$$

To find the variation in concentration of R, substitute the concentration of A from Eq. 40 into the differential equation governing the rate of change of R, Eq. 38; thus

$$\frac{dC_R}{dt} + k_2 C_R = k_1 C_{A0} e^{-k_1 t} \tag{41}$$

which is the first-order linear differential equation of the form

$$\frac{dy}{dx} + Py = Q$$

By multiplying through with the integrating factor $e^{\int P\,dx}$, the solution is

$$y e^{\int P\,dx} = \int Q e^{\int P\,dx}\,dx + \text{constant}$$

Applying this general procedure to the integration of Eq. 41, we find that the integrating factor is $e^{k_2 t}$. The constant of integration is found to be $-k_1 C_{A0}/(k_2 - k_1)$ from the boundary condition $C_{R0} = 0$ at $t = 0$, and the final expression for the variation in concentration of R is

$$C_R = C_{A0} k_1 \left(\frac{e^{-k_1 t}}{k_2 - k_1} + \frac{e^{-k_2 t}}{k_1 - k_2} \right) \tag{42}$$

Noting that for the constant-volume system there is no net change in total number of moles, we find the material balance at any time to be

$$C_{A0} = C_A + C_R + C_S$$

which with Eqs. 40 and 41 gives

$$C_S = C_{A0}\left(1 + \frac{k_2}{k_1 - k_2} e^{-k_1 t} + \frac{k_1}{k_2 - k_1} e^{-k_2 t}\right) \tag{43}$$

Thus we have found how the concentrations of components A, R, and S vary with time.

Now if k_2 is much larger than k_1, we obtain from Eq. 43

$$C_S = C_{A0}(1 - e^{-k_1 t})$$

In other words, the rate is determined by k_1 or the first step of the two-step reaction.

If k_1 is much larger than k_2, then

$$C_S = C_{A0}(1 - e^{-k_2 t})$$

which is a first-order reaction governed by k_2, the slower step in the two-step reaction. Thus for reactions in series it is the slowest step that has the greatest influence on the over-all reaction rate.

As may be expected, the values of k_1 and k_2 also govern the location and maximum concentration of R. This may be found by differentiating Eq. 42 and setting $dC_R/dt = 0$. The time at which maximum concentration of R occurs is thus

$$t_{max} = \frac{1}{k_{\log mean}} = \frac{\ln (k_2/k_1)}{k_2 - k_1} \tag{44}$$

The maximum concentration of R is found by combining Eqs. 42 and 44. Thus

$$\frac{C_{R,max}}{C_{A0}} = \left(\frac{k_1}{k_2}\right)^{k_2/(k_2 - k_1)} \tag{45}$$

Figure 13 shows the general characteristics of the concentration-time curves of the three components; A decreases exponentially, R rises to a maximum and then falls, and S rises continuously, the greatest rate of increase of S occurring where R is a maximum.

Chapter 7 discusses series reactions in more detail. Specifically, Fig. 7.1 shows how the location and value of $C_{R,max}$ are related to the k_1/k_2 ratio. These may be used to find k_1 and k_2.

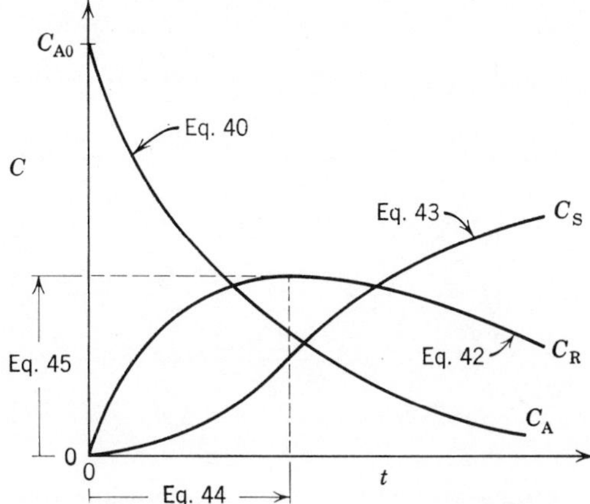

Fig. 13. Typical concentration-time curves for two consecutive first-order reactions.

The following suggestions will help in exploring the kinetics of a series reaction for which the orders of the individual steps are unknown.

1. First determine whether the reaction can be treated as irreversible by seeing whether any reactants or intermediates are still present in the mixture after a long time.

2. Then, if the reaction is irreversible, examine the concentration-time curve for the reactants. This will give the reaction order and rate constant for the first step.

3. Find how the maximum concentration of intermediate varies as the reactant concentration is changed. For example, if the first step is of first order and $C_{R,\,max}/C_{A0}$ is independent of C_{A0}, the second step of the series is first order as well. If, however, $C_{R,\,max}/C_{A0}$ drops as C_{A0} rises, the disappearance of R becomes more rapid than its formation. Therefore the disappearance, or second step, is more concentration-sensitive and consequently is of a higher order than the first step. Similarly, if $C_{R,\,max}/C_{A0}$ rises as C_{A0} rises, the second step is of a lower order than the first step.

For reversible reactions of order other than one the analysis becomes more difficult.

For a longer chain of reactions, say

$$A \rightarrow R \rightarrow S \rightarrow T \rightarrow U$$

the treatment is similar, though somewhat more cumbersome than the two-step reaction just considered. Figure 14 illustrates typical concentration-time curves for this situation. Again, as with reactions in parallel, flow reactors may be more useful than batch reactors in the study of these multiple reactions.

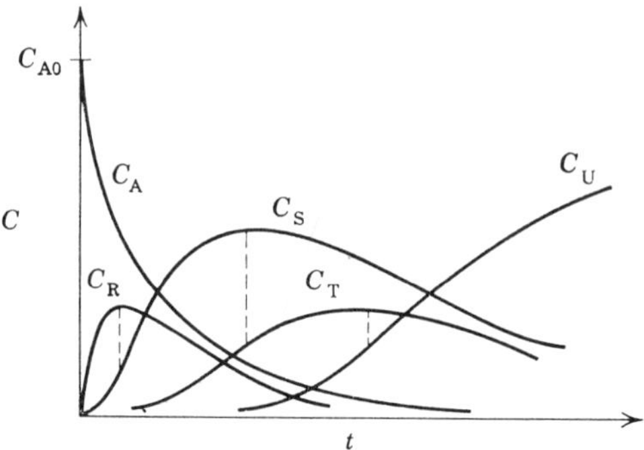

Fig. 14. Concentration-time curves for a chain of successive first-order reactions.

First-order reversible reactions. Though no reaction ever goes to completion, we can consider many reactions to be essentially irreversible because of the large value of the equilibrium constant. These are the situations we have examined up to this point. Let us now consider reactions for which complete conversion cannot be assumed. The simplest case is the opposed unimolecular-type reaction

$$A \underset{k_2}{\overset{k_1}{\rightleftharpoons}} R, \qquad K_C = K = \text{equilibrium constant}$$

Starting with concentrations C_{A0} and C_{R0}, we have the rate equation

$$\frac{dC_R}{dt} = -\frac{dC_A}{dt} = C_{A0}\frac{dX_A}{dt} = k_1C_A - k_2C_R = k_1(C_{A0} - C_{A0}X_A) - k_2(C_{R0} + C_{A0}X_A) \quad (46)$$

Now at equilibrium $dC_A/dt = 0$. Hence from Eq. 46 we find the fractional conversion of A at equilibrium conditions to be

$$X_{Ae} = \frac{K_C - C_{R0}/C_{A0}}{K_C + 1} \quad (47)$$

and the equilibrium constant to be

$$K_C = \frac{C_{Re}}{C_{Ae}} = \frac{C_{R0} + C_{A0}X_{Ae}}{C_{A0} - C_{A0}X_{Ae}} = \frac{k_1}{k_2} \quad (48)$$

Combining Eqs. 46, 47, and 48 to eliminate C_{R0} and C_{Re}, we obtain the rate equation in terms of equilibrium conversion:

$$\frac{dX_A}{dt} = (k_1 + k_2)(X_{Ae} - X_A) \quad (49)$$

With conversions measured in terms of X_{Ae}, this may be looked on as a pseudo first-order irreversible reaction which on integration gives

$$-\ln\left(1 - \frac{X_A}{X_{Ae}}\right) = -\ln\frac{C_A - C_{Ae}}{C_{A0} - C_{Ae}} = k_1\left(1 + \frac{1}{K_C}\right)t = (k_1 + k_2)t \qquad (50)$$

A plot of $-\ln(1 - X_A/X_{Ae})$ versus t as shown in Fig. 15 gives a straight line of slope $k_1(1 + 1/K_C)$.

The similarity between equations for the first-order irreversible and reversible reactions can be seen by comparing Eq. 11 with Eq. 50 or by comparing Fig. 3 with Fig. 15. The reversible reaction may be considered to be irreversible if the concentration is measured by $C_A - C_{Ae}$, or the concentration in excess of the equilibrium value. The fraction conversion is then based on 100% conversion at the maximum attainable or equilibrium conversion. On the other hand, we see that the irreversible reaction is simply the special case of the reversible reaction in which $C_{Ae} = 0$ or $X_{Ae} = 1$ or $K_C = \infty$.

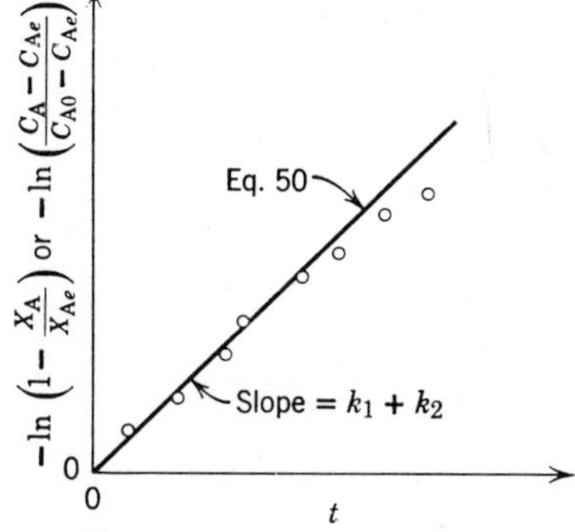

Fig. 15. Test of mechanism for unimolecular-type reversible reactions, or rate equation, Eq. 46.

Second-order reversible reactions. For bimolecular reactions with restrictions $C_{A0} = C_{B0}$ and $C_{R0} = C_{S0} = 0$ the integrated forms of the rate equations can be treated graphically. Thus for either of the reactions

$$\left.\begin{aligned} A + B &\underset{k_2}{\overset{k_1}{\rightleftharpoons}} R + S \\ 2A &\underset{k_2}{\overset{k_1}{\rightleftharpoons}} 2R \end{aligned}\right\} \qquad (51)$$

the integrated form is

$$\ln\frac{X_{Ae} - (2X_{Ae} - 1)X_A}{X_{Ae} - X_A} = 2\frac{k_1}{\sqrt{K_C}}C_{A0}t = 2k_1\left(\frac{1}{X_{Ae}} - 1\right)C_{A0}t \qquad (52)$$

For the reaction

$$2A \underset{k_2}{\overset{k_1}{\rightleftharpoons}} R + S \qquad (53)$$

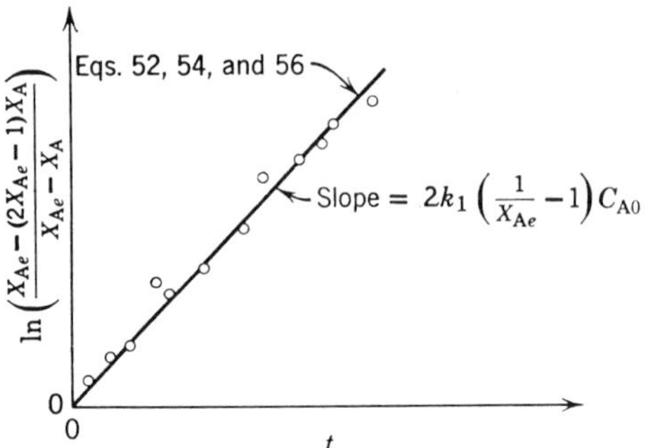

Fig. 16. Test for various reversible bimolecular reactions.

the integrated form is

$$\ln\frac{X_{Ae}-(2X_{Ae}-1)X_A}{X_{Ae}-X_A}=\frac{k_1}{\sqrt{K_C}}C_{A0}t=2k_1\left(\frac{1}{X_{Ae}}-1\right)C_{A0}t \quad (54)$$

and for the reaction

$$A+B \underset{k_2}{\overset{k_1}{\rightleftharpoons}} 2R \quad (55)$$

the integrated form is

$$\ln\frac{X_{Ae}-(2X_{Ae}-1)X_A}{X_{Ae}-X_A}=4\frac{k_1}{\sqrt{K_C}}C_{A0}t=2k_1\left(\frac{1}{X_{Ae}}-1\right)C_{A0}t \quad (56)$$

For all these integrated forms, a plot of

$$\ln\frac{X_{Ae}-(2X_{Ae}-1)X_A}{X_{Ae}-X_A}$$

versus time yields a straight line as shown in Fig. 16.

Reversible reactions in general. Integration of the rate equations for reversible reactions with orders other than one and two is difficult and does not yield conveniently to graphical method of comparison with experimental data. These reactions which do not go to completion, however, are often conveniently fitted by using differential methods on initial rate data or some of the simpler of the reversible-reaction models. With the latter approach the unimolecular-type reversible model is particularly attractive because of the simplicity of the equation involved. If this does not fit, we should then try some of the bimolecular-type equations.

For all such procedures the actual equilibrium conversion must be found. Then from this conversion and the model selected we can calculate a pseudo-equilibrium constant which may well be different from the true thermodynamic equilibrium constant. This pseudo-equilibrium constant should be used in the integrated rate expressions rather than the true equilibrium constant.

No matter what the form of the empirical rate equation, it should extrapolate logically to the extremes if it is to be valuable over a wide range of conditions. Thus at no time should the rate be infinite; in addition, as equilibrium is approached the rate should approach zero. Forms of the rate equation given above do satisfy these conditions.

Reactions with pseudo-equilibria. A number of reactions seem to have the following rate characteristics; they go, but they stop short of thermodynamic equilibrium. Such a situation may be visualized with the aid of the following analogy. Consider a block sliding down a sloped surface as shown in Fig. 17. If the sliding movement is frictionless, the block will end up at the lowest point, the equilibrium position. But if there is friction between block and surface, the block may end up short of equilibrium. Analogously, chemical reactions which stop short of thermodynamic equilibrium will have in their rate equation a frictionlike or resistance term. If K is large so that the reaction should be essentially irreversible, the rate equation for a reaction which does not go to completion is

$$-r_A = -\frac{dC_A}{dt} = f(C) - Q$$

where Q is a constant which serves to lower the rate of reaction. Thus a first-order irreversible reaction which only reaches conversion X_{Ae} will have the rate equation

$$-r_A = -\frac{dC_A}{dt} = kC_A - Q$$

When $dC_A/dt = 0$, we find that $Q = kC_{Ae}$. Therefore

$$-\frac{dC_A}{dt} = k(C_A - C_{Ae})$$

or on integrating

$$-\ln \frac{C_A - C_{Ae}}{C_{A0} - C_{Ae}} = -\ln \frac{X_{Ae} - X_A}{X_{Ae}} = kt$$

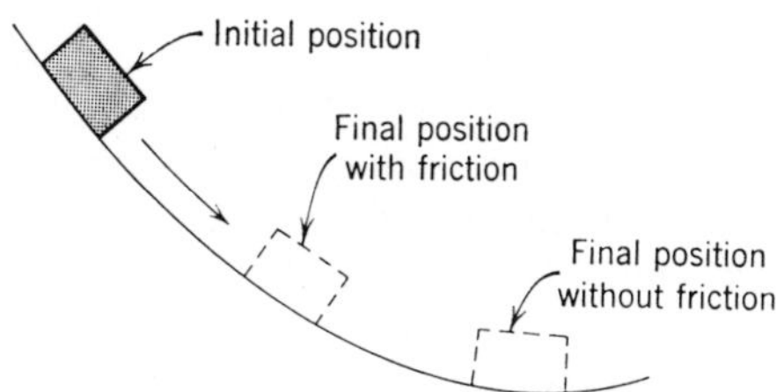

Fig. 17. Mechanical analogy to the chemical reaction which stops short of equilibrium.

which is similar to the reversible first-order reaction, Eq. 50, with equilibrium conversion X_{Ae}.

Thus we may state: treat reactions which do not go all the way to equilibrium in the same manner as reversible reactions; however, use as the equilibrium conversion the experimentally found limiting conversion of reactant.

Differential method of analysis of data

The differential method of analysis deals directly with the differential rate equation to be tested, evaluating all terms in the equation, including the derivative dC_i/dt and testing the goodness of fit of the equation with the experimental points.

We may plan the experimental program to evaluate the complete rate equation in question, or we may plan a program to evaluate separately the various parts of the rate equation which are subsequently combined to give the complete rate equation. The former method is suggested when we are testing a simple rate expression; the latter is used when no model tested by the procedures already suggested has yielded a satisfactory fit. Thus this is an exploratory procedure. These two procedures are outlined in turn.

Analysis of the complete rate equation. The analysis of the complete rate equation by the differential method may be summarized as follows.

1. Hypothesize a mechanism and from it obtain a rate equation. As with the integral analysis, it will be of the form of either

$$-r_A = -\frac{dC_A}{dt} = f(kC) \tag{7}$$

or

$$-r_A = -\frac{dC_A}{dt} = kf(C) \tag{8}$$

If it is of the latter form, proceed with step 2; if of the former, see the remarks following step 5.

2. From the experimental concentration-time curve find $-(dC_A/dt)$ at various times.

3. At the selected time intervals tabulate the concentrations of the various reactants and products as well as the derivative $-(dC_A/dt)$. From these find the value of the function $f(C)$ and tabulate.

4. Plot $-(dC_A/dt)$ versus $f(C)$. If we obtain a straight line through the origin, the rate equation is consistent with the data. Consequently, as far as kinetics can tell, the rate equation is satisfactory and the mechanism from which it is derived can be correct (Fig. 18).

5. If we do not obtain a straight line through the origin, another mechanism should be considered.

If the rate equation to be tested or to be fitted to the data is of the general type of Eq. 7, then the whole problem becomes much more involved. Then we may have to resort either to some form of least-squares analysis or to the method of finite differences to evaluate the constants of the rate equation. In the latter method the differential equation for the rate is replaced by a difference equation, values of the constants are selected, small increments of any variable are chosen, and by calculating corresponding values of the other variables from point to point the whole C versus t curve is constructed. This is then compared with the actual points. If they do not match, different values of the constants are chosen and the process is repeated. As may be expected, this procedure involves considerable trial and error, and the wisdom of its use may be questioned because it is not even known at this point whether the form of the equation being examined will give a satisfactory fit, even with the best values for the constants. In such cases it is probably better to turn to some other procedure.

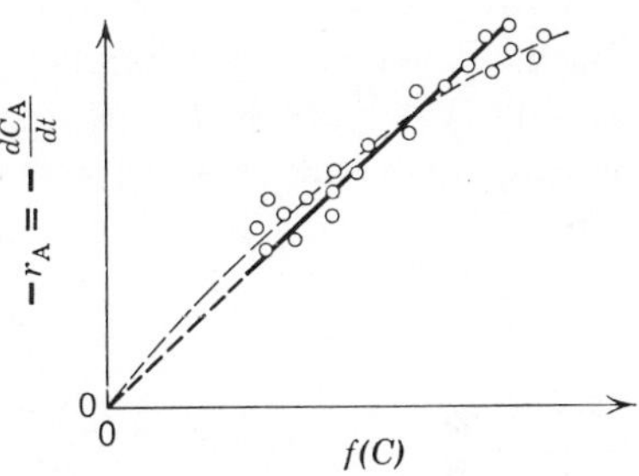

Fig. 18. Test of a rate equation by the differential method of analysis.

Partial analysis of the rate equation. Frequently we can avoid such complications by using foresight in wisely planning the experimental program and by not trying to solve the whole problem at one time. When we have no rate equation in mind, the partial solution approach is especially appealing.

As an illustration consider the reaction

$$A \rightleftharpoons R + S$$

which is not elementary. Suppose, on starting with either A or R and S, that we end up with a mixture of all three components. We may expect that one of the number of rate equations such as

$$-\frac{dC_A}{dt} = k_1 C_A{}^a - k_2 C_R{}^r C_S{}^s \qquad (57)$$

or

$$-\frac{dC_A}{dt} = \frac{k_1' C_A - k_2' C_R{}^2 C_S}{1 + k_3' C_S} \qquad (58)$$

will fit the data. How do we check this?

We could use the *method of isolation* in which we make kinetic runs starting only with reactant A, ending the run before the concentrations of R and S become appreciable. Thus the above rate equations given become

$$-\frac{dC_A}{dt} = k_1 C_A{}^a \tag{57a}$$

and

$$-\frac{dC_A}{dt} = k_1' C_A \tag{58a}$$

which are much easier to handle than the complete rate equation. Similarly, starting with pure R and S and ending before the concentration of A becomes appreciable, we have to deal only with

$$-\frac{dC_R}{dt} = k_2 C_R{}^r C_S{}^s \tag{57b}$$

and

$$-\frac{dC_R}{dt} = \frac{k_2' C_R{}^2 C_S}{1 + k_3' C_S} \tag{58b}$$

A very useful procedure for analyzing data in the absence of various components is the *method of initial rates*, in which the reaction rate is measured for a differential change in composition of reactant. Referring to Eq. 57*a*, if we start with pure A and measure the rate while this reactant has changed in concentration by but a small amount, then dC_A/dt can be replaced by $\Delta C_A/\Delta t$, the concentrations of R and S can be taken to be zero, and Eq. 57*a* becomes

$$-\frac{\Delta C_A}{\Delta t} = k_1 C_A{}^a \tag{58c}$$

A series of runs with varying concentration of reactants but with no R and S present will yield k_1 and a. Hence the key to this procedure is not to make a time run but to make a series of initial-rate determinations at different initial conditions. It should be pointed out that for this procedure precise measurements of concentrations are necessary.

Another technique, the *method of least squares*, is especially useful for the fitting of equations of the type

$$-\frac{dC_A}{dt} = kC_A{}^a C_B{}^b \cdots \tag{59}$$

where $k, a, b, \ldots$ are to be determined. The technique is described as follows. Take logarithms of Eq. 59. Thus

$$\log\left(-\frac{dC_A}{dt}\right) = \log k + a \log C_A + b \log C_B + \cdots$$

which is of the form

$$y = a_0 + a_1x_1 + a_2x_2 + \cdots$$

This may be solved [see Levenspiel et al. (1956)] to yield the values of best fit for $a_0 = \log k$, $a_1 = a$, $a_2 = b$, etc.

Alternately, using the *method of excess*, we may find the orders $a, b, \ldots$ one at a time in separate experiments by keeping in great excess all components other than the one to be examined. For example, if all but A are in great excess, their concentrations will be unchanged. Thus Eq. 59 reduces to

$$-\frac{dC_A}{dt} = k(C_{B0}{}^b \cdots)C_A{}^a$$

which may be solved simply by plotting $-(dC_A/dt)$ versus C_A on log-log paper.

With any given problem we must use good judgment in planning a fruitful experimental program. Usually the clues and partial information obtained in any set of runs will guide and suggest the line of further experimentation. Needless to say, after the various parts of the rate equation are found, the resulting complete equation should be checked to see whether all interactions have been accounted for by making an integral kinetic run in which all materials are present and are made to vary over wide concentration ranges.

VARIABLE-VOLUME BATCH REACTOR

The general form for the rate of change of component i in either the constant or variable-volume reaction system is

$$r_i = \frac{1}{V}\frac{dN_i}{dt} = \frac{1}{V}\frac{d(C_iV)}{dt} = \frac{1}{V}\frac{V\,dC_i + C_i\,dV}{dt}$$

or

$$r_i = \frac{dC_i}{dt} + \frac{C_i}{V}\frac{dV}{dt} \tag{60}$$

Hence two terms must be evaluated from experiment if r_i is to be found. Luckily, for the constant-volume system the second term drops out, leaving the simple expression

$$r_i = \frac{dC_i}{dt} \tag{1}$$

In the variable-volume reactor we may also avoid the use of the cumbersome two-term expression of Eq. 60 if we use fractional conversion rather than concentration as the primary variable. However, this simplification can only be effected if we make the restriction that the volume of reacting system varies linearily with conversion or

$$V = V_0(1 + \varepsilon_A X_A) \tag{61}$$

where ε_A is the fractional change in volume of the system between no conversion and complete conversion. Thus

$$\varepsilon_A = \frac{V_{X_A=1} - V_{X_A=0}}{V_{X_A=0}} \tag{62}$$

As an example consider the isothermal gas-phase reaction

$$A \rightarrow 4R$$

By starting with pure reactant A,

$$\varepsilon_A = \frac{4 - 1}{1} = 3$$

but with 50% inerts present two volumes of reactant mixture yield on complete conversion five volumes of product mixture; thus

$$\varepsilon_A = \frac{5 - 2}{2} = 1.5$$

We see then that ε_A accounts for both the reaction stoichiometry and the presence of inerts. Noting that

$$N_A = N_{A0}(1 - X_A) \tag{63}$$

we have, on combining with Eq. 61,

$$C_A = \frac{N_A}{V} = \frac{N_{A0}(1 - X_A)}{V_0(1 + \varepsilon_A X_A)} = C_{A0}\frac{1 - X_A}{1 + \varepsilon_A X_A}$$

or

$$\frac{C_A}{C_{A0}} = \frac{1 - X_A}{1 + \varepsilon_A X_A} \tag{64}$$

which is the relationship between conversion and concentration for variable-volume (or variable-density) systems satisfying the linearity assumption of Eq. 61. This is a reasonable restrictive assumption which holds for all practical purposes for isothermal constant-pressure systems in which no reactions in series occur, and for many nonisothermal systems.

With these relationships Eq. 60, written for reactant A, becomes

$$
\begin{aligned}
-r_A &= -\frac{1}{V}\frac{dN_A}{dt} = -\frac{1}{V_0(1+\varepsilon_A X_A)}\frac{N_{A0}d(1-X_A)}{dt} \\
&= \frac{C_{A0}}{1+\varepsilon_A X_A}\frac{dX_A}{dt}
\end{aligned}
\tag{65}
$$

which certainly is easier to handle than Eq. 60. Note that when ε_A equals zero Eq. 65 reduces to Eq. 1.

The reaction is most conveniently followed by determining the progressive change in volume of system with time. This volume change ΔV is converted into fractional conversions with Eq. 61, which can then be used in Eq. 65. These relationships apply for all compositions of active materials, either in the presence or in the absence of inerts.

The development to follow is based on the assumption made in Eq. 61 that the volume change of the system varies linearly with conversion.

Differential method of analysis

The differential method of data analysis of isothermal variable-volume reactors procedure as that for the constant-volume situation except that we must replace

$$\frac{dC_A}{dt} \text{ by } \frac{dC_A}{dt} + C_A\frac{d\ln V}{dt} \text{ or preferably by } \frac{C_{A0}}{1+\varepsilon_A X_A}\frac{dX_A}{dt}.$$

Integral method of analysis

The integral method of data analysis of isothermal variable-volume reactors requires integration of the rate expression to be tested. The resulting C versus t function is then compared with the experimental data. Thus for reactant A

$$-r_A = -\frac{1}{V}\frac{dN_A}{dt} = \frac{C_{A0}}{1+\varepsilon_A X_A}\frac{dX_A}{dt}$$

Integrating formally we obtain

$$C_{A0}\int_0^{X_A}\frac{dX_A}{(1+\varepsilon_A X_A)(-r_A)} = t \tag{66}$$

the expression for all forms of batch reactors in which the volume or density is a linear function of the conversion of material. We shall now consider special instances of this expression which are amenable to integration and simple graphical checking. Such instances are few in number when compared to those for the constant-volume reactor.

Zero-order reactions. In a zero-order reaction the rate of change of any reactant A is independent of concentration of that reactant, or

$$-r_A = -\frac{1}{V}\frac{dN_A}{dt} = \frac{C_{A0}}{1 + \varepsilon_A X_A}\frac{dX_A}{dt} = k \tag{67}$$

With Eq. 66 we obtain

$$C_{A0}\int_0^{X_A}\frac{dX_A}{1 + \varepsilon_A X_A} = \frac{C_{A0}}{\varepsilon_A}\ln(1 + \varepsilon_A X_A) = \frac{C_{A0}}{\varepsilon_A}\ln\frac{V}{V_0} = kt \tag{68}$$

As shown in Fig. 19 the logarithm of the fractional change in volume versus time yields a straight line of slope $k\varepsilon_A/C_{A0}$ for a zero-order reaction.

First-order reactions. For a unimolecular-type first-order reaction the rate of change of a reactant A is

$$-r_A = -\frac{1}{V}\frac{dN_A}{dt} = kC_A \tag{69}$$

This equation is transformed into conversion units by combining it with Eqs. 64, and 65. Thus

$$-r_A = \frac{C_{A0}}{1 + \varepsilon_A X_A}\frac{dX_A}{dt} = \frac{kC_{A0}(1 - X_A)}{1 + \varepsilon_A X_A} \tag{70}$$

Integrating, we obtain

$$\int_0^{X_A}\frac{dX_A}{1 - X_A} = -\ln(1 - X_A) = kt \tag{71}$$

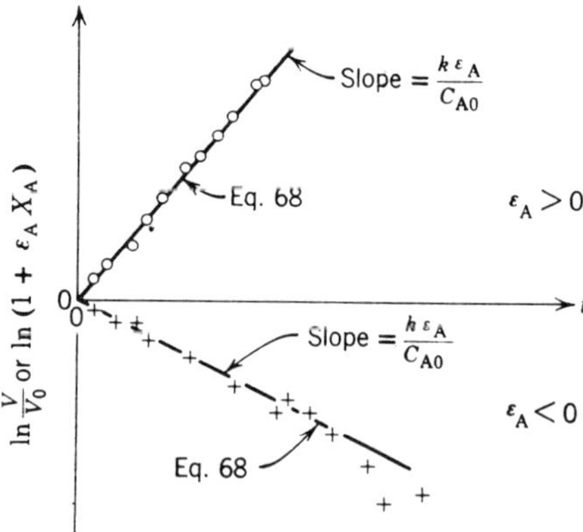

Fig. 19. Test for a zero-order reaction Eq. 67, in a constant-pressure variable-volume reactor.

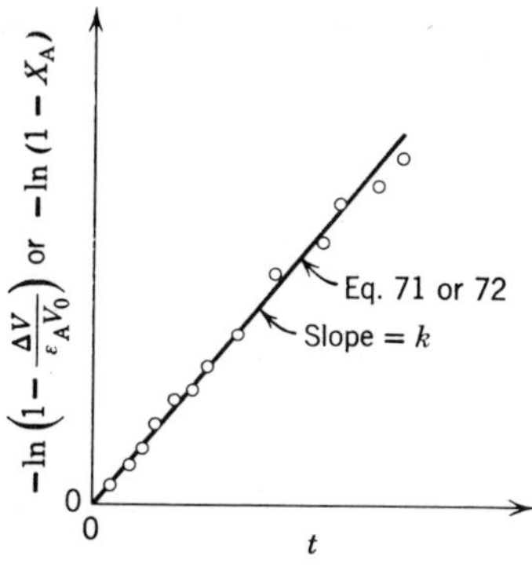

Fig. 20. Test for a first-order reaction in a constant-pressure, variable-volume reactor.

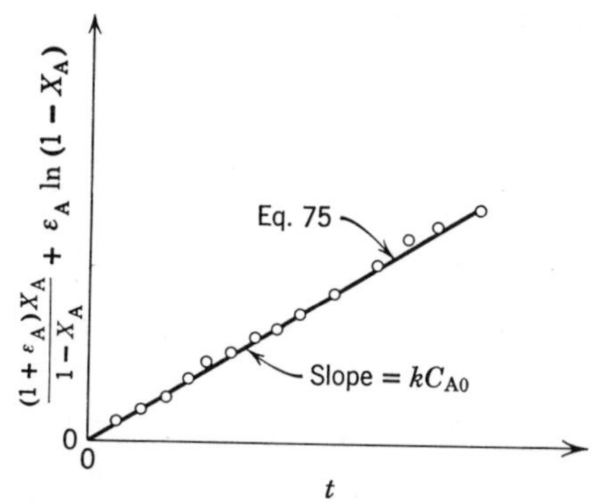

Fig. 21. Test for the second-order reaction, Eq. 73, in a constant-pressure, variable-volume reactor.

or, in terms of the total volume of the system, by combining with Eq. 61

$$-\ln\left(1-\frac{\Delta V}{\varepsilon_A V_0}\right) = kt \tag{72}$$

A semilogarithmic plot of Eq. 71 or 72 as shown in Fig. 20 yields a straight line of slope k.

Comparing this result with that found for first-order reactions in constant-volume systems, we see that the fractional conversion in both is identical; however, the concentrations of materials are not the same. The constant-pressure reactor has a lower concentration of reactant than the constant-volume reactor if $\varepsilon_A > 0$ but has a higher concentration if $\varepsilon_A < 0$. In addition, we can show for the same feed composition at any pressure that the fractional change in pressure of a constant-volume reactor and the fractional change in volume of a constant-pressure reactor are always the same. This relationship holds only for first-order reactions.

Second-order reactions. For a bimolecular-type second-order reaction,

$$2A \rightarrow \text{products}$$

or

$$A + B \rightarrow \text{products}, \qquad C_{A0} = C_{B0}$$

the rate of change of reactant A is given by

$$-r_A = kC_A^2 = k\left(\frac{N_A}{V}\right)^2 \tag{73}$$

By combining with Eq. 61, 64, and 65 this becomes in terms of conversion

$$-r_A = \frac{C_{A0}}{1+\varepsilon_A X_A}\frac{dX_A}{dt} = kC_{A0}^2\left(\frac{1-X_A}{1+\varepsilon_A X_A}\right)^2 \tag{74}$$

Separating variables, breaking into partial fractions, and integrating, we obtain

$$\int_0^{X_A} \frac{1 + \varepsilon_A X_A}{(1 - X_A)^2} dX_A = \frac{(1 + \varepsilon_A)X_A}{1 - X_A} + \varepsilon_A \ln(1 - X_A) = kC_{A0}t \quad (75)$$

With Eq. 61 this can be transformed into a V versus t relationship. Figure 21 shows how to test for such reactions.

Reactions of *n*th order. For an nth-order reaction of the type

$$-r_A = -\frac{1}{V}\frac{dN_A}{dt} = kC_A{}^n = kC_{A0}{}^n\left(\frac{1 - X_A}{1 + \varepsilon_A X_A}\right)^n \quad (76)$$

Eq. 66 becomes

$$\int_0^{X_A} \frac{(1 + \varepsilon_A X_A)^{n-1}}{(1 - X_A)^n} dX_A = C_{A0}^{n-1}\, kt \quad (77)$$

which does not yield simply to integration. For the nth order and other reactions we must integrate Eq. 66 graphically, using the appropriate rate expression. The method to be used parallels the general procedure for the integral method of analysis of constant-volume batch reactors.

TEMPERATURE AND REACTION RATE

So far we have examined the effect of concentration of reactants and products on the rate of reaction, all at a given temperature level. To obtain the complete rate equation, we also need to know the role of temperature on reaction rate. Now in a typical rate equation

$$-r_A = -\frac{1}{V}\frac{dN_A}{dt} = kf(C)$$

and it is the reaction rate constant, the concentration-independent term, which is affected by the temperature, whereas the concentration-dependent terms $f(C)$ usually remain unchanged at different temperatures.

For elementary reactions theory predicts that the rate constant should be temperature-dependent in the following manner:

1. From Arrhenius' law,

$$k \propto e^{-E/RT}$$

2. From collision or transition-state theory

$$k \propto T^m e^{-E/RT}$$

In Chapter 2 we showed that the latter expression very often reduces to the former expression because the exponential term is so temperature-sensitive that any variation caused by the T^m term is completely masked.

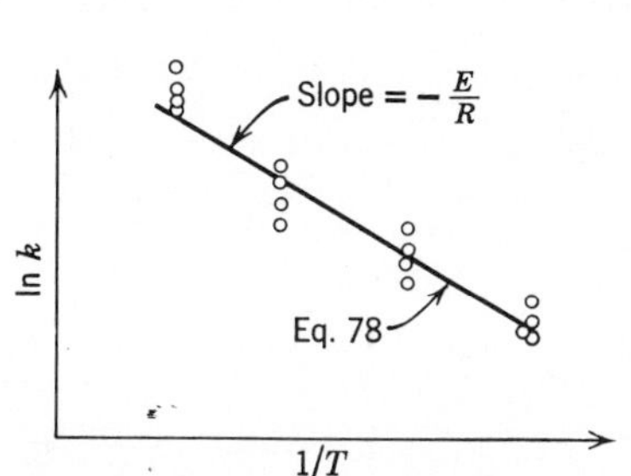

Fig. 22. Temperature dependency of a reaction according to Arrhenius' law.

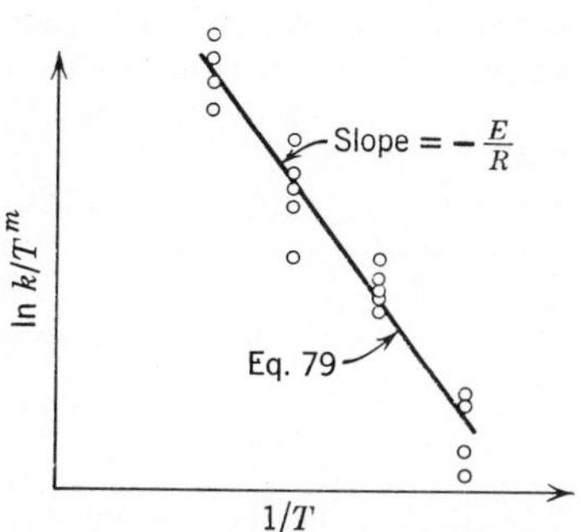

Fig. 23. Temperature dependency of a reaction according to collision theory.

Even for nonelementary reactions where the constants of the rate equations are made up of products of k values for the elementary reactions, these composite rate constants are expected to vary as $e^{-E/RT}$. This expectation has been verified experimentally.

Thus, after finding the concentration dependency of the reaction rate, we can then examine for the variation of the rate constant with temperature by an Arrhenius-type relationship

$$k = k_0 e^{-E/RT} \tag{78}$$

which is conveniently found by plotting ln k versus $1/T$ as shown in Fig. 22. With very precise data we may wish to fit the data to one of the available theories with given value for m. Then the temperature variation of the rate constant is given by

$$k = k_0 T^m e^{-E/RT} \tag{79}$$

which may be tested by plotting ln k/T^m versus $1/T$ as shown in Fig. 23.

Illustrative Example

Bodenstein and Lind (1906) studied the reaction

$$H_2 + Br_2 = 2HBr$$

and found on the basis of a careful analysis of good experimental data that the kinetics was well represented by the expression

$$-r_{H_2} = -\frac{d[H_2]}{dt} = \frac{k_1[H_2][Br_2]^{1/2}}{k_2 + [HBr]/[Br_2]} \tag{80}$$

suggesting a nonelementary reaction. Interestingly enough, this result was explained independently and almost simultaneously by Christiansen, Herzfeld, and Polanyi in terms of a chain reaction mechanism (see Example 2.1).

Using part of the data of Bodenstein and Lind, let us make a partial analysis of the kinetics of this reaction in a manner that illustrates the variety of methods which may be used in the exploration of a reaction.

Data. Let the data consist of eight time-concentration runs, four of which use equal concentrations of H_2 and Br_2. At the start of all runs no HBr is present. Columns 1 and 2 of Table 1 show the data of one of the four runs

Table 1. Time versus concentration run

(1)	(2)	(3)	(4)	(5)
Time, min	$[H_2] = [Br_2]$, moles/liter	$1/[H_2]$	$[H_2]^{-0.39}$	$[H_2]^{-0.39} - [H_2]_0^{-0.39}$
Original Data		Used in Fig. 24	Used in Fig. 29	
0	0.2250	4.444	1.789	0
20	0.1898	5.269	1.911	0.122
60	0.1323	7.559	2.200	0.411
90	0.1158	8.636	2.319	0.530
128	0.0967	10.34	2.486	0.697
180	0.0752	13.30	2.742	0.953
300	0.0478	20.92	3.275	1.486
420	0.0305	32.79	3.901	2.112

Table 2. Initial rate data

(1)	(2)	(3)
$[H_2]_0$	$[Br_2]_0$	$(-r_{H_2})10^3$
0.2250	0.2250	1.76
0.9000	0.9000	10.9
0.6750	0.6750	8.19
0.4500	0.4500	4.465
0.5637	0.2947	4.82
0.2881	0.1517	1.65
0.3103	0.5064	3.28
0.1552	0.2554	1.267

using equal concentrations of H_2 and Br_2. Table 2 shows initial rate data for these eight runs. This information will be used later.

Search for simple rate equation by integral analysis. Let us see whether the kinetics of this reaction can be described by any of the simpler rate equations. For this we use integral analysis. With Column 3 of Table 1, Fig. 24 shows the test of a second-order rate equation according to Fig. 5. The data do not lie on a straight line; hence we do not have an elementary bimolecular reaction. Figure 25 shows the test for a first-order rate equation according to Fig. 3.

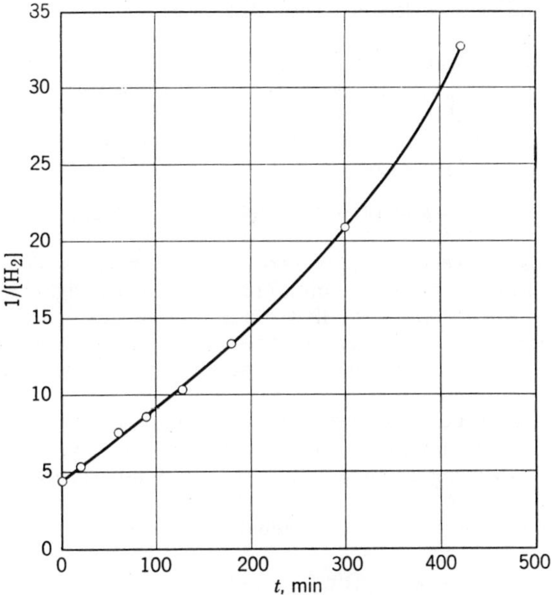

Fig. 24. Test for a second-order reaction by the integral method.

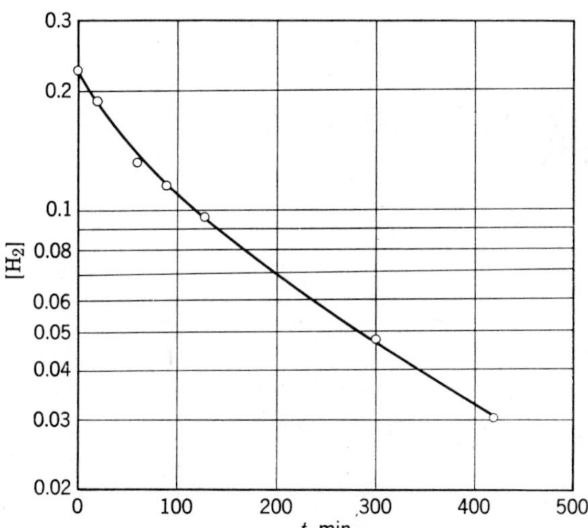

Fig. 25. Test for a first-order reaction by the integral method.

Again the data of Table 1 do not lie on a straight line, and the reaction is not of first order. Similar linearity tests with other simple forms of rate equations show negative results.

Findings of integral analysis. Kinetically the reaction is not elementary. Neither can it be satisfactorily represented by any of the simpler rate expressions which have been handled by the integral analysis.

Possible lines of investigation. Let us now see whether we can fit the rate by an expression of the form

$$-r_{H_2} = k[H_2]^a[Br_2]^b \qquad \text{with} \qquad a + b = n \tag{81}$$

To do this we may proceed in one of two ways: we may use the t versus C data of a single run or we may use initial rate data for the eight runs. If HBr influences the rate of reaction, the first procedure will lead to complications because HBr is formed during reaction. These complications are avoided if we analyze the initial rate data. Let us follow the latter procedure since it has less chance of getting us into trouble.

Find initial rate data. Initial rates of reaction are found either by plotting the C versus t curve and finding the slopes at $t = 0$ as shown in Fig. 26 for the run of Table 1, or by using a difference method. The latter procedure was used to obtain the data of Table 2.

Over-all order of reaction. For equal concentrations of H_2 and Br_2 we obtain

$$-r_{H_2} = k[H_2]^a[Br_2]^b = k[H_2]^{a+b} = k[H_2]^n$$

and taking logs this becomes

$$\log(-r_{H_2}) = \log k + n \log [H_2] \tag{82}$$

Thus from the first four runs of Table 2 we can find the over-all order of reaction.

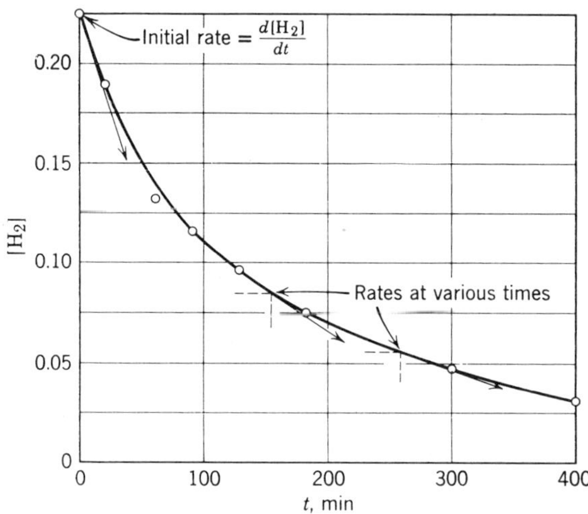

Fig. 26. Graphical procedure for finding initial rate of reaction.

This is shown in Fig. 27. Fitting by eye we find the slope to be

$$n = a + b = 1.35$$

Reaction order with respect to individual reactants. Knowing the over-all order, we can find the order with respect to each component with the following manipulation:

$$-r_{H_2} = k[H_2]^a[Br_2]^b = k[H_2]^a[Br_2]^{n-a}$$
$$= k[Br_2]^n\left(\frac{[H_2]}{[Br_2]}\right)^a$$

Taking logs and using the value of n found, we obtain

$$\log \frac{-r_{H_2}}{[Br_2]^{1.35}} = \log k + a \log \frac{[H_2]}{[Br_2]} \tag{83}$$

which when plotted as Fig. 28 with the slope determined by eye gives $a = 0.90$. Hence from the initial rate data we find

$$-r_{H_2} = k[H_2]^{0.90}[Br_2]^{0.45} \tag{84}$$

Order of reaction by the method of least squares. The method of least squares can give the order of reaction with respect to all the components all at one time. Thus this procedure replaces both of the two preceding steps.

Taking logs of the rate equation to be fitted, Eq. 81, we obtain

$$\log(-r_{H_2}) = \log k + a \log [H_2] + b \log [Br_2]$$

which is of the form

$$y = a_0 + ax_1 + bx_2$$

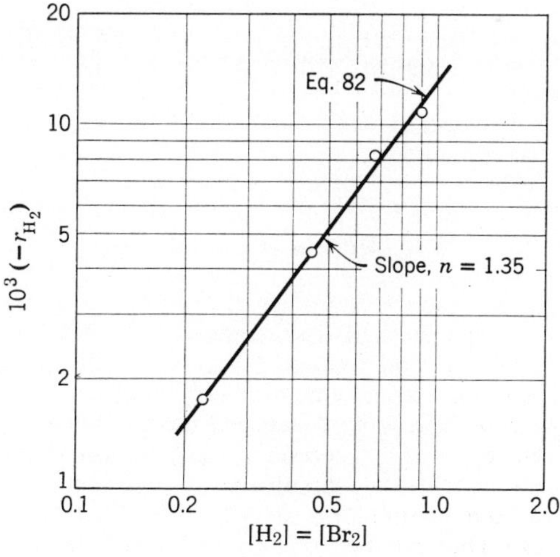

Fig. 27. Plot to give over-all order of reaction.

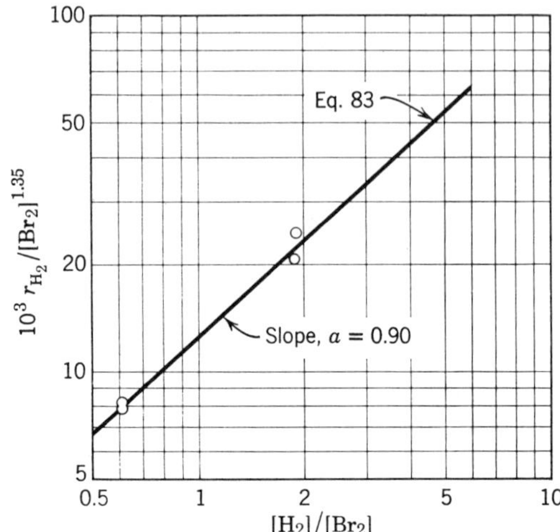

Fig. 28. Determination of order with respect to hydrogen once the over-all order is known.

The best estimate of the coefficients by the least-squares criterion is found in a straightforward manner as outlined by Levenspiel et al. (1956) and gives

$$a = 0.93$$

$$b = 0.46$$

Thus the rate equation is

$$-r_{H_2} = k[H_2]^{0.93}[Br_2]^{0.46} \tag{85}$$

which agrees closely with the results obtained by fitting graphically.

Evaluation of least-squares versus graphical procedures. The advantage of the method of least squares is that it allows us to find all the individual orders of reaction at one time by an objective method which is not influenced by the experimenter's biases in fitting lines to experimental points. Though it does give us the constants of best fit, without additional statistical analyses this method gives us no estimate or feel of how good the fit is. The graphical method allows us to estimate at each step the goodness of fit of the rate equation to the data.

Probably the best procedure is to use the graphical method to find out whether the equation type selected is satisfactory, and if it is then to use the method of least squares to find the constants of best fit. Alternatively, least squares with statistical analyses may be used exclusively.

Test of the rate equation with C versus t data. We have mentioned that to make sure a rate expression represents the reaction in all concentration ranges we should test it with data obtained when all components are present and vary widely in composition. Let us perform this test on Eq. 85 using the data of Table 1. This can be done by either the differential or integral method.

(1) In the differential method we test the fit of Eq. 85 directly. Taking logs, noting that $[H_2] = [Br_2]$, we obtain

$$\begin{aligned}\log(-r_{H_2}) &= \log k + (a + b)\log [H_2]\\ &= \log k + 1.39 \log [H_2]\end{aligned}$$

Thus if Eq. 85 holds throughout the concentration range, a plot of $\log(-r_{H_2})$ versus $\log [H_2]$ should give a straight line of slope 1.39. The rate of reaction at various conditions is found by taking slopes of the C versus t curve at various points, as shown in Fig. 26.

(2) In the integral we must first integrate Eq. 85 and then test the fit. Thus for $[H_2] = [Br_2]$

$$-r_{H_2} = -\frac{d[H_2]}{dt} = k[H_2]^{1.39}$$

Separating and integrating we obtain

$$-\int_{[H_2]_0}^{[H_2]} \frac{d[H_2]}{[H_2]^{1.39}} = k\int_0^t dt$$

or

$$[H_2]^{-0.39} - [H_2]_0^{-0.39} = 0.39kt \tag{86}$$

Thus if Eq. 85 is satisfactory at all concentrations, a plot of

$$([H_2]^{-0.39} - [H_2]_0^{-0.39}) \text{ versus } t$$

should yield a straight line.

Now which procedure should we use? Differential analysis requires taking slopes of C versus t curves and the errors and uncertainty which thereby results may well mask any trend away from linearity which may exist. In addition the differential analysis is more time consuming than the integral analysis which is quite straightforward a procedure. Thus we shall use the integral analysis.

Figure 29 is a plot of Eq. 86 based on values tabulated in Columns 4 and 5 of Table 2. It indicates that the data do not fall on a straight line. Actually, some of the other runs show this more clearly.

Concluding remarks. We can say at this point that the rate is well represented by the expression

$$-r_{H_2} = k[H_2]^{0.93}[Br_2]^{0.46} \tag{85}$$

when no HBr is present. The fact that the order changes during a run indicates that we have at hand a more complicated phenomenon than expected, and that the rate expression found only partially represents the facts, just as Eqs. 57*a* and 58*a* are only partial representations of Eqs. 57 and 58.

Since reaction orders predicted by theory are usually integers or simple fractions, as the problems in Chapter 2 show, it is reasonable to suspect that the rate expression should really be

$$-r_{H_2} = k'[H_2][Br_2]^{0.5} \tag{87}$$

The difference in goodness of fit afforded by Eqs. 85 and 87 is quite minor and can be explained in terms of experimental error.

Actually, Eq. 87 is the correct partial representation of the over-all reaction rate, Eq. 80, as found by Bodenstein and Lind; hence we are well on our way to a solution of the problem.

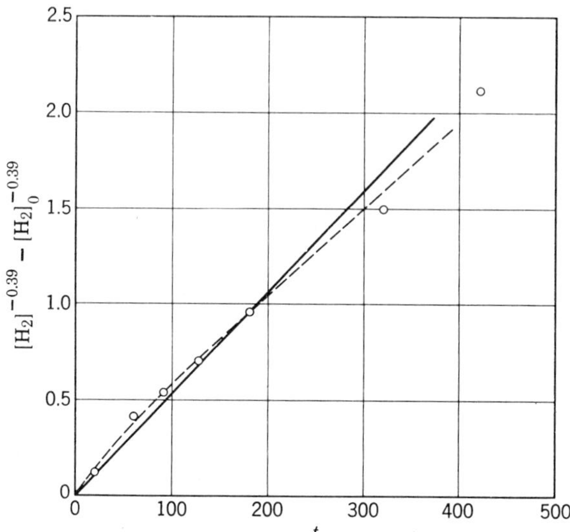

Fig. 29. Check of Eq. 86 in all concentration ranges.

COMMENTS

When we search for a rate equation and mechanism to fit a set of experimental data, we would like to have answers to two questions.

1. Have we the correct mechanism and corresponding type of rate equation?
2. Once we have the right form of rate equation, do we have the best values for the rate constants in the equation?

The second question is answered without much difficulty once the equation form is decided. To do this we decide what we mean by the words "best value" and then find the constants on the basis of this criterion. Some of the commonly used criteria are

1. Minimizing the sum of the squares of the deviation of the data points about the rate equation. This is the least-squares criterion.
2. Minimizing the sum of the absolute values of the deviations.
3. Minimizing the maximum deviation.
4. Fitting graphically by eye.

The difficult question to answer is not the second but the first question. Let us see why this is so. Recalling that each type of rate equation corresponds to a family of curves on a given plot (parabola, cubic, simple exponential, etc.), essentially what we are asking in the first question is

"Given a set of data points plotted in a certain manner, which of the various families of curves could have generated these data?"

To answer this question requires somewhat subtle logic; however, it is worthwhile for us to consider it because the reasoning involved shows what is meant by a true, correct, or verified theory in science.

Suppose we have a given plot of a fixed set of kinetic data and we wish to find out how well any one of the following families of curves—parabolas, cubics, hyperbolas, exponentials, etc.—fits these data compared with the fit of another family of curves. This is a difficult task. It cannot be done simply; neither can high-powered mathematical or statistical methods help in deciding whether one family of curves really fits the plot better than another. The one exception to this conclusion occurs when one of the families being compared is a straight line. For this situation we can simply, consistently, and fairly reliably tell whether any other family of curves fits the data better than the straight line. Thus we have essentially a negative test, one which allows us to reject a straight-line fit if it is worse than the fit of some other curve but which can never indicate whether the straight-line fit is superior to all others. At best, then, we can reject a mechanism and rate equation if evidence is against it (if the data does not fit a straight line as well as it does some other curve), but we can never tell whether a proposed mechanism and rate equation are correct (whether the fit is better than all others). As with any scientific theory or hypothesis we may, however, accept as true any unrejected hypothesis, but with the understanding that this is only done on a provisional basis.

Hence in testing a mechanism with a straight-line fit we are making sure that we are not ignoring some other mechanism which fits the data better, and this is why in all the tests presented in this chapter we have gone through numerous mathematical manipulation to obtain the data in linearized form.

There are three methods commonly used to test for the linearity of a set of points. These are as follows.

Calculation of k from individual data points. With a mechanism at hand, rate constants can be calculated for each experimental point by either the integral or differential methods. If no trend in k values is discernible, the rate equation is considered to be satisfactory and the k values are averaged.

Now the k values calculated this way are the slopes of lines joining the individual points to the origin. So for the same magnitude of scatter on the graph the k values calculated for points near the origin (low conversion) will vary widely, whereas those calculated for points far from the origin will show little variation (Fig. 30). This fact can make it difficult to decide whether k is constant and, if so, what is its best mean value.

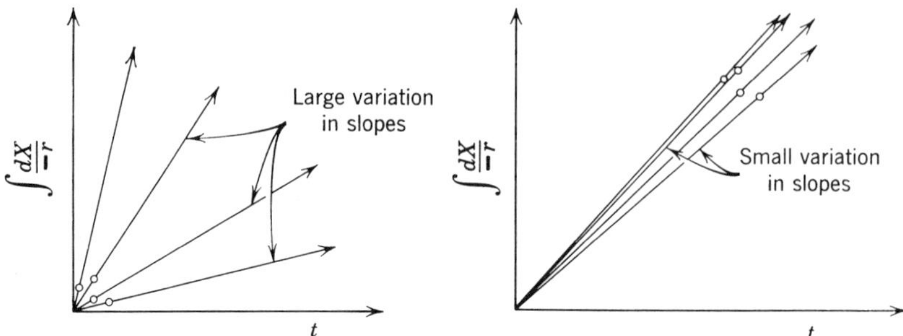

Fig. 30. How the location of the experimental points influences the scatter in calculated k values.

Calculation of k from pairs of data points. A set of k values can be calculated from each successive pair of experimental points. For large data scatter, however, or for points close together, this procedure will give widely varying k values from which k_{mean} will be difficult to determine. In fact, finding k_{mean} by this procedure for points located at equal intervals on the x axis is equivalent to considering only the two extreme data points while ignoring all the data points in between. This fact can easily be verified. Figure 31 illustrates this procedure.

This is a poor method in all respects and is not recommended for testing the linearity of data or for finding mean values of rate constants.

Graphical method. Actually, with the methods given k values can be obtained without making a plot of the data. With the graphical method the data are plotted and then examined for deviations from linearity. The decision whether a straight line gives a satisfactory fit to the data is usually made intuitively by using good judgment when looking at the

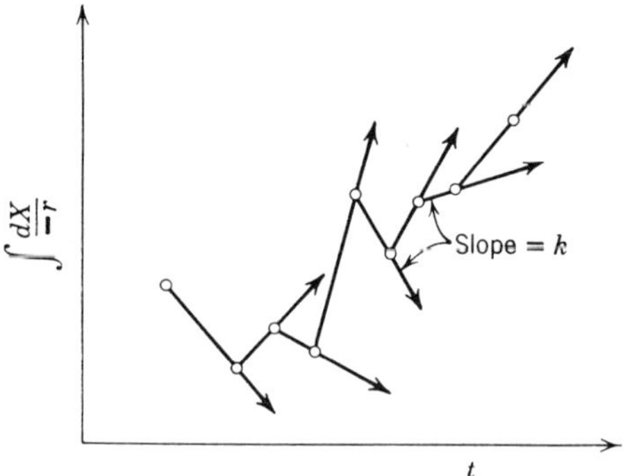

Fig. 31. Calculated k values from successive experimental points are likely to fluctuate widely.

data. When in doubt we should take more data, and occasionally (comparing second-degree polynomials with straight lines or nth degree and $n - 1$ degree polynomials) we may be able to use statistics to help us arrive at a decision.

Though statistics cannot in general compare the goodness of fit of different curves to data, it can help us compare the goodness of fit of two or more straight lines. Hence the graphical method offers an additional advantage in that it allows rational comparison of rate equations which can be represented as straight lines on a given plot. One such example is in the finding of reaction orders on a log r versus log C plot.

The graphical procedure is probably the safest and most reliable method for evaluating the fit of rate equations to the data and should be used whenever possible. For this reason we stress this method here.

RELATED READINGS

A. A. Frost and R. G. Pearson, *Kinetics and Mechanism*, second edition, John Wiley and Sons, New York, 1961.

REFERENCES

M. Bodenstein and S. C. Lind, *Z. physik. Chem.* (Leipzig), **57,** 168 (1906).
K. G. Denbigh, *The Principles of Chemical Equilibrium*, Cambridge University Press, Cambridge, England, 1955, p. 442.
M. Hellin and J. C. Jungers, *Bull. soc. chim. France*, 386 (1957).
C. H. Kunsman, *J. Am. Chem. Soc.*, **50,** 2100 (1928), see Fig. 8, p. 2108.
O. Levenspiel, N. J. Weinstein, and J. C. R. Li, *Ind. Eng. Chem.*, **48,** 324 (1956).

PROBLEMS

1. Given $-r_A = -(dC_A/dt) = 0.2$ mole/(liter)(sec) when $C_A = 1$ mole/liter. What is r_A when $C_A = 10$ moles/liter?

Note: The order of reaction is not known.

2. Given the zero-order homogeneous gas-phase decomposition $A \rightarrow 2.7R$. In a constant-volume bomb starting with 80% A, 20% inerts, we have

Time	0	1
Total pressure, atm	1	1.5

(*a*) If we introduce A at a total pressure of 10 atm, no inerts, what will be the pressure at $t = 1$?

(*b*) If we introduce A at a partial pressure of 1 atm and inerts at a partial pressure of 9 atm, what will be the total pressure at $t = 1$?

3. Given a homogeneous-phase polymerization occurring at constant temperature, with 20% of the monomer disappearing in 34 min for initial monomer concentrations of both 0.04 and 0.8 mole/liter. What can you say about the rate of disappearance of the monomer?

4. The homogeneous gas-phase reaction $A \rightarrow 3B$ has a rate constant $k = 0.5 \text{ min}^{-1}$. Tabulate the total pressure in a constant-volume reactor at 1, 2, 3 and 4 min for the following initial conditions of the reactor: (*a*) pure A at 1 atm, (*b*) pure A at 10 atm, (*c*) pure A at 1 atm, inerts at 9 atm.

5. Snake-Eyes Magoo is a man of habit. For instance, his Friday evenings are all alike—into the joint with his week's salary of $180, steady gambling at "2-up" for two hours, then home to his family leaving $45 behind. Snake-Eyes' betting pattern is predictable. He always bets in amounts proportional to his cash at hand, and his losses are also predictable—at a rate proportional to his cash at hand. This week Snake-Eyes received a raise, so he played for three hours, but as usual went home with $135. How much was his raise?

6. A small reaction bomb fitted with a sensitive pressure-measuring device is flushed out and then filled with pure reactant A at 1-atm pressure. The operation is carried out at 25°C, a temperature low enough that the reaction does not proceed to any appreciable extent. The temperature is raised as rapidly as possible to 100°C by plunging the bomb into boiling water, and the readings in Table P6 are obtained. The stoichiometric equation for the reaction is $2A \rightarrow B$,

Table P6

t, min	π, atm	t, min	π, atm
1	1.14	7	0.850
2	1.04	8	0.832
3	0.982	9	0.815
4	0.940	10	0.800
5	0.905	15	0.754
6	0.870	20	0.728

and after leaving the bomb in the bath over the week end the contents are analyzed for A; none can be found. Find a rate equation in units of lb moles, ft^3, min which will satisfactorily fit the data.

7. The reaction $A + 2B \rightarrow R$ is first order with respect to each reactant. If equimolar amounts of A and B are introduced into a constant-volume reactor and $1/m$th of A remains after time t_1, how much will remain after time $t_2 = 2t_1$?

8. In units of gram moles, liters, and seconds, find the rate expression for the decomposition of ethane at 620°C from the following information obtained at atmospheric pressure. The decomposition rate of pure ethane is 7.7%/sec, but when 85.26% inerts are present the decomposition rate drops to 2.9%/sec.

9. The aqueous-phase reaction A → R + S proceeds as follows,

Time, min	0	36	65	'100	160	∞
C_A, gram moles/liter	0.1823	0.1453	0.1216	0.1025	0.0795	0.0494

with

$$C_{A0} = 0.1823 \text{ gm mole/liter}$$
$$C_{R0} = 0$$
$$C_{S0} \approx 55 \text{ gm moles/liter}$$

Find the rate equation for this reaction.

10. Hellin and Jungers (1957) present the data in Table P10 on the reaction of sulfuric acid with diethylsulfate in aqueous solution at 22.9°C:

$$H_2SO_4 + (C_2H_5)_2SO_4 \rightarrow 2C_2H_5SO_4H$$

Initial concentrations of H_2SO_4 and $(C_2H_5)_2SO_4$ are each 5.5 gm moles/liter.

Table P10

Time, min	$C_2H_5SO_4H$ gm moles/liter	Time, min	$C_2H_5SO_4H$ gm moles/liter
0	0	180	4.11
41	1.18	194	4.31
48	1.38	212	4.45
55	1.63	267	4.86
75	2.24	318	5.15
96	2.75	368	5.32
127	3.31	379	5.35
146	3.76	410	5.42
162	3.81	∞	(5.80)

Find a rate equation for this reaction.

11. Find the over-all order of the irreversible reaction

$$2H_2 + 2NO \rightarrow N_2 + 2H_2O$$

from the accompanying constant-volume data using equimolar amounts of hydrogen and nitric oxide.

Total Pressure, mm Hg	200	240	280	320	360
Half-life, sec	265	186	115	104	67

12. Kunsman (1928) presents rate data for the decomposition of ammonia on molybdenum catalyst at both 850°C and 950°C, and reports that the rate is independent of the concentration of ammonia present. Verify this conclusion by calculating the reaction order from the data presented.

13. On p. 54 it was mentioned that the half-life method for finding reaction orders can be extended to any fractional-life data. Do this, defining $t_{1/m}$ as the time required for the reactant concentration to drop to $1/m$th of its original value.

14. Nitrogen pentoxide decomposes as follows:

$$\left.\begin{array}{lll} N_2O_5 \rightarrow \frac{1}{2}O_2 + N_2O_4, & -r_{N_2O_5} = (2.2 \times 10^{-3}\ \text{min}^{-1})\ C_{N_2O_5} \\ N_2O_4 \rightleftharpoons 2NO_2, & \text{instantaneous, } K_p = 45\ \text{mm Hg} \end{array}\right\}$$

Find the partial pressures of the contents of a constant-volume bomb after 6.5 hr if we start with pure N_2O_5 at atmospheric pressure.

15. Betahundert Bashby likes to play the gaming tables for relaxation. He does not expect to win and he doesn't, so he picks games in which losses are a given small fraction of the money bet. He plays steadily without a break, and the size of his bets are proportional to the money he has. If at "galloping dominoes" it takes him four hours to lose half of his money and if it takes him two hours to lose half of his money at "chuk-a-luck," how long can he play both games simultaneously if he starts with $100.00 and quits when he has $1.00 left, which is just enough for carfare home, a deluxe hamburger, and a shake?

16. For the reactions in series

$$A \xrightarrow{k_1} R \xrightarrow{k_2} S, \qquad k_1 = k_2$$

find when R reaches a maximum concentration and determine the value of that concentration.

17. A small reaction bomb, fitted with a sensitive pressure-measuring device, is flushed out and then filled with a mixture at 76.94% reactant A and 23.06% inert at 1-atm pressure. The operation is carried out at 14°C, a temperature low enough that the reaction does not proceed to any appreciable extent.

The temperature is raised as rapidly as possible to 100°C by plunging the bomb into boiling water, and the readings in Table P17 are obtained. The

Table P17

t, min	π, atm	t, min	π, atm
0.5	1.5	3.5	1.99
1	1.65	4	2.025
1.5	1.76	5	2.08
2	1.84	6	2.12
2.5	1.90	7	2.15
3	1.95	8	2.175

stoichiometric equation for the reaction is $A \rightarrow 2R$ and after leaving the bomb in the bath over the week end the contents are analyzed for A; none can be found. Find a rate equation in concentration units of lb moles/ft^3 which will satisfactorily fit the data.

18. The following data are obtained at 0°C in a constant-volume batch reactor using pure gaseous A.

Time, min	0	2	4	6	8	10	12	14	∞
Partial Pressure of A, mm	760	600	475	390	320	275	240	215	150

The stoichiometry of the decomposition of A is $A \rightarrow 2.5R$. Find a rate equation which satisfactorily represents this decomposition.

19. The kinetics of the liquid-phase reaction $A + 3B \rightarrow 2R$ are to be examined. It happens that the reaction can be stopped conveniently at any point and that the concentration of R can easily be measured by titration in the resulting solution. This then forms the basis for the study of the kinetics of this reaction. Chemicals A and B are prepared in various concentrations in separate flasks and at time $t = 0$ are introduced in the constant-temperature reaction vessel. After 1 min the reaction is quenched and the resultant liquid is titrated. The results in Table P19*a* are obtained.

Table P19*a*

	At $t = 0$ min		At $t = 1$ min
Run	C_{A0}, moles/liter	C_{B0}, moles/liter	C_R, moles/liter
1	1	1	0.0100
2	1	5	0.0224
3	5	1	0.0500
4	5	5	0.112

(*a*) What can we say about the rate equation and the equilibrium constant at this point?

(*b*) For run 5, we repeat run 4 without quenching and leave it over the week end. Then the solution is analyzed and R is found to be at 1 mole/liter. Now what can we say about the rate equation and the equilibrium constant?

(*c*) If in addition we make the experiment in Table P19*b*, $C_{A0} = C_{B0} = 0$, what can we say about the rate equation and equilibrium constant of the reaction?

Table P19*b*

	$t = 0$	$t = 1$ min
Run	C_{R0}, moles/liter	C_R, moles/liter
6	1	0.999
7	5	4.975
8	25	24.375

Note: The resulting equation is not thermodynamically consistent; see Denbigh (1955). Hence it would be risky to use it for conditions far from those actually examined.

20. Find the first-order rate constant for the disappearance of A in the gas-phase reaction A → 1.6R if the volume of the reaction mixture starting with pure A increases by 50% in 4 min. The total pressure within the system stays constant at 1.2 atm, and the temperature is 25°C.

21. Find the first-order rate constant for the disappearance of A in the gas-phase reaction 2A → R if, on holding the pressure constant, the volume of the reaction mixture, starting with 80% A, decreases by 20% in 3 min.

22. For a zero-order reaction, with stoichiometry A → rR taking place in a constant-volume bomb, $\pi = 1$ when $t = 0$ and $\pi = 1.5$ when $t = 1$. For the same reaction, same feed composition and initial pressure taking place in a constant-pressure setup, find V at $t = 1$ if $V = 1$ at $t = 0$.

23. For a zero-order reaction A → rR taking place in a constant-volume bomb, 20% inerts, the pressure rises from 1 to 1.3 atm in 2 min. For the same reaction, taking place in a constant-pressure batch reactor, what is the fractional volume change in 4 min if the feed is at 3 atm and consists of 40% inerts?

24. The gas-phase reaction 2A → R + 2S is approximately second order with respect to A. When pure A is introduced at 1 atm into a constant-volume batch reactor, the pressure rises 40% above the initial pressure in 3 min. For a constant-pressure batch reactor find (*a*) the time required for the same conversion, (*b*) the fractional increase in volume at that time.

25. When the first-order homogeneous gas-phase decomposition A → 2.5R is carried out in an isothermal batch reactor at 2 atm with 20% inerts present, the volume increases by 60% in 20 min. When the reaction is carried out in a constant-volume reactor, find the time required for the pressure to reach 8 atm if the initial pressure is 5 atm, 2 atm of which consist of inerts.

26. It was mentioned on p. 73 that for first-order gas-phase reactions at the same feed composition at any pressure the fractional change in pressure of a constant-volume reactor is always the same as the fractional change in volume of a constant-pressure reactor. Verify this statement.

27. Pure gaseous A which decomposes according to the reaction A → R + S is prepared under refrigeration and is introduced into a thin-walled capillary which acts as reaction vessel as shown in Fig. P27. No appreciable reaction occurs during handling. The reaction vessel is rapidly plunged into a bath of boiling water, and the volume change is noted. After the reaction has been completed, analysis of the mixture shows no A present. The following data are obtained.

Time, min	0.5	1	1.5	2	3	4	6	10	∞
Length of Capillary Occupied by Reaction Mixture, cm	6.1	6.8	7.2	7.5	7.85	8.1	8.4	8.7	9.4

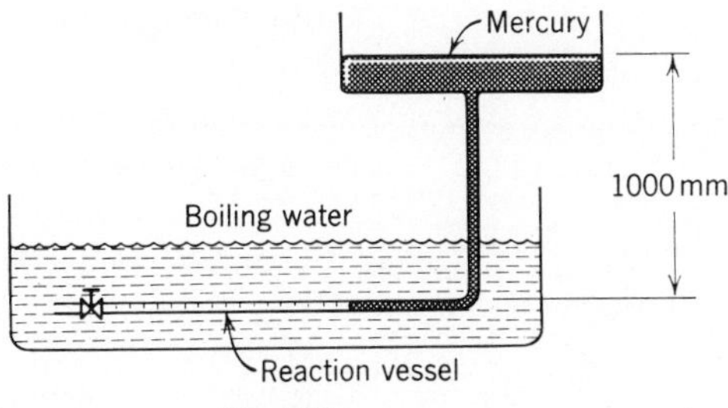

Fig. P27

Find a rate equation in concentration units, gm moles/liter, for this decomposition.

28. The kinetics of the gaseous decomposition of an unstable organic material is to be investigated in a constant-pressure reactor somewhat similar to that shown in the previous problem. A mixture of 73% reactant and 27% inerts is introduced into a thick-walled glass reaction vessel. The volume of the reactant mixture introduced is 1.1 cc at 0°C, at which temperature there is no appreciable volume change after 1 hr. The reaction vessel is placed in a bath of boiling water, and the volume of the mixture is noted at various times, all at a constant pressure of 1000 mm Hg absolute as shown in Table P28.

Table P28

Gas Volume, cc	Time, sec	Gas Volume, cc	Time, sec
1.2	<1	3.3	84
1.5	6	3.6	104
1.8	19	3.9	130
2.1	29	4.2	160
2.4	40	4.5	210
2.7	53	4.8	330
3.0	67	4.95	∞

(*a*) What can you say about the stoichiometry of the reaction?
(*b*) What can you say about the mechanism of reaction?
(*c*) Find a rate equation for this reaction.
(*d*) What can you say about the experimental equipment and procedure used, and have you any suggestions for its improvement?

29. Determine the complete rate equation in units of moles, liters, and seconds for the thermal decomposition of tetrahydrofuran

$$\begin{array}{ccc} H_2C\text{——}CH_2 & & C_2H_4 + CH_4 + CO \\ | \qquad\quad | & \nearrow & \\ H_2C \qquad CH_2 & \rightarrow & C_3H_6 + H_2 + CO \\ \diagdown \;\; \diagup & \searrow & \\ O & & \text{etc.} \end{array}$$

from the half-life data in Table P29.

Table P29

π_0, mm Hg	t, min	T, °C
214	14.5	569
204	67	530
280	17.3	560
130	39	550
206	47	539

Table P30

[A]	[B]	[C]	r_{AB}
1	3	0.02	9
3	1	0.02	5
4	4	0.04	32
2	2	0.01	6
2	4	0.03	20
1	2	0.05	12

Table P31

$[O_2]$	[NO]	$-r_{NO}$
1	1	1×10^8
2	2	4×10^8
3	1	1×10^8
1	3	9×10^8
0.0001	1	1×10^6
0.0002	2	8×10^6
0.0003	1	3×10^6
0.0001	3	9×10^6
1	0.0001	1
2	0.0002	4
3	0.0001	1
1	0.0003	9
0.0001	0.0001	0.01
0.0002	0.0002	0.08
0.0003	0.0001	0.03
0.0001	0.0003	0.09

30. The presence of substance C seems to increase the rate of reaction of A with B, $A + B \rightarrow AB$. We suspect that C acts catalytically by combining with one of the reactants to form an intermediate, which then reacts further. From the rate data in Table P30 suggest a plausible mechanism of reaction and rate equation for this reaction.

31. To explore the kinetics of the reaction

$$2NO + O_2 \rightarrow N_2O_4, \qquad \text{irreversible}$$

the rate data in Table P31 are obtained in widely different concentration ranges. What mechanism and rate equation are suggested by these data?

4

INTRODUCTION TO REACTOR DESIGN

So far we have considered the mathematical expression which describes the rate of progress of a chemical reaction. This we call the rate equation. Rate equations are suggested either by theoretical models, or if no satisfactory model can be found, we then turn to expressions representing experimental information alone. We have also considered experimental methods for finding rate equations.

Rate expressions predict the rate of change of any component i at any instant as a function of the system variables, the rate being defined as $r_i = \frac{1}{V}\frac{dN_i}{dt}$. Hence they are differential rate expressions. These are obtained to help predict the size of reactors needed to produce a given amount of product. Essentially, then, this process involves the integration of the differential rate expression across the chemical reactor. The process may pose difficulties because the temperature and composition of the reacting fluid may vary from point to point within the reactor, depending on the endothermic or exothermic character of the reaction, and depending on the rate of heat addition or removal from the system. In addition, the actual geometry of the reactor will determine the path of the fluid through the vessel and fix the gross mixing patterns which help to dilute rich feed and redistribute material and heat. Thus we see that many factors must be accounted for before we can predict the performance of a reactor.

Equipment in which homogeneous reactions are effected can be one of three general types; the batch, the steady-state flow, and the unsteady-state flow or semibatch reactor. The latter classification lumps together all reactors that do not fall into the first two categories. These types are shown in Fig. 1.

Let us briefly indicate the salient features and the main areas of application of the various reactor types. Naturally these remarks will be amplified as we treat the individual reactors. The batch reactor is simple, needs little

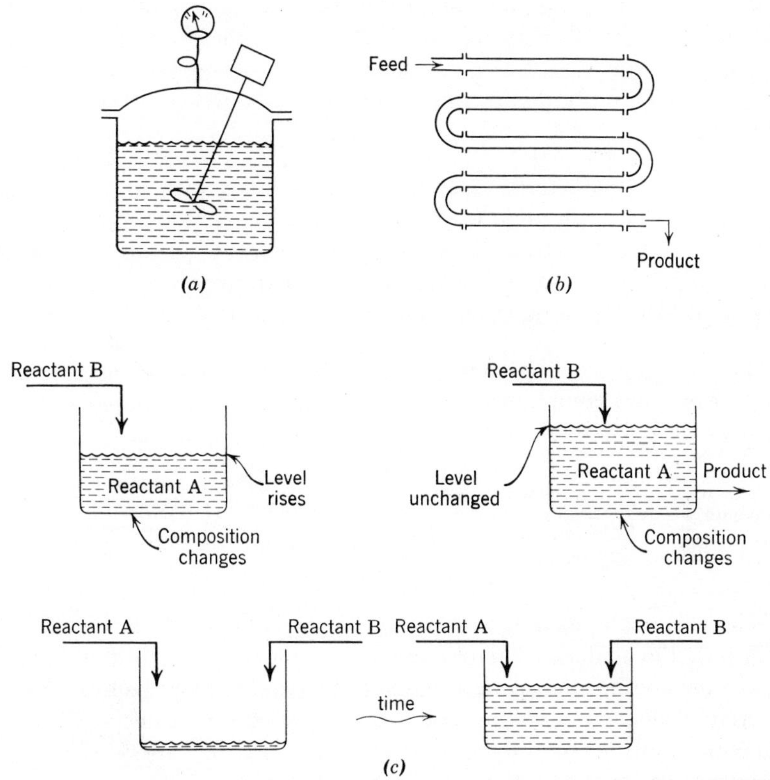

Fig. 1. Broad classification of reactor types. (*a*) The batch reactor: all reactants added at one time, composition changes with time. (*b*) The steady-state flow reactor: no accumulation of material in reactor, no change in composition of the feed or exit stream; composition at any point unchanged with time. (*c*) The semibatch reactor: composition and/or quantity of material in system changes with time, with many combinations possible; three modes of operation are illustrated.

supporting equipment, and is therefore ideal for small-scale experimental studies on reaction kinetics. Industrially it is used when either small amounts of material or relatively expensive materials are to be treated. The steady-state flow reactor is ideal for industrial purposes when large quantities of material are to be processed and when the rate of reaction is fairly high to extremely high. Supporting-equipment needs are great; however, extremely good product quality control can be obtained. As may be expected, this is the reactor which is widely used in the oil industry. The semibatch reactor is a flexible system but is more difficult to analyze than the other reactor types. It offers good control of reaction speed because the reaction proceeds as reactants are added. Such reactors are used in a variety of applications from the colorimetric titrations in the laboratory to the large open-hearth furnaces for the production of steels with special properties.

In principle we can predict the performance of a reactor if we know the following.

1. The rate characteristics of the reacting fluids with respect to heat transfer, mass transfer, and reaction.

2. The external restriction imposed by the reactor setup such as the reactor type, the actual geometry of the vessel (which affects flow and mixing patterns), and the rate of location of heat removal.

The starting point for all design is the general material balance expressed for any reaction component. Thus graphically, Fig. 2, and in equation form we have for an element of volume

$$\begin{pmatrix}\text{rate of reactant}\\ \text{flow into}\\ \text{element of}\\ \text{volume}\end{pmatrix} = \begin{pmatrix}\text{rate of reactant}\\ \text{flow out of}\\ \text{element of}\\ \text{volume}\end{pmatrix} + \begin{pmatrix}\text{rate of reactant}\\ \text{loss due to chemi-}\\ \text{cal reaction within}\\ \text{the element of}\\ \text{volume}\end{pmatrix} + \begin{pmatrix}\text{rate of}\\ \text{accumulation}\\ \text{of reactant}\\ \text{in element}\\ \text{of volume}\end{pmatrix} \quad (1)$$

Where the composition within the reactor is uniform (independent of position), the material balance may be made over the whole reactor. Where the composition is not uniform, the balance must be made over a differential element of volume and then integrated for the appropriate flow and concentration conditions. For the various reactor types this equation simplifies one way or another, and the resultant expression when integrated gives the basic design equation for that type of unit. Thus in the batch reactor the first two terms are zero, in the steady-state flow reactor the fourth term disappears, and for the semibatch reactor we may have to consider all terms.

In nonisothermal operations heat balances must be used in conjunction

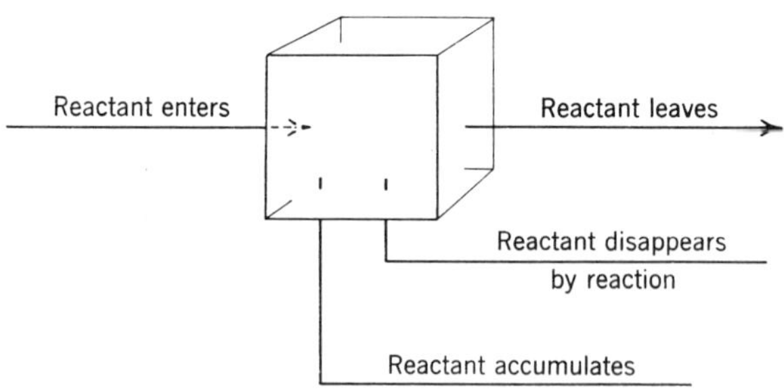

Fig. 2

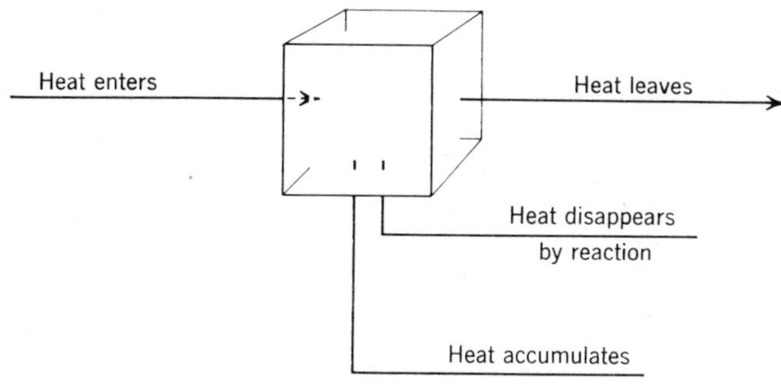

Fig. 3

with material balances. Thus graphically, Fig. 3, and in equation form for an element of reactor volume

$$\begin{pmatrix}\text{rate of heat}\\ \text{flow into}\\ \text{element of}\\ \text{volume}\end{pmatrix} = \begin{pmatrix}\text{rate of heat}\\ \text{flow out of}\\ \text{element of}\\ \text{volume}\end{pmatrix} + \begin{pmatrix}\text{rate of heat}\\ \text{disappearance}\\ \text{resulting from}\\ \text{reaction within}\\ \text{element of}\\ \text{volume}\end{pmatrix} + \begin{pmatrix}\text{rate of heat}\\ \text{accumulation}\\ \text{in the element}\\ \text{of volume}\end{pmatrix} \tag{2}$$

Again depending on the operating conditions, this balance may be taken either about a differential element of reactor or about the reactor as a whole.

Tying together both the material balance of Eq. 1 and the heat balance of Eq. 2 is a term expressing the rate of reaction and the heat effect resulting from this reaction.

Finally, when pressure drop in gas-phase flow systems is great enough to affect concentrations of materials appreciably, it must be included in design. Usually, however, this is a secondary and minor effect.

In general, then, a reactor is designed by use of the equations expressing material balances, heat balances, reaction rates, and pressure drops (particular form of momentum balance).

Since the material balance, energy balance, and rate equation, as incorporated in Eqs. 1 and 2 are the starting points for all design, in the chapters to follow we consider their integration to obtain the appropriate design equations for a variety of situations of increasing complexity.

When we can predict the response of the reacting system to changes in operating conditions (how rates and equilibrium conversion change with temperature and pressure), when we are able to compare yields of alternative designs (adiabatic versus isothermal operations, single versus multiple reactor units, flow versus batch system), and when we can estimate the economics of these various alternatives, then and only then will we feel with assurance that we can arrive at the design best fitted for the purpose at hand. Unfortunately, real situations are rarely simple. Often we do not have enough information to compare designs, we cannot solve the necessary mathematics, or more than likely we do not feel that we can afford to expend the time and manpower needed to solve the mathematics. In addition, we may not feel justified in treating design of the reactor separately from that of the chemical plant as a whole. Thus it is a matter of compromise in time and effort on the one hand and the cost of making a bad design on the other so as to maximize the probability of success in the over-all venture. Which simplifying assumptions to make? Which short cuts to take? Which factors to ignore and which to consider? To answer these questions is the role of good engineering judgment, which only comes with experience.

5
SINGLE IDEAL REACTORS

In this chapter we develop the design equations for the three types of ideal reactors, shown schematically in Fig. 1. Applications of these equations to isothermal and nonisothermal design are considered in the following three chapters.

In the batch reactor of Fig. 1*a* the reactants are initially charged into a container, are well mixed, and are then left for a certain period during which time they react. Then the resultant mixture is discharged. This is an unsteady-state operation with composition changing with time; however, at any instant the composition throughout the reactor is uniform.

The first of the two ideal flow reactors is variously known as the plug flow, slug flow, piston flow, tubular flow, and nonbackmix flow reactor and is shown in Fig. 1*b*. We refer to it as the plug flow reactor. It is characterized by the fact that the flow of fluid through the reactor is orderly with no element of fluid overtaking any other element. Consequently, no diffusion along a flow path and no difference in velocity for any two elements of flowing fluid are permitted. It is as if the material marched through the reactor in single file. Actually, for a plug flow reactor we may have lateral mixing of fluid; however, there must be no mixing of fluid

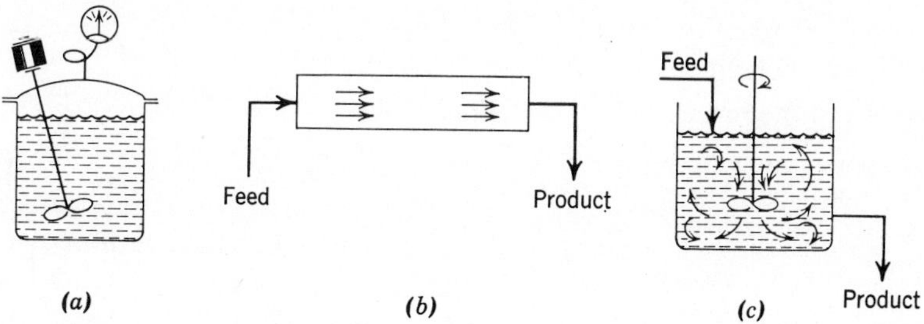

Fig. 1. The three types of ideal reactors: (*a*) batch reactor, (*b*) plug flow reactor, (*c*) backmix flow reactor.

longitudinally along the flow path. A necessary and sufficient condition for plug flow is to state that the residence time in the reactor is the same for all elements of fluid.

The other ideal steady-state flow reactor is called the backmix or total backmix reactor, the stirred tank reactor or the CFSTR (constant flow stirred tank reactor) and, as its names suggest, it is a reactor in which the contents are well stirred and uniform in composition throughout. Thus the exit stream from this reactor has the same composition as the fluid within the reactor.

These three ideal reactor types approximate a large number of real reactors, and the solution to their design equations are relatively simple; hence we treat them first. In later chapters we see how to treat the deviations of real reactors from these idealized situations. Since deviations are frequently handled by a correction factor to the design equation for the ideal reactor, we must master the design of the ideal reactor as a prerequisite to the design of the real reactor.

In the treatment to follow, when we refer to V as the reactor volume it will be understood that we are referring to the volume of reactor occupied by the reacting fluids. Void spaces in reactors above liquids and the volume of reactor occupied by solids, etc., will not be considered in V. If, say, for packed-bed reactors we wish to distinguish between volume available for reactant fluid and the gross volume of reactor, we designate the latter by V_r. Thus with ϵ as the fraction voids we have

$$V = V_r \epsilon$$

Single ideal batch reactor

Make a material balance for any component A. For such an accounting we usually select the limiting component. In a batch reactor, since the composition is uniform throughout at any instant of time, we may make the balance about the whole reactor. Hence at any instant we have from Eq. 4.1

$$+\begin{pmatrix}\text{rate of loss of}\\ \text{reactant A within}\\ \text{reactor due to}\\ \text{chemical reaction}\end{pmatrix} = -\begin{pmatrix}\text{rate of accumulation}\\ \text{of reactant A}\\ \text{within the reactor}\end{pmatrix} \tag{1}$$

Evaluating the terms of Eq. 1 we find

$$\begin{matrix}\text{Disappearance of A}\\ \text{by reaction,}\\ \text{moles/time}\end{matrix} = (-r_A)V = \left(\frac{\text{moles A reacting}}{\text{(time)(volume of reacting fluid)}}\right) \times \begin{pmatrix}\text{volume of reactor occupied}\\ \text{by reacting fluid}\end{pmatrix}$$

$$\begin{matrix}\text{Accumulation of A,}\\ \text{moles/time}\end{matrix} = \frac{dN_A}{dt} = \frac{d[N_{A0}(1 - X_A)]}{dt} = -N_{A0}\frac{dX_A}{dt}$$

By replacing in Eq. 1,

$$(-r_A)V = N_{A0}\frac{dX_A}{dt}$$

Rearranging and integrating, we obtain

$$t = N_{A0}\int_0^{X_A}\frac{dX_A}{(-r_A)V} \tag{2}$$

This is the general equation showing the time required to effect a given conversion of reactant A for either isothermal or nonisothermal operation. The volume of reacting fluid and reaction rate remain under the integral sign, for in general they both vary as reaction proceeds. This equation may be simplified for a number of situations. If the volume of mixture remains constant, we obtain

$$t = C_{A0}\int_0^{X_A}\frac{dX_A}{-r_A} = -\int_{C_{A0}}^{C_A}\frac{dC_A}{-r_A} \tag{3}$$

For all reactions in which the volume of reacting mixture changes proportionately with conversion, such as in gas-phase reactions with significant density changes, Eq. 2 becomes

$$t = N_{A0}\int_0^{X_A}\frac{dX_A}{(-r_A)V_0(1+\varepsilon_A X_A)} = C_{A0}\int_0^{X_A}\frac{dX_A}{(-r_A)(1+\varepsilon_A X_A)} \tag{4}$$

In one form or another, Eq. 2, 3, and 4 have all been encountered in Chapter 3. They are applicable to both isothermal and nonisothermal operations. For the latter the variation of rate with temperature and temperature with conversion must be known before solution is possible.

Space time and space velocity

A convenient and useful way of expressing the relation between the feed rate F_{A0} and reactor volume V in a flow system is by applying the terms space time and space velocity which are defined as follows:

$$\text{Space time} = \tau = \frac{1}{s} = \begin{pmatrix}\text{time required to process one}\\ \text{reactor volume of feed}\\ \text{measured at specified}\\ \text{conditions}\end{pmatrix} = \text{time}$$

$$\text{Space velocity} = s = \frac{1}{\tau} = \frac{\begin{pmatrix}\text{volume of entering feed at}\\ \text{specified conditions/time}\end{pmatrix}}{(\text{void volume of reactor})} = \text{time}^{-1} \tag{5}$$

Thus a space velocity of 5 hr^{-1} means that five reactor volumes of feed at specified conditions are being fed into the reactor per hour. A space time of 2 min means that every two minutes one reactor volume of feed at specified conditions is being treated in the reactor.

Now we may arbitrarily select the conditions of temperature, pressure, and state (gas, liquid, or solid) at which we choose to measure the volume of material being fed to the reactor. Certainly, then, the value for space velocity or space time depends on the conditions selected. If they are those of the stream entering the reactor, the relation between s or τ and V/F_{A0} is

$$\tau = \frac{1}{s} = \frac{C_{A0}V}{F_{A0}} = \frac{\left(\dfrac{\text{moles A entering}}{\text{volume of feed}}\right)(\text{volume of reactor})}{\left(\dfrac{\text{moles A entering}}{\text{time}}\right)}$$

$$= \frac{V}{v_0} = \frac{\begin{pmatrix}\text{reactor}\\ \text{volume}\end{pmatrix}}{\begin{pmatrix}\text{volumetric}\\ \text{feed rate}\end{pmatrix}} \tag{6}$$

It may be more convenient to measure the volumetric feed rate at some standard state, especially when the reactor is to operate at a number of temperatures. For liquids the standard state is usually taken to be 60°F, and for gases it is usually 32°F and 1 atm. If, for example, the material is gaseous when fed to the reactor at high temperature but is liquid at the standard state, care must be taken to specify precisely what standard state has been chosen. The relation between the space velocity and space time for actual entering conditions and at standard conditions (designated by primes) is given by

$$\tau' = \frac{1}{s'} = \frac{C_{A0}'V}{F_{A0}} = \tau\frac{C_{A0}'}{C_{A0}} = \frac{1}{s}\frac{C_{A0}'}{C_{A0}} \tag{7}$$

In most of what follows, we deal with the space velocity and space time based on feed at actual entering conditions; however, the conversion is easily made to any other basis.

Steady-state backmix flow reactor

The design equation for the backmix reactor is obtained from Eq. 4.1, which makes an accounting of a given component within an element of volume of the system. But since the composition is uniform throughout, the accounting may be made about the reactor as a whole. By selecting reactant A for consideration, Eq. 4.1 becomes

$$\text{Input} = \text{output} + \text{disappearance by reaction} \tag{8}$$

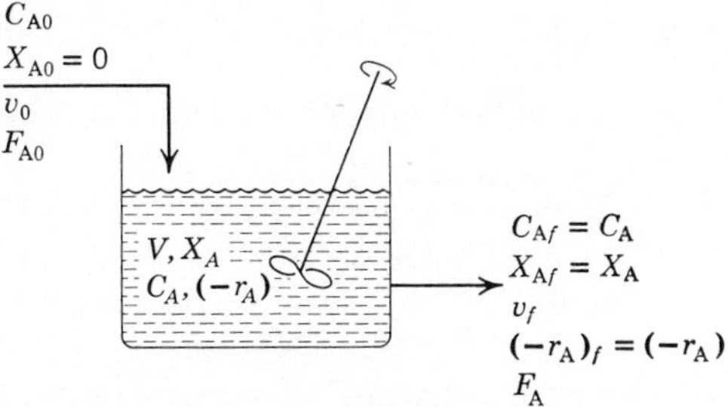

Fig. 2. Variables for a backmix flow reactor.

As shown in Fig. 2 if $F_{A0} = v_0 C_{A0}$ is the molar feed rate of component A into the reactor, then considering the reactor as a whole we have

Input of A, moles/time $= F_{A0}(1 - X_{A0}) = F_{A0}$

Output of A, moles/time $= F_A = F_{A0}(1 - X_A)$

Disappearance of A by reaction, moles/time $= (-r_A)V = \dfrac{\text{moles A reacting}}{\text{(time)(volume of reacting fluid)}} \begin{pmatrix}\text{volume of reactor}\\ \text{occupied by}\\ \text{reacting fluid}\end{pmatrix}$

Replacing in Eq. 8, we obtain

$$F_{A0} X_A = (-r_A)V$$

which on rearranging becomes

$$\frac{V}{F_{A0}} = \frac{V}{v_0 C_{A0}} = \frac{X_A}{-r_A}$$

or (9)

$$\tau = \frac{1}{s} = \frac{V}{v_0} = \frac{C_{A0} X_A}{-r_A}$$

where X_A and r_A are evaluated at exit stream conditions, which are the same as the conditions within the reactor.

More generally, if the feed on which conversion is based, subscript 0, enters the reactor partially converted, subscript i, and leaves at conditions given by subscript f, we have

$$\frac{V}{F_{A0}} = \frac{V}{v_0 C_{A0}} = \frac{X_{Af} - X_{Ai}}{(-r_A)_f}$$

or (10)

$$\tau = \frac{1}{s} = \frac{V}{v_0} = \frac{V C_{A0}}{F_{A0}} = \frac{C_{A0}(X_{Af} - X_{Ai})}{(-r_A)_f}$$

A situation in which the subscripts f and i are needed is given on p. 139.

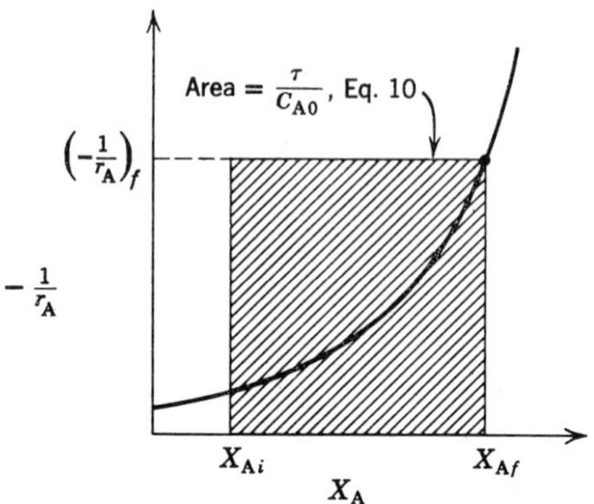

Fig. 3. Graphical representation of the design equation for backmix reactors.

Figure 3, a graphical representation of this equation, is useful when comparing performance capabilities of backmix reactors and other types of ideal reactors.

The backmix reactor has no correspondence with the batch system unless we consider it to represent the conditions within the batch reactor at a given instant of time. In this respect we may look at it somewhat as a differential reactor. The design equation for this reactor shows that knowing any three of the four terms X_A, $-r_A$, V, F_{A0} gives the fourth term directly. Thus in kinetic experiments, each run at given τ will give a corresponding value for the rate of reaction directly. The ease of interpretation of backmix reactor data can be used to advantage in kinetic studies of complex reactions for which differential analysis is required.

Example 1

The liquid-phase reaction

$$A + B \underset{k_2}{\overset{k_1}{\rightleftharpoons}} R + S$$

$$k_1 = 7 \text{ liters/(gm mole)(min)}$$
$$k_2 = 3 \text{ liters/(gm mole)(min)}$$

is to take place in a 120-liter steady-state backmix reactor. Two feed streams, one containing 2.8 gm moles A/liter, the other containing 1.6 gm moles B/liter are to be introduced in equal volumes into the reactor, and 75% conversion of limiting component is desired (see Fig. E1). What should be the flow rate of each stream? Assume a constant density throughout.

Solution. The concentration of components in the mixed feed stream is

$$C_{A0} = 1.4 \text{ moles/liter}$$
$$C_{B0} = 0.8 \text{ mole/liter}$$
$$C_{R0} = C_{S0} = 0$$

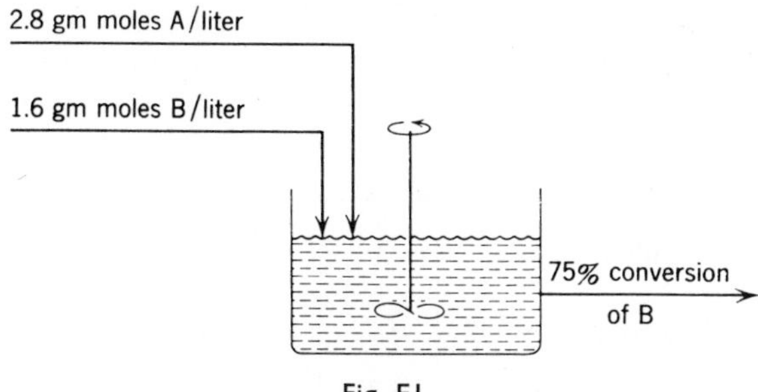

Fig. E1

For 75% conversion of B the composition within the reactor and in the exit stream, for $\varepsilon = 0$, is

$$C_A = 1.4 - 0.6 = 0.8 \text{ mole/liter}$$
$$C_B = 0.8 - 0.6 = 0.2 \text{ mole/liter}$$
$$C_R = 0.6 \text{ mole/liter}$$
$$C_S = 0.6 \text{ mole/liter}$$

Now the rate of reaction at the conditions within the reactor is

$$-r_A = -r_B = k_1 C_A C_B - k_2 C_R C_S$$

$$= \left(7 \frac{\text{liters}}{(\text{mole})(\text{min})}\right)\left(0.8 \frac{\text{mole}}{\text{liter}}\right)\left(0.2 \frac{\text{mole}}{\text{liter}}\right) - \left(3 \frac{\text{liters}}{(\text{mole})(\text{min})}\right)\left(0.6 \frac{\text{mole}}{\text{liter}}\right)^2$$

$$= (1.12 - 1.08) \frac{\text{mole}}{(\text{liter})(\text{min})} = 0.04 \frac{\text{mole}}{(\text{liter})(\text{min})}$$

For no change in density, hence $\varepsilon = 0$, Eq. 9 becomes

$$\tau = \frac{V}{v} = \frac{C_{A0} - C_A}{-r_A} = \frac{C_{B0} - C_B}{-r_B}$$

Hence the volumetric flow rate into and out of the reactor, is

$$v = \frac{V(-r_A)}{C_{A0} - C_A} = \frac{V(-r_B)}{C_{B0} - C_B}$$

$$= \frac{(120 \text{ liters})(0.04 \text{ mole/(liter)(min)})}{(0.6 \text{ mole/liter})} = 8 \frac{\text{liters}}{\text{min}}$$

or 4 liters/min of each of the two feed streams.

Example 2

From the following data find a satisfactory rate equation for the gas-phase decomposition

$$A \rightarrow R + S$$

taking place isothermally in a backmix reactor.

Run number	1	2	3	4	5
τ based on inlet feed conditions, min	0.423	5.10	13.5	44.0	192
X_A (for C_{A0} = 0.002 lb mole/ft^3)	0.22	0.63	0.75	0.88	0.96

Solution. The rates of reaction for the five runs are found by Eq. 9

$$-r_A = \frac{C_{A0}X_A}{\tau}$$

and are given in Table E2. Let us now try an equation of the type

$$-r_A = kC_A{}^n$$

Table E2

Run	τ, min	X_A	$1 - X_A$	$\frac{1 - X_A}{1 + X_A}$	$\frac{C_{A0}X_A}{\tau} = -r_A$
1	0.423	0.22	0.78	0.639	$\frac{0.002}{0.423}(0.22) = 104 \times 10^{-5}$
2	5.10	0.63	0.37	0.227	$\frac{0.002}{5.1}(0.63) = 24.7 \times 10^{-5}$
3	13.5	0.75	0.25	0.143	$\frac{0.002}{13.5}(0.75) = 11.1 \times 10^{-5}$
4	44.0	0.88	0.12	0.0638	$\frac{0.002}{44}(0.88) = 4 \times 10^{-5}$
5	192	0.96	0.04	0.021	$\frac{0.002}{192}(0.96) = 1 \times 10^{-5}$

which for constant-pressure operations with $\varepsilon_A = 1$ becomes

$$-r_A = kC_{A0}{}^n\left(\frac{1 - X_A}{1 + \varepsilon_A X_A}\right)^n = kC_{A0}{}^n\left(\frac{1 - X_A}{1 + X_A}\right)^n$$

To test this equation take logs

$$\log(-r_A) = \log(kC_{A0}{}^n) + n \log\frac{1 - X_A}{1 + X_A}$$

and plot, using the information in Table E2 to see whether a straight line results.

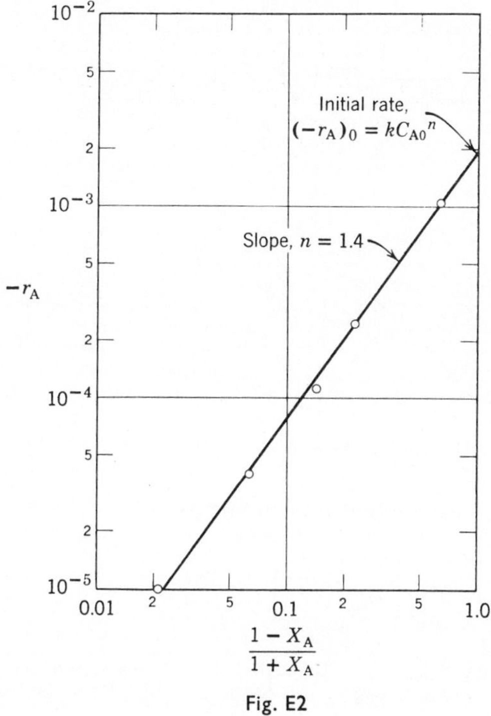

Fig. E2

Figure E2 shows that this rate equation represents the data with

$$n = 1.4$$

The rate constant is found from the intercept. Thus

$$kC_{A0}{}^n = k\left(0.002 \frac{\text{lb mole}}{\text{ft}^3}\right)^{1.4} = 2 \times 10^{-3} \frac{\text{mole}}{(\text{ft}^3)(\text{min})}$$

Hence the complete rate equation is

$$-r_A = \left[12 \left(\frac{\text{ft}^3}{\text{lb mole}}\right)^{0.4} \frac{1}{\text{min}}\right]\left(C_A \frac{\text{lb moles}}{\text{ft}^3}\right)^{1.4}$$

Steady-state plug flow reactor

In a plug flow reactor the composition of the fluid varies from position to position along a flow path; consequently, the material balance for a reaction component must be made for a differential element of volume dV. Thus for A we obtain

$$\text{input} = \text{output} + \text{disappearance by reaction} \tag{8}$$

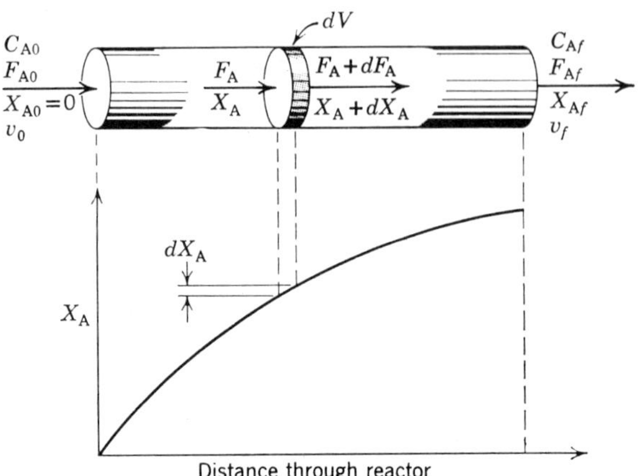

Fig. 4. Variables for a plug flow reactor.

Referring to Fig. 4 we see that for volume dV

Input of A, moles/time $= F_A$

Output of A, moles/time $= F_A + dF_A$

Disappearance of A by reaction, moles/time $= (-r_A)\,dV = \left(\dfrac{\text{moles A reacting}}{(\text{time})(\text{volume of reacting fluid})}\right) \times \left(\begin{matrix}\text{volume of fluid in the section}\\ \text{of reactor considered}\end{matrix}\right)$

Introducing these three terms in Eq. 8, we obtain

$$F_A = (F_A + dF_A) + (-r_A)\,dV$$

Noting that

$$dF_A = d[F_{A0}(1 - X_A)] = -F_{A0}\,dX_A$$

we obtain on replacement

$$F_{A0}\,dX_A = (-r_A)\,dV \tag{11}$$

This then is the equation accounting for A in the differential section of reactor having volume of fluid dV. For the reactor as a whole the expression must be integrated. Now F_{A0}, the feed rate, is constant, but r_A is certainly dependent on the concentration of materials or conversion. Thus grouping the terms accordingly we obtain

$$\int_0^V dV \Big/ F_{A0} = \int_0^{X_{Af}} \frac{dX_A}{-r_A}$$

Thus

$$\frac{V}{F_{A0}} = \int_0^{X_{Af}} \frac{dX_A}{-r_A}$$

or

$$\tau = \frac{1}{s} = \frac{V}{v_0} = C_{A0} \int_0^{X_{Af}} \frac{dX_A}{-r_A} \tag{12}$$

Equation 12 allows the determination of reactor size for a given feed rate and conversion. Compare Eqs. 9 and 12. The difference is that in the plug flow reactor r_A varies, whereas in the backmix reactor r_A is constant.

As a more general expression for plug flow reactors, if the feed on which conversion is based, subscript 0, enters the reactor partially converted, subscript i, and leaves at a conversion designated by subscript f, we have

$$\frac{V}{F_{A0}} = \frac{V}{C_{A0}v_0} = \int_{X_{Ai}}^{X_{Af}} \frac{dX_A}{-r_A}$$

or

$$\tau = \frac{1}{s} = \frac{V}{v_0} = C_{A0} \int_{X_{Ai}}^{X_{Af}} \frac{dX_A}{-r_A} \tag{13}$$

A case in which the different subscripts i and f are used is given on p. 137.

The plug flow reactor can be used for kinetic studies. Graphical analysis of plug flow reactor data follows closely that for batch systems with two modifications; τ is used in place of t, and the appropriate rate expression must account for the changing fluid density. Because of the expansion term integral analysis of plug flow systems becomes more difficult. Where $\varepsilon = 0$, however, this procedure becomes identical to that for constant-volume batch systems.

For irreversible reactions of order n

$$\tau = C_{A0} \int_0^{X_A} \frac{dX_A}{kC_A{}^n} \tag{14}$$

and with expansion proportional to conversion

$$C_A = \frac{N_A}{V} = \frac{N_{A0}(1 - X_A)}{V_0(1 + \varepsilon_A X_A)} = C_{A0} \frac{1 - X_A}{1 + \varepsilon_A X_A}$$

Therefore

$$\tau = \frac{1}{kC_{A0}^{n-1}} \int_0^{X_A} \frac{(1 + \varepsilon_A X_A)^n \, dX_A}{(1 - X_A)^n} \tag{15}$$

For *zero-order* reactions Eq. 15 becomes

$$k\tau = C_{A0} X_A \tag{16}$$

For *irreversible first-order* reactions

$$k\tau = (1 + \varepsilon_A) \ln \frac{1}{1 - X_A} - \varepsilon_A X_A \tag{17}$$

For *irreversible second-order* reactions with one reactant A or two reactants with equal concentrations

$$C_{A0} k\tau = 2\varepsilon_A(1 + \varepsilon_A) \ln (1 - X_A) + \varepsilon_A{}^2 X_A + (\varepsilon_A + 1)^2 \frac{X_A}{1 - X_A} \tag{18}$$

For *reversible* reactions with or without inerts

$$A \underset{k_2}{\overset{k_1}{\rightleftharpoons}} rR$$

which are approximated by first-order reversible kinetics, we have for plug flow reactors

$$k_1\tau = \frac{N + M\varepsilon_A}{N^2} \ln \frac{M}{M - NX_A} - \frac{\varepsilon_A X_A}{N}$$

where (19)

$$M = 1 - \frac{k_2 C_{R0}}{k_1 C_{A0}}; \; N = 1 + \frac{rk_2}{k_1}$$

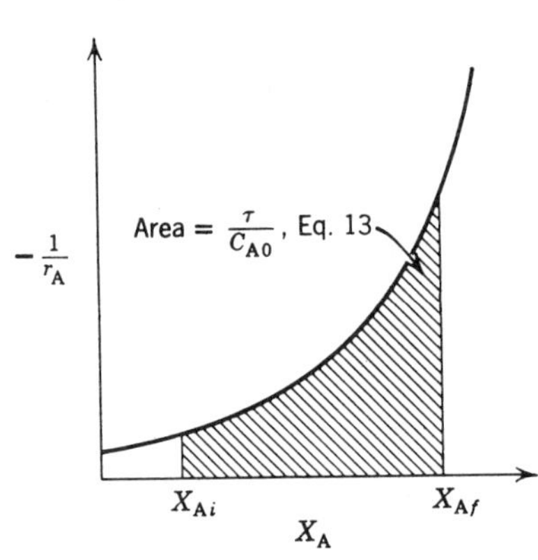

Fig. 5. Graphical solution of the design equation for plug flow reactors.

For all other rate equations graphical integration is recommended. This is done by plotting $-1/r_A$ versus X_A and evaluating the area under this curve between the appropriate limits, as shown in Fig. 5.

Example 3

The homogeneous gas-phase decomposition of phosphine proceeds at 1200°F,

$$4PH_3(g) \rightarrow P_4(g) + 6H_2$$

with first-order rate

$$-r_{PH_3} = (10/\text{hr})C_{PH_3}$$

What size of plug flow reactor operating at 1200°F and 4.6 atm can produce 80% conversion of a feed consisting of 4 lb moles of pure phosphine per hour.

Solution. Let A = PH_3, R = P_4, S = H_2. Then the reaction becomes

$$4A \rightarrow R + 6S$$

with

$$-r_A = (10/\text{hr})C_A$$

The volume of plug flow reactor is given by Eq. 12; thus

$$V = F_{A0} \int_0^{X_A} \frac{dX_A}{-r_A} = F_{A0} \int_0^{X_A} \frac{dX_A}{kC_A}$$

Now at constant pressure

$$C_A = C_{A0}\frac{1 - X_A}{1 + \varepsilon_A X_A}$$

Hence

$$V = \frac{F_{A0}}{kC_{A0}}\int_0^{X_A}\frac{1 + \varepsilon_A X_A}{1 - X_A}\,dX_A$$

Integrating, we obtain Eq. 17, or

$$V = \frac{F_{A0}}{kC_{A0}}\left[(1 + \varepsilon_A)\ln\frac{1}{1 - X_A} - \varepsilon_A X_A\right]$$

Evaluating the terms

$$F_{A0} = 4 \text{ lb moles/hr}$$

$$k = 10/\text{hr}$$

$$C_{A0} = \frac{p_{A0}}{RT} = \frac{4.6 \text{ atm}}{\left(0.729\dfrac{\text{ft}^3\text{ atm}}{(\text{lb mole})(°\text{R})}\right)(1660°\text{R})} = 0.0038\,\frac{\text{lb mole}}{\text{ft}^3}$$

$$\varepsilon_A = \frac{7 - 4}{4} = 0.75$$

$$X_A = 0.8$$

Hence the volume of reactor

$$V = \frac{(4 \text{ lb moles/hr})}{(10/\text{hr})(0.0038 \text{ lb mole/ft}^3)}\left[(1 + 0.75)\ln\frac{1}{0.2} - 0.75(0.8)\right]$$

$$= 234 \text{ ft}^3$$

Example 4

Consider the elementary gas-phase reaction

$$A + B \underset{k_2}{\overset{k_1}{\rightleftharpoons}} R$$

occurring isothermally in a plug flow reactor.

(*a*) Set up the design equation for a feed consisting of A, B, R, and inerts.

(*b*) Show how space time is found for a feed consisting of equimolar quantities of A and B.

Solution. (*a*) *Feed of* A, B, R, *and inerts.* For this elementary reaction the rate is

$$-r_A = k_1 C_A C_B - k_2 C_R = k_1\frac{N_A}{V}\frac{N_B}{V} - k_2\frac{N_R}{V}$$

At constant pressure by basing fractional expansion and conversion on substance A,

$$-r_A = k_1\frac{N_{A0} - N_{A0}X_A}{V_0(1 + \varepsilon_A X_A)}\,\frac{N_{B0} - N_{A0}X_A}{V_0(1 + \varepsilon_A X_A)} - k_2\frac{N_{R0} + N_{A0}X_A}{V_0(1 + \varepsilon_A X_A)}$$

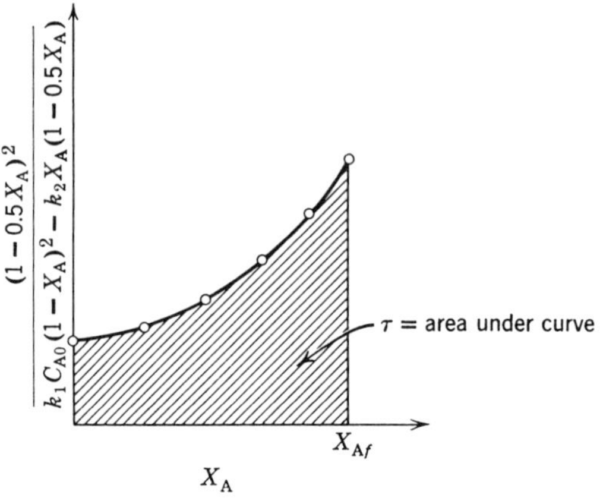

Fig. E4

Letting $M = C_{B0}/C_{A0}$, $M' = C_{R0}/C_{A0}$, we obtain

$$-r_A = k_1C_{A0}{}^2\frac{(1 - X_A)(M - X_A)}{(1 + \varepsilon_A X_A)^2} - k_2C_{A0}\frac{M' + X_A}{1 + \varepsilon_A X_A}$$

Hence the design equation for plug flow reactors is

$$\tau = C_{A0}\int_0^{X_{Af}} \frac{dX_A}{-r_A}$$

$$= \int_0^{X_{Af}} \frac{(1 + \varepsilon_A X_A)^2\, dX_A}{k_1C_{A0}(1 - X_A)(M - X_A) - k_2(M' + X_A)(1 + \varepsilon_A X_A)}$$

In this expression ε_A accounts for inerts present in the feed.

(*b*). *Equimolar feed of* A *and* B. For $C_{A0} = C_{B0}$, $C_{R0} = 0$, and no inerts we have $M = 1$, $M' = 0$, $\varepsilon_A = -0.5$; hence the expression for part *a* becomes

$$\tau = \int_0^{X_{Af}} \frac{(1 - 0.5X_A)^2\, dX_A}{k_1C_{A0}(1 - X_A)^2 - k_2X_A(1 - 0.5X_A)}$$

Graphical evaluation of this integral gives the required space time as shown in Fig. E4.

Reactor holding time (mean residence time) and space time (reciprocal space velocity)

When the density of the fluid stream is the same at all points within the reactor, we may write

$$t = \frac{V}{v} = \frac{VC_{A0}}{F_{A0}} = \frac{1}{s} = \tau \tag{20}$$

This equation shows that the mean residence time for fluid in the reactor (or reactor holding time) and space time (reciprocal space velocity) can be used interchangeably.

When constant density cannot reasonably be assumed, the reactor holding time is not related in a simple way to the other variables and must be found for each specific situation. These relationships will now be derived for the various reactor types.

Batch reactor. The residence time t of fluid in a batch reactor is given by Eq. 2, 3, or 4 and corresponds to the time for cooking the batch. Consider a long period of operation covering a large number of batches with average shut down time t_s for dumping, cleaning, and refilling the reactor. Then the capacity of the reactor over long periods of time is given by

$$F_{A0} = \frac{N_{A0}}{t + t_s} = \frac{\text{(moles A charged/batch)}}{\text{(total processing time/batch)}}$$

Hence from Eq. 6 we have

$$\tau = \frac{1}{s} = \frac{C_{A0}V}{F_{A0}} = \frac{C_{A0}V(t + t_s)}{N_{A0}} \tag{21}$$

Backmix reactor. As each element of fluid has an equal chance of being withdrawn from the reactor at any instant, no matter how long it has been in the system, the residence time is not a single value and has little significance. But if we wish to determine $\bar{t}$, the mean residence time (or the reactor holding time), it is found as follows. By definition

$$\bar{t} = \frac{V}{v_f}$$

In general the incoming and outgoing volumetric flow rates differ because of change in fluid density. In such a case note that it is the volumetric rate of the outgoing stream which is used to determine $\bar{t}$. This is because the exit stream represents the conditions within the reactor.

Now with Eq. 9 we get

$$\bar{t} = \frac{F_{A0}X_A}{(-r_A)_f v_f} = \frac{C_{A0}X_A}{(-r_A)_f \dfrac{v_f}{v_0}} = \tau \frac{v_0}{v_f} \tag{22}$$

For the special case where the change in fluid density is proportional to conversion we have

$$\frac{v_f}{v_0} = 1 + \varepsilon_A X_{Af}$$

in which case Eq. 22 becomes

$$\bar{t} = \frac{\tau}{1 + \varepsilon_A X_{Af}} = \frac{C_{A0} X_A}{(-r_A)_f (1 + \varepsilon_A X_{Af})} \tag{23}$$

Plug flow reactor. The residence time in a plug flow reactor does have physical meaning, for each element of fluid actually stays in the reactor for that length of time. Now, in general, as the composition of fluid changes from point to point within the reactor, so does its density. As a result the velocity of flow varies as the fluid passes through the reactor. Hence, to find the flow rate of fluid, we must find the residence time dt in an element of volume dV and then integrate across the reactor. Thus, at conversion X_A for element of volume dV,

$$dt = \frac{dV}{v} = \frac{\text{(element of volume)}}{\text{(volumetric flow rate at conversion } X_A)} \tag{24}$$

but from Eq. 11 for any differential section of plug flow reactor

$$dV = \frac{F_{A0}}{-r_A} dX_A$$

Therefore on combining

$$dt = \frac{F_{A0} dX_A}{(-r_A) v}$$

and on integrating along the reactor

$$t = F_{A0} \int_0^{X_{Af}} \frac{dX_A}{(-r_A) v} = C_{A0} \int_0^{X_{Af}} \frac{dX_A}{(-r_A) \dfrac{v}{v_0}} \tag{25}$$

Where the fluid density change is proportional to conversion, this becomes

$$t = C_{A0} \int_0^{X_{Af}} \frac{dX_A}{(-r_A)(1 + \varepsilon_A X_A)} \tag{26}$$

We may note in comparing Eq. 26 with Eq. 12 that in general space time and holding time are not related in a simple way.

Comparison of usefulness of holding time and space time

We have introduced two capacity measures for a chemical reactor, holding time and space time. Table 1 shows how these capacity measures t and τ can be found by the combination of material balances and rate equations. General and special forms of these equations are also shown for the various reactor types.

Comparing these expressions we see that, when the fluid density remains constant, then

$$t_{\text{batch},\pi=\text{const}} = t_{\text{batch},\,V=\text{const}} = t_{\text{plug flow}} = \tau_{\text{plug flow}} \tag{27}$$

For all conditions in addition

$$t_{\text{batch},\,\pi=\text{const}} = t_{\text{plug flow}} \tag{28}$$

This relationship becomes apparent if the plug flow reactor is visualized as a system through which elements of fluid pass in succession, each in its own little constant-pressure reactor. The residence time of each element passing through the plug flow reactor is identical to that of the stationary constant-pressure batch reactor.

In batch systems holding time is used exclusively as the capacity measure of a reactor. For flow system, however, we introduced a new measure, space time (and its related variables, space velocity, and V/F). Why was this done? Are there any advantages to using these new variables instead of holding time? Why not use the latter directly as in batch processes?

First of all we see that distinction between these two measures exists only when density changes occur in the system. Hence to assess the relative advantages of these two measures, let us only consider flow systems with density changes.

Now the flow system equations are used for one of two purposes: (1) to find the rate equation from flow experiments, (2) to determine the size requirement of a reactor from kinetic data.

For finding a rate equation we need either t versus X_A or τ versus X_A data. Now in plug flow reactors t cannot be found directly from experimental measurements. It must be calculated from Eq. 26. But Eq. 26 can only be solved if we know the reaction rate beforehand. Thus we are at an impasse. In contrast, τ is a direct measure of the feed rate to the reactor and can be found directly from the imposed experimental conditions.

A similar situation exists in determining the capacity of a plug flow reactor, for knowing the holding time (calculated by Eq. 26) still does not tell us the size of reactor required. Finding the space time will give the reactor size required directly.

Thus when space time and holding time differ from each other, space time is the more useful of the two variables because it is an independent

Table 1. Summary of design expressions for single ideal reactors

Type of Reactor	Capacity Measure	General Design Relationship	Design Equation with $V = V_0(1 + \varepsilon_A X_A)$	Design Equation for Isothermal nth Order Reaction with $V = V_0(1 + \varepsilon_A X_A)$
Batch $V = \text{const}$	t	$= C_{A0}\int \frac{dX_A}{-r_A}$		$= \frac{1}{kC_{A0}^{n-1}}\int \frac{dX_A}{(1 - X_A)^n}$
Batch $\pi = \text{const}$	t	$= N_{A0}\int \frac{dX_A}{V(-r_A)}$	$= C_{A0}\int \frac{dX_A}{(1 + \varepsilon_A X_A)(-r_A)}$	$= \frac{1}{kC_{A0}^{n-1}}\int \frac{(1 + \varepsilon_A X_A)^{n-1}}{(1 - X_A)^n}\, dX_A$
Plug flow[a]	t	$= F_{A0}\int \frac{dX_A}{v(-r_A)}$	$= C_{A0}\int \frac{dX_A}{(1 + \varepsilon_A X_A)(-r_A)}$	$= \frac{1}{kC_{A0}^{n-1}}\int \frac{(1 + \varepsilon_A X_A)^{n-1}}{(1 - X_A)^n}\, dX_A$
Plug flow	$\tau = \frac{1}{s}$	$= C_{A0}\int \frac{dX_A}{-r_A}$	$= C_{A0}\int \frac{dX_A}{-r_A}$	$= \frac{1}{kC_{A0}^{n-1}}\int \frac{(1 + \varepsilon_A X_A)^{n}}{(1 - X_A)^n}\, dX_A$
Backmix reactor	$\tau = \frac{1}{s}$	$= \frac{C_{A0}X_A}{-r_A}$	$= \frac{C_{A0}X_A}{-r_A}$	$= \frac{1}{kC_{A0}^{n-1}} \cdot \frac{X_A(1 + \varepsilon_A X_A)^n}{(1 - X_A)^n}$
Backmix reactor[a]	$\bar{t}$	$= \frac{F_{A0}X_A}{v_f(-r_A)}$	$= \frac{C_{A0}X_A}{(1 + \varepsilon_A X_A)(-r_A)}$	$= \frac{1}{kC_{A0}^{n-1}} \cdot \frac{X_A(1 + \varepsilon_A X_A)^{n-1}}{(1 - X_A)^n}$

[a] Not recommended for use.

Note: $C_{A0}X_A = C_{A0} - C_A$ and $C_{A0}\, dX_A = -dC_A$ only when $\varepsilon_A = 0$.

variable, directly related to the conditions imposed upon the system, whereas holding time cannot be considered to be an independent variable, for it cannot be found except by a knowledge of the progressive changes occurring within the reactor.

Because of these reasons we use space time, space velocity, or V/F as capacity measures for plug flow reactors rather than holding or mean residence time. It is interesting that the analogous situation occurs in the design equations for steady-state operations in other areas of chemical engineering such as the mass transfer operations; time does not enter explicitly into the design equations.

For the backmix reactors integration of an expression such as Eq. 26 is not needed to find $\bar{t}$. Both capacity measures are related in a single way by Eq. 23; hence either can be used.

Example 5

Two groups of experimenters alpha and beta studied the kinetics of the decomposition of A, for which the stoichiometry is

$$A \rightarrow R + S + T$$

Using a feed consisting of pure A at 650°C and 1.2 atm, group alpha reports that a space time $\tau = 2.7$ min (based on entering feed conditions) is needed to achieve 95% conversion in a plug flow reactor. Group beta reports for the identical experimental conditions and conversion that a residence time $t = 1$ min is needed.

Using in turn the data of these two groups, determine the size of reactor needed to treat 100 ft³/min of A at 650°C and 1.2 atm so as to obtain 95% conversion of reactant.

Solution. (*a*) *Use the data of group alpha.* By Eq. 6

$$V = \tau v_0 = (2.7 \text{ min})\ (100 \text{ ft}^3/\text{min}) = 270 \text{ ft}^3$$

(*b*) *Use the data of group beta.* The required reactor size is found from residence time data through the use of Eqs. 26 and 12. Thus with $\varepsilon_A = 2$

$$t = 1 \text{ min} = C_{A0}\int_0^{X_{Af}} \frac{dX_A}{(1 + \varepsilon_A X_A)(-r_A)} = C_{A0}\int_0^{0.95} \frac{dX_A}{(1 + 2X_A)(-r_A)}$$

and

$$\tau = \frac{V}{v_0} = C_{A0}\int_0^{X_{Af}} \frac{dX_A}{-r_A} = C_{A0}\int_0^{0.95} \frac{dX_A}{-r_A}$$

With $-r_A$ not specified, we cannot proceed further with the data of group beta to determine the reactor size.

To solve the problem, let us then specify in addition that the decomposition is second order with respect to A:

$$-r_A = kC_A^2 = kC_{A0}^2\left(\frac{1 - X_A}{1 + \varepsilon_A X_A}\right)^2$$

Note that this information is not required if space time rather than residence time is specified. Then the t and τ expressions become

$$t = 1 = \frac{1}{kC_{A0}} \int_0^{X_{Af}} \frac{1 + \varepsilon_A X_A}{(1 - X_A)^2} dX_A$$

$$\tau = \frac{1}{kC_{A0}} \int_0^{X_{Af}} \frac{(1 + \varepsilon_A X_A)^2}{(1 - X_A)^2} dX_A$$

Integrating and putting $X_A = 0.95$ and $\varepsilon_A = 2$, we obtain

$$ktC_{A0} = \varepsilon_A \ln (1 - X_A) + (\varepsilon_A + 1) \frac{X_A}{1 - X_A} = 51$$

and from Eq. 18

$$k\tau C_{A0} = 2\varepsilon_A(\varepsilon_A + 1) \ln (1 - X_A) + (\varepsilon_A + 1)^2 \frac{X_A}{1 - X_A} + \varepsilon_A{}^2 X_A = 138.8$$

Dividing and putting $t = 1$ min, we obtain

$$\tau = \frac{138.8}{51}$$

Therefore

$$V = (100 \text{ ft}^3)\left(\frac{138.8}{51}\right) = 272 \text{ ft}^3$$

This example shows that where $\varepsilon \neq 0$, scale-up using τ is simple and direct and requires less information than when t is used. It shows in addition that these terms cannot be used interchangeably.

REFERENCE

R. N. Pease, *J. Am. Chem. Soc.*, **51**, 3470 (1929).

PROBLEMS

1. Consider a gas-phase reaction 2A = R + 2S with unknown kinetics. If a space velocity of 1/min is needed for 90% conversion of A in a plug flow reactor, find the corresponding (*a*) space time, (*b*) mean residence time or holding time of fluid in the reactor.

2. In a batch reactor operating isothermally 70% of a liquid reactant is converted in 13 min. What space time, space velocity, and holding time are needed to effect this conversion in (*a*) a plug flow reactor, (*b*) a backmix reactor.

3. Consider a gas-phase reaction A = 3.2R with unknown kinetics. If 0.3% of reactant is converted in 4 min in an isothermal constant pressure batch reactor, what space velocity, space time, and holding time will yield this conversion in (*a*) a plug flow reactor, (*b*) a backmix reactor.

4. A homogeneous liquid-phase constant-density reaction is being studied at a fixed temperature in a laboratory reactor using stoichiometric quantities of reactants with the following results:

Time t, min	0	1	4
Fraction of limiting reactant converted X	0	0.20	0.80

(*a*) Find the order of the reaction.

(*b*) What ratio of volumes of backmix to plug flow reactors will produce identical quantities of material at 80% conversion of limiting reactant?

(*c*) What is the ratio of residence times in these two reactors?

5. The slow gas-phase reaction $A \rightarrow 2.4R$ with unknown kinetics takes place isothermally in a constant-volume bomb. Starting with pure A at 1 atm the pressure in the bomb rises to 1.8 atm in 75 min. What space time, space velocity, and holding time is needed to effect this conversion in (*a*) a plug flow reactor, (*b*) a backmix reactor.

6. In a study of the partial oxidation of ethane in a jet reactor it was reported that the following conditions were employed:

Pressure in the reactor = 65 psia

Temperature in the reactor = 2408°F

Space velocity based on gaseous feed at 25°C and 1 atm = 5.6×10^6 hr^{-1}

Assuming $\varepsilon = 0$, what holding time in seconds was used in this run?

7. The reaction $A \rightarrow 2R + S$ takes place isothermally in a constant-pressure experimental reactor. Starting with a mixture of 75% A and 25% inerts, the volume doubles in 8 min. (*a*) What conversion is achieved? (*b*) What volume of plug flow reactor can treat 500 ft³/hr of this feed to obtain the same conversion as that obtained in the batch reactor experiment?

8. Two gas-phase reactions $A \rightarrow R + S$, $A' \rightarrow R'$ have the same rate equations $r = k$.

(*a*) At a given feed rate to a backmix reactor, are fractional conversions and outlet concentrations the same for these two reactions? If not which is greater?

(*b*) Repeat part *a* for a plug flow reactor.

9. The aqueous-phase decomposition of A is studied in an experimental backmix reactor. The results in Table P9 are obtained in steady-state runs.

To obtain 75% conversion of reactant in a feed, $C_{A0} = 0.8$ gm mole/liter, what holding time is needed (*a*) in a plug flow reactor, (*b*) in a backmix flow reactor.

10. (*a*) Write the general design equation for backmix and plug flow reactors in terms of concentrations rather than fractional conversions, using as capacity measures both t and τ.

(*b*) Comment on the relative ease of using these various equations.

11. The homogeneous gas-phase reaction $A \rightarrow 3R$ follows second-order kinetics. For a feed rate of 40 ft³/hr of pure A at 5 atm and 350°C, an experimental reactor consisting of a standard 1-in. pipe 6 ft long gives 60% conversion

Table P9

Concentration of A, gm moles/liter		
In Feed	In Exit Stream	Holding Time, sec
2.00	0.65	300
2.00	0.92	240
2.00	1.00	250
1.00	0.56	110
1.00	0.37	360
0.48	0.42	24
0.48	0.28	200
0.48	0.20	560

of feed. A commercial plant is to treat 3200 ft^3/hr of feed consisting of 50% A, 50% inerts at 25 atm and 350°C to obtain 80% conversion.

(*a*) How many 6-ft lengths of standard 1-in. pipe are required?

(*b*) Should they be placed in parallel or in series?

Assume plug flow, negligible pressure drop, and ideal gas.

12. HOLMES: You say he was last seen tending this vat . . ..

SIR BOSS: You mean "overflow backmix reactor," Mr. Holmes.

HOLMES: You must excuse my ignorance of your particular technical jargon, Sir Boss.

SIR BOSS: That's all right; however, you must find him Mr. Holmes. Imbibit was a queer chap; always staring into the reactor, taking deep breaths, and licking his lips, but he was our very best operator. Why since he left, our conversion of googliox has dropped from 80% to 75%.

HOLMES: (*Tapping the side of the vat idly*) By the way, what goes on in the vat?

SIR BOSS: Just an elementary second-order reaction, between ethanol and googliox, if you know what I mean. Of course, we maintain a large excess of alcohol, about 100 to 1 and . . .

HOLMES: (*Interrupting*) Intriguing, we checked every possible lead in town and found not a single clue.

SIR BOSS: (*Wiping away the tears*) We'll give the old chap a raise—about twopence per week—if only he'll come back.

DR. WATSON: Pardon me, but may I ask a question?

HOLMES: Why certainly, Watson.

WATSON: What is the capacity of this vat, Sir Boss?

SIR BOSS: A hundred Imperial gallons, and we always keep it filled to the brim. That is why we call it an overflow reactor. You see we are running at full capacity—profitable operation you know.

HOLMES: Well, my dear Watson, we must admit that we're stumped, for without clues deductive powers are of no avail.

WATSON: Ahh, but that is where you are wrong, Holmes. (*Then turning to the manager*) Imbibit was a largish fellow—say about 18 stone—was he not?

SIR BOSS: Why yes, how did you know?

HOLMES: (*With awe*) Amazing, my dear Watson!

WATSON: (*Modestly*) Why it's quite elementary, Holmes. We have all the clues necessary to deduce what happened to the happy fellow. But first of all, would someone fetch me some dill.

With Sherlock Holmes and Sir Boss impatiently waiting, Dr. Watson casually leaned against the vat, slowly and carefully filled his pipe, and—with the keen sense of the dramatic—lit it. There our story ends.

(*a*) What momentous revelation was Dr. Watson planning to make and how did he arrive at this conclusion?

(*b*) Why did he never make it?

13. The data in Table P13 have been obtained on the gas-phase decomposition of reactant A in a constant volume reactor at 100°C.

Table P13

t, sec	p_A, atm	t, sec	p_A, atm
0	1.00	140	0.31
20	0.80	200	0.17
40	0.68	260	0.09
60	0.58	330	0.04
80	0.49	420	0.01
100	0.42		

The stoichiometry of the reaction is $2A \rightarrow R + S$. What size plug flow reactor (in liters) operating at 100°C and 1 atm can treat 100 gm moles A/hr in a feed consisting of 20% inerts to obtain 95% conversion of A?

14. A 55-gal tank is to be used as a backmix reactor to effect the reaction of the previous problem. For identical feed and identical operating conditions, what conversion of A may be expected from this reactor?

15. An aqueous-phase chemical reaction is being studied in a laboratory-sized steady-state flow system. The reactor is a 5-liter flask whose contents (5 liters of fluid) are well stirred and uniform in composition. The stoichiometric equation for the reaction is $A \rightarrow 2R$, and reactant A is introduced at a concentration of 1 gm mole/liter. Results of the experimental investigation are summarized in Table P15. What is the rate expression for this reaction?

16. The homogeneous gas-phase reaction $A \rightarrow 2B$ is run at 100°C at a constant pressure of 1 atm in an experimental batch reactor. The data in Table P16 were obtained starting with pure A. What size plug flow reactor operated at 100°C and 10 atm would yield 90% conversion of A for a total feed rate of 300 lb moles/hr, the feed containing 40% inerts?

Table P15

Run	Feed Rate, cc fluid/sec	Temperature of Run, °C	Conc. of R in Effluent, moles R/liter
1	2	13	1.8
2	15	13	1.5
3	15	84	1.8

Table P16

Time, min	$\frac{V}{V_0}$	Time, min	$\frac{V}{V_0}$
0	1.00	8	1.82
1	1.20	9	1.86
2	1.35	10	1.88
3	1.48	11	1.91
4	1.58	12	1.92
5	1.66	13	1.94
6	1.72	14	1.95
7	1.78		

17. Find the rate equation for the decomposition of A from the results of the kinetic runs made in a backmix reactor at steady state (Table P17).

Table P17

Conc. of A in Feed, gm moles/liter	Conc. of A in Reactor, gm moles/liter	Mean Residence Time of Fluid in Reactor, sec	Temperature, °C
1.0	0.4	220	44
1.0	0.4	100	57
1.0	0.4	30	77
1.0	0.1	400	52
1.0	0.1	120	72
1.0	0.1	60	84

18.* At 600°K the gas-phase reaction

$$C_2H_4 + Br_2 \underset{k_2}{\overset{k_1}{\rightleftharpoons}} C_2H_4Br_2$$

has rate constants

$$k_1 = 8000 \text{ ft}^3/(\text{lb mole})(\text{hr})$$

$$k_2 = 0.032 \text{ hr}^{-1}$$

If a plug flow reactor is to be fed 20,000 ft^3/hr of gas containing 60% Br_2 and 30% C_2H_4 and 10% inerts by volume at 600°K and 1.5 atm absolute, compute (*a*) the maximum possible fractional conversion of C_2H_4 into $C_2H_4Br_2$, (*b*) the volume of reaction vessel required to obtain 60% of this maximum conversion.

19. It has been reported that the reaction

$$\underset{\substack{\text{ethylene}\\\text{chlorhydrin}}}{\begin{matrix}CH_2OH\\|\\CH_2Cl\end{matrix}} + \underset{\substack{\text{sodium}\\\text{bicarbonate}}}{NaHCO_3} \rightarrow \underset{\substack{\text{ethylene}\\\text{glycol}}}{\begin{matrix}CH_2OH\\|\\CH_2OH\end{matrix}} + NaCl + CO_2$$

is elementary with rate constant k = 5.2 liters/(gm mole)(hr) at 180°F. On the basis of this information we wish to construct a pilot plant to determine the economic feasibility of producing ethylene glycol from two available feeds, a 15 wt % aqueous solution of sodium bicarbonate and a 30 wt % aqueous solution of ethylene chlorhydrin.

(*a*) What volume of tubular (plug flow) reactor will produce 100 lb/hr ethylene glycol at 95% conversion of an equimolar feed produced by intimately mixing the appropriate quantities of the two available feed streams.

(*b*) What size backmix reactor is needed for the same feed, conversion, and production rate as in part *a*?

Assume all operations at 180°F, at which temperature the specific gravity of the mixed reacting fluid is 1.02.

20. Experimental work by Pease (1929) indicates that the pyrolitic polymerization of acetylene in the gas phase follows second-order kinetics and occurs so that 0.009 of the acetylene is converted into an average tetramer complex, $4C_2H_2 \rightarrow (C_2H_2)_4$, in 1 sec at 550°C and 1 atm absolute pressure. An estimation of plant performance is to be made from this information. The units available consist of five identical tubular furnaces, each comprising 37 tubes; the tubes are 10 ft long and have an inside diameter of 2 in. The five units are to be operated continuously in parallel, are to be fed gas at 20 atm absolute pressure, and are to be maintained at such a temperature that the reaction may be considered to occur isothermally at 550°C. The total gas feed rate to the plant is to be 25,000 ft^3/hr measured at 20 atm absolute pressure and 550°C. The analysis of the feed gas is 80 vol% acetylene and 20 vol% inerts. For estimation purposes

---

* Problems 5.18, 5.20, 7.9, 14.16, and 14.18 either are taken directly from or are modified versions of problems given in *Chemical Engineering Problems*, 1946, edited by the Chemical Engineering Education Projects Committee, American Institute of Chemical Engineers, 1955.

the pressure drop through the system may be neglected, and the ideal gas law may be assumed to apply.

(*a*) Compute the production rate of the tetramer complex for the entire plant in pounds per hour.

(*b*) If the five units are operated in series, compute the gas feed rate that may be used if the fraction of conversion of acetylene is to be the same as it is in part *a*.

6

DESIGN FOR SINGLE REACTIONS

Many reactor systems may be considered for a given job. These may include the single-batch, backmix, or plug flow reactors, or multistage setups such as reactors in series or parallel. In addition, we may consider various feed ratios, the introduction of feed between stages, interstage cooling or heating, recycle of material, and many other possibilities. Now the factors that influence the selection of one design in preference to a competing design could be the reaction type, rate of production and product desired, the relative costs of equipment and necessary instrumentation, operational stability, control and flexibility of operation, feed material and operating costs, equipment life expectancy, length of time that the product is expected to be manufactured, ease of convertibility of the equipment to modified operating conditions or to new and different processes. With the wide choice of systems available and with the many factors to be considered, no neat formula can be expected to give the optimum setup. Experience, engineering judgment, and a sound knowledge of the characteristics of the various reactor systems are all needed in selecting a design close to the optimum, and, needless to say, the choice in the last analysis will be dictated by the economics of the over-all process.

Reactor design controls two factors which may profoundly influence the economics of the over-all process. These two factors are the reactor size and the distribution of products of reaction. By reactor size is meant the volume required for the reactive materials and not for the whole setup including auxiliary equipment. Sizes of reactor may vary by a factor of 10,000% among competing designs. The second factor, product distribution, is probably the prime consideration in the choice of reactor system for multiple reactions, since the distribution of products may be greatly affected by the type of flow existing in the reactor. Thus a reactor with the appropriate type of flow will maximize the production of the desired product and at the same time depress formation of undesired materials.

In this chapter we deal with single reactions. These are reactions whose progress can be described and followed adequately by using one and only one rate expression coupled with the necessary stoichiometric and equilibrium expressions. For such reactions product distribution is fixed and not a variable; hence the important factor in comparing designs is the reactor size requirement. We consider in turn the size comparison of various single and multiple reactor systems, first for irreversible reactions nth order and then for reactions with arbitrary kinetics. Finally we treat a rather unique type of reaction, the autocatalytic reaction.

Design for multiple reactions, for which the primary consideration is product distribution, is given in the next chapter.

SIZE COMPARISON OF SINGLE REACTORS

Batch reactor

First of all, before we compare the flow reactor systems, let us mention the batch reactor briefly. The batch reactor has the advantage of small instrumentation cost, and flexibility of operation (may be shut down easily and quickly). It has the disadvantage of high labor and handling cost, often considerable shutdown time to empty, clean out, and refill, and poorer quality control of the product. Hence we may generalize to state that the batch reactor is well suited to produce small amounts of material or to produce many different products from one piece of equipment. On the other hand, for the chemical treatment of materials in large amounts the continuous process is nearly always found to be more economical.

Regarding reactor sizes, if $\varepsilon = 0$ and $t_s = 0$, we see from Eqs. 5.3, 5.12, and 5.20 that the volumes of batch and plug flow reactor to do a given job are the same. Of course, on a long-term production basis we must correct our size requirement estimates for the additional factor of shutdown time t_s between batches. Thus we can easily relate the performance capabilities of the batch reactor with the plug flow reactor.

Backmix versus plug flow reactors, first- and second-order reactions

We may expect, and it is true, that in general the ratio of sizes of backmix and plug flow reactors will be influenced by the extent of reaction, the reaction type, and the rate equation. For the general case a comparison of Eqs. 5.9 and 5.12 will give the ratio of backmix to plug flow reactor sizes required for a given conversion. However, a number of design charts are presented which will allow rapid comparison of the frequently encountered reaction types, the first- and second-order reactions.

A large class of reactions approximate the simple type of rate law

$$-r_A = -\frac{1}{V}\frac{dN_A}{dt} = kC_A{}^n$$

where n varies anywhere from zero to at the most three. For reactions of this type comparisons of conversions in plug and backmix flow reactors are found as functions of feed rate, feed composition, reaction order, and expansion factor from expressions derived in Chapter 5. Thus from Table 5.1 we have for nth-order reactions in backmix flow reactors

$$\tau_b = \left(\frac{C_{A0}V}{F_{A0}}\right)_b = \frac{C_{A0}X_A}{-r_A} = \frac{1}{kC_{A0}^{n-1}}\frac{X_A(1+\varepsilon_A X_A)^n}{(1-X_A)^n}$$

whereas in plug flow reactors

$$\tau_p = \left(\frac{C_{A0}V}{F_{A0}}\right)_p = C_{A0}\int_0^{X_A}\frac{dX_A}{-r_A} = \frac{1}{kC_{A0}^{n-1}}\int_0^{X_A}\frac{(1+\varepsilon_A X_A)^n\,dX_A}{(1-X_A)^n}$$

Dividing we find that

$$\frac{(\tau C_{A0}^{n-1})_b}{(\tau C_{A0}^{n-1})_p} = \frac{\left(\dfrac{C_{A0}{}^n V}{F_{A0}}\right)_b}{\left(\dfrac{C_{A0}{}^n V}{F_{A0}}\right)_p} = \frac{\left[X_A\left(\dfrac{1+\varepsilon_A X_A}{1-X_A}\right)^n\right]_b}{\left[\displaystyle\int_0^{X_A}\frac{(1+\varepsilon_A X_A)^n}{(1-X_A)^n}\,dX_A\right]_p} \tag{1}$$

With density constant, or $\varepsilon = 0$, we obtain

$$\frac{(\tau C_{A0}^{n-1})_b}{(\tau C_{A0}^{n-1})_p} = \frac{\left[\dfrac{X_A}{(1-X_A)^n}\right]_b}{\left[\displaystyle\int_0^{X_A}\frac{dX_A}{(1-X_A)^n}\right]_p}$$

which on integration yields

$$\frac{(\tau C_{A0}^{n-1})_b}{(\tau C_{A0}^{n-1})_p} = \frac{\left[\dfrac{X_A}{(1-X_A)^n}\right]_b}{\dfrac{-1}{1-n}[(1-X_A)^{1-n}-1]_p}, \qquad n \neq 1$$

or (2)

$$\frac{(\tau C_{A0}^{n-1})_b}{(\tau C_{A0}^{n-1})_p} = \frac{\left(\dfrac{X_A}{1-X_A}\right)_b}{-\ln(1-X_A)_p}, \qquad n = 1$$

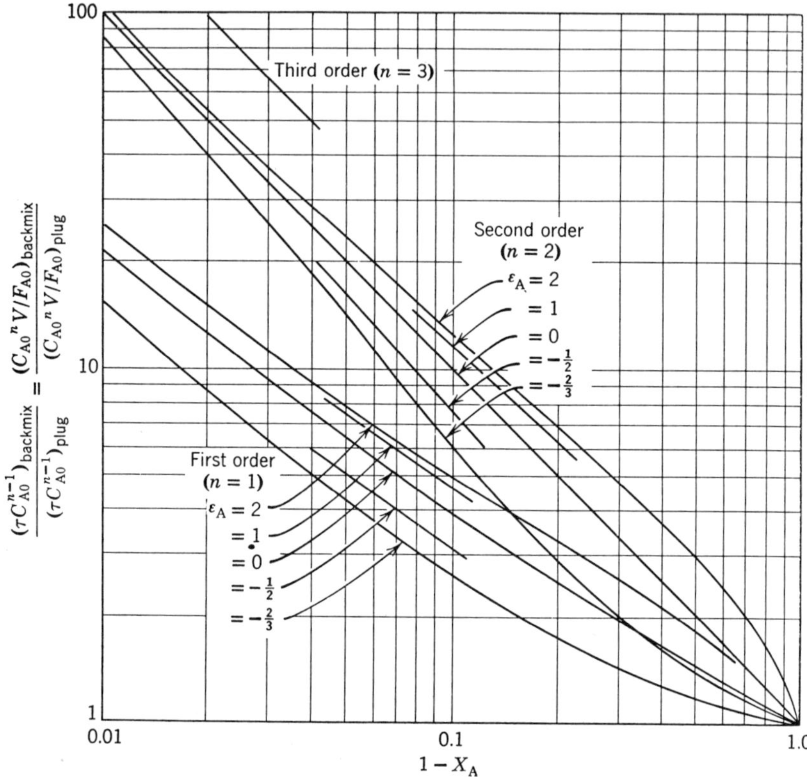

Fig. 1. Comparison of performances of single backmix and plug flow reactors for the nth-order reaction

$$aA \rightarrow \text{products}, \qquad -r_A = kC_A{}^n$$

The ordinate becomes the volume ratio V_b/V_p or space-time ratio τ_b/τ_p if the same quantities of identical feed are used.

Equations 1 and 2 are presented in graphical form for first- and second-order reactions in Fig. 1, which provides a quick comparison of the performance of single plug flow with backmix flow reactors. For identical feed composition C_{A0} and flow rate F_{A0} the ordinate of this figure gives directly the volume ratio of backmix to plug flow reactors required for any specified conversion. Figure 1 shows the following.

1. The backmix reactor is always larger than the plug reactor for all positive reaction orders. The ratio of volumes increases with order. For zero-order reactions reactor size is independent of the type of flow.

2. When conversion is small, the reactor performance is only slightly affected by flow type for all reactions, the volume ratio approaching unity as conversion approaches zero. The ratio increases very rapidly at high

conversion; consequently knowledge of the type of flow becomes very important to design in this range of conversion.

3. Density variation during reaction as measured by the expansion factor affects design; however, it is generally of secondary importance compared to the difference in flow type. Expansion (or density decrease) during reaction increases the volume ratio, in other words further decreases the effectiveness of the backmix reactor with respect to the plug flow reactor; density increase during reaction has the opposite effect.

Variation of reactant ratios for second-order reactions

For reactions of type A + B → products with rate law

$$-r_A = -r_B = kC_AC_B \tag{3.12}$$

Fig. 1 compares sizes of plug flow and backmix reactors when equimolar feed ratios are used. However, it is usually more economical in cost of reactants and equipment (reactor size) to use unequal molar quantities of the two active feed components. The optimum setup depends on a number of factors, including cost of separation of the products from unused reactants, recycle cost of components, density of various feed compositions, etc. Let us compare the ratio of backmix to plug flow reactor size required to effect a given conversion of limiting reactant A for various initial reactant ratios $C_{B0}/C_{A0} = M > 1$. Assume in the following treatment that density changes during reaction can be neglected.

For a plug flow reactor with $M \neq 1$, we find from Eq. 3.13 that

$$\tau_{M\neq1} = \left(\frac{C_{A0}V}{F_{A0}}\right)_{M\neq1} = \frac{1}{kC_{A0}(M-1)} \ln \frac{M - X_A}{M(1 - X_A)}, \qquad M \neq 1 \tag{3a}$$

and for $M = 1$ we find from Eq. 3.14*b*

$$\tau_{M=1} = \left(\frac{C_{A0}V}{F_{A0}}\right)_{M=1} = \frac{1}{kC_{A0}} \frac{X_A}{1 - X_A}, \qquad M = 1 \tag{3b}$$

With Eqs. 3 we can compare the performance of plug flow reactors at various C_{A0}, F_{A0}, M, and X_A with $\varepsilon = 0$. Figure 2 shows the interrelationship among the many variables in this situation.

For a backmix reactor with $M \neq 1$, Eqs. 3.12 and 5.9 give

$$\tau_{M\neq1} = \left(\frac{C_{A0}V}{F_{A0}}\right)_{M\neq1} = \frac{X_A}{kC_{A0}(1 - X_A)(M - X_A)}, \qquad M \neq 1 \tag{4a}$$

and for $M = 1$, Eqs. 3.14 and 5.9 give

$$\tau_{M=1} = \left(\frac{C_{A0}V}{F_{A0}}\right)_{M=1} = \frac{X_A}{kC_{A0}(1 - X_A)^2}, \qquad M = 1 \tag{4b}$$

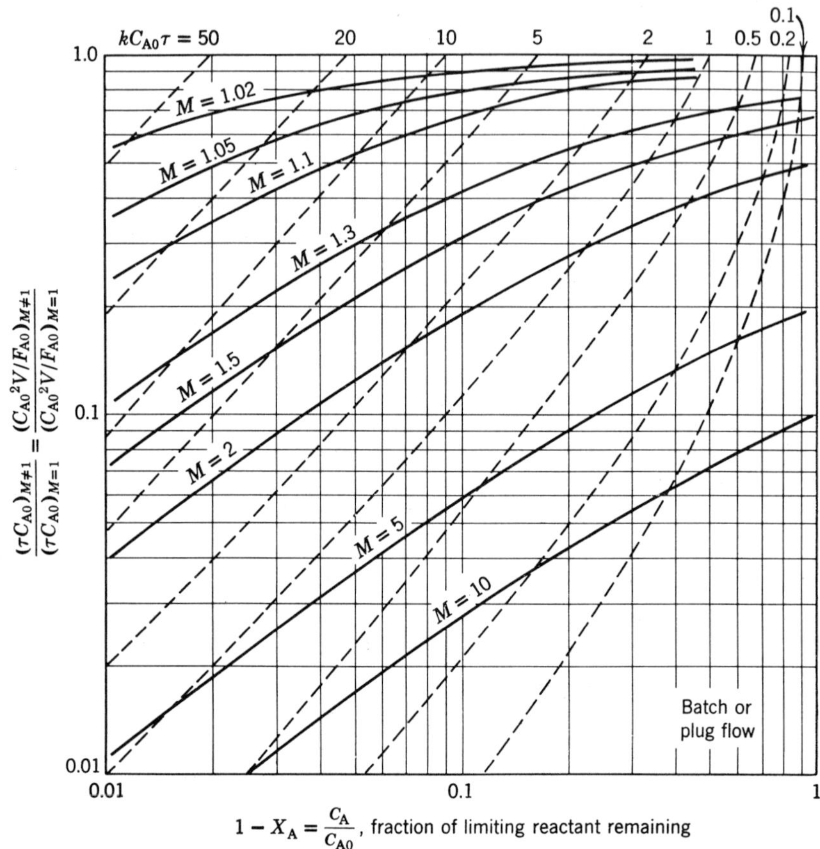

Fig. 2. Performance of a batch or plug flow reactor as influenced by the mole ratio of reactants in the feed, $M = C_{B0}/C_{A0}$, for the second-order reaction

$$A + B \rightarrow \text{products}, \qquad -r_A = kC_AC_B, \quad \varepsilon = 0$$

For identical F_{A0} and C_{A0} the ordinate becomes the volume ratio $V_{M\neq1}/V_{M=1}$ or the space-time ratio $\tau_{M\neq1}/\tau_{M=1}$.

With Eqs. 4 we can compare the performance of backmix reactors at various operating conditions and conversions if $\varepsilon = 0$. Figure 3 shows the interrelationship among the many variables for this situation.

With identical feed rates F_{A0} and identical initial concentration of limiting reactant C_{A0} for the two conditions, the ordinates of Figs. 2 and 3 compare directly the volumes of reactors needed for processing. For this situation we see that changing the molar feed ratio away from unity increases the capacity of a reactor for both backmix and plug flow. This

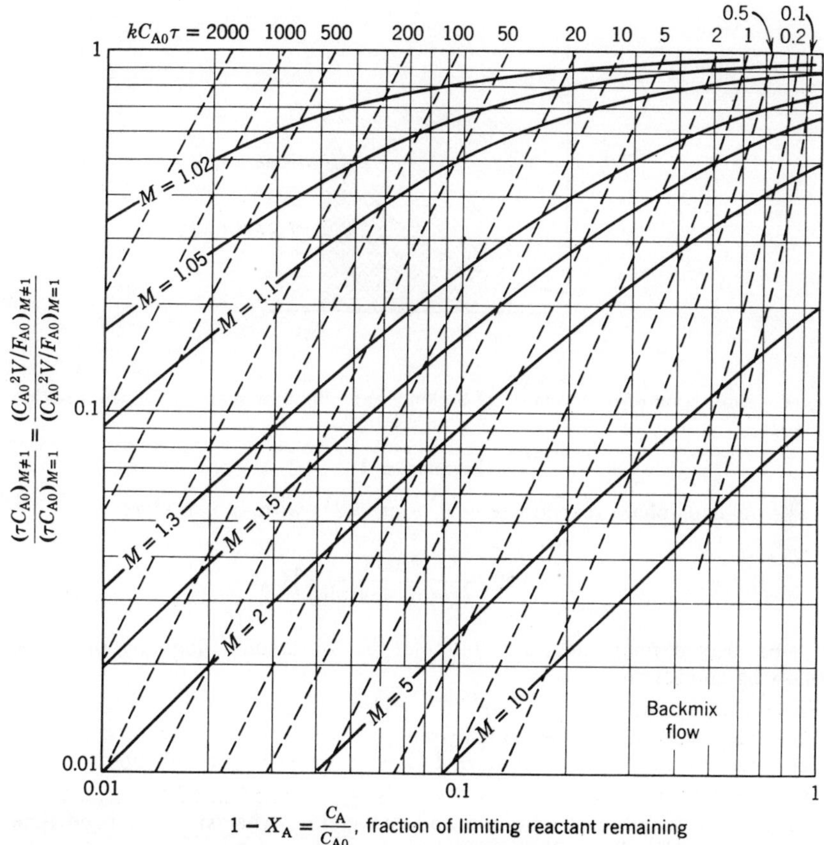

Fig. 3. Performance of a backmix reactor as influenced by the mole ratio of reactants in the feed, $M = C_{B0}/C_{A0}$, for the second-order reaction

$$A + B \rightarrow \text{products}, \qquad -r_A = kC_AC_B, \quad \varepsilon = 0$$

For identical F_{A0} and C_{A0} the ordinate becomes the volume ratio $V_{M\neq1}/V_{M=1}$ or the space-time ratio $\tau_{M\neq1}/\tau_{M=1}$.

effect is more pronounced at high conversions than at low and in backmix reactors than in plug flow reactors.

Example 1 illustrates the use of these charts.

General graphical procedure

For reactions with arbitrary but known rate the performance capabilities of backmix and plug flow reactors are best compared by using the graphical representations of Figs. 5.3 and 5.5. This is illustrated in Fig. 4. The ratio of shaded areas gives the ratio of space times needed in these two reactors.

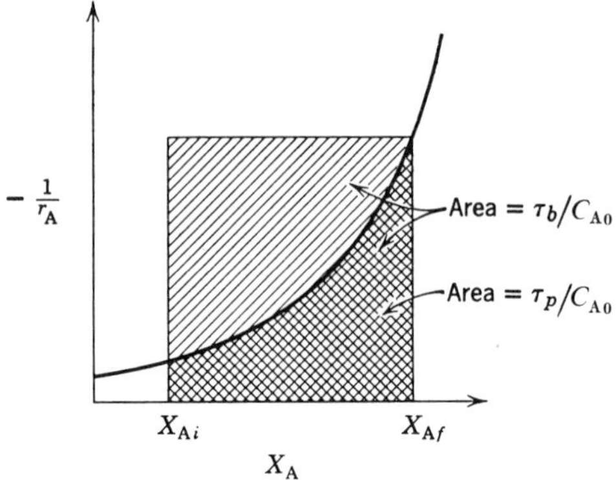

Fig. 4. Comparison of performance of backmix and plug flow reactors for any reaction kinetics.

Example 1

The aqueous-phase reaction A + B → products with known kinetics

$$-r_A = \left(500 \frac{\text{liters}}{(\text{gm mole})(\text{min})}\right) C_A C_B$$

is to be effected in an experimental tubular reactor (assume plug flow) under the following conditions:

volume of reactor $V = 0.1$ liter
volumetric feed rate $v = 0.05$ liter/min
concentration of reactants in feed, $C_{A0} = C_{B0} = 0.01$ gm mole/liter

(*a*) What fractional conversions of reactants can be expected?

(*b*) For the same treatment rate and conversion, what size of stirred tank reactor (assume backmix flow) is needed?

(*c*) For the same treatment rate, what conversion can be expected in a backmix reactor of size equal to the plug flow reactor?

Introduce into the original plug flow reactor a modified feed in which the concentration of B is increased 50% while the concentration of A remains unchanged. Thus $C_{B0} = 0.015$ gm mole/liter, $C_{A0} = 0.010$ gm mole/liter.

(*d*) For the same volumetric feed rate using the new feed, what conversion of limiting reactant A can be expected in the original reactor?

(*e*) For the same conversion of limiting reactant, by what fraction can the volumetric treatment rate be increased when the new feed is used?

(*f*) What volumetric treatment rate of new feed can be used in a semicommercial-sized backmix reactor, $V = 100$ liters, for 99% conversion of limiting reactant A?

Solution. The sketches in Fig. E1 show how the various charts are used.

(*a*) *Conversion in plug flow reactor.* Since

$$\tau = t = \frac{VC_{A0}}{F_{A0}} = \frac{V}{v} = \frac{0.1 \text{ liter}}{0.05 \text{ liter/min}} = 2 \text{ min}$$

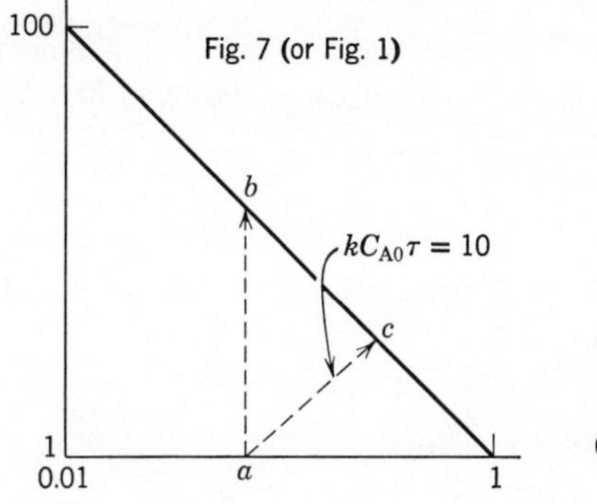

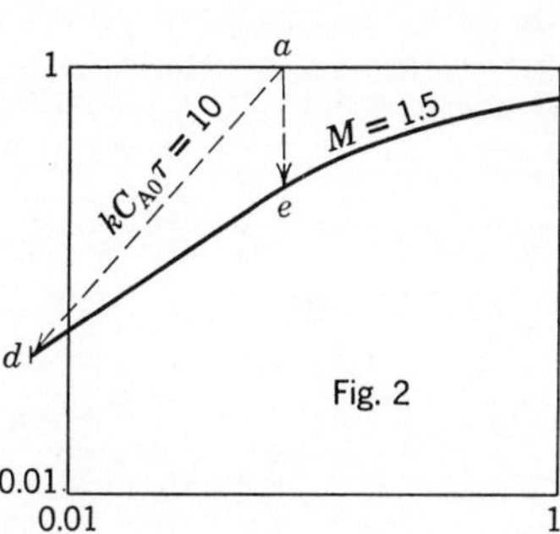

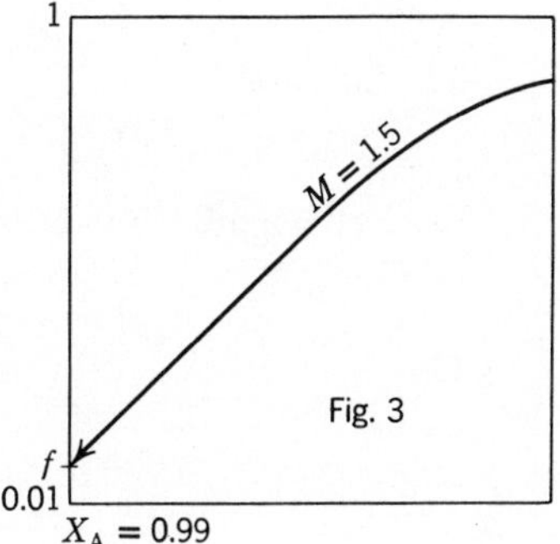

Fig. E1

therefore

$$kC_{A0}\tau = \left(\frac{500 \text{ liters}}{(\text{gm mole})(\text{min})}\right)(2 \text{ min})\left(\frac{0.01 \text{ gm mole}}{\text{liter}}\right) = 10$$

From the plug flow line of Fig. 2 or 7 and the value calculated for the dimensionless reaction rate group, $kC_{A0}\tau$, we find

Conversion: $X_A = X_B = 0.91$

(*b*) *Size of backmix reactor for identical performance.* For identical C_{A0} and F_{A0} in both backmix and plug flow reactor the ordinate of Fig. 1 or 7 is simply the volume ratio of the two reactors V_b/V_p.

Thus for the same X_A we find

$$\frac{V_b}{V_p} = 11$$

Hence

$$V_b = (11)(0.1 \text{ liter}) = 1.1 \text{ liters}$$

(*c*) *Conversion in a backmix reactor of the same size.* For the same-sized reactor we must remain on the same $kC_{A0}\tau$ line. Thus moving along this line from plug to backmix flow in Fig. 7 we find

Conversion: $X_A = 0.73$

(*d*) *Conversion in same reactor with* $M = 1.5$. For identical v, V, and C_{A0} the dimensionless reaction group $kC_{A0}\tau$ must be the same in the plug flow reactor for both feeds. Hence, moving along the $kC_{A0}\tau = 10$ line of Fig. 2 from the point found in part *a* on the $M = 1$ line to the $M = 1.5$ line we find (on extrapolating)

Conversion: $X_A = 0.994$

(*e*) *Treatment rate when* $M = 1.5$. For identical conversion we find from Fig. 2 that

$$\frac{(\tau C_{A0})_{M=1.5}}{(\tau C_{A0})_{M=1}} = \frac{\left(\dfrac{V}{v} C_{A0}\right)_{M=1.5}}{\left(\dfrac{V}{v} C_{A0}\right)_{M=1}} = 0.295$$

But C_{A0} and V are identical in the two cases; hence the new feed rate is

$$v_{M=1.5} = (v_{M=1})\left(\frac{1}{0.295}\right) = 0.17 \text{ liter/min}$$

which represents an increase in processing rate of 240%.

(*f*) *Volumetric treatment rate in a backmix reactor*. Figure 3 for backmix reactors shows that when $X_A = 0.99$ and $M = 1.5$

$$kC_{A0}\tau = kC_{A0}\frac{V}{v} = 190$$

Hence

$$v = \frac{kC_{A0}V}{190} = \frac{(500 \text{ liters/(gm mole)(min)})(0.01 \text{ mole/liters})(100 \text{ liters})}{190}$$
$$= 2.63 \text{ liters/min.}$$

These charts may be used in the repetitive calculations which are made in search of optimum operating conditions. Analytic solution is also possible and in some cases is just as quick as the graphical method. However, the graphical method was used in this example simply to illustrate the use of these charts.

The following examples illustrate the analytic approach to the search for optimum operating conditions.

Example 2

One hundred gram moles of R are to be produced hourly from a feed consisting of a saturated solution of A ($C_{A0} = 0.1$ gm mole/liters). The reaction is

$$A \rightarrow R$$

with rate

$$r_R = (0.2 \text{ hr}^{-1})C_A$$

Cost of reactant at $C_{A0} = 0.1$ gm mole/liter is

$$\$_A = \$0.50/\text{gm mole A}$$

Cost of backmix reactor including installation, auxiliary equipment, instrumentation overhead, labor, depreciation, etc., is

$$\$_b = \$0.01/(\text{hr})(\text{liter})$$

What size of backmix reactor, feed rate, and conversion should be used for optimum operations? What is the unit cost of R for these conditions? Unreacted A is discarded.

Solution. This is an optimization problem between high fractional conversion (low reactant cost) in a large reactor (high equipment cost) on the one hand versus low fractional conversion in a small reactor. The solution involves finding an expression for the total cost of the operation and minimizing it. On an hourly basis the total cost is

$$\$_t = \begin{pmatrix}\text{volume of}\\ \text{reactor}\end{pmatrix}\left(\frac{\text{cost}}{(\text{hr})(\text{volume of reactor})}\right) + \begin{pmatrix}\text{feed rate}\\ \text{of reactant}\end{pmatrix}\begin{pmatrix}\text{unit cost of}\\ \text{reactant}\end{pmatrix}$$

$$= V\$_b + F_{A0}\$_A$$

Now for a first-order reaction Eq. 5.9 gives

$$V = \frac{F_{A0}X_A}{kC_{A0}(1 - X_A)}$$

Noting that the rate of production of R

$$F_R = F_{A0}X_A = 100 \text{ moles/hr}$$

we can eliminate F_{A0} and can write the total cost expression in terms of one variable alone, X_A. Thus

$$\$_t = \frac{F_R}{kC_{A0}(1 - X_A)}\$_b + \frac{F_R}{X_A}\$_A$$

$$= \frac{100}{(0.2)(0.1)(1 - X_A)}(0.01) + \frac{100}{X_A}(0.5)$$

$$= \frac{50}{1 - X_A} + \frac{50}{X_A}$$

To find the conditions for minimum cost differentiate this expression and set to zero. Thus

$$\frac{d(\$_t)}{dX_A} = 0 = \frac{50}{(1 - X_A)^2} - \frac{50}{X_A^2}$$

or

$$X_A = 0.5$$

Hence the optimum conditions are

Conversion: $X_A = 0.5$

Feed rate: $F_{A0} = \dfrac{F_R}{X_A} = \dfrac{100}{0.5} = 200 \text{ moles A/hr}$

$$\text{Reactor size:}\quad V = \frac{F_{A0}X_A}{kC_{A0}(1 - X_A)} = \frac{100}{(0.2)(0.1)(0.5)} = 10{,}000 \text{ liters}$$

$$\text{Cost of product:}\quad \frac{\$_t}{F_R} = \frac{V\$_b + F_{A0}\$_A}{F_R} = \frac{10{,}000(0.01) + 200(0.5)}{100}$$

$$= \$2.00/\text{gm mole R}$$

Example 3

Suppose all unreacted A of the product stream of Example 2 can be reclaimed by an extraction process and can be brought up to the initial concentration $C_{A0} = 0.1$ gm mole/liter, at a total cost $\$_r = \$0.125$/gm mole A processed (Fig. E3). With this reclaimed A as a recycle stream, find the new optimum operating conditions and unit cost of producing R.

Solution. The solution involves finding a balance between low reactor and high recycle cost on the one hand and high reactor and low recycle cost on the other. Referring to the accompanying sketch which indicates all flowing streams in terms of F, the hourly molar flow rate, we find by material balance that

$$F_R = F_{Ai}X_A = F_{A0} = 100 \text{ moles/hr}$$

The total hourly cost

$$\$_t = \begin{pmatrix}\text{volume of}\\ \text{reactor}\end{pmatrix}\begin{pmatrix}\text{hourly cost}\\ \text{per unit}\\ \text{volume of}\\ \text{reactor}\end{pmatrix} + \begin{pmatrix}\text{feed rate}\\ \text{of fresh}\\ \text{reactant}\end{pmatrix}\begin{pmatrix}\text{unit cost}\\ \text{of fresh}\\ \text{reactant}\end{pmatrix} + \begin{pmatrix}\text{feed rate}\\ \text{of reclaimed}\\ \text{reactant}\end{pmatrix}\begin{pmatrix}\text{unit cost}\\ \text{of reclaimed}\\ \text{reactant}\end{pmatrix}$$

$$= V\$_b + F_{A0}\$_A + F_{A_i}(1 - X_A)\$_r$$

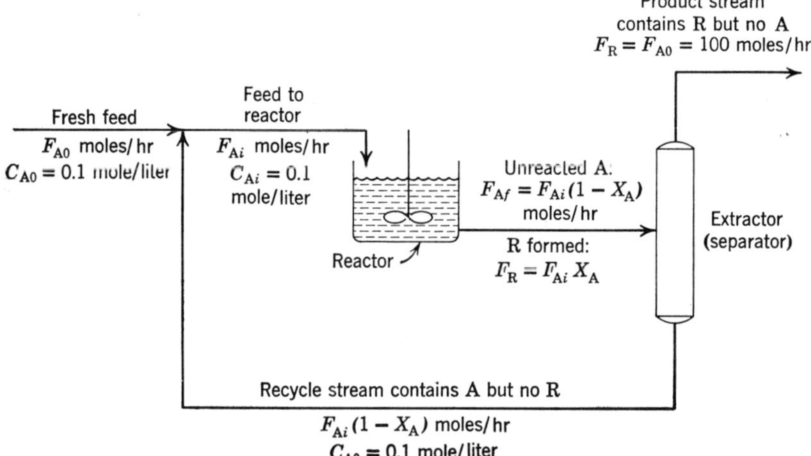

Fig. E3

With feed rate to the reactor F_{Ai} we have

$$V = \frac{F_{Ai}X_A}{kC_{A0}(1 - X_A)}$$

Eliminating F_{Ai} by the material balance, the total cost expression can be then written as a function of a single variable X_A. Thus

$$\begin{aligned}
\$_t &= \frac{F_{A0}}{kC_{A0}(1 - X_A)}\$_b + F_{A0}\$_A + \frac{F_{A0}}{X_A}(1 - X_A)\$_r \\
&= \frac{(100)}{(0.2)(0.1)(1 - X_A)}(0.01) + (100)(0.5) + (100)\left(\frac{1 - X_A}{X_A}\right)(0.125) \\
&= \frac{50}{1 - X_A} + 50 + 12.5\frac{1 - X_A}{X_A}
\end{aligned}$$

By the differentiating and setting to zero the condition for minimum cost is obtained. Thus

$$\frac{d\$_t}{dX_A} = 0 = \frac{50}{(1 - X_A)^2} - \frac{12.5}{X_A^{\,2}}$$

or

$$X_A = 0.33$$

Hence for optimum operations

Conversion within reactor: $X_A = 0.33$

Reactor size: $V = \dfrac{100}{(0.2)(0.1)(0.67)} = 7500 \text{ liters}$

Flow rate into reactor: $F_{Ai} = \dfrac{F_{A0}}{X_A} = 300 \text{ gm moles A/hr}$

$\qquad = 3000 \text{ liters/hr}$

Recycle rate: $F_{Ai} - F_{A0} = 200 \text{ gm moles A/hr}$

$\qquad = 2000 \text{ liters/hr}$

Cost of product:

$$\frac{\$_t}{F_R} = \frac{50/0.67 + 50 + 12.5(0.67/0.33)}{100} = \$1.50/\text{gm mole R}$$

MULTIPLE-REACTOR SYSTEM

Plug flow reactors in series and/or in parallel

Consider j plug flow reactors connected in series, and let $X_1, X_2, \ldots, X_j$, be the fractional conversion of component A leaving reactor $1, 2, \ldots, j$. Basing the material balance on the feed rate of A to the first reactor, we find for the ith reactor from Eq. 5.13

$$\frac{V_i}{F_0} = \int_{X_{i-1}}^{X_i} \frac{dX}{-r}$$

Hence, for the j reactors in series

$$\frac{V}{F_0} = \sum_{i=1}^{j} V_i \Big/ F_0 = \frac{V_1 + V_2 + \cdots + V_j}{F_0}$$

$$= \int_{X_0=0}^{X_1} \frac{dX}{-r} + \int_{X_1}^{X_2} \frac{dX}{-r} + \cdots + \int_{X_{j-1}}^{X_j} \frac{dX}{-r}$$

$$= \int_0^{X_j} \frac{dX}{-r}$$

Hence the j plug flow reactors in series with a total volume V gives the same fractional conversion as a single plug flow reactor of volume V.

For plug flow reactors connected in parallel or in any parallel-series combination, we can treat the whole system as a single plug flow reactor of volume equal to the total volume of the individual units if the feed is distributed in such a manner that fluid streams which meet have the same composition. Thus for reactors in parallel V/F or τ must be the same for each parallel line. Any other way of feeding is less efficient.

Example 4

A reactor setup as shown in Fig. E4 consists of three plug flow reactors in two parallel branches. Branch D has a reactor of volume 50 ft³ followed by a reactor of volume 30 ft³. Branch E has a reactor of volume 40 ft³. What fraction of the feed should go to branch D?

Solution. Branch D consists of two reactors in series; hence it may be considered to be a single reactor of volume

$$V_D = 50 + 30 = 80 \text{ ft}^3$$

Now for reactors in parallel V/F must be identical if the conversion is to be the same in each branch. Therefore

$$\left(\frac{V}{F}\right)_D = \left(\frac{V}{F}\right)_E$$

or

$$\frac{F_D}{F_E} = \frac{V_D}{V_E} = \frac{80}{40} = 2$$

Therefore two-thirds of the feed must be fed to branch D.

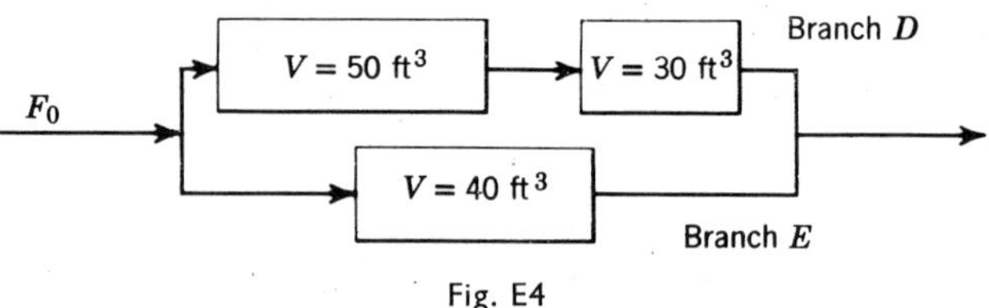

Fig. E4

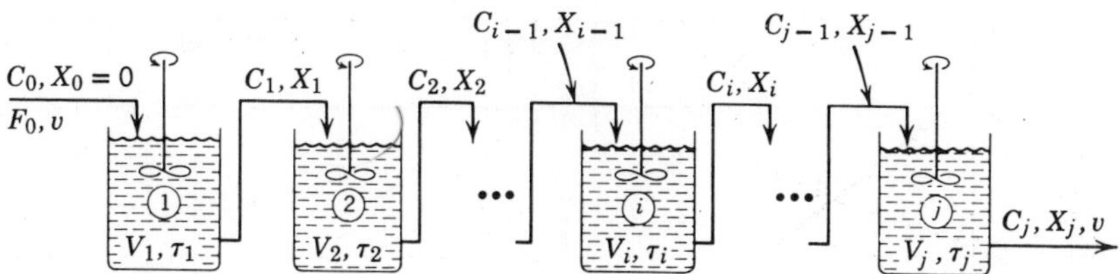

Fig. 5. Variables for a system of j equal-sized backmix reactors in series.

Equal-sized backmix reactors in series

In a plug flow reactor the concentration of reactants decreases progressively as fluid passes through the system; in a backmix reactor the concentration drops immediately to a low value. Because of this fact a plug flow reactor is more efficient than a backmix reactor for reactions whose rate is dependent only on the reactant concentration, such as nth-order irreversible reactions, $n > 0$.

Now consider a system consisting of j backmix reactors connected in series. Though the concentration is uniform in each reactor, there is nevertheless a change in concentration as fluid moves from reactor to reactor. If the number of backmix reactors is increased indefinitely, the volume of each being reduced so that the total volume remains constant, we see in the limit that the volume of the system required approaches that of the plug flow system.

Let us now quantitatively evaluate the behavior of a series of j equal-sized backmix reactors. Density changes will be assumed to be negligible; hence $\varepsilon = 0$ and $\bar{t} = \tau$. As a rule, with backmix reactors it is more convenient to develop the necessary equations in terms of concentrations rather than fractional conversions; therefore we use this approach. The nomenclature used is shown in Fig. 5 with subscript i referring to the ith vessel.

First-order reactions. From Eq. 5.10 a material balance about vessel i for component A gives

$$\tau_i = \frac{C_0 V_i}{F_0} = \frac{V_i}{v} = \frac{C_0(X_i - X_{i-1})}{-r_i}$$

As $\varepsilon = 0$ this may be written in terms of concentrations. Hence

$$\tau_i = \frac{C_0[(1 - C_i/C_0) - (1 - C_{i-1}/C_0)]}{kC_i} = \frac{C_{i-1} - C_i}{kC_i}$$

or

$$\frac{C_{i-1}}{C_i} = 1 + k\tau_i \tag{5}$$

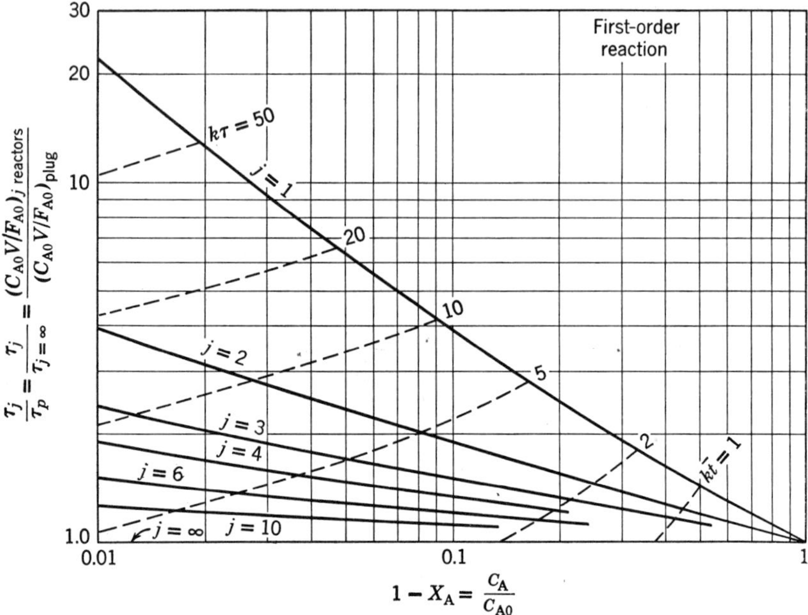

Fig. 6. Comparison of performance of a plug flow reactor with a series of j equal-sized backmix reactors for the first-order reaction

$$A \rightarrow R, \quad \varepsilon = 0$$

For the same processing rate of identical feed the ordinate measures the volume ratio V_j/V_p directly.

Now the space time τ (or mean residence time $\bar{t}$) is the same in all the j equal-sized reactors of volume V_i. Therefore

$$\frac{C_0}{C_j} = \frac{1}{1 - X_j} = \frac{C_0}{C_1}\frac{C_1}{C_2}\cdots\frac{C_{j-1}}{C_j} = (1 + k\tau_i)^j \tag{6a}$$

Rearranging, we find for the system as a whole

$$\tau_{j\text{reactors}} = j\tau_i = \frac{j}{k}\left[\left(\frac{C_0}{C_j}\right)^{1/j} - 1\right] \tag{6b}$$

In a plug flow reactor

$$\tau_p = \frac{1}{k}\ln\frac{C_0}{C} \tag{7}$$

With Eqs. 6*a* and 7 we can compare performance of *j* reactors in series with a plug flow reactor or with a single backmix reactor. This comparison is shown in Fig. 6 for first-order reactions in which density variations are negligible.

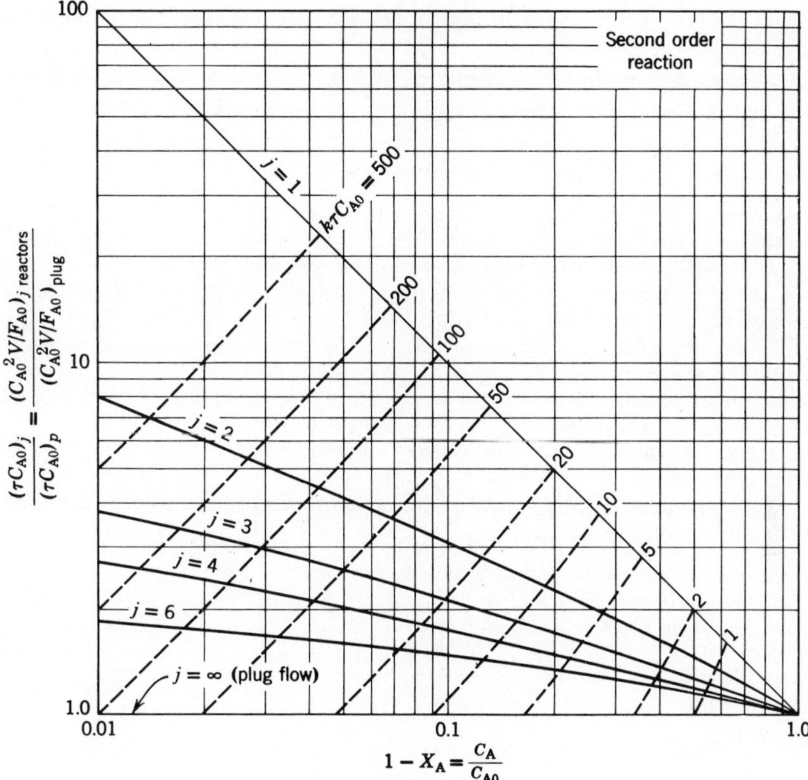

Fig. 7. Comparison of performance of a plug flow reactor with a series of j equal-sized backmix reactors for the second-order reactions

$$2A \rightarrow R$$
$$A + B \rightarrow R, \qquad C_{A0} = C_{B0}$$

with negligible expansion. For the same processing rate of identical feed the ordinate measures the volume ratio V_j/V_p or space-time ratio τ_j/τ_p directly.

Second-order reactions. We may evaluate the performance of backmix reactors in series for a second-order, bimolecular-type reaction, no excess of either reactant, by a procedure similar to that shown for a first-order reaction. Thus for j reactors in series

$$C_j = \frac{1}{2k\tau_i}\left(-1 + \sqrt{-1 \cdots + 2\sqrt{-1 + 2\sqrt{1 + 4C_0k\tau_i}^{\,j=1}}}^{\,j}\right) \tag{8a}$$

whereas for plug flow

$$\frac{C_0}{C} = 1 + C_0k\tau \tag{8b}$$

The results are presented in Fig. 7.

Figures 6 and 7 support our intuition by showing that the volume of system required for a given conversion decreases to plug flow volume as the number of reactors in series is increased, the greatest change taking place with the addition of a second vessel to a one-vessel system.

Example 5

At present 90% of reactant A is converted into product by a second-order reaction in a single backmix reactor. We plan to replace this reactor with two reactors with the same total volume as the one we now have.

(*a*) For the same 90% conversion, by how much can the treatment rate be increased?

(*b*) For the same treatment rate as that used at present, how will this replacement affect conversion of reactant?

Rather than replace the reactor now operating, suppose we place a second reactor similar to the one being used in series with it.

(*c*) For the same 90% conversion, by how much can the treatment rate be increased?

(*d*) For the same treatment rate as that used at present, how will this addition affect conversion of reactant?

Solution. Figure E5 shows how Fig. 7 is used.

(*a*) *Treatment rate for $j = 2$ for same total size.* For 90% conversion we find in moving from the $j = 1$ to $j = 2$ that

$$\frac{\tau_{j=1}}{\tau_p} = 10 \qquad \text{and} \qquad \frac{\tau_{j=2}}{\tau_p} = 3.05$$

or dividing

$$\frac{\tau_{j=1}}{\tau_{j=2}} = \frac{(C_0V/F_0)_{j=1}}{(C_0V/F_0)_{j=2}} = \frac{10}{3.05} = 3.28$$

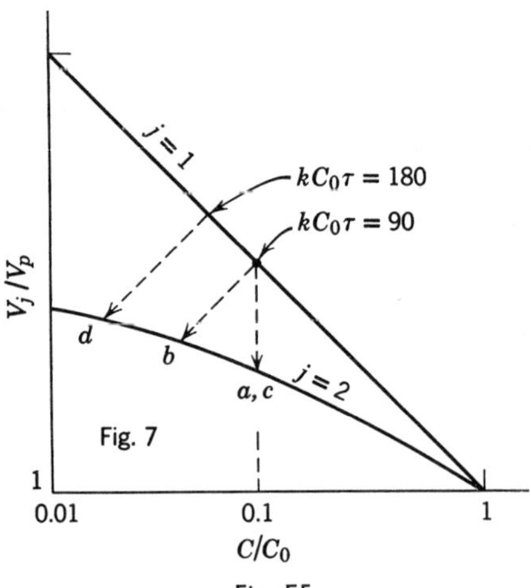

Fig. E5

But C_0 and V are identical in both cases; thus

$$\frac{(F_0)_{j=2}}{(F_0)_{j=1}} = 3.28$$

Hence the treatment rate can be increased by 2.28 times.

(*b*) *Conversion for same treatment rate.* For the same treatment rate in the same reactor size, F_0 and C_0, and hence $kC_0\tau$, are constant. Moving along this line from $j = 1$ to $j = 2$, we find from Fig. 7 that conversion

$$X = 95.4\%$$

(*c*) *Treatment rate for two reactors.* For 90% conversion we find as in part *a* that

$$\frac{\tau_{j=1}}{\tau_{j=2}} = 3.28$$

But for double the total size $V_{j=2} = 2V_{j=1}$; hence

$$\frac{(F_0)_{j=2}}{(F_0)_{j=1}} = 2(3.28) = 6.56$$

Therefore treatment rate can be increased by 5.56 times.

(*d*) *Conversion for same treatment rate.* For the single reactor with 90% conversion we have from Fig. 7

$$kC_0\tau = 90$$

For the two reactors the holding time is doubled; hence

$$kC_0\tau = 180$$

This line cuts the $j = 2$ line at a conversion $X = 97.4\%$.

Graphical methods different from those shown in Figs. 1, 2, 3, 6, and 7 are given by MacMullin and Weber (1935), Jenney (1955), Lessells (1957), and Schoenemann (1958).

Arbitrary network of ideal reactors

The more general problems of determining performance of backmix reactors of different sizes in series, any series of plug flow and backmix reactors, or any parallel-series network of plug flow and backmix reactors for reactions of any type can be solved by the simultaneous solution of the appropriate design equations.

Graphical solution for backmix reactors in series. A graphical solution of these equations is easily obtained for reactions with negligible density change taking place in a series of backmix reactors of various sizes [see Jones (1951)]. All that is needed is an r_A versus C_A curve to represent the reaction rate at various concentrations.

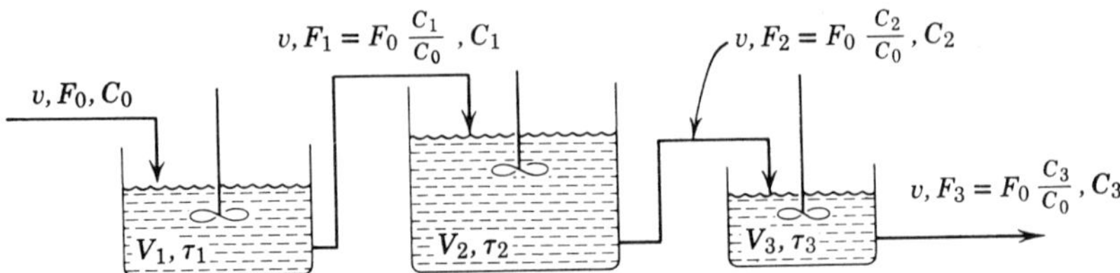

Fig. 8. Variables for a system of unequal-sized backmix reactors in series.

Let us illustrate the use of this method by considering three backmix reactors in series with volumes, feed rates, concentrations, space time (equal to residence time because $\varepsilon = 0$), and volumetric flow rates as shown in Fig. 8. Now from Eq. 5.9, noting that $\varepsilon = 0$, we may write for component A in the first reactor

$$\tau_1 = \bar{t}_1 = \frac{V_1}{v} = \frac{C_0 - C_1}{(-r)_1}$$

or

$$-\frac{1}{\tau_1} = \frac{(-r)_1}{C_1 - C_0} \tag{9}$$

Similarly from Eq. 5.10 for the ith reactor we may write

$$-\frac{1}{\tau_i} = \frac{(-r)_i}{C_i - C_{i-1}} \tag{10}$$

Plot the C versus r curve for component A and suppose that it is as shown in Fig. 9. To find the conditions in the first reactor note that (*a*) the inlet concentration C_0 is known (point L), (*b*) C_1 and $(-r)_1$ correspond to a point on the curve to be found (point M), (*c*) the slope of the line $LM = MN/NL = (-r)_1/(C_1 - C_0) = -(1/\tau_1)$ from Eq. 9. Hence from C_0

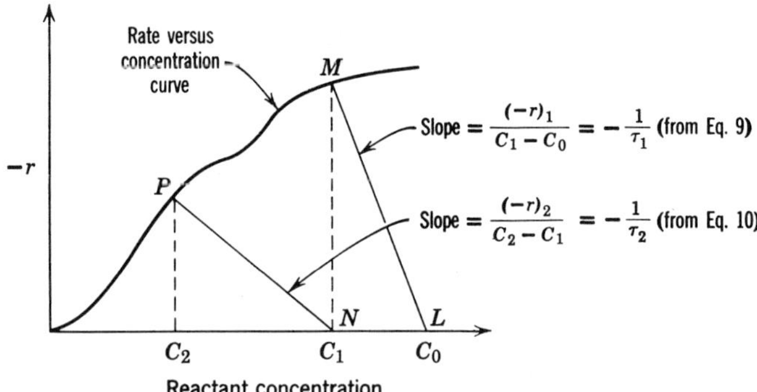

Fig. 9. Graphical procedure for finding compositions in a series of backmix reactors.

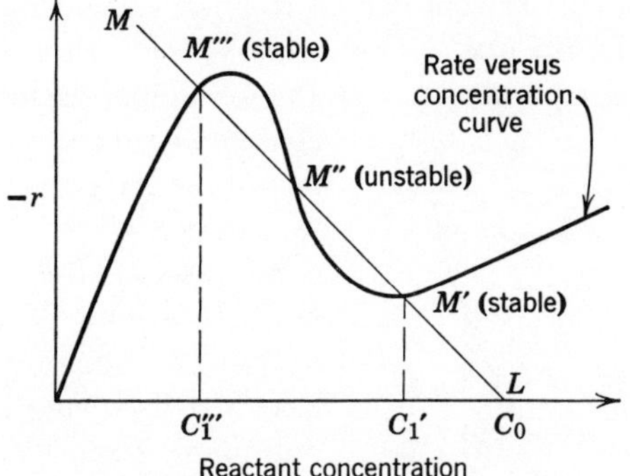

Fig. 10. With unusual rate characteristics either of two stable operating conditions can result.

draw a line of slope $-(1/\tau_1)$ until it cuts the curve. This gives C_1. In a like manner we find from Eq. 10 that a line of slope $-(1/\tau_2)$ from point N cuts the curve at P, giving the concentration C_2 of material leaving the second reactor. This procedure is then repeated as many times as needed.

For a reaction with an unusual rate concentration curve, shown in Fig. 10, which can be cut by a line LM at more than one point, say M', M'', and M''', more than one outlet concentration is possible. Both M' and M''' are stable operating conditions; however, M'' is unstable in the sense that a slight displacement to higher or lower concentrations will result in a shift to points M' or M'''. This shift is analogous to that of autothermal reactions treated in Chapter 8. For these reactions point M'' is called the ignition point (see Fig. 8.12)

With slight modification this graphical method can be extended to reactions in which density changes are appreciable.

Reactors of different types in series. If reactors of different types are put in series, such as a backmix reactor followed by a plug flow reactor which in turn is followed by a backmix reactor as shown in Fig. 11, we may write for the three reactors

$$\frac{V_1}{F_0} = \frac{X_1 - X_0}{(-r)_1}, \qquad \frac{V_2}{F_0} = \int_{X_1}^{X_2} \frac{dX}{-r}, \qquad \frac{V_3}{F_0} = \frac{X_3 - X_2}{(-r)_3}$$

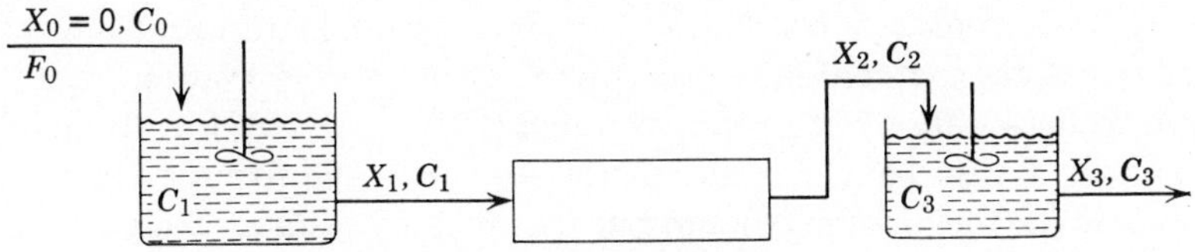

Fig. 11. Various types of reactors in series.

These relationships are represented in graphical form in Fig. 12. This allows us to predict the over-all conversions for such systems, or conversions at intermediate points between the individual reactors. These intermediate conversions are needed to determine the duty of interstage heat exchangers.

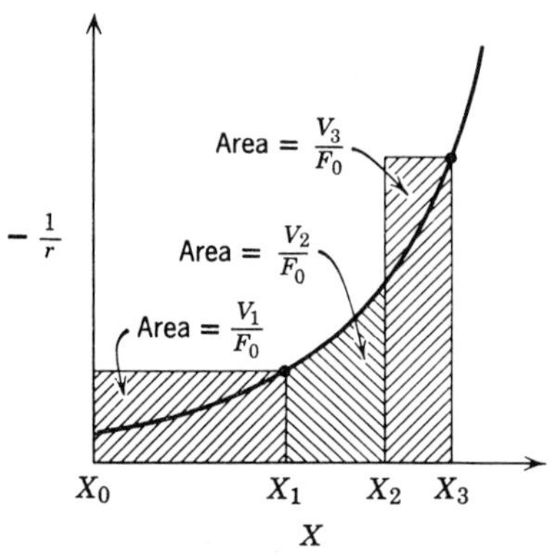

Fig. 12. Graphical design procedure for reactors in series.

Series-parallel network. In multiple-reactor systems of any type in any parallel-series network we have the following guiding rules for optimum performance (maximum capacity).

1. Flow in parallel branches of the network should be so adjusted that fluid streams which meet have the same composition.

2. For reactions in which the rate-concentration curve is concave, for example, reactions with order greater than unity, the given system of reactors in series should be arranged so that the concentration of reactant is kept as high as possible; if the rate-concentration curve is convex, the reactors should be arranged to keep the concentration as low as possible.

AUTOCATALYTIC REACTIONS

Autocatalytic reactions deserve special attention because their rates, influenced by both reactants and products, lead to rather unusual optimization problems.

Qualitative discussion. When a reactant disappears by a first- or second-order rate in a batch reactor, the rate of reaction is rapid at the start when the concentration of reactant is high. This rate slows down continually as reactant is consumed. In an autocatalytic reaction, however, the rate at the start is low because little product is present; it increases to a maximum as product is formed and then drops again to a low value as reactant is consumed. Figure 13 shows a typical situation.

If we wish to process material in a batch or plug flow reactor from state 1 to state 3, the material must pass progressively in composition from the initial to final state while passing through this sequence of low to high to low rates. But to have a small reactor size we would like the reactor to operate in the region of maximum rate (point 2) if possible. How can this be done? Now in a backmix reactor material does not pass through the whole range of compositions but drops immediately to the reactor exit conditions. Thus by introducing feed into a backmix reactor, operating under the conditions of state 2, we can avoid the slow transition from state 1 to state 2. The material will react at its maximum rate. By the same line of reasoning, to process reactant from state 2 to state 3 we should then switch to the plug flow reactor which will not take the material down to the composition with low rate all in one step.

Thus for autocatalytic reactions which are processing material past point 2 the optimum setup is a backmix reactor followed by plug flow reactor, a rather surprising conclusion.

Quantitative treatment. Consider the constant density ($\varepsilon = 0$) reaction

$$\mathrm{A + R \rightarrow R + R} \qquad \text{or} \qquad \mathrm{A \rightarrow R}$$

with a fairly general form of rate expression

$$-r_A = -\frac{dC_A}{dt} = kC_A{}^aC_R{}^r = kC_A{}^a(C_0 - C_A)^r$$

where $$C_0 = C_A + C_R = C_{A0} + C_{R0} \tag{11}$$

The extreme in rate is found by differentiating Eq. 11 and setting to zero. Thus

$$\frac{d(-r_A)}{dC_A} = akC_A^{a-1}(C_0 - C_A)^r - rkC_A{}^a(C_0 - C_A)^{r-1} = 0 \tag{12}$$

or $$aC_R = rC_A \tag{13}$$

To verify that the condition of Eq. 13 represents a maximum (point 2 of

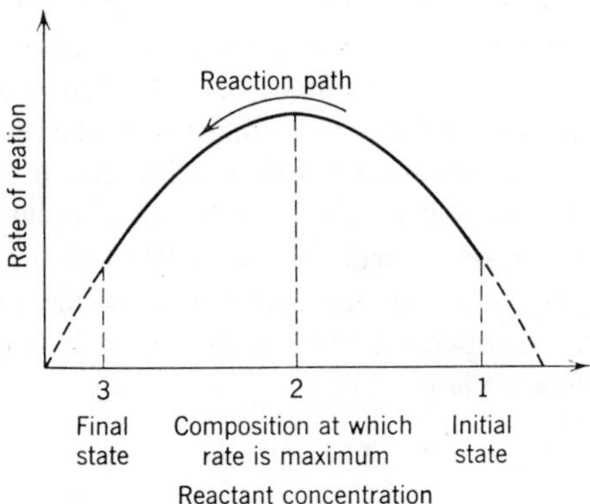

Fig. 13. Rate-concentration characteristics of an autocatalytic reaction in a batch reactor.

Fig. 13), differentiate a second time at $C_R/C_A = r/a$. Thus

$$\frac{d^2(-r_A)}{dC_A{}^2} = -kC_A^{a-1}C_R^{r-1}(a + r) < 0 \tag{14}$$

Table 1 compares the performance of plug flow and backmix reactors at different concentrations. It is important to note in terms of over-all performance of single reactors that the point of equal efficiency of single reactors is not given by Eq. 13. This is illustrated by parts f of the following two examples.

Table 1. Comparison of efficiency of ideal flow reactors with autocatalytic reactions

Condition	More Efficient Reactor	Remarks
$\frac{C_A}{C_R} > \frac{a}{r}$	Backmix	Occurs at high reactant concentration
$\frac{C_A}{C_R} = \frac{a}{r}$	Both reactors equally efficient	The composition for maximum efficiency of conversion
$\frac{C_A}{C_R} < \frac{a}{r}$	Plug flow	Occurs at low reactant concentration

Optimum design for autocatalytic reactions may involve operating at intermediate conversions with subsequent separation and recycle of unused reactants, thus taking advantage of the high reaction rate at this concentration. Consequently the backmix reactor is often found to be very efficient for this type of reaction, in contrast with other reaction types.

Though true homogeneous phase autocatalytic reactions are not common, there are many actual reactions which have characteristics of autocatalytic reactions. For example, consider the exothermic reaction (say oxidation) in which reactants enter the system at a temperature too low to support combustion. In such a reaction, called autothermal, heat may be considered to be the product which sustains the reaction. Thus with plug flow of reactants the reaction will die—with backmixing the reaction will be self-sustaining because the heat generated by the reaction can raise fresh reactants to a temperature at which they will react. Autothermal reactions are considered later.

Example 6

We wish to explore various reactor setups for the transformation of A into R. The feed contains 99% A, 1% R; the desired product is to consist of 10% A,

90% R. The transformation takes place by means of the elementary reaction

$$A + R \rightarrow R + R$$

with rate constant $k = 1$ liter/(mole)(min). The concentration of active materials is

$$C_{A0} + C_{R0} = C_A + C_R = C_0 = 1 \text{ mole/liter}$$

throughout.

Show the relation between the reactor holding time and fraction of A in the exit stream (*a*) for a plug flow reactor and (*b*) for a backmix reactor.

What reactor holding time will yield a product in which $C_R = 0.9$ mole/liter (*c*) in a plug flow reactor, (*d*) in a backmix reactor, and (*e*) in a minimum-sized setup without recycle.

At low conversions the backmix reactor is more efficient; for high conversions it is not. (*f*) For what conditions are the two single reactors equally efficient?

If the reactor outlet stream is richer in A than desired, suppose that it can be separated into two streams, one containing the desired product, 90% R, 10% A, and the other containing pure A at 1 mole/liter. The pure A stream is then recycled.

(*g*) Under these conditions find the minimum holding time if the reactor is operated at the conditions of maximum efficiency.

Solution. (*a*) The C_A versus t relationship for a plug flow reactor is given by Eq. 5.12, or

$$t = \int_{C_{A0}}^{C_A} \frac{-dC_A}{kC_A(C_0 - C_A)}$$

The integrated form, given by Eq. 3.35, is

$$C_0 kt = \ln \frac{C_{A0}(C_0 - C_A)}{C_A(C_0 - C_{A0})}$$

Replacing values from this problem we obtain

$$t = \ln \frac{99(1 - C_A)}{C_A} \tag{i}$$

which is plotted as curve MN in Fig. E6.

(*b*) The C_A versus t relationship in a backmix reactor is obtained with Eq. 5.9. Thus

$$\bar{t} = \frac{C_{A0}X_A}{-r_A} = \frac{C_{A0} - C_A}{kC_A(C_0 - C_A)} = \frac{0.99 - C_A}{C_A(1 - C_A)} \tag{ii}$$

which is plotted as line PQ in the figure.

(*c*) From the figure or from Eq. i the holding time necessary to obtain $C_R = 0.9$ in a plug flow reactor is

$$t = 6.8 \text{ min}$$

(*d*) For a backmix reactor from the figure or from Eq. ii

$$\bar{t} = 9.9 \text{ min}$$

(*e*) The most efficient reactor setup without recycle is one in which we switch from backmix to plug flow where the slopes of the C versus t curves are equal,

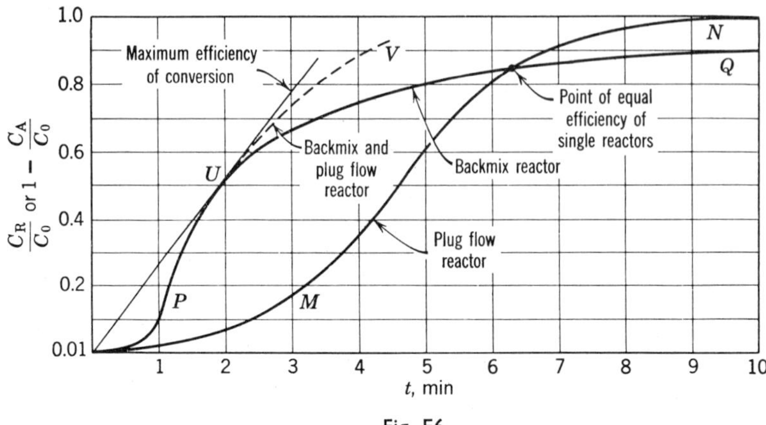

Fig. E6

or where $C_A = C_R = 0.5$ mole/liter. This is shown by the backmix curve plus dotted line PUV, U being the point on the backmix curve where $C_A = 0.5$ mole/liter. The holding time is thus

$$t_{b+p} = 4.2 \text{ min}$$

(*f*) Single plug flow and backmix reactors are equally efficient at the point where the curves intersect or for $C_R/C_0 = 0.84$, $C_A/C_0 = 0.16$. The holding time for either of the two reactors for this condition is

$$t_p = \bar{t} = 6.3 \text{ min}$$

(*g*) The minimum holding time is found by keeping the reactor contents at the composition at which the rate of reaction is maximum, or when $C_A = C_R = 0.5$. Thus we must use a backmix reactor for which from Eq. ii

$$\bar{t} = \frac{0.99 - 0.5}{(0.5)(0.5)} = 1.96 \text{ min}$$

Alternately, this may be found by simply referring to the backmix curve PQ and reading off the holding time corresponding to a reactor composition of $C_A = C_R = 0.5$ (point U).

Note that the holding time drops from 6.8 min for the best single-reactor setup to 4.2 min for the best two-reactor setup to 1.96 min for a single reactor plus recycle.

The general graphical procedure can also be used for autocatalytic reactions as illustrated in the following example.

Example 7

Solve Example 6 using the general graphical procedure.

Solution. Here it is more convenient to use concentrations rather than conversions. Thus Table E7 presents the necessary data to prepare the $-1/r_A$ versus C_A chart.

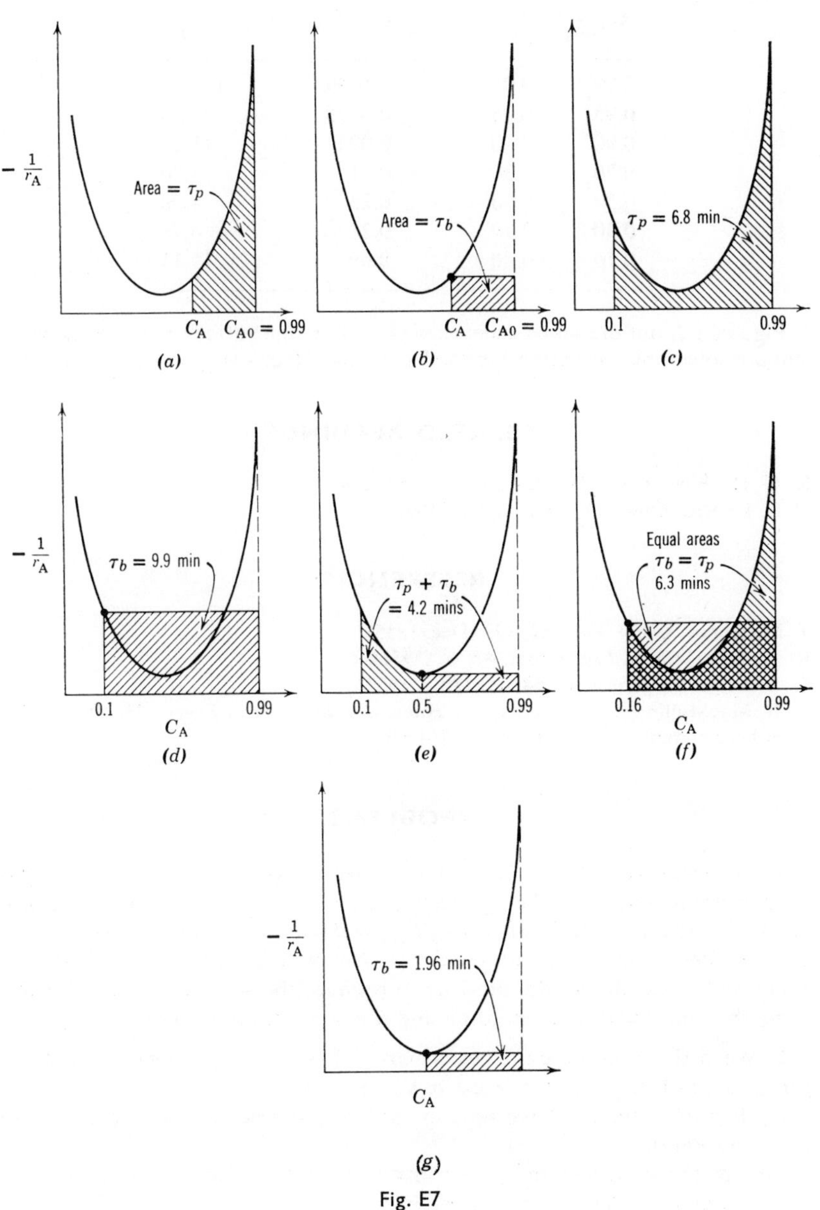

$-\frac{1}{r_A}$
Area = τ_p
C_A $C_{A0} = 0.99$
(a)
Area = τ_b
C_A $C_{A0} = 0.99$
(b)
τ_p = 6.8 min
0.1
0.99
(c)
$-\frac{1}{r_A}$
τ_b = 9.9 min
0.1
0.99
C_A
(d)
$\tau_p + \tau_b$
= 4.2 mins
0.1
0.5
0.99
(e)
Equal areas
$\tau_b = \tau_p$
6.3 mins
0.16
0.99
C_A
(f)
$-\frac{1}{r_A}$
τ_b = 1.96 min
C_A
(g)

Fig. E7

Table E7

C_A	C_R	$-r_A = C_A C_R$	$-\frac{1}{r_A}$
0.99	0.01	0.0099	101.01
0.95	0.05	0.0475	21.05
0.90	0.10	0.09	11.11
0.70	0.30	0.21	4.76
0.50	0.50	0.25	4.00
0.30	0.70	0.21	4.76
0.10	0.90	0.09	11.11

Figures E7, not drawn to scale, then show how the various parts of the problem are solved by measuring the shaded areas of the $-1/r_A$ versus C_A curve.

RELATED READINGS

K. G. Denbigh, *Trans. Faraday Soc.*, **40,** 352 (1944).
V. R. Leclerc, *Chem. Eng. Sci.*, **2,** 213 (1953).

REFERENCES

T. M. Jenney, *Chem. Eng.*, **62,** 198 (Dec. 1955).
R. W. Jones, *Chem. Eng. Progr.*, **47,** 46 (1951).
G. A. Lessells, *Chem. Eng.*, **64,** 251 (Aug. 1957).
R. B. MacMullin and M. Weber, Jr., *Trans. Am. Inst. Chem. Engrs.*, **31,** 409 (1935).
K. Schoenemann, *Chem. Eng. Sci.*, **8,** 161 (1958).

PROBLEMS

1. The reaction A + B → R is first order with respect to each of the reactants. At present the reaction is being effected in the liquid phase in a 5-ft^3 plug flow reactor using a mole ratio $M = C_{B0}/C_{A0} = 2$ with 90% conversion of A. We are considering replacing the present system with a 25-ft^3 backmix reactor. What mole ratio M' would allow us to produce the same amount of product using the same initial concentration and fractional conversion of A?

2. We wish to compare the performance of backmix and plug flow reactors for the zero-order gas-phase reaction A → R + S.

(*a*) For the same residence time in each, which reactor gives a greater conversion of A?

(*b*) For the same feed rate and conversion of A, which reactor needs to be larger and what is the ratio V_b/V_p?

(*c*) For the same feed rate and conversion of A, what is the ratio of residence times $\bar{t}_b/t_p$?

3. Is it more advantageous to connect two plug flow reactors in series than in parallel? How does reaction order, expansion, and degree of conversion affect your answer?

4. At present we have one reactor giving 99% conversion of reactant A. We buy a second unit identical to the first. For the same conversion, how much is our capacity increased if we operate these two units in parallel or in series?

(*a*) The reaction is first order, the reactor is backmix.
(*b*) The reaction is first order, the reactor is plug flow.
(*c*) The reaction is second order, the reactor is backmix.
(*d*) The reaction is second order, the reactor is plug flow.

5. Your company has two backmix reactors of unequal size which it would like to use in the production of a specified product formed by homogeneous first-order reaction. How should these reactors be hooked up to achieve a maximum production rate?

6. The kinetics of the aqueous-phase decomposition of A is investigated in two backmix reactors in series, the second having twice the volume of the first reactor. At steady state with a feed concentration of 1 gm mole A/liter and mean residence time of 96 sec in the first reactor, the concentration in the first reactor is 0.5 gm mole A/liter and in the second is 0.25 gm mole A/liter. Find the kinetic equation for the decomposition.

7. Two unequal-sized backmix reactors are connected in series. It is suspected that the order in which these vessels are connected as well as the reaction type may affect the degree of conversion for a given feed rate. Determine in general for reactions with concave or convex rate concentration curves which reactor should come first. How does this apply to *n*th-order reactions?

8. The elementary reaction $A + B \rightarrow R + S$ is being carried out at present in a setup consisting of a backmix reactor in which the two reactant solutions are mixed followed by a plug flow reactor. A large enough excess of B is used so that the reaction is pseudo first order.

(*a*) Various ways of increasing production have been suggested, one of which is to reverse the order of the two units. How would this change affect conversion?

(*b*) If the backmix reactor has a volume four times that of the plug flow reactor, conversion of A is 99%, what would be the percentage increase in production if the two reactors were connected in parallel?

9.(*a*) Derive an expression for the concentration of reactant in the effluent from a series of backmix reactors of different sizes. Let the reaction follow first-order kinetics and let the holding time in the *i*th reactor be τ_i.

(*b*) Show that this expression reduces to the appropriate equation in this chapter when the reactors are all the same size.

10. A certain material polymerizes at high temperature. With temperature above 220°F a product with undesirable properties is obtained; therefore an operating temperature of 215°F is selected. At this temperature the polymerization proceeds by means of a reaction which can be represented adequately by a

1.5-order rate law with respect to the monomer. At present the monomer is being treated in two equal-sized backmix reactors in series yielding a product in which the monomer content is about 20%. An increase in production is contemplated by adding a reactor similar to those being used.

(*a*) By what percentage can we increase the feed rate and still obtain a product containing no more than 20% monomer if the third reactor is connected to receive the effluent of the second reactor? Thus we have three vessels connected in series.

(*b*) By what percentage can the feed rate be increased if the third reactor is connected in parallel with the two existing reactors? For this arrangement what fraction of the monomer should be fed to each of the two branches?

11. Based on the fact that a color indicator shows when the concentration of A falls below 0.1 gm mole/liter, the following scheme is devised to explore the kinetics of the decomposition of A. A feed of 0.6 gm mole A/liter is introduced into the first of the two backmix reactors in series, each having a volume of 400 cc. The color change occurs in the first reactor for a steady-state feed rate of 10 cc/min and in the second reactor for a steady-state feed rate of 50 cc/min. Find the rate equation for the decomposition of A based on this information.

12. The elementary irreversible aqueous-phase reaction $A + B \rightarrow R + S$ is carried out isothermally as follows. Equal volumetric flow rates of two liquid streams are introduced into a 1-ft^3 mixing tank. One stream contains 0.020 mole A/liter, the other 1.400 moles B/liter. The mixed stream is then passed through a 4-ft^3 plug flow reactor. We find that some R is formed in the mixing tank, its concentration being 0.002 mole/liter. Hence the mixing tank acts as a backmix reactor. Find the concentration of R at the exit of the plug flow reactor as well as the fraction of initial A that has been converted in the system.

13. At present the elementary liquid-phase reaction $A + B \rightarrow 2R + S$ takes place in a plug flow reactor using equimolar quantities of A and B. Conversion is 96%, $C_{A0} = C_{B0} = 1$ mole/liter.

(*a*) If a backmix reactor ten times as large as the plug flow reactor were hooked up in parallel with the existing unit, by what fraction could production be increased?

(*b*) If these two units were connected in series, which should come first and by what fraction could production be increased for that setup?

(*c*) Does the concentration level of the feed affect the answer, and if so in what way?

Note: Conversion is to remain unchanged.

14. A first-order liquid-phase reaction, 92% conversion, is taking place in a backmix reactor. It has been suggested that a fraction of the product stream, with no additional treatment, be recycled.

(*a*) If the feed rate remains unchanged, in what way would this affect conversion?

(*b*) Repeat part *a* with a plug flow reactor instead of a backmix reactor.

(*c*) How does reaction order affect your answer?

(*d*) What can you conclude from this about recycle for *n*th order irreversible reactions?

15. One hundred moles of A per hour are available in a concentration of 0.01 lb mole/ft³ by a previous process. This stream is to be reacted with B to produce R and S. The reaction proceeds by the aqueous-phase elementary reaction

$$A + B \xrightarrow{k} R + S, \qquad k = 500 \text{ ft}^3/(\text{lb mole})(\text{hr})$$

The amount of R required is 95 lb moles/hr. In extracting R from the reacted mixture, A and B are destroyed; hence recycle of unused reactants is out of the question. Calculate the optimum reactor size and type as well as feed composition for this process.

Data: B costs \$1.25/lb mole in crystalline form. It is highly soluble in the aqueous solution and even when present in large amounts does not change the concentration of A in solution. Capital and operating costs are \$0.015/(hr)(ft³) for plug flow reactors, \$0.004/(hr)(ft³) for backmix reactors.

16. A commercial installation produces 40 lb moles R/hr by hydrolysis in a backmix reactor of a feed stream containing 0.04 lb mole/ft³ of reactant A. Because of the large excess of water used the reaction may be considered to be first order, or A → 2R even though it is bimolecular. The system effluent stream from the reactor goes to a countercurrent extraction column in which R is quantitatively extracted. Two per cent of the incoming A passes through the system unreacted. Fixed and operating costs for this process are \$10/hr, reactant cost is \$1.00/lb mole, and R can be sold at \$0.66/lb mole. It is suspected that the plant is not being operated at optimum conditions. Therefore you have been asked to study the operations with the aim of optimizing them.

(*a*) What are the present profits on an hourly basis?

(*b*) How should the installation be operated (feed rate of A, conversion of A, and production rate of R) to maximize the profit per unit of R? What is this profit?

(*c*) How should the installation be operated to maximize profits? What are these profits on an hourly basis?

Note: All R produced may be sold. Separation equipment is flexible since it has been designed to adapt to large changes in capacity.

17. A process is to be designed to produce 720,000 lb R/year. This material is formed by the elementary homogeneous liquid-phase reaction A + B → 2R.

(*a*) Using a backmix reactor, find the optimum reactor size and feed composition to the reactor.

(*b*) Determine the cost of producing R by this process.

(*c*) Prepare a process flow sheet for the final design chosen showing flow rates of A, B, and R in all streams.

(*d*) Write the expression in terms of X_{Af} and M for the cost of producing R in a plug flow reactor system.

Data: Cost of reactants: A = \$7.50/lb, B = \$0.01/lb.
The molecular weights of the reactants: A = 40, B = 80.

Pure liquid A, dissolved solid B and the appropriate amount of water (inert and diluent) enter the reactor as a single liquid stream. Water and A are miscible in all proportions, B has a solubility of 8 gms/liter.

The reaction takes place only in the liquid phase and has a rate constant of 0.001 liter/(gm mole)(sec), based on the rate of disappearance of A or B.

Specific gravity of all solutions is approximately unity.

Reactant B may be extracted quantitatively and recycled from the mixture of products by an organic solvent. Ignore cost of recovery of B.

Recovery of A is impractical because of the high cost of separation.

Capital and operating costs of reactor with all supporting equipment, based on 24 hr/day operation 300 days/yr, is estimated to be \$14/(yr)(gal) for backmix flow, \$200/(yr)(gal) for plug flow.

18. The reaction by which R is formed is A → R with rate equation

$$-r_A = (0.1\ \text{ft}^3/(\text{lb mole})(\text{hr}))C_A C_R$$

From a feed of pure A (1 lb mole/ft^3, \$1.00/lb mole) 100 lb moles R/hr are to be produced using either a backmix reactor alone or a backmix reactor followed by an A-R separator, in which case unreacted A may be recycled and reused.

The separator operates by an extraction process which, because of a favorable phase equilibrium, yields streams of essentially pure A and pure R. Its cost is \$8/hr + \$0.1/ft^3 of fluid treated. The hourly cost of backmix reactor is \$8 + \$0.01/ft^3 of reactor. Consider the density of all A-R mixtures to be constant.

(*a*) What reactor system is most economical and what is the unit cost of R produced by this setup?

The manufacturer of the separator is afraid that, because of some technical difficulty which can only be overcome by increasing the size and consequently the cost of the separation equipment by a large amount, he cannot guarantee a clean separation of A + R. He is quite sure that the recycle stream (A stream) will be free of R; however, he states that the product stream may be contaminated with up to 7.4% A.

(*b*) On the basis of maximum contamination, what is the unit cost of producing R?

(*c*) Qualitatively, how does this inefficiency affect reactor size, separator size, recycle rate?

19. Present facilities for the production of R cannot keep up with the demand for the material; hence you are asked to make an exploratory study to see whether production can be increased.

Product R is formed by the elementary irreversible reaction of A with B in a backmix reactor. Because a large excess of B is used the reaction may be considered to be first order with respect to A with rate constant k. R is quantitatively separated from the reactor effluent stream which is then discarded. The separation equipment is rather flexible and can easily handle greatly different flow rates.

(*a*) In general if feed A at \$$\alpha$/lb mole enters a backmix reactor of volume V ft^3 at a concentration C_{A0} lb moles/ft^3 and rate F_{A0} lb moles/hr, find the conversion of A at which unit cost of product R is a minimum. Let fixed and operating costs be $\$\gamma$/hr.

(*b*) Under present operating conditions, what is the unit cost of producing R?

(*c*) Have you any suggestions for how the plant should be operated (conversion of reactant and production rate of R) so as to maximize production but still maintain the present unit cost of product?

(*d*) What is the minimum unit cost of producing R, and at what conversion of reactant and at what production rate will this occur?

Data: A is supplied at \$4/lb mole at a concentration of 0.1 lb mole/ft^3. The cost of B is negligible.

Fixed and operating charges for the reactor and separation system are \$20/hr.

At present the production rate $F_R = 25$ lb moles R/hr at conversion $X_A = 0.95$

20. We wish to expand the operating facilities of the previous problem to produce more R than is produced at present with no change in unit cost of product. It has been suggested that reclaiming unreacted A should help raise production of R. With such a treatment of the waste stream from the product separator followed by recycle to the reactor inlet of reconcentrated A at $C_{A0} =$ 0.1 lb mole/ft^3, how much R can be produced?

Data: Capital and operating costs of the reclaiming equipment are \$4/hr + \$0.50/lb mole A recycled. Four per cent of A entering reclaiming equipment is not recoverable.

7

DESIGN FOR MULTIPLE REACTIONS

In the preceding chapter on single reactions we showed that the size of chemical reactor was greatly affected by the type of reactor used. We now extend the discussion to multiple reactions and show that for these reactions both reactor size and distribution of the products of reaction are affected by the type of reactor and contacting pattern of fluids used. We may recall at this point that the distinction between a *single* reaction and *multiple* reactions is that the single reaction requires only one rate expression to describe its kinetic behavior completely, whereas multiple reactions require more than one rate expression.

Since multiple reactions are varied in type and seem to have very little in common, we may despair of finding general guiding principles for design. Fortunately this is not so because all multiple-reaction schemes can be considered to be made up of a combination of two primary reaction types, *competing* or *parallel* reactions and *consecutive* or *series* reactions. Because these two reaction types are the building blocks or components for more involved reaction schemes called *mixed* reactions, we study them first. Then we shall select a mixed reaction, find its characteristics, and show how these characteristics can be arrived at by breaking the reaction down into its component parallel and series reactions.

Let us consider the general approach and nomenclature. First of all, we find it more convenient to deal with concentrations than conversions. Secondly, in examining product distribution the procedure is to eliminate the time variable by dividing one rate equation by another. We end up then with equations relating the rates of change of certain components with respect to other components of the systems. Such relationships are amenable to simple analysis and interpretation. Thus we see that two distinct analysis are used, one for reactor size determination and the other for the study of product distribution.

The two requirements, small reactor size and maximization of desired product, may run counter to each other in that a design may be good with respect to one requirement and poor with respect to the other. Now which requirement is more important to satisfy? Economic analysis, balancing increased reactor cost on the one hand versus higher treatment cost on the other, is always the final answer to this question. In general, product distribution controls (*a*) when the reaction is not very slow; (*b*) when the cost of raw materials is greater than the cost of the equipment, both being calculated on the same time basis; (*c*) when the cost of equipment for the separation, purification, and recycle of materials is of higher order than that of the reactor. In the majority of situations encountered, product distribution is the controlling factor.

This chapter is concerned primarily with optimizing design with respect to product distribution, which factor plays no role in single reactions. If reactor size controls, the treatment of multiple reactions follows with little modification the kinetic treatment of single reactions.

Finally, we ignore expansion effects in this chapter; thus we take $\varepsilon = 0$ throughout. This means that we may use the terms mean residence time, reactor holding time, space time, and reciprocal space velocity interchangeably.

REACTIONS IN PARALLEL

Qualitative discussion about product distribution. Consider the decomposition of A by either one of two paths:

$$\mathrm{A} \xrightarrow{k_1} \mathrm{R} \quad \text{(desired product)} \tag{1a}$$

$$\mathrm{A} \xrightarrow{k_2} \mathrm{S} \quad \text{(unwanted product)} \tag{1b}$$

with corresponding rate equations

$$r_\mathrm{R} = \frac{dC_\mathrm{R}}{dt} = k_1 C_\mathrm{A}{}^{a_1} \tag{2a}$$

$$r_\mathrm{S} = \frac{dC_\mathrm{S}}{dt} = k_2 C_\mathrm{A}{}^{a_2} \tag{2b}$$

Dividing Eq. 2*b* by Eq. 2*a*, we obtain a measure of the relative rates of formation of R and S. Thus

$$\frac{r_\mathrm{S}}{r_\mathrm{R}} = \frac{dC_\mathrm{S}}{dC_\mathrm{R}} = \frac{k_2}{k_1} C_\mathrm{A}^{a_2 - a_1} \tag{3}$$

Increasing or decreasing the right-hand side of Eq. 3 will result in a corresponding increase or decrease in the S/R ratio. Examining this equation, we see that the only factor we can control in the right-hand side is C_A because k_1, k_2, a_1, and a_2 are all constant for a specific system at a given temperature.

Now we can keep C_A at a very low value throughout the reaction by one of the following means.

1. By using a backmix reactor, in which case the reactant drops immediately to its outlet and lowest concentration and stays there. The conversion should preferably be large.

2. By using a large recycle stream to dilute the incoming feed, thus lowering the concentration of A in the reactor.

3. By lowering the pressure or increasing the inerts in a gas-phase system.

We can, on the contrary, keep C_A at a high value.

1. By using a batch or plug flow reactor, in which C_A starts at a high value, then drops progressively. Low conversions should be used.

2. By increasing the total pressure of a gas-phase system or by eliminating inerts in the feed stream. Both these measures help raise the concentration of active materials in the feed to the reactor.

3. By eliminating recycle of products.

Let us see whether the concentration of A should be kept high or low.

If $a_1 > a_2$, or the order of the desired reaction is higher than the order of the unwanted reaction, then $a_2 - a_1$ is negative. From Eq. 3 we see that the S/R ratio becomes small for high C_A. This is exactly what we wish to happen because S is not wanted. As a result a batch or plug flow reactor would favor formation of product R and would require a minimum reactor size.

If $a_1 < a_2$, or the desired reaction has a lower order than the unwanted reaction, we need a low reactant concentration to favor formation of R. But this would also require large reactor size. Unfortunately, the demand for a desirable product distribution works against that of small reactor size. In such a case optimum design is achieved by the economic balance of cost of separation of undesired material S versus the greater capital and operating costs required for larger equipment.

If $a_1 = a_2$, or the two reactions are of the same order, then Eq. 3 becomes

$$\frac{r_S}{r_R} = \frac{dC_S}{dC_R} = \frac{k_2}{k_1} = \text{constant}$$

Hence product distribution is fixed by k_2/k_1 alone and is unaffected by type of reactor used. Thus the reactor volume requirement will govern the design.

Besides this method, we may control product distribution by varying k_2/k_1. This can be done in two ways.

1. By changing the temperature level of operation. If the activation energies of the two reactions are different, k_2/k_1 can be made to vary. Chapter 8 considers this problem.

2. By using a catalyst. One of the most important features of a catalyst is its selectivity in depressing or accelerating specific reactions. This may be a much more effective way of controlling product distribution than any of the methods discussed so far.

For other reactions in parallel the reasoning is analogous to that presented. For example, consider the reactions

$$A + B \xrightarrow{k_1} R \quad \text{(desired product)} \tag{4a}$$

$$A + B \xrightarrow{k_2} S \quad \text{(unwanted product)} \tag{4b}$$

with rate equations

$$r_R = \frac{dC_R}{dt} = k_1 C_A{}^{a_1} C_B{}^{b_1} \tag{5a}$$

$$r_S = \frac{dC_S}{dt} = k_2 C_A{}^{a_2} C_B{}^{b_2} \tag{5b}$$

Dividing Eq. 5*b* by Eq. 5*a* we obtain

$$\frac{r_S}{r_R} = \frac{dC_S}{dC_R} = \frac{k_2}{k_1} C_A^{a_2 - a_1} C_B^{b_2 - b_1} \tag{6}$$

As R is the desired product, we want to minimize

$$\frac{dC_S}{dC_R} \quad \text{or} \quad \frac{k_2}{k_1} C_A^{a_2 - a_1} C_B^{b_2 - b_1}$$

Thus we must examine separately whether $a_2 - a_1$ and $b_2 - b_1$ are positive or negative. This will determine whether A or B are to be kept at low or high concentrations.

We may summarize our qualitative findings on product distribution for parallel reactions as follows.

For reactions of the same order product distribution is unaffected by reactor type or concentration of reactants. For reactions of different order a high concentration favors the reaction of higher order; a low concentration favors the reaction of lower order.

From this discussion we see that various combinations of high and low reactant concentrations may be desired during reaction depending on the kinetics of the competing reactions. Besides changing the concentration of feed materials the most direct and the simplest way of controlling the concentrations is by using the correct contacting pattern of reacting fluids. Figures 1 and 2 illustrate methods of contacting two reacting fluids in continuous and noncontinuous operations that keep the concentrations of these two fluids both high, both low, one high, the other low. In general, the number of reacting fluids involved, the possibility of recycle, and the cost of possible alternative setups must all be considered before the most desirable contacting pattern can be arrived at.

In any case the use of the proper contacting pattern is the critical factor in obtaining a favorable distribution of products of complex reactions.

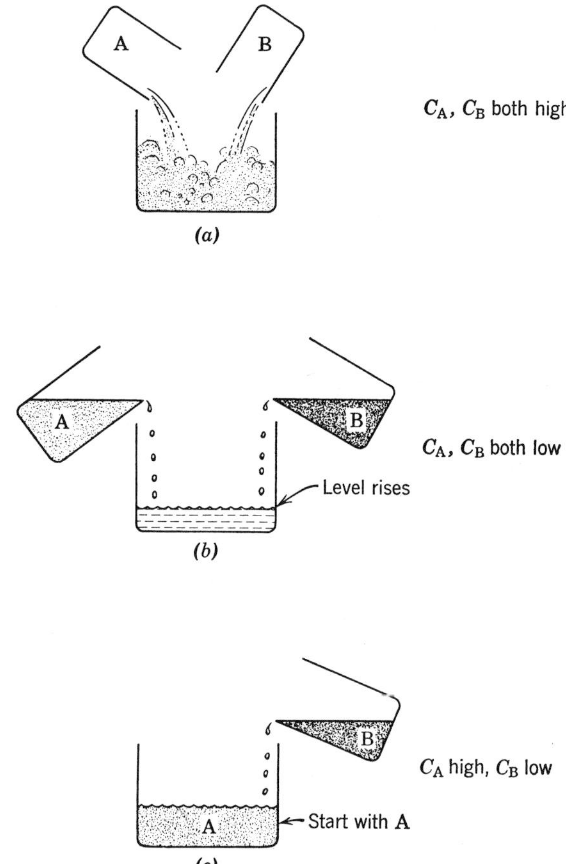

Fig. 1. Contacting patterns for various combinations of high and low concentrations of reactants in batch and semibatch operations. (*a*) Add both reactants all at one time before reaction starts. (*b*) Add reactants slowly, letting reaction proceed nearly to completion before adding more. (*c*) Add B slowly, letting it react nearly to completion before adding more reactant.

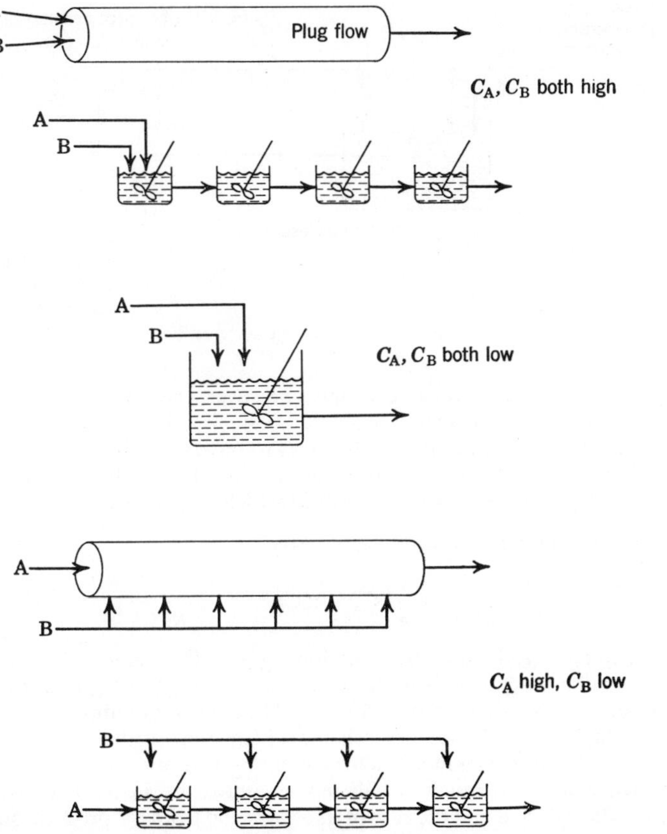

Fig. 2. Contacting patterns for various combinations of high and low concentrations of reactants in steady-state flow operations.

Example 1

Suppose that the desired liquid-phase reaction

$$A + B \xrightarrow{k_1} R + T$$

is accompanied by the undesired side reaction

$$A + B \xrightarrow{k_2} S + U$$

which we wish to depress. The rates of formation of product by the two reactions are found to be well approximated by the following rate equation

$$\frac{dC_R}{dt} = \frac{dC_T}{dt} = k_1 C_A C_B^{0.3} \qquad \text{(i)}$$

and

$$\frac{dC_S}{dt} = \frac{dC_U}{dt} = k_2 C_A^{0.5} C_B^{1.8} \qquad \text{(ii)}$$

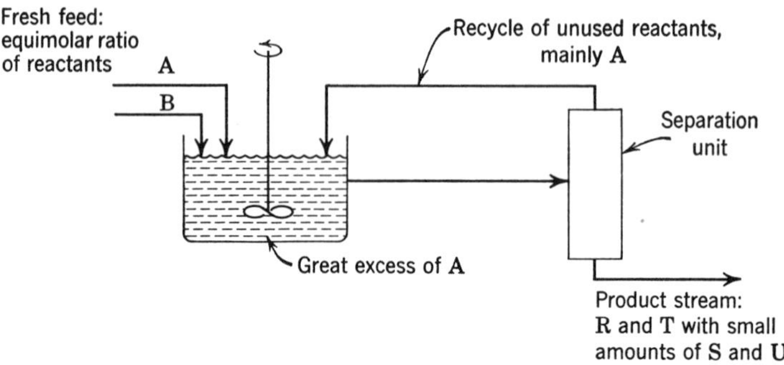

Fig. E1

The cost of reactants is relatively high; however, they can be cleanly separated from the products of the reaction at small cost. In addition, it is more important to depress formation of S and U than it is to have a small reactor setup because of the high cost of separation of S and U from R and T and because of high reactant cost. Suggest a reactor setup in which to produce R and T.

Solution. Divide Eq. ii by Eq. i. Thus

$$\frac{dC_S}{dC_R} = \frac{k_2}{k_1} C_A^{0.5-1.0} C_B^{1.8-0.3} = \frac{k_2}{k_1} \frac{C_B^{1.5}}{C_A^{0.5}} \tag{iii}$$

Now dC_S/dC_R is to be minimized by having high C_A and low C_B. In addition, the ratio to be minimized is more sensitive to changes in C_B than to changes in C_A because of the higher power on C_B. Thus it is more important to have low C_B than high C_A. The reactor scheme which best satisfies these requirements on C_A and C_B is a backmix reactor operating with an excess of A. However, with such conditions much A will remain unreacted in the exit stream of the reactor. Its high cost and the ease of its separation from the products immediately suggest that it be recycled. Thus the scheme selected is a backmix reactor with separation equipment as shown in Fig. E1.

From Eq. iii, lowering C_B results in a more favorable distribution of products. Hence for a given production rate we should have as large a backmix reactor as is practical. An economic balance between separation cost of reactants and products, cost of chemical A tied up, and pumping and capital and operating costs for the large reactor on the one hand and the cost of having large quantities of impurities T and U on the other will determine the optimum size of equipment to use.

Example 2 quantitatively determines the distribution of products for this reaction for various setups.

Quantitative treatment of product distribution and of reactor size. If rate equations are known for the individual reactions, we can quantitatively determine product distribution and reactor-size requirements. Consider the reactions and rates given by Eqs. 1 and 2, and let us define two terms related to the ratio S/R. Let φ be the fraction of A reacting at any instant that is transformed into R. This term may be called the "instantaneous fractional yield of R." Thus

$$\varphi = \frac{r_R}{-r_A} = \frac{dC_R}{-dC_A} = \frac{dC_R}{dC_R + dC_S} \tag{7}$$

As illustration φ for the reaction of Eq. 2 is

$$\varphi = \frac{k_1 C_A{}^{a_1}}{k_1 C_A{}^{a_1} + k_2 C_A{}^{a_2}} = \frac{1}{1 + (k_2/k_1)C_A^{a_2 - a_1}} \tag{8}$$

In general C_A may vary through the reactor, in which case φ will also vary. So let us define Φ as the fraction of all the A reacted which has been converted into R. Let us call this the "over-all fractional yield of R." If subscript 0 and f refer to the reactor inlet and outlet conditions, respectively, the over-all fractional yield of R is given by

$$\Phi = \frac{C_{Rf}}{C_{A0} - C_{Af}} = \left(\frac{C_R}{C_R + C_S}\right)_f \tag{9}$$

It is this over-all fractional yield Φ which really concerns us, for it gives the product distribution at the reactor outlet. At the reactor outlet C_R is found in terms of the instantaneous fractional yields by Eq. 7. Thus

$$C_{Rf} = \int_0^{C_{Rf}} dC_R = -\int_{C_{A0}}^{C_{Af}} \varphi \, dC_A \tag{10}$$

The over-all fractional yield can be found from Eq. 9.

So far the fractional yields of product R have been defined on the basis of the amount of single reactant A consumed. More generally, when more than one reactant is involved, the fractional yield can be based on a single reactant consumed, on all reactants consumed, or on all products formed. It is simply a matter of convenience which definition is used. Thus in general $\varphi(M/N)$ is the instantaneous fractional yield of M, based on the disappearance or formation of N.

Let us next find the fraction of reacted A which is converted to R in the various reactor types. From Eqs. 9 and 10 we have for plug flow reactors

$$\Phi_{\text{plug}} = \frac{C_{Rf}}{C_{A0} - C_{Af}} = \frac{-1}{C_{A0} - C_{Af}} \int_{C_{A0}}^{C_{Af}} \varphi \, dC_A \tag{11}$$

Again taking as illustration the rate expressions of Eq. 2, this becomes on combining with Eq. 8

$$\Phi_{\text{plug}} = \frac{-1}{C_{A0} - C_{Af}} \int_{C_{A0}}^{C_{Af}} \frac{dC_A}{1 + (k_2/k_1)C_A^{a_2 - a_1}} \tag{12}$$

For single backmix reactors the instantaneous fractional yield is constant; hence we have

$$\Phi_{\text{backmix}} = \varphi \tag{13}$$

which for the case of Eq. 2 becomes

$$\Phi_{\text{backmix}} = \frac{1}{1 + (k_2/k_1)C_A^{a_2-a_1}}$$

For a series of 1, 2, . . . , j backmix reactors in which the concentrations of A are $C_{A1}, C_{A2}, \ldots, C_{Aj}$, the over-all fractional yield is obtained by summing the fractional yields in each of the j vessels and weighting by the amount of reaction occurring in each vessel. Thus we have

$$\varphi_1(C_{A0} - C_{A1}) + \varphi_2(C_{A1} - C_{A2}) + \cdots + \varphi_j(C_{Aj-1} - C_{Aj}) = \Phi_{j\,\text{backmix}}(C_{A0} - C_{Aj})$$

from which

$$\Phi_{j\text{backmix}} = \sum_{i=1}^{j} \varphi_i\, \Delta C_i \Big/ \sum_{i=1}^{j} \Delta C_i = \frac{\varphi_1(C_{A0} - C_{A1}) + \varphi_2(C_{A1} - C_{A2}) + \cdots + \varphi_j(C_{Aj-1} - C_{Aj})}{C_{A0} - C_{Aj}} \tag{14}$$

and for the rate expressions of Eq. 2 this becomes

$$\Phi_{j\text{backmix}} = \frac{\dfrac{-\Delta C_1}{1 + (k_2/k_1)C_{A1}^{a_2-a_1}} + \dfrac{-\Delta C_2}{1 + (k_2/k_1)C_{A2}^{a_2-a_1}} + \cdots + \dfrac{-\Delta C_j}{1 + (k_2/k_1)C_{Aj}^{a_2-a_1}}}{C_{A0} - C_{Aj}} \tag{15}$$

Thus we can find the S/R ratio for any reactor system, and this procedure may be extended to other types of parallel reactions.

The determination of reactor volume is no different from that for a single reaction if we recall that the over-all rate of disappearance of reactant by a number of competing paths is simply the sum of the rates of the individual paths or

$$r = r_1 + r_2 + \cdots$$

Example 2

For the competitive liquid-phase reactions

$$A + B \xrightarrow{k_1} R, \qquad \text{desired reaction}$$

$$A + B \xrightarrow{k_2} S, \qquad \text{unwanted side reaction}$$

with rate equations

$$\frac{dC_R}{dt} = 1.0 C_A C_B^{0.3} \text{ moles/(liter)(min)}$$

$$\frac{dC_S}{dt} = 1.0 C_A^{0.5} C_B^{1.8} \text{ moles/(liter)(min)}$$

find the fraction of impurity S in the product for the following situations.

(*a*) Equimolar feed, plug flow reactor, 90% conversion.

(*b*) Equimolar feed, backmix reactor, 90% conversion.

(*c*) It was suggested that we operate with large excess of A to depress the unwanted reaction (see Example 1) as well as recycle the unreacted A if this reactant is expensive. Let us assume that reactant A is inexpensive and need not be recycled. For this condition find the fraction of impurity in the product for a feed containing 99 mole % A, 1 mole % B, with a 90% conversion of limiting reactant.

(*d, e, f*) For the operating conditions of parts *a*, *b*, and *c*, find the volume of reactor required to treat 100 moles B/min.

Additional data: Pure A and B each has a density of 20 moles/liter.

Solution. The instantaneous fraction yield of R is given by

$$\varphi = \frac{dC_R}{dC_R + dC_S} = \frac{k_1 C_A C_B^{0.3}}{k_1 C_A C_B^{0.3} + k_2 C_A^{0.5} C_B^{1.8}} = \frac{1}{1 + C_A^{-0.5} C_B^{1.5}}$$

(*a*) For an equimolar feed of pure A and B, 90% conversion

$$C_A = C_B \qquad \begin{aligned} C_{A0} &= 10 \text{ moles/liter} \\ C_{B0} &= 10 \text{ moles/liter} \end{aligned} \qquad \begin{aligned} C_{Af} &= 1 \text{ mole/liter} \\ C_{Bf} &= 1 \text{ mole/liter} \end{aligned}$$

Hence the over-all fractional yield of R in a plug flow reactor is given by

$$\Phi_{\text{plug}} = \frac{-1}{C_{A0} - C_{Af}} \int_{C_{A0}}^{C_{Af}} \varphi \, dC_A$$

$$= \frac{-1}{10 - 1} \int_{10}^{1} \frac{dC_A}{1 + C_A} = \frac{1}{9} \ln (1 + C_A) \Big|_1^{10} = 0.19$$

Therefore impurities in the product = 81%.

(*b*) For a backmix reactor, with the same feed and products given in part *a*, we have

$$\Phi_{\text{backmix}} = \varphi = \frac{1}{1 + C_{Af}} = \frac{1}{1 + 1} = 0.5$$

Therefore impurities in the product = 50%.

(*c*) For an A to B feed ratio of 99 to 1, 90% conversion of B

$$C_A \neq C_B \qquad \begin{aligned} C_{A0} &= 20(0.99) = 19.8 \text{ moles/liter} \\ C_{B0} &= 20(0.01) = 0.2 \text{ moles/liter} \end{aligned} \qquad \begin{aligned} C_{Af} &= 19.8 - (0.2 - 0.02) \\ &= 19.62 \text{ moles/liter} \\ C_{Bf} &= (0.2)(0.1) \\ &= 0.02 \text{ mole/liter} \end{aligned}$$

Hence the over-all fractional yield of R in a backmix reactor is given by

$$\Phi_{\text{backmix}} = \varphi = \frac{1}{1 + C_A^{-0.5} C_B^{1.5}}$$

$$= \frac{1}{1 + (19.62)^{-0.5}(0.02)^{1.5}} = 0.99936$$

Therefore impurities in the product = 0.064%.

(*d*) The volume of plug flow reactor required to treat 100 moles A/min under the conditions of part *a* is given by the usual type relationship shown next. However, we include the units of all terms involved to avoid any possible confusion. We use these units throughout the problem. Thus

$$\frac{V,\ \text{liters}}{F_{A0},\ \text{moles A introduced/min}} = \int_0^{X_{Af}} \frac{dX_A,\ \text{dimensionless}}{-r_A,\ \text{moles A/(liter)(min)}}$$

But

$$-r_A = -\frac{dC_A}{dt} = \frac{dC_R}{dt} + \frac{dC_S}{dt}$$

Therefore

$$\frac{V}{F_{A0}} = \int_{X_{A0}}^{X_{Af}} \frac{dX_A}{k_1 C_A C_B^{0.3} + k_2 C_A^{0.5} C_B^{1.8}} = \int_{X_{A0}}^{X_{Af}} \frac{dX_A}{C_A^{1.3} + C_A^{2.3}}$$

Now at this point it seems easier to transform fractional conversions into concentrations. This is done by noting that

$$C_A = C_{A0}(1 - X_A) \qquad \text{and} \qquad dX_A = -\frac{dC_A}{C_{A0}}$$

Therefore

$$V = \frac{F_{A0}}{C_{A0}} \int_{C_{A0}}^{C_{Af}} \frac{-dC_A}{C_A^{1.3} + C_A^{2.3}} = \frac{100\ \text{moles A/min}}{10\ \text{moles A/liter}} \int_{1\ \text{mole/liter}}^{10\ \text{moles/liter}} \frac{dC_A}{C_A^{1.3}(1 + C_A)}$$

Graphically evaluating the integral we find

$$V = \left(\frac{100}{10}\right)(0.477) = 4.8\ \text{liters}$$

(*e*) The volume of backmix reactor for the conditions of part *b* is given by

$$\frac{V}{F_{A0}} = \frac{X_{Af} - X_{A0}}{-r_{Af}} = \frac{1 - (C_{Af}/C_{A0})}{k_1 C_{Af} C_{Bf}^{0.3} + k_2 C_{Af}^{0.5} C_{Bf}^{1.8}}$$

Therefore

$$V = \frac{F_{A0}(1 - C_{Af}/C_{A0})}{C_{Af}^{1.3} + C_{Af}^{2.3}} = \frac{(100\ \text{moles A/min})(1 - 1/10)}{(1 + 1)\text{moles/(liter)(min)}} = 45\ \text{liters}$$

The answers of parts *d* and *e* can be shown to be consistent with each other by taking the reaction to be approximately second order and using the methods of the previous chapter.

(*f*) The volume of backmix reactor for the conditions of part *c* is given by

$$\frac{V}{F_{A0}} = \frac{X_{Af}}{-r_{Af}} \qquad \text{or} \qquad \frac{V}{F_{B0}} = \frac{X_{Bf}}{-r_{Bf}}$$

The latter form is slightly easier to handle; therefore let us use it. Thus

$$\begin{aligned} V &= \frac{F_{B0}(1 - C_{Bf}/C_{B0})}{k_1 C_{Af} C_{Bf}^{0.3} + k_2 C_{Af}^{0.5} C_{Bf}^{1.8}} \\ &= \frac{(100\ \text{moles B/min})(1 - 1/10)}{(19.62)(0.02)^{0.3} + (19.62)^{0.5}(0.02)^{1.8}\ \text{moles B/(liter)(min)}} \\ &= \frac{(100)(0.9)}{6.08 + 0.00385} \\ &= 14.8\ \text{liters} \end{aligned}$$

The results, summarized in Table E2, show that for this set of reactions favorable product distribution can be obtained without sacrificing too much in reactor size, but by wasting large amounts of A.

Table E2. Summary of results for 90% conversion of 100 moles B/min

Reactor Type	Ratio of A to B in Feed	Impurities in the Product, %	Volume of Reactor, liters
Plug flow	1:1	81	4.8
Backmix	1:1	50	45
Backmix	99:1	0.064	14.8

REACTIONS IN SERIES

Successive first-order reactions

For easy visualization consider that the reactions

$$A \xrightarrow{k_1} R \xrightarrow{k_2} S \tag{16}$$

proceed only in the presence of light, and that the reactions stop the instant the light is shut off.. For a given intensity of radiation, the rate equations for the materials involved in these reactions are then

$$\frac{dC_A}{dt} = -k_1C_A \tag{17}$$

$$\frac{dC_R}{dt} = k_1C_A - k_2C_R \tag{18}$$

$$\frac{dC_S}{dt} = k_2C_R \tag{19}$$

Our discussion will center about these reactions

Qualitative discussion about product distribution. Consider the following two ways of treating a beaker containing A; first, the contents are irradiated all at one time and, second, a small stream is continuously withdrawn from the beaker, irradiated, and returned to the beaker, the rate of absorption of radiant energy being the same in the two cases. The two schemes are shown in Figs. 3 and 4. During this process A disappears and products are formed. Is the product distribution of R and S different in the two beakers? Let us see whether we can answer this question qualitatively for all values of the rate constants.

In the first beaker when the contents are being irradiated all at the same time, the first bit of light will attack A alone because only A is present at the start. The result is that R is formed. With the next bit of light both A and R will compete; however, A is in very large excess so it will preferentially absorb the radiant energy to decompose and form more R. Thus the concentration of R will rise. This will continue until R is present in high enough concentration so that it can compete favorably with A for the radiant energy. When this happens, a maximum R concentration is reached. After this the decomposition of R becomes more rapid than its rate of formation, and its concentration drops. A typical concentration time curve is shown in Fig. 3.

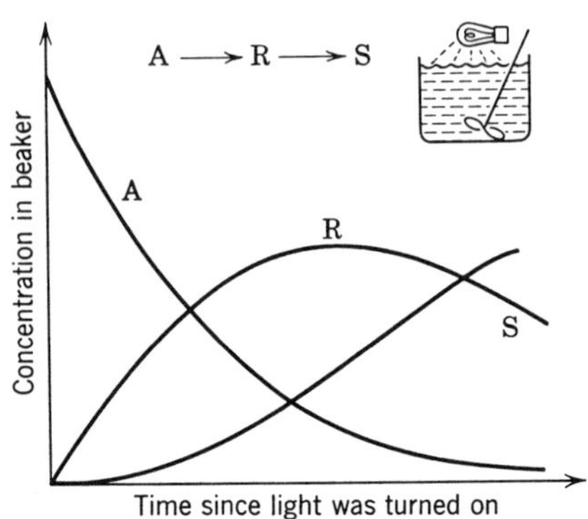

Fig. 3. Concentration-time curves if the contents of the beaker are irradiated all at one time.

In the alternate way of treating A a small fraction of the beaker contents is continuously removed, irradiated, and returned to the beaker. Since the total absorption rate is the same in the two cases, however, the intensity of radiation received by the fluid removed is greater, and it could well be, if the flow rate is not too high, that the fluid being irradiated reacts essentially to completion. In this case, then, A is removed and S is returned to the beaker. So as time proceeds the concentration of A slowly decreases in the beaker, and S rises while R is absent. This progressive change is shown in Fig. 4.

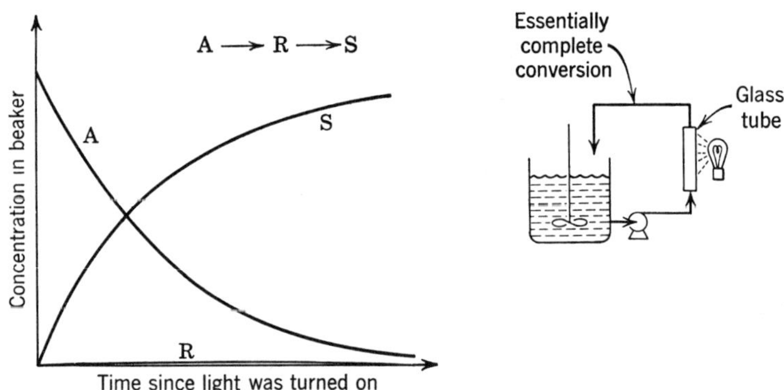

Fig. 4. Concentration-time curves for the contents of the beaker if only a part of the fluid is irradiated at any instant.

These two methods of reacting the contents of the beaker yield different product distributions and represent the two extremes in possible operations, one with a maximum possible formation of R and the other with a minimum, or no formation, of R. Now how can we best characterize this behavior? We note that in the first method the contents of the beaker remain homogeneous throughout, all changing slowly with time, whereas in the second a stream of reacted fluid is continually being mixed with fresh fluid. In other words, we are mixing two streams of different compositions. Thus we have the following general principles governing product distribution for reactions in series.

For a given conversion of reactant a maximum amount of intermediate is formed when the mixture is homogeneous or when mixing of material at different stages of conversion does not occur. Other ways of operating give lower yields of intermediate. In the extreme no intermediate is formed.

As intermediate R is frequently the desired reaction product, this principle controls the selection of the reactor system. With it we can already evaluate the relative worths of various reactor systems. For example, plug flow and batch systems should give a maximum R yield because in both these systems there is no mixing of two fluid streams of different compositions. On the other hand the backmix reactor should not give as high an R yield as possible because a fresh stream of pure A is being mixed continually with an already reacted fluid in the reactor.

The following examples illustrate the point just made. We then give a quantitative treatment of the actual concentrations involved which will bear out these qualitative findings.

Example 3

From each of the following pair of reactor setups in Fig. E3 select the method of operation which will maximize the concentration of R and briefly explain why this should be so. The reaction is

$$A \xrightarrow{\text{light}} R \xrightarrow{\text{light}} S$$

In all cases the same fractional conversion of A is used.

Solution. (*a*) For a relatively slow reaction either setup is satisfactory, yielding a maximum R concentration, but for a fast reaction with insufficient fluid mixing the concentration of products in the beam of light of the second setup may rise above that in the surrounding fluid. The resulting heterogeneity results in a lowering in R yield. Thus for fast reactions the first setup is preferable.

Note: The special problems of extremely fast reactions are considered in Chapter 10.

(*b*) For reactions which are slow enough so that the conversion per pass is very small, either setup should be satisfactory; however, for a fast reaction the second setup is preferred because the conversion of reactant per pass is approximately

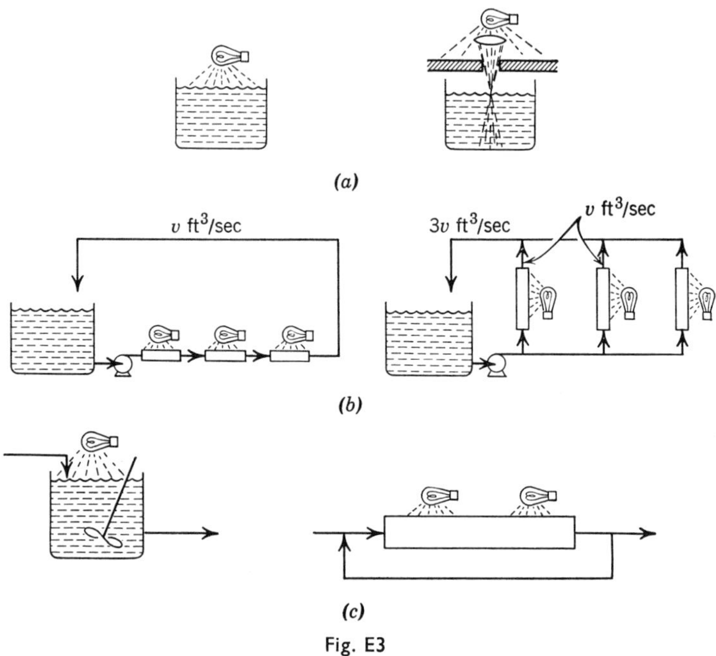

Fig. E3

one-third that for the first setup. Thus streams with smaller concentrations differences are being mixed.

(*c*) To examine this situation first consider various extents of recycle in the second setup. With no recycle we have a plug flow system with no mixing of streams of different compositions, hence a maximum R yield. As the recycle rate is increased the second setup approaches the backmix reactor with a resultant decrease in R yield, hence the second setup with no recycle is preferred.

Quantitative treatment, plug flow or batch reactor. In Chapter 3 we developed the equations relating concentration with time for all components of the unimolecular-type reactions

$$A \xrightarrow{k_1} R \xrightarrow{k_2} S$$

in batch reactors. The derivations assumed that the feed contained no reaction products R or S. If we take t to be the holding time, these equations apply equally well for plug reactors and are now summarized.

$$\frac{C_A}{C_{A0}} = e^{-k_1 t} \tag{3.40}$$

$$\frac{C_R}{C_{A0}} = \frac{k_1}{k_2 - k_1}(e^{-k_1 t} - e^{-k_2 t}) \tag{3.42}$$

$$C_S = C_{A0} - C_A - C_R$$

The maximum concentration and time at which it occurs is given by

$$\frac{C_{R,max}}{C_{A0}} = \left(\frac{k_1}{k_2}\right)^{k_2/(k_2-k_1)} \tag{3.45}$$

$$t_{max} = \frac{1}{k_{log\ mean}} = \frac{\ln (k_2/k_1)}{k_2 - k_1} \tag{3.44}$$

This is also the point at which the rate of increase of S is the most rapid.

Figure 5 prepared for various k_2/k_1 values illustrates how this ratio governs the concentration-time curves of the intermediate product R. Figure 6, a time-independent plot, relates the concentration of all reaction components.

Quantitative treatment, backmix reactor. Let us find concentration–holding time curves for this reaction when it takes place in a backmix reactor. This may be done by referring to Fig. 7. Again the derivation will be limited to a feed which contains no reaction product R or S.

By the steady-state material balance we obtain for any component

$$\text{Input} = \text{Output} + \text{Disappearance by reaction} \tag{4.1}$$

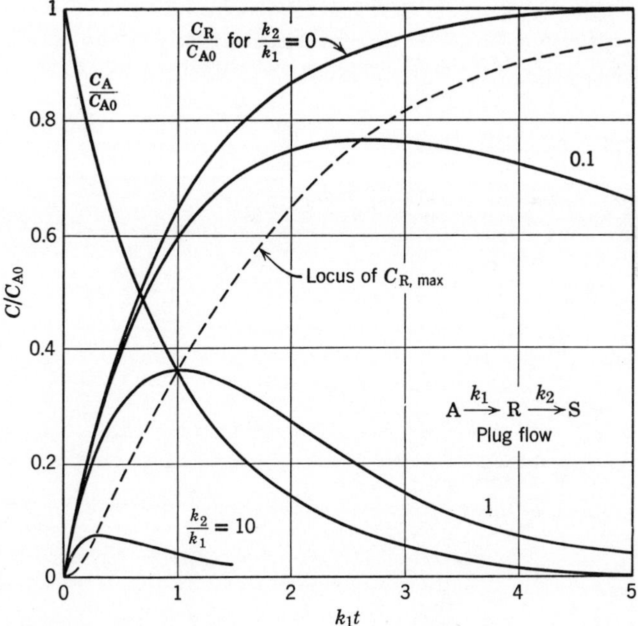

Fig. 5. Concentration–holding time curves in a plug flow reactor for the unimolecular-type reactions $A \xrightarrow{k_1} R \xrightarrow{k_2} S$.

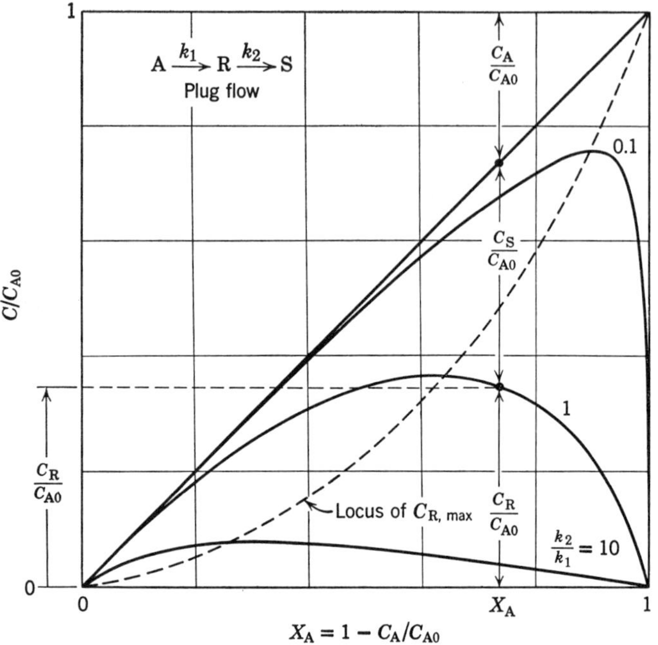

Fig. 6. Relative concentration of the reaction components in a plug flow reactor for the unimolecular-type reactions $A \xrightarrow{k_1} R \xrightarrow{k_2} S$.

which for reactant A becomes

$$F_{A0} = F_A + (-r_A)V$$

or

$$vC_{A0} = vC_A + k_1 C_A V$$

Noting that

$$\frac{V}{v} = \bar{t} \tag{20}$$

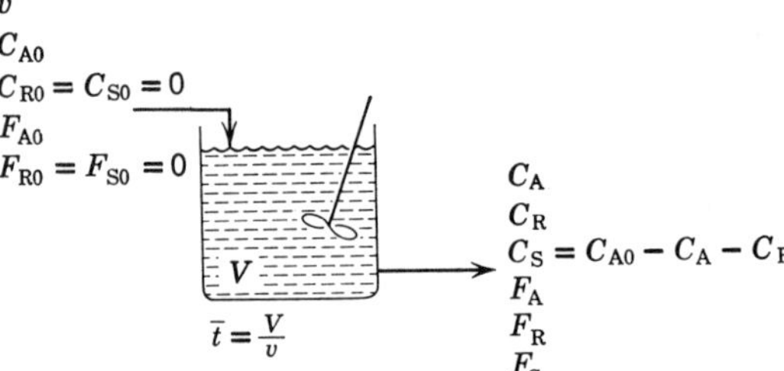

Fig. 7. Backmix reactor variables for a reaction in series $A \rightarrow R \rightarrow S$, no R or S in the feed.

we obtain, on rearranging,

$$\frac{C_A}{C_{A0}} = \frac{1}{1 + k_1\bar{t}} \tag{21}$$

For component R the material balance, Eq. 4.1, becomes

$$vC_{R0} = vC_R + (-r_R)V$$

or

$$0 = vC_R + (-k_1C_A + k_2C_R)V$$

With Eqs. 20 and 21 and rearranging we obtain

$$\frac{C_R}{C_{A0}} = \frac{k_1\bar{t}}{(1 + k_1\bar{t})(1 + k_2\bar{t})} \tag{22}$$

C_S is found by simply noting that at any time

$$C_A + C_R + C_S = C_{A0} = \text{constant}$$

or

$$\frac{C_S}{C_{A0}} = \frac{k_1k_2\bar{t}^2}{(1 + k_1\bar{t})(1 + k_2\bar{t})} \tag{23}$$

The location and maximum concentration of R are found by taking $dC_R/d\bar{t} = 0$. Thus

$$\frac{dC_R}{d\bar{t}} = 0 = \frac{C_{A0}k_1(1 + k_1\bar{t})(1 + k_2\bar{t}) - C_{A0}k_1\bar{t}[k_1(1 + k_2\bar{t}) + (1 + k_1\bar{t})k_2]}{(1 + k_1\bar{t})^2(1 + k_2\bar{t})^2}$$

which simplifies neatly to give

$$\bar{t}_{max} = \frac{1}{\sqrt{k_1k_2}} \tag{24}$$

The corresponding concentration of R is given by replacing Eq. 24 in Eq. 22. On rearranging this becomes

$$\frac{C_{R,max}}{C_{A0}} = \frac{1}{[(k_2/k_1)^{1/2} + 1]^2} \tag{25}$$

Typical concentration-time curves for various k_2/k_1 values are shown in Fig. 8. A time-independent plot, Fig. 9, relates the concentrations of all reactants and products.

Remarks on performance characteristics, kinetic studies, and design. Figures 5 and 8 show the general time-concentration characteristics for plug and backmix flow reactors and are an aid in visualizing the

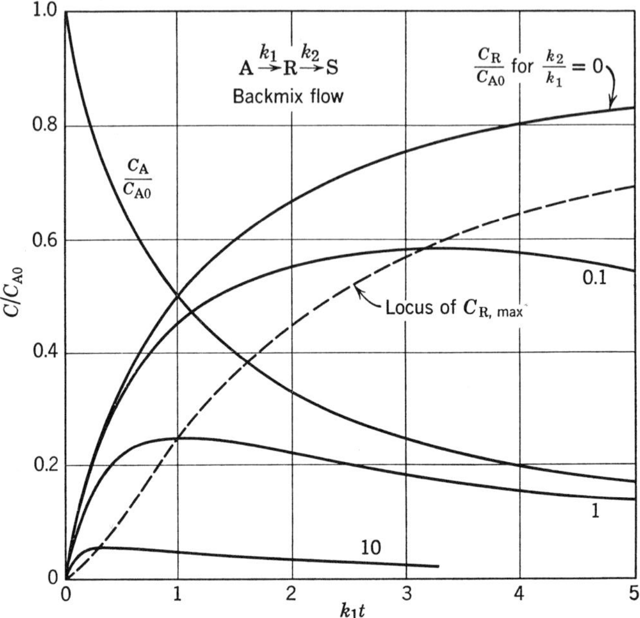

Fig. 8. Concentration–holding time curves in a backmix reactor for the unimolecular-type reactions $A \xrightarrow{k_1} R \xrightarrow{k_2} S$.

actual progress of the reaction. Comparison of these figures shows that except when $k_1 = k_2$ the plug flow reactor requires smaller holding times than does the backmix reactor to achieve a maximum concentration of R, the difference in holding time becoming progressively larger as k_2/k_1 departs from unity. This fact may be verified with Eqs. 24 and 3.44. These figures also show that for a given reaction the maximum obtainable concentration of R in a plug flow reactor is always higher than the maximum obtainable in a backmix reactor (see Eqs. 25 and 3.45). This verifies the conclusions arrived at by qualitative reasoning.

Figures 6 and 9, time-independent plots, show the distribution of materials during reaction. Such plots find the most use in kinetic studies since they allow the determination of k_2/k_1 by matching the experimental points with one of the family of curves on the appropriate graph. Figures 15 and 16 are more detailed representations of these two figures.

Though not shown in the figures, C_S can easily be found by difference between C_{A0} and $C_A + C_R$. For reactor holding times $t < t_{max}$ the S formed is small. For $t \gg t_{max}$ the C_S curve approaches asymptotically that for a simple one-step reaction. Alternately, we can look at the

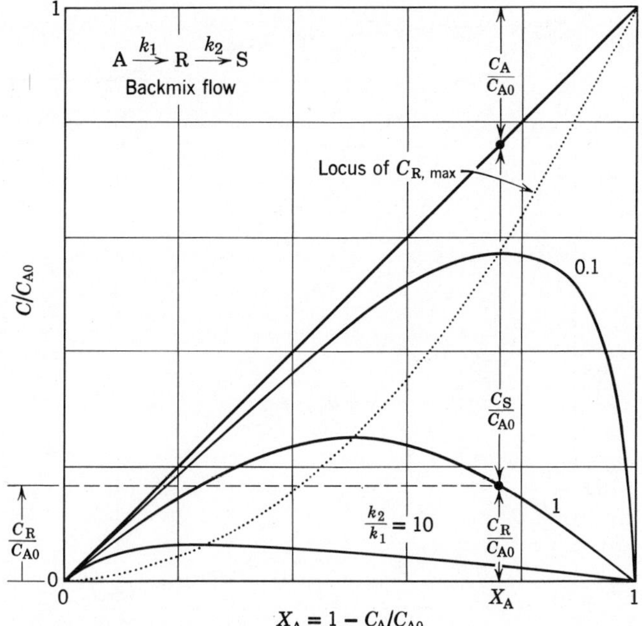

Fig. 9. Relative concentration of the reaction components in a backmix reactor for the unimolecular-type reactions $A \xrightarrow{k_1} R \xrightarrow{k_2} S$.

formation of S as a simple one-step reaction with an induction period which becomes relatively unimportant as holding times increase. Thus the ratio of reactor sizes needed to obtain a given concentration of S is given to an increasingly better approximation by the figure for the simple first-order reaction, Fig. 6.6.

Figure 10 shows the fractional yield of R in both the backmix and plug flow systems and finds the most use in guiding the proper design of reactor systems involving successive first-order reactions. This figure again shows that the fractional yield of R is always greater in the plug flow reactor than in the backmix reactor. Hence if R is the desired product and the cost of materials is not negligible, we should naturally favor the use of the plug flow or batch reactor. A second important observation in this figure concerns the extent of conversion of A we should plan for. If for the reaction considered k_2/k_1 is much smaller than unity, we should design for a large conversion of A and probably dispense with recycling of unused reactant, the latter point depending on the processing cost situation. However, if k_2/k_1 is greater than unity, the fractional yield drops very sharply even with a small conversion. Hence to avoid obtaining unwanted S instead of R we

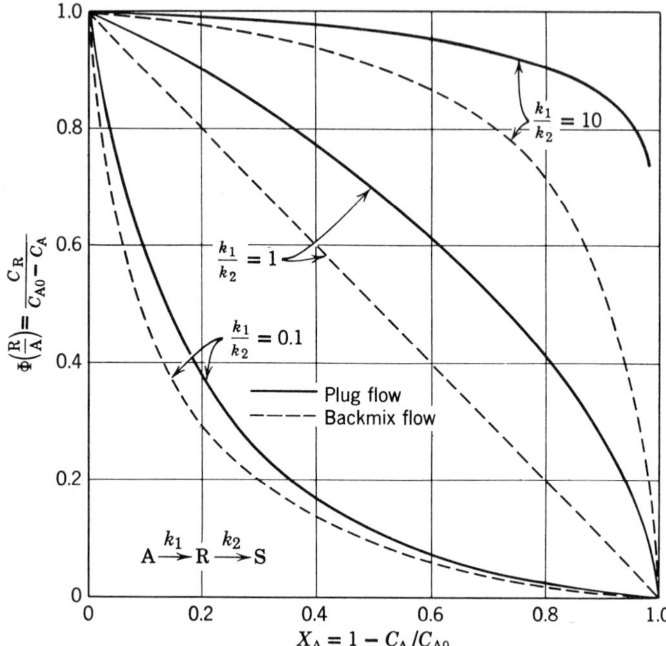

Fig. 10. Comparison of the fractional yields of R in backmix and plug flow reactors for the unimolecular-type reactions $A \xrightarrow{k_1} R \xrightarrow{k_2} S$.

must plan for a very small conversion of A per pass with separation of R and recycle of unused reactant. In such a case large quantities of material will have to be treated in the A-R separator and recycled; hence this part of the process will figure prominently in cost considerations.

Successive irreversible reactions of different orders

In principle concentration–holding time curves can be constructed for all successive reactions of different orders. For the plug flow or batch reactor this will involve simultaneous solution of the governing differential equations, while for the backmix reactor we have only simultaneous algebraic equations to deal with. In both these cases explicit solutions are difficult and can be obtained only for specific cases. Thus numerical methods provide the best tool for treating such reactions. But in all cases these curves exhibit the same qualitative characteristics as the successive first-order reactions; therefore we may generalize the conclusions for that reaction to all irreversible reactions in series.

Product distribution curves for these reactions are of little generality for they are dependent on the concentration of reactant in the feed. As with reactions in parallel a rise in concentration favors the higher-order reaction; a lower concentration favors the lower-order reaction. This characteristic is used to control the product distribution, for it will cause $C_{R, max}$ to vary.

Successive reversible reactions

Solution of the equations for successive reversible reactions is quite formidable even for the first-order case,

$$A \rightleftharpoons R \rightleftharpoons S$$

Thus we illustrate only the general characteristics for a few typical cases.

Consider the first-order reversible reaction

$$A \leftrightharpoons R \leftrightharpoons S \rightleftharpoons \cdots$$

Figure 11 shows the concentration-time curves for the components in a batch or plug flow reactor for different values of the rate constants.

For the reaction

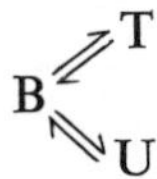

Fig. 12 shows the concentration-time curves for the components in a batch or plug flow reactor for different values of the rate constants.

Figure 11 shows that an intermediate in a reversible series reaction need not exhibit a maximum concentration. Such a maximum only occurs if the rate constants governing its formation are high when compared to those governing its disappearance. Figure 12 also shows that a product may exhibit a maximum concentration typical of an intermediate in the irreversible series reactions; however, the reaction may be of a different kind.

Comparing Figs. 11 and 12 we see that many of the curves are very similar in shape, making it difficult to select the correct mechanisms of reaction by experiment, especially if the kinetic data are somewhat scattered. Probably the best clue in distinguishing between parallel and successive reactions is to examine initial rate data—data obtained for very small conversion of reactant. For successive reactions the time-concentration curve for S has a zero slope, whereas for parallel reactions this is not so. In any case, we must be warned that obtaining a good fit for some data does not necessarily mean that the mechanism suggested is the true one. We must first reject all likely alternate mechanisms that could give such curves. This means exploring mechanisms that are not first order—a discouraging prospect.

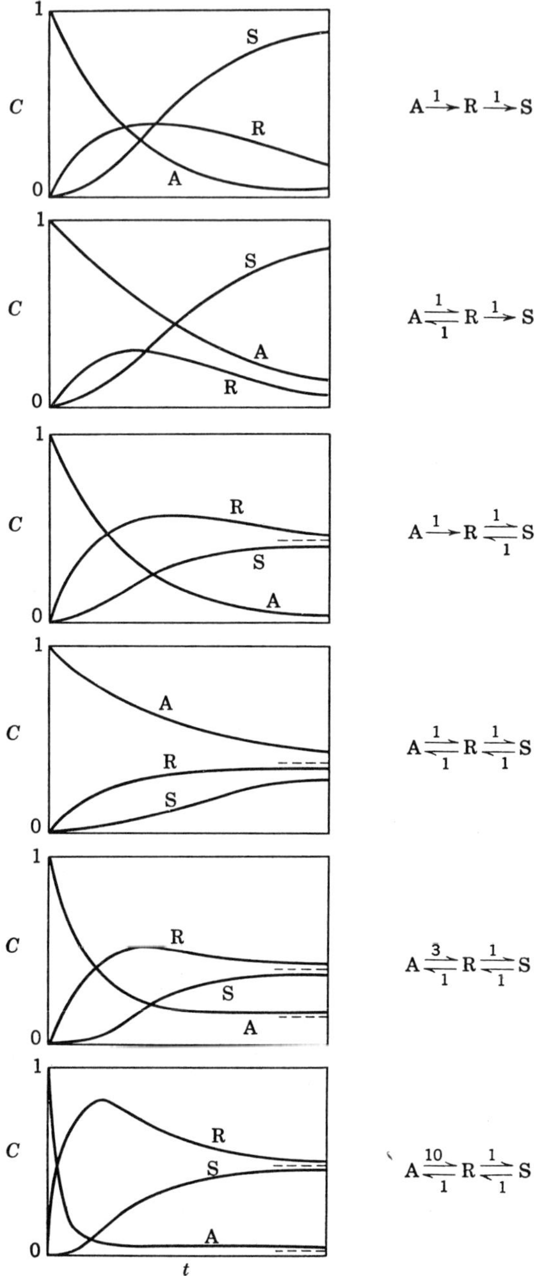

Fig. 11. Concentration-time curves for the elementary reversible reactions A $\underset{k_2}{\overset{k_1}{\rightleftharpoons}}$ R $\underset{k_2}{\overset{k_1}{\rightleftharpoons}}$ S; from Jungers et al. (1958), p. 207.

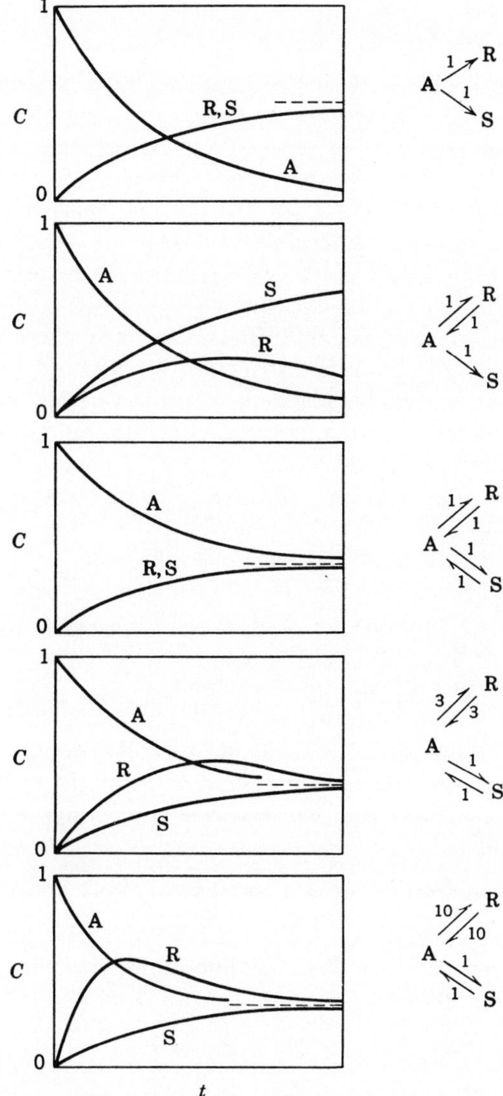

Fig. 12. Concentration-time curves for reversible parallel reactions

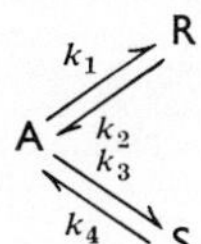

from Jungers et al. (1958), p. 207.

MIXED REACTIONS

Multiple reactions which consist of steps in series and steps in parallel are called mixed reactions. As we mentioned earlier, all mixed reactions can be treated by separate analyses of their two primary reaction types.

Mixed reactions complicate the task of analyzing the kinetics and of finding a satisfactory mechanism. However, though the kinetics may be more complicated, there is a bright side to mixed reactions; with the stoichiometry and kinetics known these reactions become more amenable to control. For example, if k_2/k_1 is fixed, there is nothing we can do to change the product distribution for first-order parallel reactions; similarly, for irreversible reactions of the same order in series there is no way of obtaining more than a certain fixed concentration of intermediate. On the contrary, mixed reactions exhibit great flexibility in product distribution. For example, the mode of mixing of two reactants (whether A is added to B, or vice versa) will very likely change the product distribution radically. Thus mixed reactions afford the good design engineer a fertile opportunity to display his talents in devising ingenious reactor systems which optimize yield of desirable product while depressing the formation of the unwanted product. For this reason the design engineer seeks the correct mechanism of reaction.

The best way to illustrate the points just made is to treat in detail one type of mixed reaction, developing the necessary design charts and working out problems which are based on that reaction. In addition, it is desirable to select a reaction type that has wide application in industry. This we shall do now.

Consecutive-competing (or series-parallel) reactions

The successive attack of a compound and its products by a reactive material is a common, industrially important type of reaction. The general representation of such a reaction is

$$\left.\begin{aligned} A + B &\xrightarrow{k_1} R \\ R + B &\xrightarrow{k_2} S \\ S + B &\xrightarrow{k_3} T \\ &\text{etc.} \end{aligned}\right\} \qquad (26)$$

or

$$A \xrightarrow{+B,\, k_1} R \xrightarrow{+B,\, k_2} S \xrightarrow{+B,\, k_3} T$$

where A is the compound to be attacked, B is the reactive material added, and R, S, T, etc., are the polysubstituted materials formed during reaction. Examples of such reactions may be found in the successive substitutive halogenation (or nitration) of hydrocarbons, say benzene or methane, to form monohalo, dihalo, trihalo, etc., derivatives as shown below:

$$C_6H_6 \xrightarrow{+Cl_2} C_6H_5Cl \xrightarrow{+Cl_2} \cdots \xrightarrow{+Cl_2} C_6Cl_6$$

$$C_6H_6 \xrightarrow{+HNO_3} C_6H_5NO_2 \xrightarrow{+HNO_3} \cdots \xrightarrow{+HNO_3} C_6H_3(NO_2)_3$$

$$CH_4 \xrightarrow{+Cl_2} CH_3Cl \xrightarrow{+Cl_2} \cdots \xrightarrow{+Cl_2} CCl_4$$

Another important example is the addition of alkene oxides, say ethylene oxide, to compounds of the proton donor class such as amines, alcohols, water, and hydrazine to form monoalkoxy, dialkoxy, trialkoxy, etc., derivatives, some examples of which are shown below:

$$\begin{matrix} H \\ / \\ N-H \\ \backslash \\ H \end{matrix} \xrightarrow{+\overset{O}{\triangle}\,CH_2-CH_2} \begin{matrix} CH_2-CH_2OH \\ / \\ N-H \\ \backslash \\ H \end{matrix} \quad \cdots \xrightarrow{+\overset{O}{\triangle}\,CH_2-CH_2} N\equiv(CH_2-CH_2OH)_3$$

$$\begin{matrix} H \\ / \\ O \\ \backslash \\ H \end{matrix} \xrightarrow{+\overset{O}{\triangle}\,CH_2-CH_2} \underset{\text{ethylene glycol}}{\begin{matrix} CH_2-CH_2OH \\ / \\ O \\ \backslash \\ H \end{matrix}} \xrightarrow{+\overset{O}{\triangle}\,CH_2-CH_2} \underset{\text{diethylene glycol}}{O=(CH_2-CH_2OH)_2}$$

Such processes are frequently bimolecular, irreversible, hence second order kinetically. When occurring in the liquid phase they are also essentially constant-density reactions.

We first consider two consecutive reactions where the first substitution product is desired. Actually for an n-step reaction the third and succeeding reactions do not occur to any appreciable extent and may be ignored if the mole ratio of A to B is high (see qualitative treatment given next). The reaction is thus

$$\left.\begin{aligned} A + B &\xrightarrow{k_1} R \\ R + B &\xrightarrow{k_2} S \end{aligned}\right\} \tag{27}$$

With the assumption that the reaction is irreversible, bimolecular, and of constant density, the rate expressions at any instant are given by

$$r_A = \frac{dC_A}{dt} = -k_1 C_A C_B \tag{28}$$

$$r_B = \frac{dC_B}{dt} = -k_1 C_A C_B - k_2 C_R C_B \tag{29}$$

$$r_R = \frac{dC_R}{dt} = k_1 C_A C_B - k_2 C_R C_B \tag{30}$$

$$r_S = \frac{dC_S}{dt} = k_2 C_B C_R \tag{31}$$

Note that this reaction may be considered to be parallel with respect to B but consecutive with respect to A, R, and S. We shall show that this correspondence is not just superficial but carries over into the product distribution analysis so that the generalization arrived at for parallel reactions and series reactions applies to the corresponding components of this reaction.

Qualitative discussion about product distribution. To get the "feel" for what takes place when A and B react according to Eq. 27, imagine that we have two beakers, one containing reactant A and the other containing reactant B. Should it make any difference in the final mixture how we mix A and B? To find out, consider the following three ways of mixing the contents of the beakers; (*a*) A added slowly to B, (*b*) B added slowly to A, and finally (*c*) A and B mixed together rapidly.

For the first mixing pour A a little at a time into the beaker containing B, stirring thoroughly and making sure that all the A is used up and that the reaction stops before the next bit is added. With each addition a bit of R is produced in the beaker. But this R finds itself in an excess of B so it will react further to form S. The result is that at no time during the slow addition of A will A and R be present in any appreciable amount because in the large excess of B they will rapidly react away. Thus the mixture becomes progressively richer in S and poorer in B. This continues until the beaker contains only S. Figure 13 shows this progressive change.

Now pour B a little at a time into the beaker containing A, again stirring thoroughly. The first bit of B will be used up, reacting with A to form R. This R cannot react further for there is now no B present in the mixture. With the next addition of B, both A and R will compete with each other for the B added, and since A is in very large excess it will react with most of the B, producing even more R. This process will be repeated with progressive buildup of R and depletion of A until the concentration of R is high enough so that it will compete favorably with A for the B added.

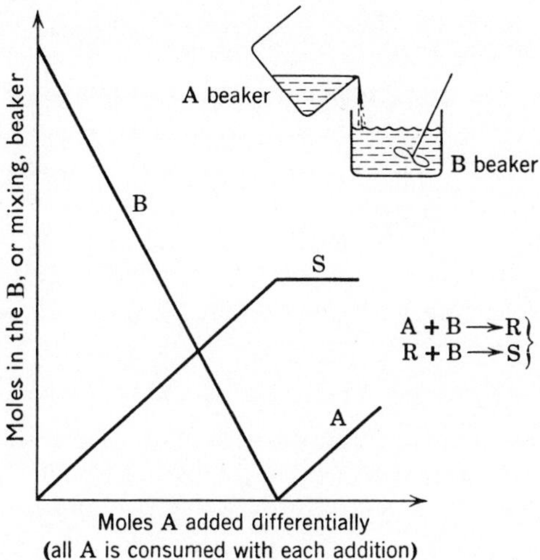

Fig. 13. Distribution of materials in B beaker for mode of mixing shown.

When this happens, the concentration of R reaches a maximum, then drops off. Finally, after addition of 2 moles of B for each mole of A, we end up with a solution containing only S. This progressive change is shown in Fig. 14.

Now consider the third alternative where the contents of the two beakers are rapidly mixed together, the reaction being slow enough so that it does

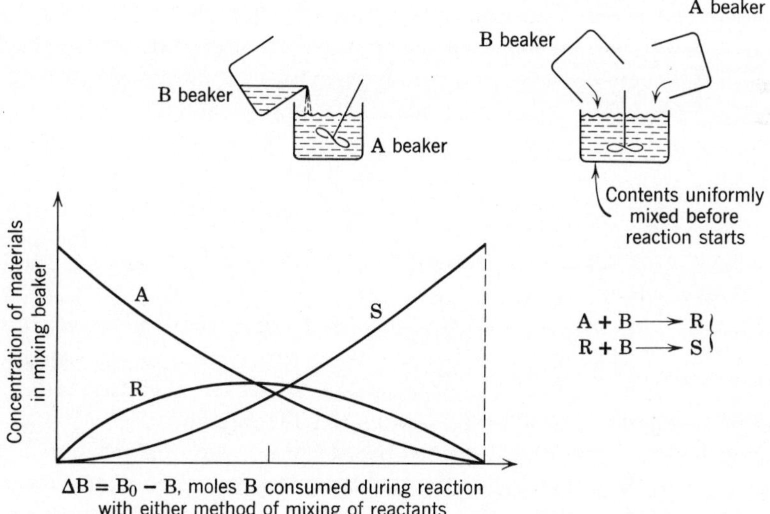

Fig. 14. Distribution of materials in mixing beaker for modes of mixing shown.

not proceed to any appreciable extent before the mixture becomes uniform. During the first few reaction increments R finds itself competing with a large excess of A for B and hence is at a disadvantage. Carrying through this line of reasoning, we find the same type of distribution curve as for the mixture in which B is added slowly to A. This situation is also shown in Fig. 14.

Examining these curves we see that the way we bring together the reactants greatly affects the composition of the mixture. How do we explain this behavior? The clue is to observe that the reaction is consecutive with respect to A, R, and S or

$$A \xrightarrow{+B} R \xrightarrow{+B} S$$

and then compare Figs. 13 and 14 with Figs. 3 and 4. Because of the similar shape of these curves, we are led to suspect that the same factors affecting the R yield in consecutive reactions affects it here. So for materials reacting in series:

For a given conversion of reactant A a maximum amount of intermediate is formed when we do not mix materials at different stages of conversion. Other ways of operating give lower yields of intermediate, and in the extreme case no intermediate is formed.

Now consider the second and third method of bringing the reactants together. We see that in one method we add B all at one time (high C_B) to the beakerful of A; in the other we add B a bit at a time (low C_B) to the beakerful of A. In both methods the product distribution follows the same path, implying that B does not influence product distribution. Now this is exactly what we find for reactions in parallel where the order is the same in both reactions. So in mixed reactions, if a component acts in parallel

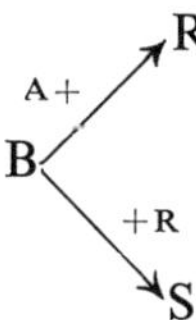

its effect on product distribution can be found by considering parallel reactions alone.

Thus we have shown what we intended to show, that mixed reactions can be treated by considering their component parallel and series reactions. This conclusion is then the guide to proper design. The quantitative treatment to follow verifies these qualitative findings.

Now let us consider what type of reactor to use with this reaction. The choice naturally depends on the product desired. If S is the desired product, we have no problem. However, if R is the desired product, and this is usually the case, we need to keep the composition uniform in A and

R. We must not mix a partly reacted mixture with pure A, for this will result in a lower R concentration than can be expected without this mixing. We consider in what follows that R is always the product desired.

If the reaction is slow, we may mix reactants in a *batch* reactor and let them react to the desired extent. Since the mixture is homogeneous in A, R, and S, we obtain the highest possible concentration of R.

If the reaction is fast, in the mixing of A and B, zones of reaction will form between B-rich and A-rich regions of fluid. In these zones, R will be present in high concentration and will react away more rapidly than in the surrounding regions. The net result of this nonhomogeneity is a decrease in R yield. This undesirable effect may be avoided by slowing down the reaction by dilution or a lowering in temperature, or else by adding B a bit at a time, which involves *semibatch* operations. Unfortunately, for extremely fast reactions this last-mentioned procedure does not help, for even if B were added a drop at a time, zones of nonhomogeneity would still be created between the drop and the rest of the fluid with resultant decrease in R concentration. The problems of mixing in fast reactions are considered further in Chapter 10.

The same remarks can be made for the *plug flow* reactor as are made for the batch reactor.

Backmix operations require mixing an incoming A stream with an already reacted mixture. The resulting nonhomogeneity again lowers the yield in R.

In the following sections we quantitatively treat consecutive competing reactions with the understanding that R, the intermediate, is the desired product, and that the reaction is slow enough so that we may ignore the problems of partial reaction during mixing of reactants.

Quantitative treatment, plug flow or batch reactor. In general, taking the ratio of two rate equations eliminates the time variable and gives information on the product distribution. So dividing Eqs. 30 and 28 we obtain the first-order linear differential equation

$$\frac{r_R}{r_A} = \frac{dC_R}{dC_A} = -1 + \frac{k_2 C_R}{k_1 C_A} \tag{32}$$

the method of solution for which is shown in Chapter 3. With some R present in the feed the limits of integration are C_{A0} to C_A for A and C_{R0} to C_R for R; the solution of this differential equation is

$$\begin{aligned} \frac{C_R}{C_{A0}} &= \frac{1}{1 - k_2/k_1}\left[\left(\frac{C_A}{C_{A0}}\right)^{k_2/k_1} - \frac{C_A}{C_{A0}}\right] + \frac{C_{R0}}{C_{A0}}\left(\frac{C_A}{C_{A0}}\right)^{k_2/k_1}, \qquad \frac{k_2}{k_1} \neq 1 \\ \frac{C_R}{C_{A0}} &= \frac{C_A}{C_{A0}}\left(\frac{C_{R0}}{C_{A0}} - \ln\frac{C_A}{C_{A0}}\right), \qquad \frac{k_2}{k_1} = 1 \end{aligned} \tag{33}$$

This gives the relationship between C_R and C_A at any time in a batch or plug flow reactor. To find the concentrations of the other components at any time, simply make a material balance. An A balance gives

$$C_{A0} + C_{R0} + C_{S0} = C_A + C_R + C_S$$

or

$$\Delta C_A + \Delta C_R + \Delta C_S = 0 \tag{34}$$

from which C_S can be found as a function of C_A and C_R. Finally a balance about B gives

$$\Delta C_B + \Delta C_R + 2\Delta C_S = 0 \tag{35}$$

from which C_B can be found.

Quantitative treatment, backmix reactor. Writing the design equation for backmix reactors in terms of A and R gives

$$\tau = \bar{t} = \frac{C_{A0} - C_A}{-r_A} = \frac{C_{R0} - C_R}{-r_R}$$

or

$$\tau = \bar{t} = \frac{C_{A0} - C_A}{k_1 C_A C_B} = \frac{C_{R0} - C_R}{k_2 C_R C_B - k_1 C_A C_B}$$

Rearranging, we obtain

$$\frac{C_{R0} - C_R}{C_{A0} - C_A} = -1 + \frac{k_2 C_R}{k_1 C_A}$$

which is the integrated form of Eq. 32 with the right-hand-side constant. Rearranging gives

$$C_R = \frac{C_A(C_{A0} - C_A + C_{R0})}{C_A + (k_2/k_1)(C_{A0} - C_A)} \tag{36}$$

which relates the concentrations of A and R. Equations 34 and 35, material balances about A and B in plug flow reactors, hold equally well for backmix reactors and serve to complete the set of equations giving complete product distribution in this reactor.

Graphical representation. Figures 15 and 16, time-independent plots, show the distribution of materials in plug and backmix flow reactor and are prepared from Eqs. 33 to 36. As mentioned earlier, A, R, and S seem to have characteristics of the components in a first-order reaction in series. Comparing Figs. 15 and 16 with Figs. 6 and 9, we see that the distribution of these materials is the same in both cases. As the reaction proceeds, the composition of A and R follows the corresponding k_2/k_1 curve from left to right. The ratio of A to R in the feed and product streams will indicate the starting point and end point on the curve. As this happens, B is progressively used up. The lines of slope 2 on these charts show the amount of B consumed to reach that locus of positions for

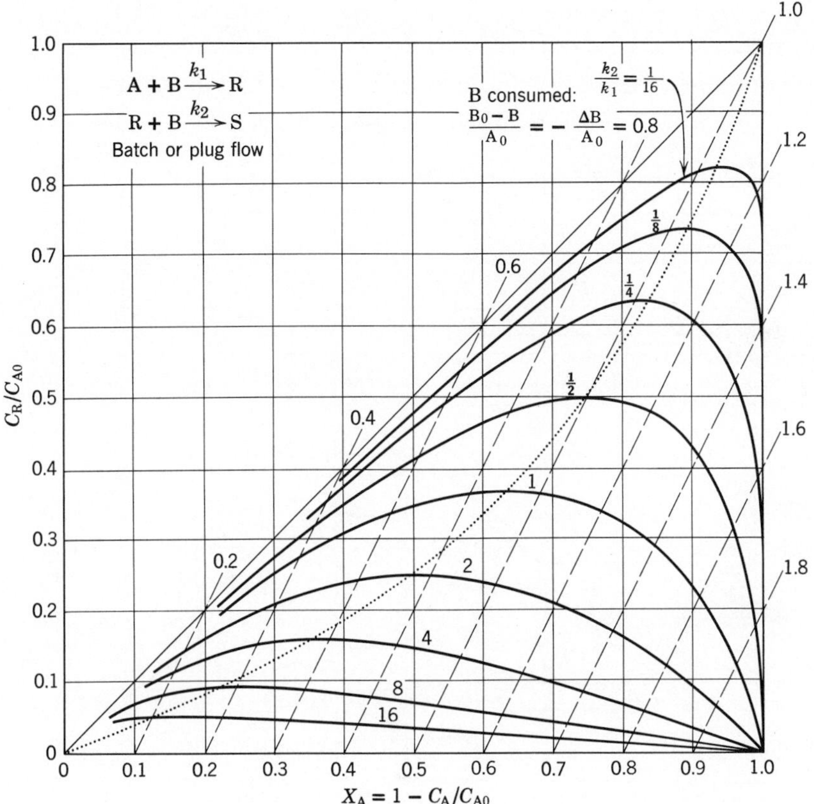

Fig. 15. Distribution of materials in a batch or plug flow reactor for the elementary reactions

$$A + B \xrightarrow{k_1} R$$
$$R + B \xrightarrow{k_2} S$$

any k_2/k_1. It makes no difference whether B is added all at one time as in a batch reactor or a bit at a time as in a semibatch reactor; in either case the same point on the chart will be reached when the same total amount of B is consumed.

These figures indicate that no matter what reactor system is selected, when the fractional conversion of A is low the fractional yield of R is large. Thus if it is possible to separate cheaply small amounts of R from a large reactant stream, the optimum setup for producing R is to have small conversions per pass coupled with a separation of R and recycle of unused A. The actual mode of operation will, as usual, depend on the economics of the system under study.

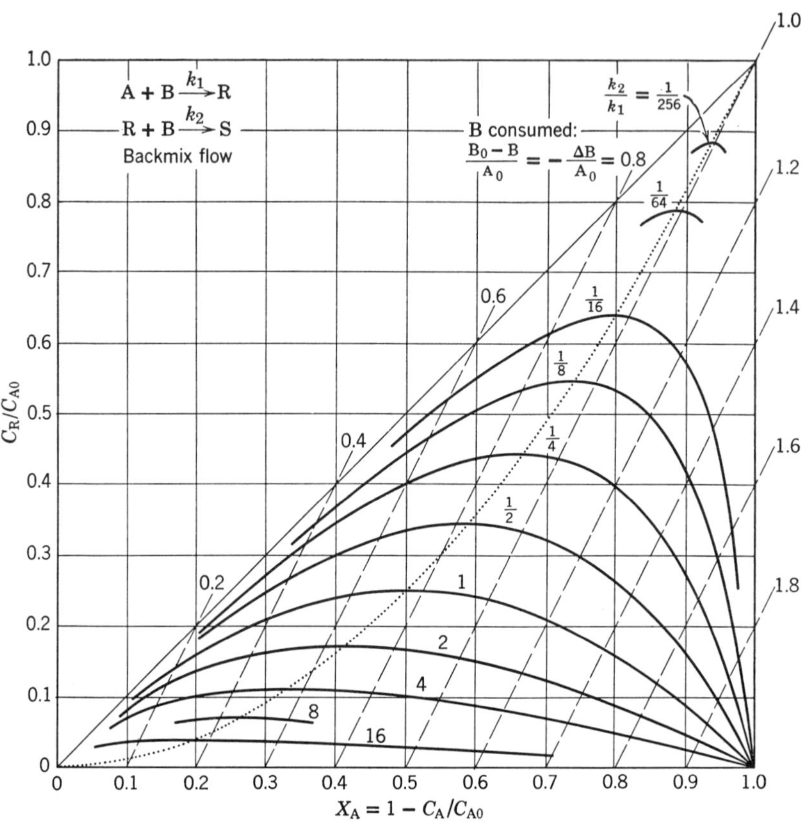

Fig. 16. Distribution of materials in a backmix reactor for the elementary reactions

$$A + B \xrightarrow{k_1} R$$

$$R + B \xrightarrow{k_2} S$$

Experimental determination of the kinetics of reaction. The ratio k_2/k_1 may be found as follows. Analyze the products of reaction from any ideal reactor at any instant, calculate the product distribution of materials, and locate the corresponding point on the design chart. For a batch, semibatch, or plug flow reactor, the appropriate chart is Fig. 15. For a backmix reactor the appropriate chart is Fig. 16. Though this method is general, probably the simplest way to find k_2/k_1 is to use different ratios of B to A in a batch reactor, allowing the reaction to go to completion each time. For each run a value of k_2/k_1 can be determined. The best mole ratios to use in experimental work can be estimated from Figs. 15 and 16 to occur where the lines of constant k_2/k_1 are the furthest apart, or $-(\Delta B/A_0) \approx 1.0$.

Now if there is a third reaction in the series it will not proceed to any appreciable extent if only a little B has been used, since it uses S as a starting material

$$S + B \xrightarrow{k_3} T$$

So if there is a third reaction to the series, it is best to keep $-(\Delta B/A_0)$ low.

With k_2/k_1 known, all that is needed is k_1 which must be found by kinetic experiments. Since the rate of reaction between A and B is initially second order when R is absent in the feed, k_1 can be found by extrapolating rate data to zero holding time. In other words, k_1 is found from initial rate data. Another way is to deal directly with Eqs. 28–33, fitting the best values of the constants by a least-squares procedure. This may become somewhat difficult, however.

Frost and Pearson (1961) consider in detail the experimental determination of the rate constants of this reaction.

Intermediate in feed or recycle stream. If R is present in the feed to the reactor, either from the initial feed or recycle stream, its effect can easily be found because the progress of the reaction will still be along the same k_2/k_1 line of Fig. 15 or 16 but starting from the point where this line cuts a second line of slope $-(C_R/C_A)_{\text{initial}}$ and emanating from $C_A = C_R = 0$. The effect of this R in the feed reduces the net fractional yield of R.

Example 4

From each of the following experiments, what can we say about the rate constants of the multiple reaction

$$A + B \xrightarrow{k_1} R$$

$$R + B \xrightarrow{k_2} S$$

(*a*) Half a mole of B is poured bit by bit, with stirring, into a flask containing a mole of A. The reaction proceeds slowly, and when completed B is entirely consumed but 0.67 mole of A remains unreacted.

(*b*) One mole of A and 1.25 moles of B are rapidly brought together. The reaction is slow enough so that it does not proceed to any appreciable extent before homogeneity in A and B is achieved. On completion of the reaction 0.5 mole of R is found to be present in the mixture.

(*c*) One mole of A and 1.25 moles of B are rapidly brought together. The reaction is slow enough so that it does not proceed to any appreciable extent before homogeneity in A and B is achieved. At the time when 0.9 mole of B is consumed 0.3 mole of S is present in the mixture.

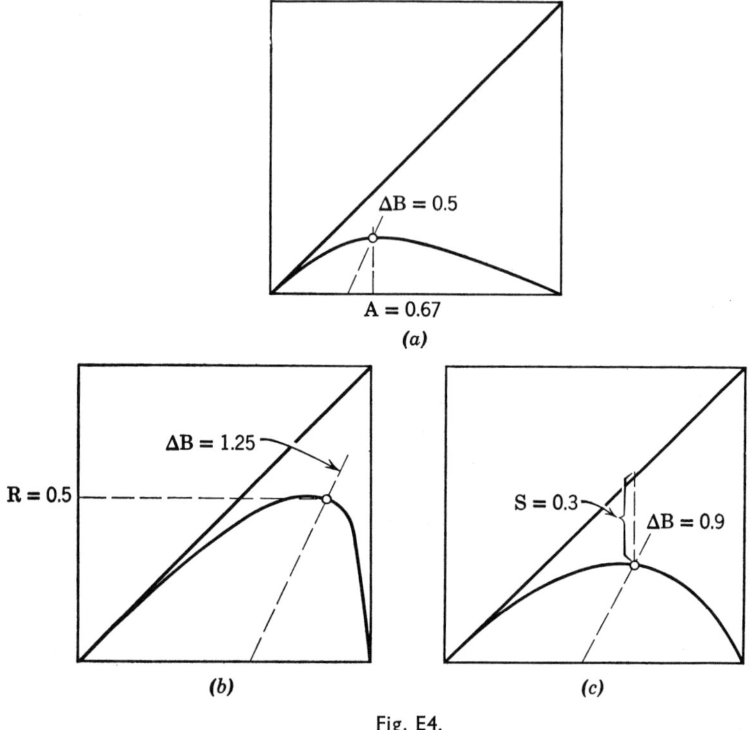

Fig. E4.

Solution. The sketches in Fig. E4 show how Fig. 15 is used to find the desired information. The data given determine specific product distribution curves. Thus

$$(a)\ k_2/k_1 = 4,\ (b)\ k_2/k_1 = 0.4,\ (c)\ k_2/k_1 = 1.45.$$

Extensions and applications

Analysis of three or more reactions can be made by procedures analogous to those presented. Of course, the mathematics becomes more involved; however, much of the extra labor can be avoided by selecting experimental conditions in which only two reactions need be considered at any time. Product distribution curves for one such reaction, the progressive chlorination of benzene, is shown in Fig. 17. Note the similarity in shape with the time-concentration curves for successive first-order reactions in series, Fig. 3.14. The curves of Fig. 17 may be replotted in the manner of Figs. 15 and 16 for a three-step reaction [see Jungers et al. (1958)]. Unfortunately, because paper is only two dimensional, a separate graph is needed for each value of k_2/k_1. Again, as with the two-step reaction, we find that a plug flow reactor yields higher maximum concentration of intermediates

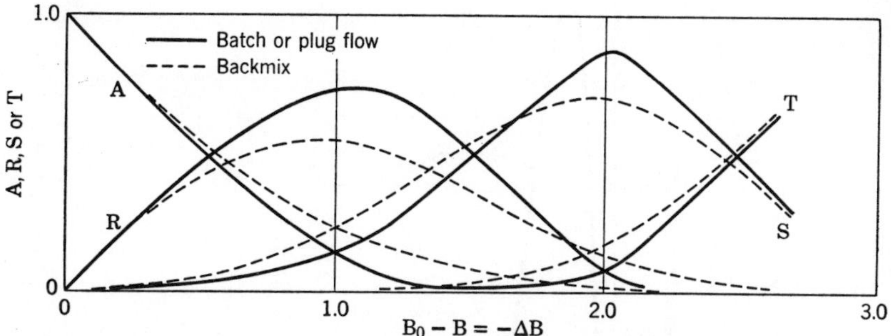

Fig. 17. Product distribution in the progressive chlorination of benzene:

$$\begin{array}{llll} A + B \xrightarrow{k_1} R + U & & C_6H_6 + Cl_2 \xrightarrow{k_1} C_6H_5Cl + HCl \\ R + B \xrightarrow{k_2} S + U & \text{or} & C_6H_5Cl + Cl_2 \xrightarrow{k_2} C_6H_4Cl_2 + HCl \\ S + B \xrightarrow{k_3} T + U & & C_6H_4Cl_2 + Cl_2 \xrightarrow{k_3} C_6H_3Cl_3 + HCl \end{array}$$

with $k_2/k_1 = \frac{1}{8}$ and $k_3/k_1 = \frac{1}{240}$; from MacMullin (1948).

than does a backmix reactor. Hence we may generalize observations on the formation of intermediate in various reactor types from a two-step reaction to an n-step reaction.

The field of polymerization affords an opportunity for a fruitful application of these ideas. Often hundreds or even thousands of reactions in series occur in the formation of polymers, and the type of cross linking and molecular weight distribution of these products are what gives these materials their particular physical properties of solubilities, density, flexibility, etc.

Since the mode of mixing of monomers with their catalysts profoundly affects product distribution, and therefore molecular weight distribution, great importance must be paid to this aspect of processing and scale up if the product is to have the desired physical and chemical properties. Denbigh (1947, 1951) considered some of the many aspects of this problem, and Figs. 18 and 19 show for various kinetics how reactor type influences molecular weight distribution of products.

CONCLUSION

The key to optimum design for multiple reactions is proper contacting and proper flow pattern of fluids within the reactor. These requirements are determined by the stoichiometry and observed kinetics.

To obtain high yields of a desired product we may have to maintain high concentrations or low concentrations (parallel reactions), or homogeneity

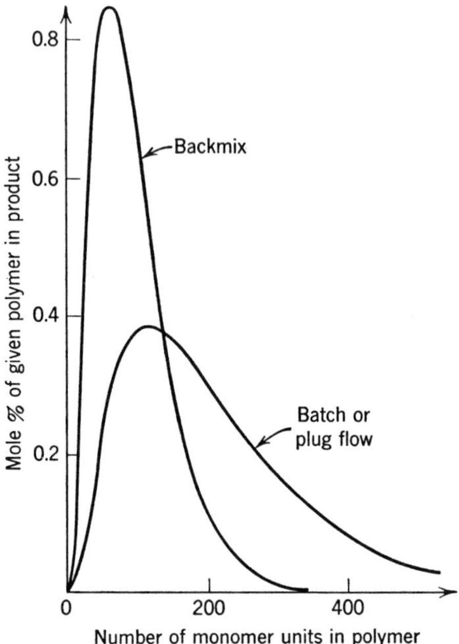

Fig. 18. Molecular weight distribution of polymer where duration of polymerization reaction (life of active polymer) is short compared to reactor holding time. Adapted from Denbigh (1947).

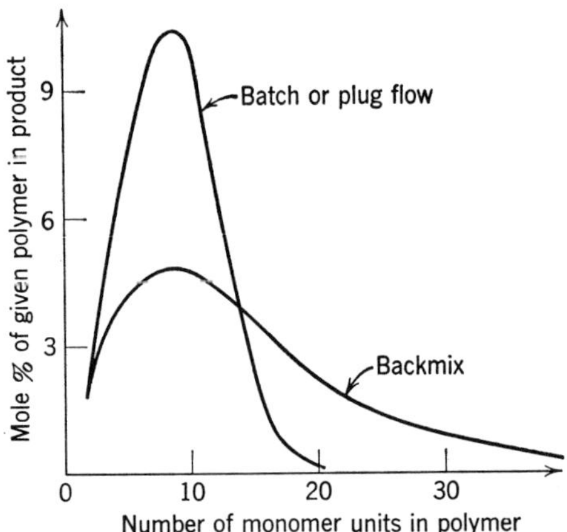

Fig. 19. Molecular weight distribution of polymer where duration of polymerization reaction is long compared to the holding reactor time, or where the polymerization has no termination reaction. Adapted from Denbigh (1947).

of composition (series reactions) for the various reactants. With these requirements known desirable contacting patterns can then be devised by using the appropriate batch, semibatch, backmix, or plug flow unit with slow or rapid introduction of the various feeds.

Usually qualitative reasoning is sufficient to determine the correct contacting scheme. This is done by breaking the reaction stoichiometry into its component parallel and series reactions. Naturally, to determine the actual equipment size requires quantitative considerations.

When the kinetics and stoichiometry are not known, well-planned experimentation guided by the principles enunciated here should result in a reasonably close approach to optimum operations.

Additional discussions of how product distribution is affected by the contacting pattern and temperature of operations are given in Chapters 10 and 8 and in the chapters on heterogeneous systems.

RELATED READINGS

K. G. Denbigh, *Trans. Faraday Soc.*, **40,** 352 (1944).

J. C. Jungers et al., *Cinétique chimique appliquée*, Technip, Paris, 1958, Ch. 4.

REFERENCES

K. G. Denbigh, *Trans. Faraday Soc.*, **43,** 648 (1947).

———, *J. Appl. Chem.*, **1,** 227 (1951).

A. A. Frost and R.G. Pearson, *Kinetics and Mechanism*, second edition, John Wiley and Sons, New York, 1961.

J. C. Jungers et al., *Cinétique chimique appliquée*, Technip, Paris, 1958.

R. B. MacMullin, *Chem. Eng. Progr.*, **44,** 183 (1948).

PROBLEMS

1. In one sentence state the distinguishing characteristic of each of the following reactions: single, multiple, elementary, nonelementary.

2. Under appropriate conditions A decomposes as follows:

$$\mathrm{A} \xrightarrow{k_1=0.1/\mathrm{min}} \mathrm{R} \xrightarrow{k_2=0.1/\mathrm{min}} \mathrm{S}$$

R is to be produced from 1000 liters/hr of feed in which $C_{A0} = 1$ mole/liter, $C_{R0} = C_{S0} = 0$.

(*a*) What size plug flow reactor will maximize the yield of R, and what is the concentration of R in the effluent stream of this reactor?

(*b*) What size backmix reactor will maximize the yield of R, and what is $C_{R,\max}$ in the effluent stream of this reactor?

3. It is mentioned in this chapter (and we can see by comparing Figs. 15 and 16 with Figs. 6 and 9) that the distribution of A, R, and S for the two sets of elementary reactions

$$\begin{aligned} &A \xrightarrow{k_1} R \xrightarrow{k_2} S \\ &A \xrightarrow{+B,\, k_1'} R \xrightarrow{+B,\, k_2'} S \end{aligned} \qquad \text{with } \frac{k_2}{k_1} = \frac{k_2'}{k_1'}$$

is identical. Verify this analytically.

4. At Sandy's Rock and Gravel Company they want to shift a mountain of gravel, estimated at about 20,000 tons, from one side of their yard to the other. For this they intend to use a steam shovel to fill a hopper, which in turn feeds a belt conveyer. The latter then transports the gravel to the new location. The shovel scoops up large amounts of gravel at first; however, as the gravel supply decreases the handling capacity of the shovel also decreases because of the increased time required to move away from the hopper for a load and then return and dump. Roughly, then, we may estimate that the shovel's gravel-handling rate is proportional to the size of the pile still to be moved, its initial rate being 10 tons/min. The conveyer, on the other hand, transports the gravel at a uniform 5 tons/min. At first the shovel will work faster than the conveyer, then slower. Hence the storage bin will accumulate material, then empty.

(*a*) What will be the largest amount of gravel in the bin?
(*b*) When will this occur?
(*c*) When will the rates of bin input and output be equal?
(*d*) When will the bin become empty?

5. Consider the following elementary reactions

$$A + B \xrightarrow{k_1} R$$

$$R + B \xrightarrow{k_2} S$$

(*a*) One mole A and 3 moles B are rapidly mixed together. The reaction is very slow, allowing analysis of compositions at various times. When the 2.2 moles B remain unreacted, 0.2 mole S is present in the mixture. What should be the composition of the mixture (A, B, R and S) when the amount of S present is 0.6 mole?
(*b*) One mole A is added bit by bit with constant stirring to 1 mole B. Left overnight, then analyzed, 0.5 mole S is found. What can we say about k_2/k_1?
(*c*) One mole A and 1 mole B are thrown together and mixed in a flask. The reaction is very rapid and goes to completion before any rate measurements can be made. On analysis of the products of reaction 0.25 mole S is found to be present. What can we say about k_2/k_1?

6. A and B react with each other as follows:

$$\begin{aligned} 2A &\rightarrow R, \qquad & r_R &= k_1 C_A^2 \\ A + B &\rightarrow S, \qquad & r_S &= k_2 C_A C_B \\ 2B &\rightarrow T, \qquad & r_T &= k_3 C_B^2 \end{aligned}$$

Find what ratio of A to B should be maintained in a backmix reactor so that the production of S is maximized.

7. We have a mixture consisting of 90 mole % A (45 moles/liter) and 10 mole % impurity B (5 moles/liter). To be of satisfactory quality the mole ratio of A to B in the mixture must be 100 to 1 or higher. D reacts with both A and B as follows:

$$\mathrm{A + D \rightarrow R}, \qquad -\frac{dC_{\mathrm{A}}}{dt} = 21 C_{\mathrm{A}} C_{\mathrm{D}}$$

$$\mathrm{B + D \rightarrow S}, \qquad -\frac{dC_{\mathrm{B}}}{dt} = 147 C_{\mathrm{B}} C_{\mathrm{D}}$$

Assuming that the reactions go to completion, how much D need be added to a given batch of mixture to bring about the desired quality?

8. We suspect that A and B react as follows:

$$\mathrm{A + B} \xrightarrow{k_1} \mathrm{R}$$

$$\mathrm{R + B} \xrightarrow{k_2} \mathrm{S}$$

To see if this is so we mix different proportions of A and B in test tubes and leave them standing overnight. The reaction is slow, and we question whether the reaction has come to a stop or not when we analyze the contents of the test tubes (Table P8).

Table P8

Feed		Concentration of S after an Overnight Wait,
C_{A0}	C_{B0}	C_{S}
0.20	0.80	0.20
0.25	0.75	0.26
0.33	0.67	0.33
0.50	0.50	0.21
0.67	0.33	0.11
0.75	0.25	0.07
0.80	0.20	0.05

(*a*) Have we waited long enough for the reaction to go to completion?
(*b*) Could the reaction mechanism be correct? If so, what is k_2/k_1?
(*c*) We plan four more runs. In what concentration region should they be made to find k_2/k_1 more precisely?

9. When A (benzenesulfonic acid, mol wt = 158) reacts with B (nitric acid, mol wt = 63), products R, S, and T (ortho-, meta-, and paranitrobenzenesulfonic acids, mol wt = 203) are formed by the elementary reactions

$$\mathrm{A + B} \begin{matrix} \nearrow \mathrm{R} \\ \rightarrow \mathrm{S} \\ \searrow \mathrm{T} \end{matrix}$$

During a laboratory nitration test when A and B are mixed in a mole ratio of 2 to 1 in the presence of dehydrating agent, one-third of the A is consumed in 40 min yielding 21% R, 72% S, 7% T.

If these data are used as a basis for computing yields for this reaction carried out on a commercial scale and 3160 lb of A is to be mixed with 1260 lb of B under conditions identical to the laboratory conditions, compute the composition of the mixture (pounds of A, B, R, S, and T) after 90 min have elapsed.

10. A and B react as follows:

$$\mathrm{A + 2B \rightarrow 2R + S}, \qquad (r_\mathrm{A})_1 = -k_1 C_\mathrm{A} C_\mathrm{B}^2$$

$$\mathrm{A + B \rightarrow T + U}, \qquad (r_\mathrm{A})_2 = -k_2 C_\mathrm{A} C_\mathrm{B}$$

Equimolar quantities of A and B are introduced into a batch reactor and are left to react to completion. With all B consumed, $C_\mathrm{A} = 0.1C_{\mathrm{A}0} = 0.1$. What information does this experiment give us about the rate constants for the reactions?

11. D reacts with both A and B as follows:

$$\mathrm{A + D} \xrightarrow{k_1} \mathrm{R}, \qquad r_\mathrm{R} = k_1 C_\mathrm{A} C_\mathrm{D}$$

$$\mathrm{B + D} \xrightarrow{k_2} \mathrm{S}, \qquad r_\mathrm{S} = k_2 C_\mathrm{B} C_\mathrm{D}$$

One feed stream contains a fixed ratio of A to B, the other D. To maximize the fractional yield of R in steady-state operations of single reactors show

(*a*) when $k_2/k_1 > 1$ use backmix flow and high conversions,
(*b*) when $k_2/k_1 < 1$ use plug flow and low conversions,
(*c*) when $k_2/k_1 = 1$ product distribution is unaffected by reactor type and extent of conversion.
(*d*) Illustrate these conclusions by sketching and showing the general characteristic of the $\Phi(\mathrm{R/R + S})$ versus X_A plot for backmix reactors.

Note: These conclusions also hold for the elementary reactions

$$\mathrm{A} \xrightarrow{k_1} \mathrm{R}$$

$$\mathrm{B} \xrightarrow{k_2} \mathrm{S}$$

commonly found in catalytic systems.

12. Consider the reactions of Problem 11 with $k_2/k_1 = 0.2$ occurring in a backmix reactor with an equimolar feed of A, B, and D.

(*a*) If 50% of the incoming A is consumed, find what fraction of the product formed is R.
(*b*) If 50% of the incoming D is consumed, find what fraction of the products formed is R.

13. For single reactions we have seen that if the reactor system consists of a number of backmix reactors in series, its performance (volume or capacity) lies between plug flow and the single backmix reactor; the larger the number of reactors in series, the closer the approach to plug flow. We may expect the same behavior to occur with multiple reactions with respect not only to capacity but to product distribution as well. Let us see if it is true for one particular case. Consider the reaction

$$A \xrightarrow{k_1=1,\, n_1=1} R \xrightarrow{k_2=1,\, n_2=1} S$$

For a single plug flow reactor

$$\frac{C_{R,max}}{C_{A0}} = \frac{1}{e} = 0.368 \quad \text{and} \quad t_{R,max} = \frac{1}{k_{\text{log mean}}} = 1$$

For a single backmix reactor

$$\frac{C_{R,max}}{C_{A0}} = 0.25 \quad \text{and} \quad t_{R,max} = \frac{1}{\sqrt{k_1 k_2}} = 1$$

For two backmix reactors in series find $C_{R,max}/C_{A0}$ and $t_{R,max}$, and see whether these lie between the values found for the plug flow and single backmix reactor systems.

14. The elementary reactions

$$A + B \xrightarrow{k_1} R$$

$$2B \xrightarrow{k_2} S$$

occur when A and B are contacted in the presence of a homogeneous catalyst. Reactants are available in separate feed streams. If R is the desired product, determine the optimum contacting scheme for given conversion of B at fixed temperature in (*a*) batch or noncontinuous operations, (*b*) continuous operations, (*c*) continuous operations with separation and recycle of one reactant.

15. A process stream consisting of a mixture of A and B of a definite ratio can, under suitable conditions, be made to react by the elementary reactions

$$A + B \xrightarrow{k_1} R, \qquad \frac{dC_R}{dt} = k_1 C_A C_B$$

$$2B \xrightarrow{k_2} S, \qquad \frac{dC_S}{dt} = k_2 C_B^2$$

To maximize the fractional yield of R in steady-state operations of single reactors show

(*a*) when $2k_2/k_1 > 1 - C_{A0}/C_{B0}$ use backmix flow and high conversions,
(*b*) when $2k_2/k_1 < 1 - C_{A0}/C_{B0}$ use plug flow and low conversions,
(*c*) when $2k_2/k_1 = 1 - C_{A0}/C_{B0}$ product distribution is unaffected by reactor type and extent of conversion.

Note: These conditions imply that when $k_1 < 2k_2$, then backmix flow and high conversions are always favored.

16. Analyze qualitatively the following elementary reactions and determine the methods of contacting that will maximize formation of the desired product R.

(*a*) $A + A \rightarrow R$
$R + A \rightarrow S$

(*b*) $A + A \rightarrow S$
$A + B \rightarrow R$
$S + B \rightarrow T$
$R + A \rightarrow T$

Assume that recycle is not permitted.

17. The great naval battle, to be known to history as the battle of Trafalgar (1805), was soon to be joined. Admiral Villeneuve proudly surveyed his powerful fleet of 33 ships stately sailing in single file in the light breeze. The British fleet under Lord Nelson was now in sight, 27 ships strong. Estimating that it would still be two hours before the battle, Villeneuve popped open another bottle of burgundy and point by point reviewed his carefully thought out battle strategy. As was the custom of naval battles at that time, the two fleets would sail in single file parallel to each other and in the same direction, firing their cannons madly. Now, by long experience in battles of this kind, it was a well-known fact that the rate of destruction of a fleet was proportional to the fire power of the opposing fleet. Considering his ships to be on a par, one for one, with the British, Villeneuve was confident of victory. Looking at his sundial, Villeneuve sighed and cursed the light wind—he'd never get it over with in time for his favorite television western. "Oh well," he sighed "c'est la vie." He could see the headlines next morning. "British Fleet annihilated, Villeneuve's losses are . . . ." Villeneuve stopped short. How many ships would he lose? Villeneuve called over his chief bottle cork popper, Monsieur Dubois, and asked this question. What answer did he get?

At this very moment, Nelson, who was enjoying the air on the poop deck of the *Victory*, was struck with the realization that all was ready except for one detail—he had forgotten to formulate his battle plan. Commodore Archibald Forsythe-Smythe, his trusty trusty, was hurriedly called over for a conference. Being familiar with the firepower law, Nelson was loathe to fight the whole French fleet (he could see the headlines too). Now certainly it was no disgrace for Nelson to be defeated in battle by superior forces, so long as he did his best and played the game; however, he had a sneaking suspicion that maybe he could pull a fast one. With a nagging conscience whether it was cricket or not, he proceeded to investigate this possibility.

It was possible to "break the line," in other words, to start parallel to the French fleet, and then cut in and divide the enemy fleet into two sections. The rear section could be engaged and disposed of before the front section could turn around and get back into the fray. Now to the $64 question. Should he split the French fleet and if so at what point should it be done and with how many ships should he engage the fore and after sections of the enemy? Commodore Forsythe-Smythe, who was so rudely taken from his grog, grumpily agreed to consider this question and to advise Nelson at what point to split the French fleet so as to maximize their chance of success. He also agreed to predict the outcome of the battle using this strategy.

18. The desired product R is formed as follows

$$A + B \rightarrow R, \qquad r_R = k_1 C_A C_B$$

Under conditions which favor this reaction, however, B also dimerizes to form unwanted S:

$$2B \rightarrow S, \qquad r_S = k_2 {C_B}^2$$

At present R is produced in a backmix reactor using a large excess of A so as to depress formation of unwanted dimer. Feeds of A and B are so adjusted that the mole ratio of A to B in the reactor is kept at 40 to 1. Unreacted A is cleanly separated from the rest of the materials in the reactor effluent stream and is returned to the reactor. Unreacted B cannot be simply separated and is discarded. R and S are produced in equimolar quantities, and 50% of entering B is unreacted and is discarded unused.

(*a*) Find the fractional yield of R based on A consumed, on B consumed, on total entering B, and on the sum of all products formed.

This scheme seems to be inefficient because much B forms the wrong product or is wasted by remaining unreacted. To improve utilization of B, let us connect a second reactor in series with the present reactor, leaving the conditions within the first reactor unchanged. Both reactors are to be of the same size, and separation of A to be recycled occurs after passage of fluid through both reactors. Because it is in great excess, assume that the concentration of A is constant throughout the system.

(*b*) Find the fraction of R present in the R-S product and the fraction of B in the feed which has been transformed into R.

(*c*) With unchanged feed rate of B and unchanged concentration of A within the system, repeat part *b* if the two backmix reactors are connected in parallel rather than in series.

19. A 20 ft^3 backmix reactor is to treat a reactant which decomposes as follows:

$$A \rightarrow R, \qquad r_R = k_1 C_A = (4/\text{hr})C_A$$
$$A \rightarrow S, \qquad r_S = k_2 C_A = (1/\text{hr})C_A$$

Find the feed rate and conversion of reactant so as to maximize profits. What are these on an hourly basis?

Data: Feed material A costs \$1.00/lb mole at $C_{A0} = 1$ lb mole/ft^3, product R sells for \$5.00/mole, and S has no value. The total operating cost of reactor and product separation equipment is \$25/hr + \$1.25/mole A treated. Unconverted A is not recycled.

20. Chemical R is to be produced by the decomposition of A in a given backmix reactor. The reaction proceeds as follows:

$$A \rightarrow R, \qquad r_R = k_1 C_A$$
$$2A \rightarrow S, \qquad r_S = k_2 {C_A}^2$$

Let the molar cost ratio $\$_R/\$_A = M$ (S is waste material of no value), and for convenience let $k_1 = N k_2 C_{A0}$. In the feed C_{A0} is fixed.

(*a*) Ignoring operating costs, find what conversion of A should be maintained in the reactor to maximize the gross earnings and therefore the profits.

(*b*) Repeat part *a* with the hourly operating cost dependent on the feed rate and given by $\alpha + \beta F_{A0}$.

21. Chemicals A and B react as follows:

$$\text{A} + \text{B} \rightarrow \text{R}, \qquad r_R = k_1 C_A C_B = [68.8 \text{ liters/(hr)(gm mole)}] C_A C_B$$

$$2\text{B} \rightarrow \text{S}, \qquad r_S = k_2 C_B^2 = [34.4 \text{ liters/(hr)(gm mole)}] C_B^2$$

In this reaction 100 gm moles R/hr are to be produced at minimum cost in a backmix reactor. Find the feed rates of A and B to be used and the size of reactor required.

Data: Reactants are available in separate streams at $C_{A0} = C_{B0} = 0.1$ gm mole/liter and both cost \$0.50/gm mole. The cost of reactor is \$0.01/(hr)(liter).

8

TEMPERATURE AND PRESSURE EFFECTS

In our search for the optimum conditions at which to effect reactions, we have already considered how reactor type and size influence the extent of conversion and distribution of products obtained. The reaction temperature and pressure also influence the progress of reactions, and it is the role of these variables that we now consider.

A number of factors must be considered here. First of all, we need to know how equilibrium yield, rate of reaction, and product distribution are affected by changes in operating temperatures and pressures. This will allow determination of the optimum temperature progression: in time for batch reactors, along the length of plug flow reactors, and from reactor to reactor in a series of backmix reactors. This information can then be used as a guide for proper design.

Secondly, chemical reactions are invariably accompanied by heat effects. When these are large enough to result in a significant change in temperature of the reacting mixture, these effects must be accounted for in design. More important still, we should know how to use these effects to proper advantage by the selection of the proper reactor type and by use of appropriate heat exchange.

So with the emphasis on finding the optimum conditions and then seeing how best to approach it in actual design rather than determining what specific reactors will do, let us start with discussions of single reactions and follow this with the special considerations of multiple reactions.

SINGLE REACTIONS

With single reactions we are concerned with extent of conversion and reactor stability. Questions of product distribution do not occur.

Thermodynamics gives two important pieces of information related to the extent of reaction and reactor stability, the first being the heat liberated or absorbed for a given extent of reaction, the second being the thermodynamic equilibrium or the maximum expected extent of reaction. Let us now briefly summarize these findings. More detailed treatments and justification of the expressions to follow and their many special forms and extensions can be found in standard thermodynamics texts for chemical engineers and will not be considered here.

Heats of reaction from thermodynamics

The heat liberated or absorbed during reaction depends on the nature of the reacting system, the amount of material reacting, and the temperature and pressure of the reacting system, and is calculated from the heat of reaction ΔH_r for the reaction in question. When this is not known, it can in most cases be calculated from known and tabulated thermochemical data on heats of formation ΔH_f, or heats of combustion ΔH_c of the individual components of the reaction. As a brief reminder consider the reaction

$$a\text{A} \rightarrow r\text{R} + s\text{S}$$

By convention we define the heat of reaction at temperature T as the heat transferred *to* the reacting system from the surroundings when a moles of A disappear to produce r moles of R and s moles of S with the system measured at the same temperature and pressure before and after the change. Thus

$$a\text{A} \rightarrow r\text{R} + s\text{S}, \qquad \Delta H_{r,T} \begin{cases} \text{positive, endothermic} \\ \text{negative, exothermic} \end{cases} \tag{1}$$

Heats of reaction and temperature. The heat of reaction at temperature T_2 in terms of the heat of reaction at temperature T_1 is found by the law of conservation of energy as follows:

$$\begin{pmatrix}\text{heat absorbed} \\ \text{during reaction} \\ \text{at temperature} \\ T_1\end{pmatrix} = \begin{pmatrix}\text{heat added} \\ \text{to reactants} \\ \text{to change their} \\ \text{temperature} \\ \text{from } T_1 \text{ to } T_2\end{pmatrix} + \begin{pmatrix}\text{heat absorbed} \\ \text{during reaction} \\ \text{at temperature} \\ T_2\end{pmatrix} + \begin{pmatrix}\text{heat added} \\ \text{to products} \\ \text{to bring them} \\ \text{back to } T_1 \\ \text{from } T_2\end{pmatrix} \tag{2}$$

In terms of enthalpies of reactants and products this becomes

$$\Delta H_{r2} = -(H_2 - H_1)_{\text{reactants}} + \Delta H_{r1} + (H_2 - H_1)_{\text{products}} \tag{3}$$

where subscripts 1 and 2 refer to quantities measured at temperatures T_1 and T_2. In terms of specific heats

$$\Delta H_{r2} = \Delta H_{r1} + \int_{T_1}^{T_2} \nabla C_p \, dT \tag{4}$$

where

$$\nabla C_p = rC_{p\text{R}} + sC_{p\text{S}} - aC_{p\text{A}} \tag{5}$$

When the specific heats are functions of temperature as follows,

$$\begin{aligned} C_{pA} &= \alpha_A + \beta_A T + \gamma_A T^2 \\ C_{pR} &= \alpha_R + \beta_R T + \gamma_R T^2 \\ C_{pS} &= \alpha_S + \beta_S T + \gamma_S T^2 \end{aligned} \tag{6}$$

we obtain

$$\begin{aligned} \Delta H_{r2} &= \Delta H_{r1} + \int_{T_1}^{T_2} (\nabla\alpha + \nabla\beta T + \nabla\gamma T^2)\, dT \\ &= \Delta H_{r1} + \nabla\alpha(T_2 - T_1) + \frac{\nabla\beta}{2}(T_2^2 - T_1^2) + \frac{\nabla\gamma}{3}(T_2^3 - T_1^3) \end{aligned} \tag{7}$$

where

$$\begin{aligned} \nabla\alpha &= r\alpha_R + s\alpha_S - a\alpha_A \\ \nabla\beta &= r\beta_R + s\beta_S - a\beta_A \\ \nabla\gamma &= r\gamma_R + s\gamma_S - a\gamma_A \end{aligned} \tag{8}$$

Knowing the heat of reaction at any one temperature and pressure as well as the specific heats of the reactants and products in the temperature range concerned allows determination of the heat of reaction at any other temperature or pressure. From this the heat effects of the reaction can be found.

Equilibrium constants from thermodynamics

From the second law of thermodynamics, equilibrium constants, hence equilibrium compositions of reacting systems, may be calculated. We must remember, however, that real systems do not necessarily achieve this conversion (see Chapter 3); therefore the conversions calculated from thermodynamics are only suggested attainable values.

As a brief reminder, the standard free energy ΔF° for the reaction of Eq. 1 at temperature T is

$$\begin{aligned} \Delta F^\circ &= rF^\circ_R + sF^\circ_S - aF^\circ_A = -RT\ln K \\ &= -RT\ln \frac{\left(\dfrac{f}{f^\circ}\right)_R^r \left(\dfrac{f}{f^\circ}\right)_S^s}{\left(\dfrac{f}{f^\circ}\right)_A^a} \end{aligned} \tag{9}$$

where f is the fugacity of the component at the equilibrium conditions, f° is the fugacity of the component at the arbitrarily selected standard state at temperature T, the same one used in calculating ΔF°, F° are the standard free energies of the reacting components, tabulated for many compounds, and K is the thermodynamic equilibrium constant for the reaction.

Standard states at given temperature are commonly chosen as follows:

Gases—Pure component at one atmosphere at which pressure ideal gas behavior is closely approximated

Solid—Pure solid component at unit pressure

Liquid—Pure liquid at its vapor pressure

Solute in liquid—1 molar solution

—Such dilute concentrations that the activity is unity

Define for convenience

$$K_f = \frac{f_R^{\,r} f_S^{\,s}}{f_A^{\,a}}, \qquad K_p = \frac{p_R^{\,r} p_S^{\,s}}{p_A^{\,a}},$$
$$K_y = \frac{y_R^{\,r} y_S^{\,s}}{y_A^{\,a}}, \qquad K_C = \frac{C_R^{\,r} C_S^{\,s}}{C_A^{\,a}} \tag{10}$$

and

$$r + s - a = \Delta n$$

Now simplified forms of Eq. 9 can be obtained for various systems. For *gas-phase* reactions standard states are usually chosen at a pressure of 1 atm. At this low pressure the deviation from ideality invariably is small; hence fugacity and pressure are identical and $f^\circ = p^\circ = 1$ atm. Thus

$$K = K_f\{p^\circ = 1 \text{ atm}\}^{-\Delta n} = e^{-\Delta F^\circ/RT} \tag{11}$$

The term in braces in this equation and Eq. 13 is always unity but is retained to keep the equations dimensionally correct.

For ideal gases

$$f_i = p_i = y_i\pi = C_i RT \tag{12}$$

for any component *i*. Hence

$$K_f = K_p$$

and

$$K = K_p\{p^\circ = 1 \text{ atm}\}^{-\Delta n} = K_y \pi^{\Delta n}\{p^\circ = 1 \text{ atm}\}^{-\Delta n}$$
$$= K_c(RT)^{\Delta n}\{p^\circ = 1 \text{ atm}\}^{-\Delta n} \tag{13}$$

For a *solid component* taking part in a reaction, fugacity variations with pressure are small and can usually be ignored. Hence

$$\left(\frac{f}{f^\circ}\right)_{\text{solid component}} = 1 \tag{14}$$

Equilibrium and temperature. Now the equilibrium composition, as governed by the equilibrium constant, changes with temperature. From thermodynamics the rate of this change is given by

$$\frac{d(\ln K)}{dT} = \frac{\Delta H_r}{RT^2} \tag{15}$$

This expression shows that for an increase in temperature equilibrium yields drop for exothermic reactions, and equilibrium yields rise for endothermic reactions. Integrating Eq. 15 we see precisely how the equilibrium constant changes as the temperature changes from T_1 to T_2. When the heat of reaction ΔH_r can be considered to be constant in the temperature interval considered integration yields

$$\ln \frac{K_2}{K_1} = -\frac{\Delta H_r}{R}\left(\frac{1}{T_2} - \frac{1}{T_1}\right) \tag{16}$$

When the variation of ΔH_r is to be accounted for in the integration we have

$$\ln \frac{K_2}{K_1} = \frac{1}{R}\int_{T_1}^{T_2} \frac{\Delta H_r}{T^2}\, dT \tag{17}$$

In terms of specific heats for the reaction of Eq. 1, the variation of ΔH_r with temperature is given by a special form of Eq. 4,

$$\Delta H_r = \Delta H_{r0} + \int_{T_0}^{T} \nabla C_p \, dT \tag{18}$$

where subscript 0 refers to the base temperature. With Eq. 17 we obtain

$$R \ln \frac{K_2}{K_1} = \nabla\alpha \ln \frac{T_2}{T_1} + \frac{\nabla\beta}{2}(T_2 - T_1) + \frac{\nabla\gamma}{6}(T_2^2 - T_1^2)$$
$$+ \left(-\Delta H_{r0} + \nabla\alpha T_0 + \frac{\nabla\beta}{2} T_0^2 + \frac{\nabla\gamma}{3} T_0^3\right)\left(\frac{1}{T_2} - \frac{1}{T_1}\right) \tag{19}$$

These expressions allow us to find the variation of the equilibrium constant, hence conversion, with temperature.

The following conclusions may be drawn from thermodynamics. These are illustrated in part by Figs. 1 and 2.

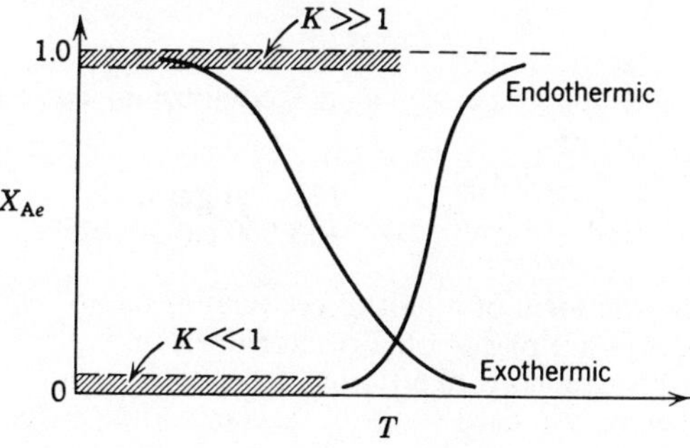

Fig. 1. Effect of temperature on equilibrium conversion as predicted by thermodynamics (pressure fixed).

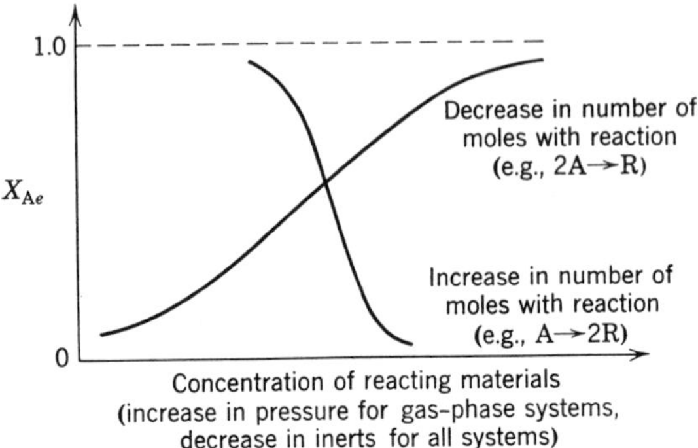

Fig. 2. Effect of pressure and inerts on equilibrium conversion as predicted by thermodynamics (temperature fixed).

1. The thermodynamic equilibrium constant is unaffected by the pressure of the system, by the presence or absence of inerts, or by the kinetics of the reaction, but it is affected by the temperature of the system.

2. Though the thermodynamic equilibrium constant is unaffected by pressure or inerts, the equilibrium concentration of materials and fractional conversion of reactants can be influenced by these variables.

3. $K \gg 1$ indicates that practically complete conversion is possible and that the reaction can be considered to be irreversible. $K \ll 1$ indicates that reaction will not proceed to any appreciable extent.

4. For an increase in temperature, equilibrium conversion rises for endothermic reactions and drops for exothermic reactions.

5. For an increase in pressure in gas-phase reactions, conversion rises when the number of moles decreases with reaction and drops when the number of moles increases with reaction.

6. A decrease in inerts for all reactions acts in the way that an increase in pressure acts for gas-phase reactions.

Example 1

(*a*) Between 0 and 100°C determine the equilibrium conversion of A for the aqueous-phase reaction

$$A \rightleftharpoons R \qquad \begin{aligned} \Delta F^\circ_{298} &= -1744 \text{ cal/gm mole} \\ \Delta H_{r,298} &= -18{,}000 \text{ cal/gm mole} \end{aligned}$$

Present the result in the form of a plot of conversion versus temperature.

(*b*) What restrictions are placed on a reactor operating isothermally if we are to obtain fractional conversions of 50% or higher?

Assume the following standard states of reactants and products,

$$C^\circ_R = C^\circ_A = 1 \text{ mole/liter}$$

and ideal solutions, in which case

$$K = \frac{C_R/C^\circ_R}{C_A/C^\circ_A} = \frac{C_R}{C_A} = K_C$$

In addition, assume specific heats of all solutions equal to that of water.

Solution. (*a*) With all specific heats alike, $\nabla C_p = 0$. Then from Eq. 4 the heat of reaction is independent of temperature and is given by

$$\Delta H_r = \Delta H_{r,298} = -18{,}000 \text{ cal/gm mole} \tag{i}$$

From Eq. 9 the equilibrium constant at 25°C is given by

$$\begin{aligned} K_{298} &= \exp(-\Delta F^\circ_{298}/RT) \\ &= \exp \frac{1744 \text{ cal/gm mole}}{(1.98 \text{ cal/(gm mole)(°K))(298°K)}} = 19 \end{aligned} \tag{ii}$$

Since the heat of reaction does not change with temperature, the equilibrium constant K at any temperature T is now found from Eq. 16. Thus

$$\ln \frac{K}{K_{298}} = -\frac{\Delta H_r}{R}\left(\frac{1}{T} - \frac{1}{298}\right)$$

which with Eqs. i and ii gives

$$\ln \frac{K}{19} = \frac{18{,}000}{1.98}\left(\frac{1}{T} - \frac{1}{298}\right)$$

or

$$\ln K = \frac{9060}{T} - 27.46 \tag{iii}$$

Values of ln K and K, calculated from Eq. iii, are shown for 10°C intervals in Table E1. From thermodynamics

$$K = \frac{C_{Re}}{C_{Ae}} = \frac{C_{A0} - C_{Ae}}{C_{Ae}} = \frac{X_{Ae}}{1 - X_{Ae}}$$

Hence the fractional conversion at equilibrium is given by

$$X_{Ae} = \frac{K}{1 + K} \tag{iv}$$

Table E1 also gives the values of X_{Ae} calculated from Eq. iv, and Fig. E1 shows the changing equilibrium conversion as a function of temperature in the range of 0 to 100°C.

(*b*) From the graph we see that the temperature must stay below 57°C if conversions of 50% or higher are to be obtained.

Effect of operating temperature level on conversion

Consider a given feed being processed at isothermal conditions in a plug flow, backmix, or batch reactor. Let us see how the operating temperature level affects the conversion of limiting reactant.

Table E1

Selected Temperature °C	Selected Temperature °K	ln K from Eq. iii	K	X_{Ae} from Eq. iv
5	278	5.14	170.5	0.9945
15	288	4.0	54.6	0.982
25	298	2.94	18.92	0.950
35	308	1.94	6.96	0.8748
45	318	1.03	2.80	0.7370
55	328	0.15	1.162	0.5375
65	338	−0.66	0.517	0.3406
75	348	−1.44	0.237	0.1915
85	358	−2.15	0.1165	0.1044
95	368	−2.85	0.0579	0.0547

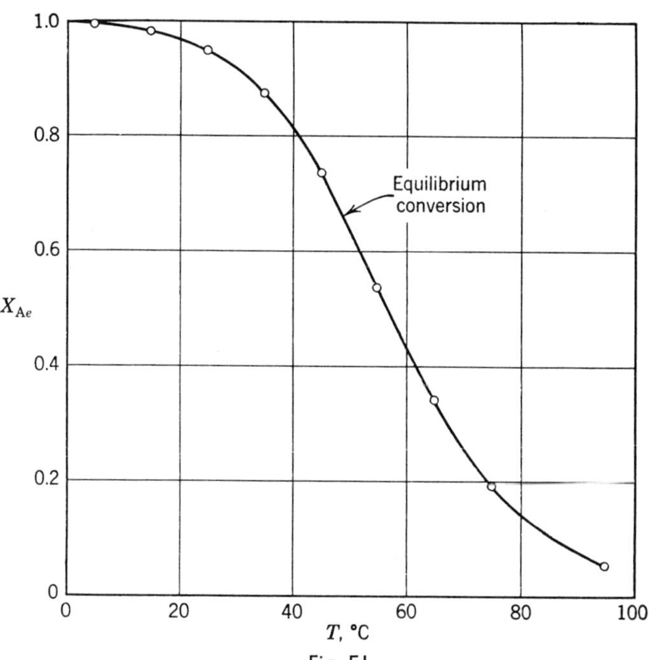

Fig. E1.

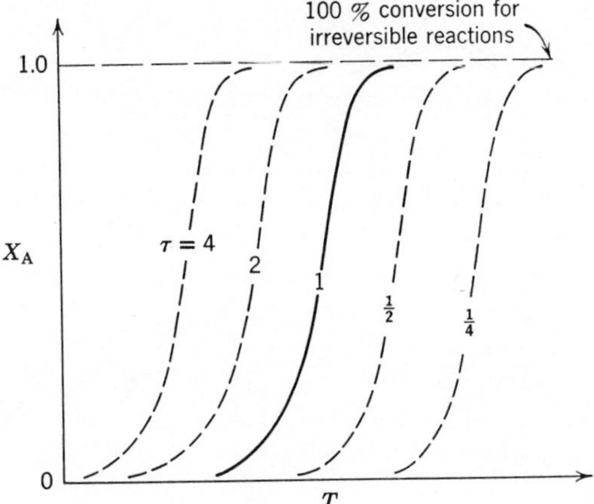

Fig. 3. Locus of conversion versus reactor temperature level for irreversible reactions occurring isothermally in any kind of reactor, backmix, plug flow, or batch.

Irreversible reactions. Figure 3 shows the general characteristics of the conversion versus temperature-level curve at fixed processing rate; hence fixed τ. Let us follow this curve. At low temperatures reaction will be so slow that conversion is negligible. Now let the temperature level of the reactor be raised. Since the rate constant is ordinarily given by Arrhenius' law,

$$k = k_0 e^{-E/RT}$$

and therefore rises exponentially with temperature, a certain temperature range is reached where conversion rises rapidly. Here a small rise in temperature level will result in practically complete conversion. At high conversions the depletion in available reactant will cause the rate to slow again. The over-all effect of the rapidly increasing rate constant followed by depletion of reactant gives the characteristic steep S-shaped curve shown in Fig. 3.

Increasing the space time or reactor holding time results in higher conversion at a given temperature. The over-all effect is simply a shift of the characteristic curve to the left. Since

$$\tau = \frac{C_{A0} V}{F_{A0}}$$

this displacement to the left can be obtained by using a larger reactor, a higher feed concentration (decreasing inerts), or a smaller processing rate. A shift to the right is obtained by decreasing τ.

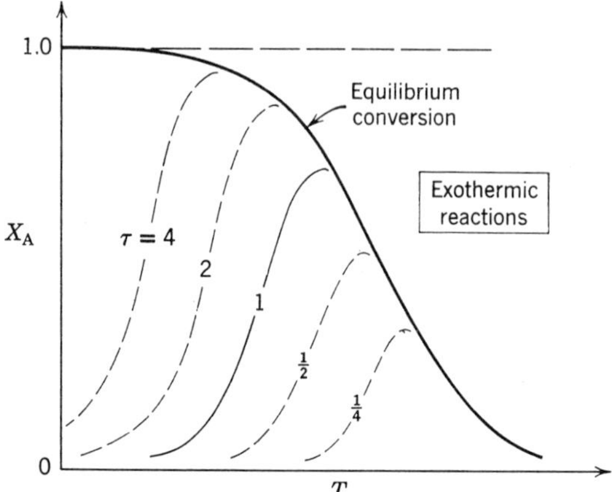

Fig. 4. Locus of conversion versus reactor temperature level for reversible exothermic reactions occurring isothermally in any kind of reactor, backmix, plug flow, or batch.

In gaseous reacting systems the main effect of a pressure increase is to raise the concentration of reacting materials, increasing the rate and shifting the curve to the left.

Reversible reactions. Changing the temperature level with reversible reactions results in the same characteristic S-shaped curve as that for irreversible reactions. However, this curve approaches equilibrium rather than 100% conversion. Since the change in equilibrium conversion is given by Fig. 1, we then have the curves of Figs. 4 and 5 for this situation.

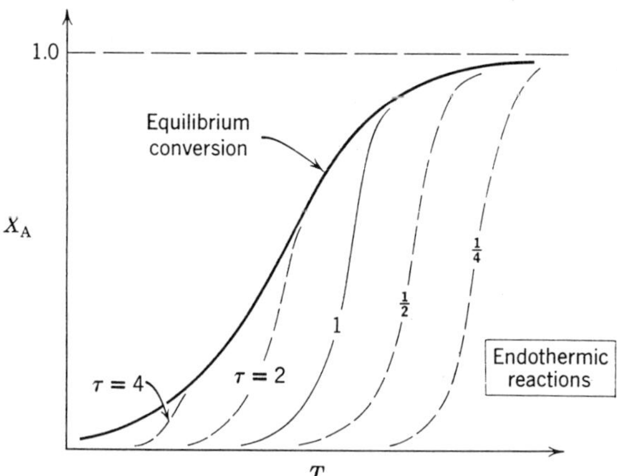

Fig. 5. Locus of conversion versus reactor temperature for reversible endothermic reactions occurring at isothermal conditions in any kind of reactor, backmix, plug flow, or batch.

It is interesting to note that with exothermic reactions conversion reaches a maximum, decreasing at higher temperature because of the unfavorable equilibrium.

With curves such as those in Figs. 3, 4 and 5, processing rate, temperature, and other variables for satisfactory or optimum isothermal operations can be determined.

Example 2

Starting with R-free solution, the reaction of Example 1 is to be effected in a plug flow reactor. Feed rate, reactant concentration, and reactor size are such that $\tau = 10$ min.

(*a*) Determine the conversion of A obtained if the reactor is run at room temperature, 25°C.

(*b*) Determine the conversion of A obtained if the reactor is run at its maximum allowable operating temperature, 65°C.

(*c*) Find the optimum temperature level of operation and the conversion obtained at this condition.

Kinetic experiments in a batch reactor starting with R-free solution give 79.3% conversion in 19 min at 25°C, 69.1% conversion in 8 min at 35°C.

Assume that the reaction is well described by first-order reversible kinetics.

Solution. *Integrate the reactor design equation.* For first-order reversible reactions in plug flow reactors

$$\tau = C_{A0}\int \frac{dX_A}{-r_A} = C_{A0}\int \frac{dX_A}{k_1 C_A - k_2 C_R} = \frac{1}{k_1}\int_0^{X_A} \frac{dX_A}{1 - X_A/X_{Ae}}$$

From Eq. 3.50 or Eq. 5.19, integration of this equation yields

$$k_1\tau = -\frac{K}{K+1}\ln\left(1 - \frac{K+1}{K}X_A\right) = -X_{Ae}\ln\left(1 - \frac{X_A}{X_{Ae}}\right) \tag{i}$$

or

$$X_A = X_{Ae}(1 - e^{-k_1\tau/X_{Ae}}) \tag{ii}$$

Calculate the forward rate constant. From the batch kinetic run at 25°C, noting from Example 1 that $X_{Ae} = 0.95$, we find with Eq. i

$$k\ (19\text{ min}) = -0.95\ln\left(1 - \frac{0.793}{0.95}\right)$$

or

$$k_{1,298} = 0.09/\text{min} \tag{iii}$$

Similarly for the batch run at 35°C we find

$$k_{1,308} = 0.1706/\text{min} \tag{iv}$$

The complete form of the rate constant

$$k = k_0 e^{-E/RT}$$

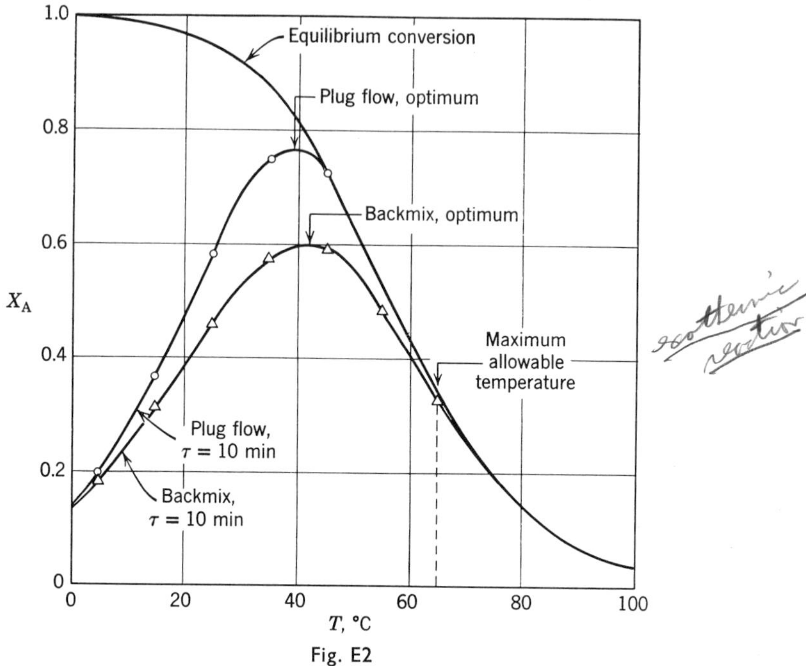

Fig. E2

is found by taking the ratio of the k_1 values, or

$$\frac{k_{1,298}}{k_{1,308}} = \frac{k_{01}e^{-E_1/R(298)}}{k_{01}e^{-E_1/R(308)}} = \exp\left[-\frac{E_1}{R}\left(\frac{1}{298} - \frac{1}{308}\right)\right]$$

Solving with Eqs. iii and iv, we find that the activation energy of the forward reaction is

$$E_1 = 11{,}600 \text{ cal/gm mole}$$

from which the complete forward rate constant is found to be

$$k_1 = (3 \times 10^7)e^{-(11{,}600 \text{ cal/gm mole})/RT} \tag{v}$$

Find conversion versus temperature curve. Solving Eqs. ii and v at 10°C intervals gives the conversion at various temperatures for $\tau = 10$ min. This conversion is plotted in Fig. E2, and the details of the calculations are shown in Table E2. As expected, this curve rises to a maximum and then drops as predicted by Fig. 4.

(*a*) From Fig. E2 we find

$$X_A = 0.58, \qquad \text{at } 25°\text{C}$$

Here reaction kinetics is the important factor, and increasing the space time τ gives a rise in conversion.

Table E2

Selected Temperature °C	°K	X_{Ae} from Ex. 1.	k_1 from Eq. v	$e^{-k_1\tau/X_{Ae}}$	X_A from Eq. ii
5	278	0.9945	0.02218	0.800	0.1989
15	288	0.982	0.0456	0.6282	0.365
25	298	0.950	0.09	0.3878	0.582
35	308	0.8748	0.1706	0.142	0.750
45	318	0.7370	0.311	0.01468	0.726
55	328	0.5375	0.544	0.00004	0.5375
65	338	0.3406	0.926	–	0.34

(*b*) From Fig. E2

$$X_A = 0.34, \qquad \text{at } 65°\text{C}$$

This shows that conversion is rather low at the maximum operating temperature. Since equilibrium controls here, no improvement in yield is possible with change in reactor size or feed rate.

(*c*) From Fig. E2 the optimum operating temperature and corresponding conversion are

$$T = 39°\text{C}$$
$$X_A = 0.76$$

This example shows that substantial improvements in yield are possible by selecting the optimum temperature of operation.

Example 3

Repeat Example 2 using a backmix reactor in place of a plug flow reactor

Solution. The design equation for backmix flow is

$$\tau = \frac{C_{A0}X_A}{-r_A} = \frac{X_A}{k_1(1 - X_A/X_{Ae})}$$

which on rearranging gives

$$X_A = \frac{X_{Ae}k_1\tau}{X_{Ae} + k_1\tau} \qquad \text{(i)}$$

Using the values of X_{Ae} and k_1 from Table E2 and replacing them in Eq. i, we obtain the values given in Table E3 and plotted in Fig. E2.

(*a*) From Fig. E2 we find

$$X_A = 0.46, \qquad \text{at } 25°\text{C}$$

(*b*) From Fig. E2 we find

$$X_A = 0.33, \qquad \text{at } 65°\text{C}$$

(*c*) From Fig. E2 the optimum operating temperature and corresponding conversion are

$$T = 42°\text{C}$$
$$X_A = 0.60$$

The graph shows that as temperature is lowered conversions drop and the performances of plug flow and backmix reactors approach each other. At high temperatures, when equilibrium determines the performance, these reactors also act alike. Only at intermediate and close to optimum temperatures is the difference in performance significant.

Table E3

Selected Temperature		X_A
°C	°K	from Eq. i
5	278	0.1814
15	288	0.313
25	298	0.4622
35	308	0.5788
45	318	0.596
55	328	0.489
65	338	0.3294

Optimum temperature progression

Let us determine the optimum temperature progression to be used, optimum in the sense that it maximizes the production rate of a given reactor. This optimum may be isothermal or it may be a varying temperature: in time for a batch reactor, along the length of a plug flow reactor, or from reactor to reactor in a series of backmix reactors.

For *irreversible reactions* the maximum possible conversion is unaffected by temperature, as shown in Fig. 3, whereas, with an Arrhenius temperature dependency the rate of reaction rises with temperature. Hence maximum production is achieved at the highest allowable operating temperature. This maximum temperature is limited by the materials of construction of the reactor or by the possible increasing importance of side reactions.

For *reversible endothermic reactions* a rise in temperature increases both the equilibrium conversion and rate (Fig. 1). Thus, as with irreversible reactions, the highest allowable temperature should be used.

Now consider an *exothermic reversible reaction* taking place in a plug flow reactor, as shown in Fig. 4. An increase in temperature increases the rate of forward reaction but, in opposition to this, it decreases the maximum attainable conversion. Thus near the reactor inlet where the reacting fluid is far from equilibrium, it is advantageous to use a high temperature. Near the reactor outlet where equilibrium conditions are approached, the temperature should be lowered so that the equilibrium will shift to the more favorable values of higher conversions. This suggests, and it is generally

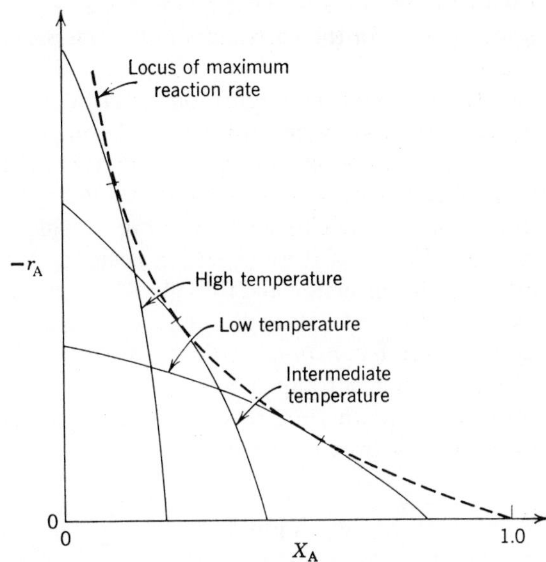

Fig. 6. Reaction rate as a function of conversion and temperature for reversible exothermic reactions using a given feed material. Dashed line shows the temperature to use at each composition for optimum operations.

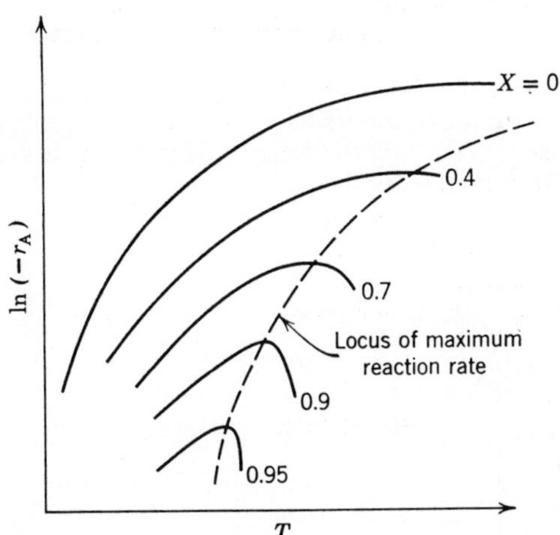

Fig. 7. Reaction rate as a function of conversion and temperature for reversible exothermic reactions using a given feed material. Dashed line shows the optimum temperature progression.

found to be so for reversible exothermic reactions, that optimum processing is achieved with the use of a varying temperature progression. The temperature should be high in the early stages of conversion, decreasing as conversion rises.

To find the optimum temperature progression, and from it the maximum production rate, we need to know the entering feed composition and the rate of reaction as a function of temperature. From this information the rate of reaction as a function of both conversion and temperature may be calculated and then plotted as in either Fig. 6 or Fig. 7, whichever is more convenient. The dashed lines on these figures indicate the locus of maximum reaction rate at each conversion and thus gives the optimum temperature profile. By using this rate at each corresponding conversion and graphically integrating for batch or plug flow systems, or by using the graphical procedure outlined in Chapter 6 for j tanks in series, the maximum production rate for exothermic reversible reactions can be found. The following examples illustrate the procedure.

Example 4

Using the optimum temperature progression in a plug flow reactor for the reaction of the previous examples, $C_{A0} = 1$ mole/liter, calculate the space time required to achieve 76% conversion and find how much production can be increased by using this optimum temperature progression over the isothermal operating conditions of Example 2.

Note that the maximum allowable operating temperature is 65°C.

Solution. We have the choice of preparing a graph such as Fig. 6 or Fig. 7. Now for first-order reactions, reversible or irreversible, the lines of Fig. 6 are straight; hence this figure is easy to prepare. Thus we make use of such a plot, rather than one like Fig. 7.

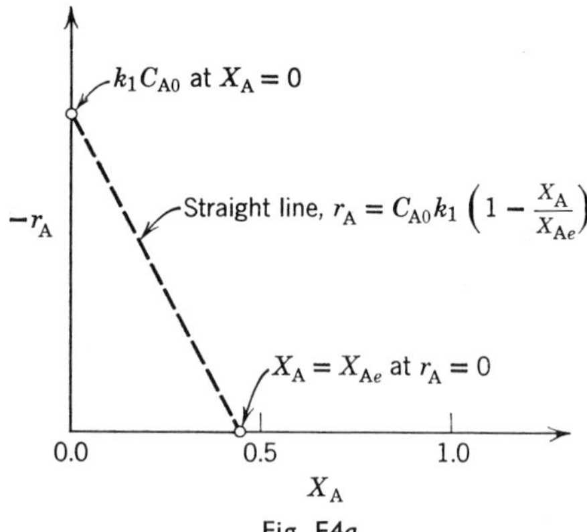

Fig. E4*a*

The rate of reaction is

$$-r_A = k_1 C_{A0}\left(1 - \frac{X_A}{X_{Ae}}\right)$$

Now at

$$X_A = 0, \qquad -r_A = k_1 C_{A0} = k_1 \tag{i}$$

and at

$$X_A = X_{Ae}, \qquad -r_A = 0 \tag{ii}$$

These values locate the end points for the $-r_A$ versus X_A curve as shown in Fig. E4*a*. These values are given at various temperatures in Table E2 and are plotted in Fig. E4*b*. From this figure the optimum temperature and corresponding rate are found, as shown by the heavy line of Fig. E4*b*. From this the required space time is then found by graphical integration of the design equation

$$\tau = \int_0^{0.76} \frac{dX_A}{(-r_A)_{\text{optimum}}}$$

From Fig. E4*c* the value of the integral is found to be

$$\tau = 7.71 \text{ min}$$

Thus the ratio of production rates is

$$\frac{\tau_{\text{optimum}}}{\tau_{\text{isothermal}}} = \frac{(VC_{A0}/F_{A0})_{\text{optimum}}}{(VC_{A0}/F_{A0})_{\text{isothermal}}} = \frac{F_{A0,\text{isothermal}}}{F_{A0,\text{optimum}}} = \frac{7.71}{10}$$

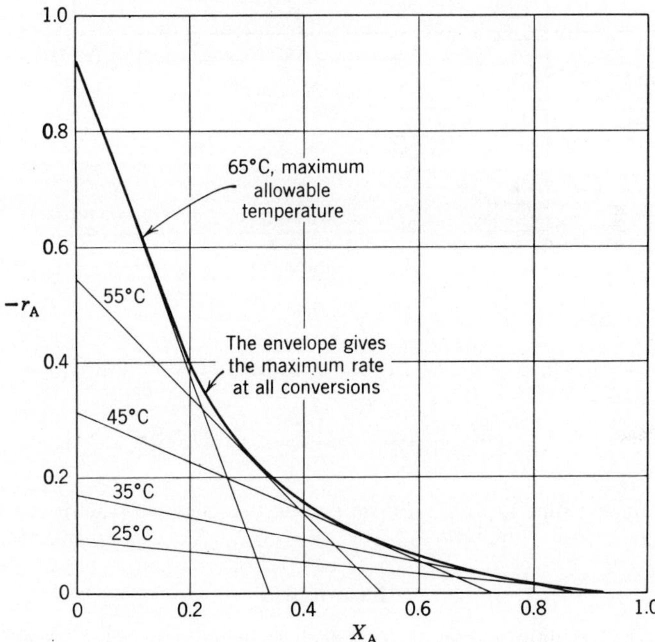

Fig. E4*b*

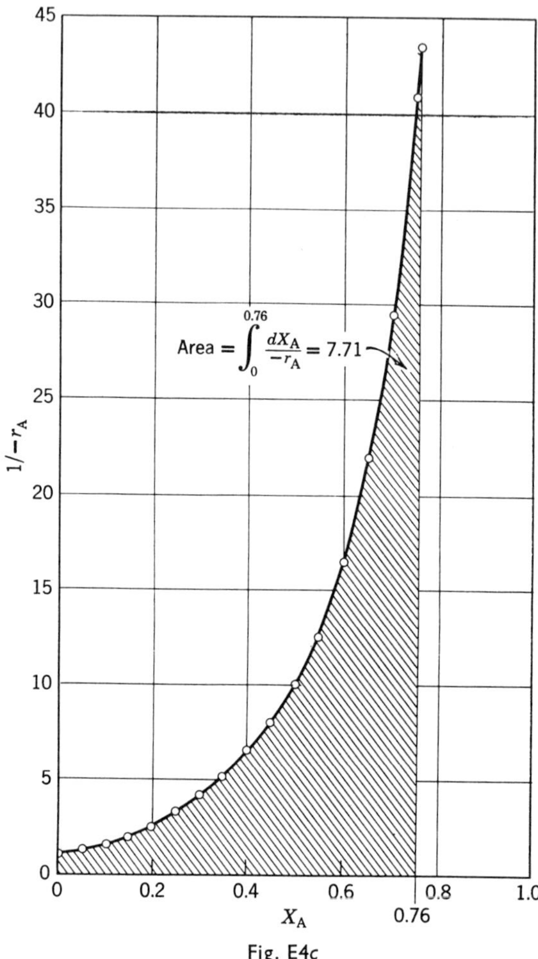

Fig. E4c

and the increase in production rate over isothermal operation is

$$\frac{10 - 7.71}{7.71} = 0.297, \qquad \text{or } 29.7\%$$

The optimum temperature progression along the length of reactor can be found from Fig. E4*c* with Fig. E4*b*.

Example 5

Using the optimum temperature in each of two equal-sized backmix reactors for the reaction of the previous examples, $C_{A0} = 1$ mole/liter, (*a*) calculate the space time required to achieve 60% conversion; (*b*) show how much production can be increased over the optimum isothermal operating conditions of a single reactor (see Example 3); and (*c*) give the temperature and conversion that should be maintained in each reactor.

Solution. (*a*) By trial and error, using the graphical procedure of Fig. 6.9, we find from Fig. E5 that the slope of the curve for the two reactors is

$$\frac{-(r_A)_{out}}{X_{A,out} - X_{A,in}} = \frac{0.134}{0.4} = \frac{0.335 \text{ gm mole}}{(\text{liter})(\text{min})} \tag{i}$$

But from the backmix reactor design equation for each reactor

$$\tau = \frac{C_{A0}(X_{A,out} - X_{A,in})}{(-r_A)_{out}} \tag{ii}$$

Combining Eqs. i and ii, noting that $C_{A0} = 1$ mole/liter, we have for each reactor

$$\tau = 3 \text{ min}$$

(*b*) In terms of total holding time for the two-reactor system

$$\frac{\tau_{j=1}}{\tau_{j=2}} = \frac{(C_{A0}V/F_{A0})_{j=1}}{(C_{A0}V/F_{A0})_{j=2}} = \frac{F_{A0,j=2}}{F_{A0,j=1}} = \frac{10}{6}$$

Hence the increase in production over operations in one backmix reactor is

$$\frac{10 - 6}{6} = 0.667 \qquad \text{or } 66.7\%$$

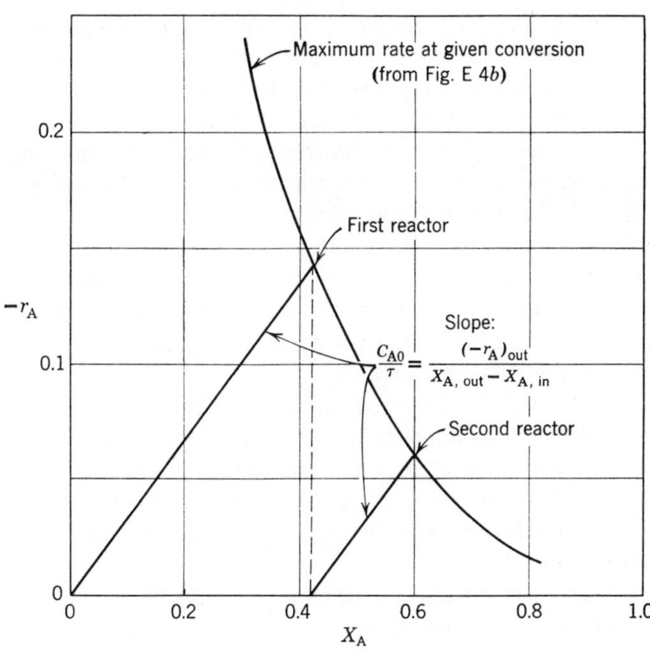

Fig. E5

(*c*) From Fig. E5 conversions within the two reactors are found. Figure E4*b* then gives the corresponding temperatures. Thus,

$$\text{in the first reactor} \quad X_A = 0.42, \quad T = 49°\text{C}$$

and

$$\text{in the second reactor} \quad X_A = 0.60, \quad T = 42°\text{C}$$

Heat effects, qualitative discussion

Transfer of heat with surroundings is often necessary to bring reactants to the desired temperature and to maintain the desired temperature profile within the reactor. Now when the heat absorbed or released by reaction can change significantly the temperature of the reacting fluids, this heat should be considered in design since it can often serve to reduce or even eliminate the external heat requirement.

Let us now examine the interplay between the heat of reaction and the external heat load in reactors of different types, both for endothermic and exothermic reactions.

Endothermic reactions. For endothermic reactions temperature drops as reaction proceeds. Thus in adiabatic operations a hot reactant stream enters and a cool product stream leaves the reactor. Now for a favorable equilibrium shift and for high rate (see Fig. 5), the temperature should be kept high. If it drops so low that the desired conversion cannot be achieved, heat should be added to the reacting mixture. In these situations the rate of heat transfer is often the rate-controlling factor, and design becomes primarily a heat transfer problem.

Figure 8 illustrates the characteristics of a number of arrangements of reactors and heat exchangers. Arrangements such as these are frequently encountered in heterogeneous operations.

Exothermic reactions. As exothermic reactions proceed, heat is liberated and the temperature of the reacting mixture rises. When the increase in rate resulting from the rise in temperature more than compensates for the drop in rate caused by a decrease in reactant concentration, backmix flow of fluids is desirable.

When enough heat is liberated during reaction to raise the cold reactants to a high enough temperature to make the reaction self-sustaining, an external supply of heat becomes unnecessary and the reaction is appropriately called autothermal. Considering the heat liberated as a "product" of the reaction, the analogy with autocatalytic reactions of Chapter 6 is evident.

Since too high a temperature may cause an undesirable shift in equilibrium conversion, it may be advantageous to use a tubular reactor with appropriate heat exchange between various parts of the reactor so as to

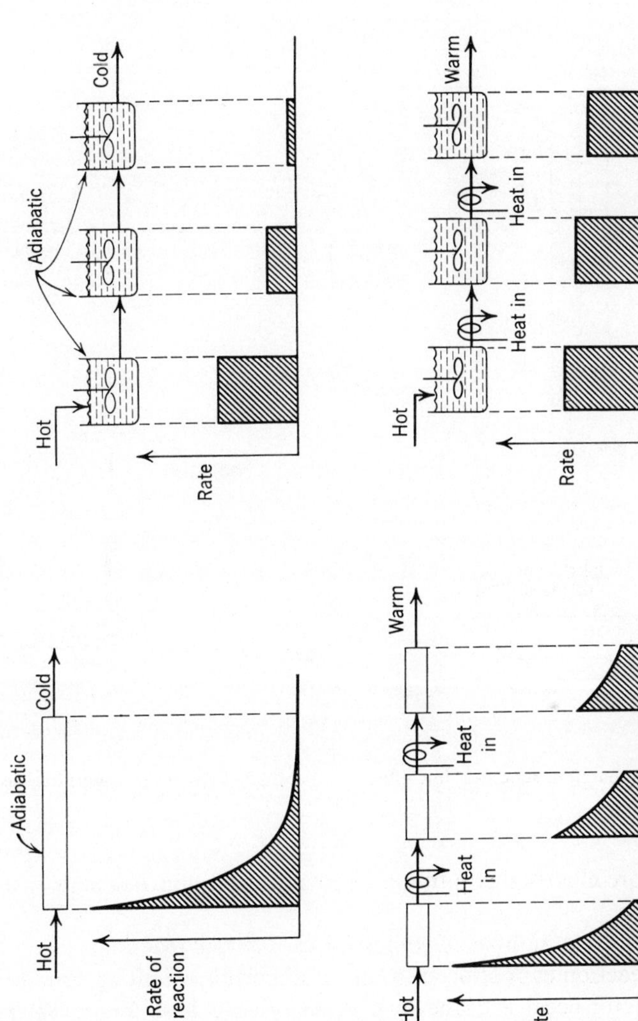

Fig. 8. Rate characteristics of various reactor and heat exchanger combinations used for endothermic reactions.

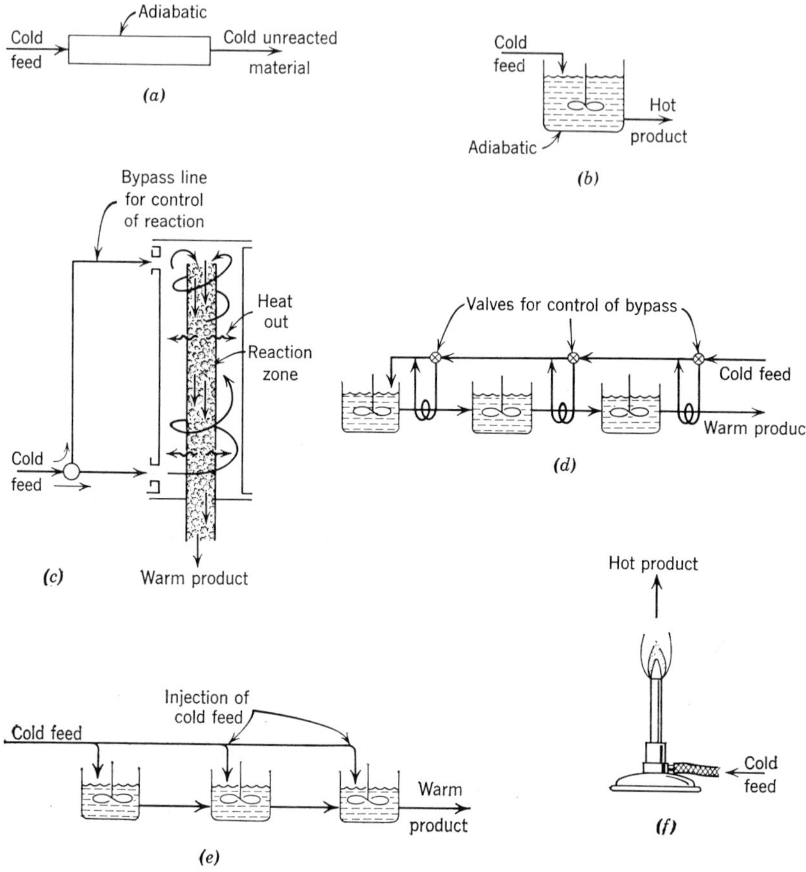

Fig. 9. Various reaction schemes for effecting exothermic reactions without use of external heat.

approach more closely the optimum temperature profile calculated earlier in the chapter.

Figure 9 shows a number of setups for exothermic reactions. Figure 9*a* shows that reaction cannot occur to any appreciable extent in an adiabatic plug flow reactor because of the very nature of plug flow. Figure 9*b* shows that once ignited a backmix reactor can sustain an autothermal reaction.

Many schemes can be used to aid in the interchange of heat between hot and cold fluid. These are particularly applicable for reversible reactions because with proper design the temperature progressions in such reactors can be made to approach reasonably closely the optimum desired temperature profiles. Figures 9*c* and *d* show two such schemes. Figure 9*c* uses a plug flow reactor and is particularly useful in heterogeneous systems with reaction in packed catalyst beds. Figure 9*d* uses a series of interconnected backmix reactors and is the most applicable to liquid-phase reactions. Figure 9*e* shows how the injection of cold feed at several locations can also be used to control the termperature progression in the reactor system. The most common example of a gas-phase autothermal reaction is the gas flame of Fig. 9*f*. Here convection and molecular conduction serve to heat the reactant gases to their ignition temperature. The combustions of solid and liquid fuels are other examples of autothermal reactions.

Heat effects, quantitative treatment

Since the temperature of the reacting fluids changes as a result of heat effects, the solution of design problems requires the simultaneous consideration of both the heat and material balance expressions, Eqs. 4.1 and 4.2, rather than the former expression alone, which was the starting point of our analyses of the isothermal operations of Chapters 5 and 6.

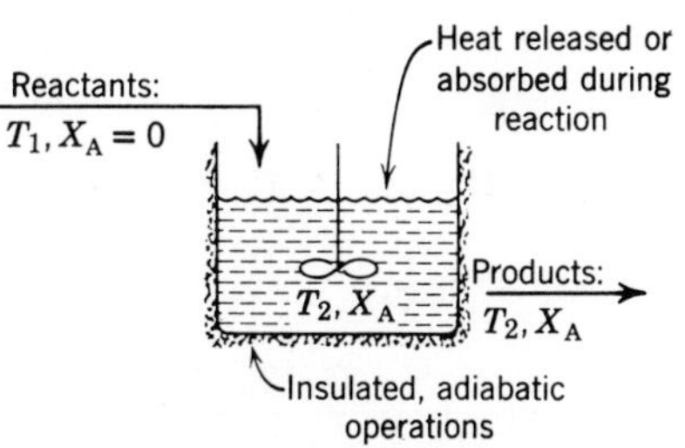

Fig. 10. Adiabatic operation of a backmix reactor. The reaction is accompanied by large enough heat effects to cause temperature changes in the reacting fluid.

Irreversible reactions, adiabatic operation in backmix reactors. Let us start with an irreversible reaction occurring adiabatically in a backmix reactor as shown in Fig. 10. This treatment will then be extended to situations involving both reversible reactions and heat interchange with surroundings.

In Chapters 5 and 6 one component, usually the limiting reactant, was selected as the basis for all material balance calculations. The same procedure is followed here, with limiting reactant A taken as the basis. Let

Subscripts 1, 2 refer to temperatures of entering and leaving streams

$\mathbf{C}_p', \mathbf{C}_p''$ = mean specific heat of unreacted feed stream and of completely converted product stream per mole of entering reactant A

$\mathbf{H}', \mathbf{H}''$ = enthalpy of unreacted feed stream and of completely converted product stream per mole of entering reactant A.

$\Delta\mathbf{H}_r$ = heat of reaction per mole of entering reactant A.

With T_1 as the reference temperature on which enthalpies and heats of reaction are based we have at conversion X_A

Enthalpy of entering feed:

$$\mathbf{H}_1' = \mathbf{C}_p'(T_1 - T_1) = 0$$

Enthalpy of leaving stream:

$$\mathbf{H}_2''X_A + \mathbf{H}_2'(1 - X_A) = \mathbf{C}_p''(T_2 - T_1)X_A + \mathbf{C}_p'(T_2 - T_1)(1 - X_A) \text{ cal/gm mole A}$$

Energy absorbed by reaction:

$$\Delta\mathbf{H}_{r1}X_A \text{ cal/gm mole A}$$

Replacing these quantities in the energy balance,

$$\text{Input} = \text{Output} + \text{Accumulation} + \text{Disappearance by reaction} \tag{4.2}$$

we obtain at steady state

$$0 = [\mathbf{C}_p''(T_2 - T_1)X_A + \mathbf{C}_p'(T_2 - T_1)(1 - X_A)] + 0 + \Delta\mathbf{H}_{r1}X_A \tag{20}$$

By rearranging,

$$X_A = \frac{\mathbf{C}_p'(T_2 - T_1)}{-\Delta\mathbf{H}_{r1} - (\mathbf{C}_p'' - \mathbf{C}_p')(T_2 - T_1)} = \frac{\mathbf{C}_p'\,\Delta T}{-\Delta\mathbf{H}_{r1} - (\mathbf{C}_p'' - \mathbf{C}_p')\,\Delta T} \tag{21}$$

or with Eq. 18

$$X_A = \frac{\mathbf{C}_p'\,\Delta T}{-\Delta\mathbf{H}_{r2}} \tag{22}$$

which for complete conversion becomes

$$-\Delta\mathbf{H}_{r2} = \mathbf{C}_p'\Delta T, \qquad \text{for } X_A = 1 \tag{23}$$

The last form of the equation simply states that the heat released by reaction just balances the heat necessary to raise the reactants from T_1 to T_2.

The relation between temperature and conversion as given by the energy balances of Eqs. 21 or 22 is shown in Fig. 11. The resulting lines are straight for all practical purposes since the variable term in the denominator of these equations is relatively small. When $\mathbf{C}_p'' - \mathbf{C}_p' = 0$, the heat of reaction is independent of temperature and Eqs. 21 and 22 reduce to

$$X_A = \frac{\mathbf{C}_p\,\Delta T}{-\Delta\mathbf{H}_r} \tag{24}$$

which is a straight line in Fig. 11.

This figure shows the shape of the energy balance curves for both endothermic and exothermic reactions. With increased inerts $\mathbf{C}_p$ rises, and these curves become more closely vertical. A vertical line indicates that temperature is unchanged as reaction proceeds. This then is the special case of isothermal reactions treated in Chapters 5–7.

Figure 11 also represents the energy balance expression for adiabatic operations in plug flow reactors.

Now the material balance determines the conversion obtained in a reactor of given size operated at a fixed temperature and is represented graphically by the S-shaped curve on the X_A versus T plot of Fig. 3.

The simultaneous solution of the energy and material balances gives the permissible operating states of the reactor. These conditions are the points of intersection of the material and energy balance curves. As shown in Fig. 12, three types of situations may be encountered. In Fig. 12*a* the heat liberated by reaction is insufficient to raise the temperature to a high enough level for the reaction to be self-sustaining. Hence conversion is negligible. In Fig. 12*b* practically complete conversion is obtained; actually more heat is available than is required. Figure 12*c* indicates three solutions to the material and energy equations, points M', M'', and M'''. However, point M'' is an unstable state because with a small rise in temperature the heat produced (with the rapidly rising material balance curve) is much greater than the heat consumed by the reacting mixture (energy balance curve). The excess heat produced will make the temperature rise until point M''' is reached. By similar reasoning, if the temperature drops slightly below M'',

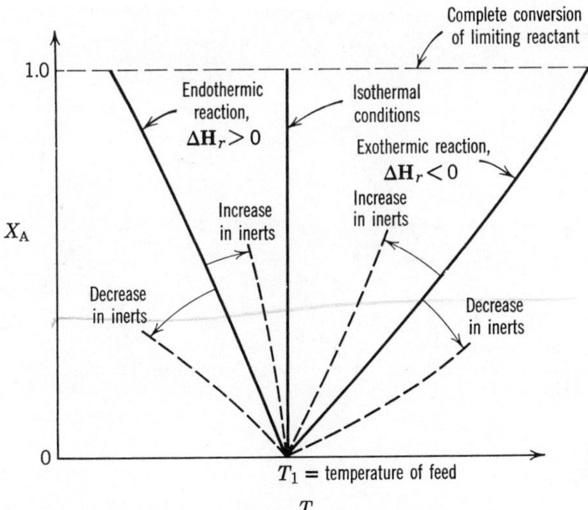

Fig. 11. Graphic representation of energy balance equation for adiabatic operation.

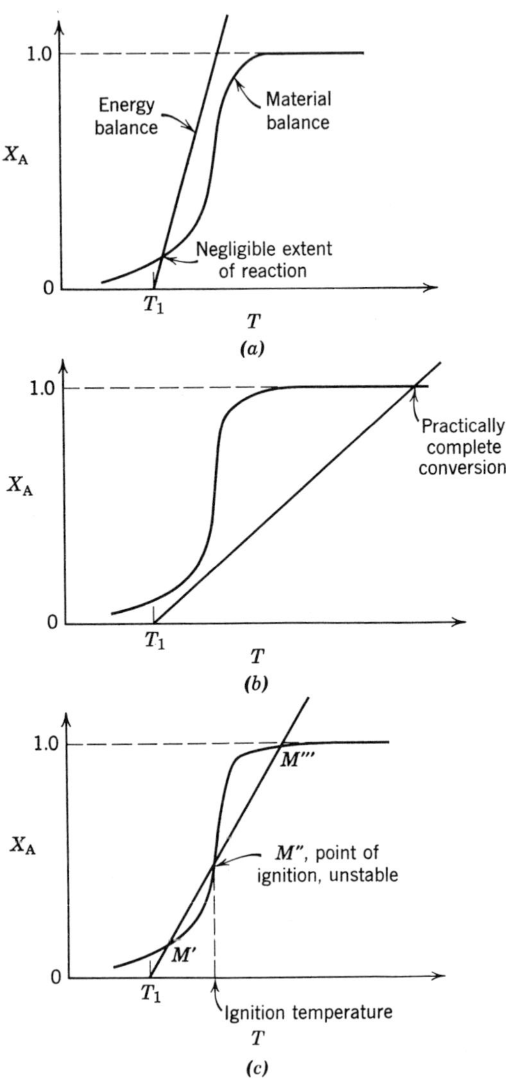

Fig. 12. Three types of solution to the energy and material balances for exothermic irreversible reactions.

it will continue to drop until point M' is reached. Thus we may look upon point M'' as the ignition point. If the mixture can be raised above this temperature, the reaction will be self-sustaining. Note the similarity with the autocatalytic situation illustrated in Fig. 6.10. The study of reactor dynamics, stability, and proper start-up procedures is important for all auto-induced reactions such as these.

Though it is a much more complex situation, a gas flame illustrates very well the three solutions of Fig. 12*c*, the unreacted state, the reacted state, and the ignition point.

An important property of autothermal irreversible reactions is that the reacted state will usually lie in the region of practically complete conversion of limiting component.

Reversible reactions, adiabatic operations in backmix reactors. The only difference from irreversible reactions is that we here use the appropriate material balance curve as shown in Fig. 4 or 5 and find its intersection with the energy balance curve. With reversible exothermic reactions Fig. 13 shows that an optimum point of intersection exists. Above or below this temperature conversion drops; thus good control of heat input is essential to satisfactory operation of the reactor.

Optimum reactor type or reactor combination for adiabatic operations. If a given feed is reacted under adiabatic conditions, every extent of conversion has associated with it a particular temperature of fluid given by Eq. 22 and therefore a definite value of reaction rate. The forms of the rate-conversion relationship for these varying temperature conditions are shown in Figs. 14 and 15.

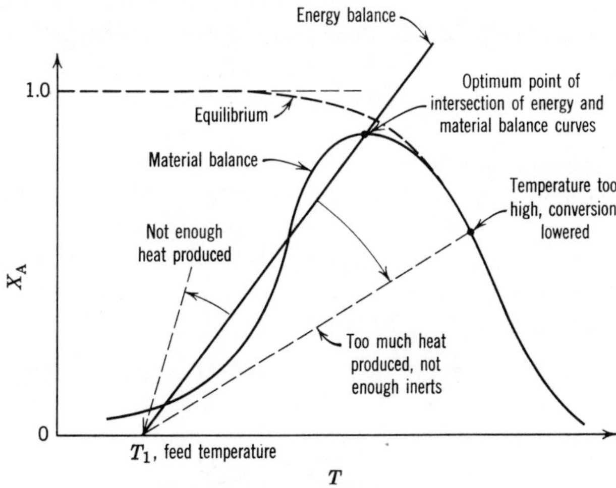

Fig. 13. Solution of energy and material balances for reversible exothermic reactions.

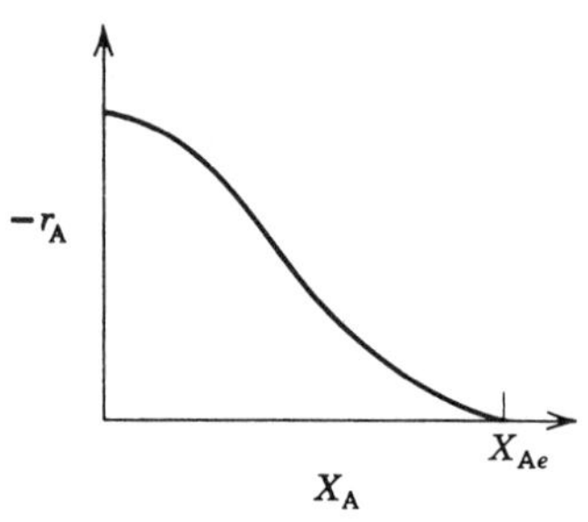

Fig. 14. Where the rate decreases progressively with conversion, plug flow is the most efficient in converting material.

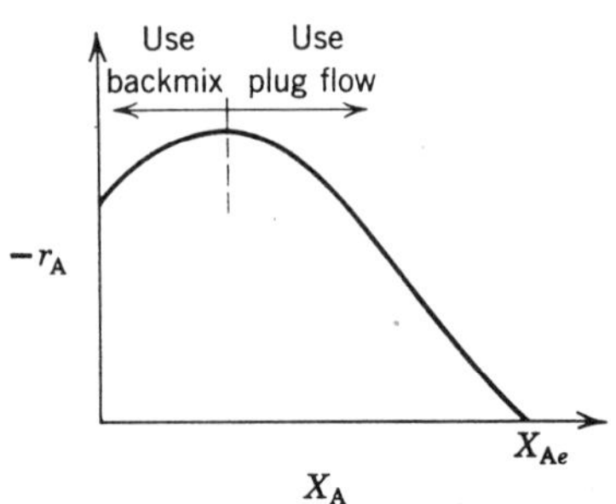

Fig. 15. Where the rate-conversion curve exhibits a maximum, backmix followed by plug flow is the most efficient in converting material.

Figure 14 shows a progressive decrease in rate with conversion which is representative of all endothermic reactions (temperature drops with conversion) and also the particular exothermic reactions in which, because of relatively minor heat release, the rise in rate resulting from the rise in temperature is not sufficient to compensate for the drop in rate resulting from the lowered reactant concentration. For reactions of this type plug flow is always advantageous.

Figure 15 illustrates reactions in which the rate rises to a maximum and then falls to zero. This progressive behavior occurs when the rise in rate resulting from the rise in temperature more than offsets the drop in rate resulting from the consumption of reactants and is representative of reversible or irreversible exothermic reactions with sufficiently large heat release. For reactions of this type the optimum setup is a backmix unit followed by a plug flow unit. The method of treatment to find the optimum size of each unit is analogous to the treatment of autocatalytic reactions in Chapter 6. Aris (1962) considers this question of optimization in detail.

Nonadiabatic operations. To obtain the desired intersection of the material and energy balance curves at favorable high conversions, it may be necessary deliberately to introduce or remove heat from the reactor as shown in Fig. 16. If $\mathbf{Q}$ equals total heat added to reactor per mole of entering reactant A and if we let this heat also include the heat losses to surroundings, Eq. 20 becomes

$$\mathbf{Q} = \mathbf{C}_p''(T_2 - T_1)X_A + \mathbf{C}_p'(T_2 - T_1)(1 - X_A) + \Delta\mathbf{H}_{r1}X_A$$

which on rearrangement gives

$$X_A = \frac{\mathbf{C}_p'\,\Delta T - \mathbf{Q}}{-\Delta\mathbf{H}_{r1} - (\mathbf{C}_p'' - \mathbf{C}_p')\,\Delta T} \tag{25}$$

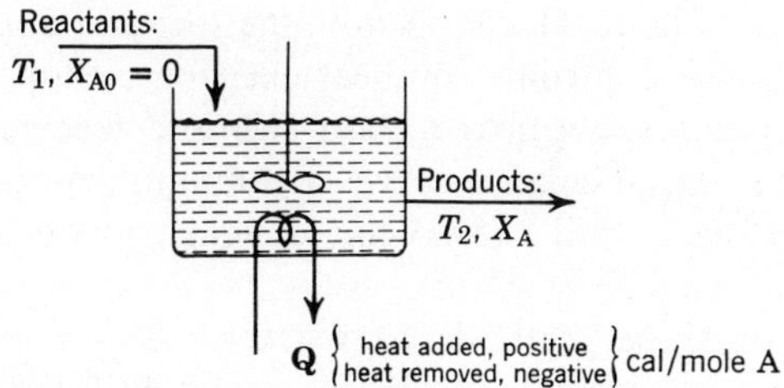

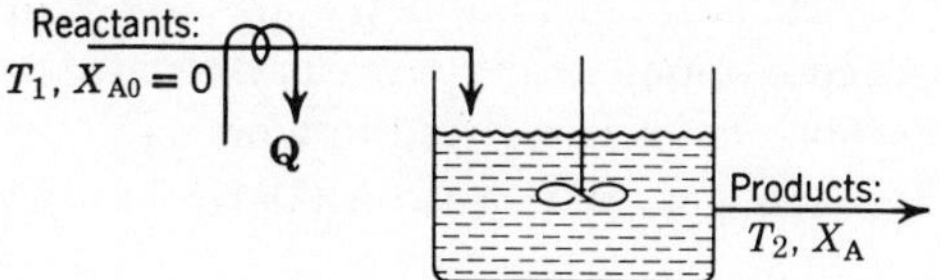

Fig. 16. Operation of a backmix reactor with addition or removal of heat.

and for $\mathbf{C}_p'' = \mathbf{C}_p'$, which is a reasonable approximation,

$$X_A = \frac{\mathbf{C}_p \Delta T - \mathbf{Q}}{-\Delta \mathbf{H}_r} \tag{26}$$

Constant addition or removal of heat independent of conversion results in a horizontal translation in energy balance line. With heat input proportional to $\Delta T = T_2 - T_1$ a rotation in energy balance line is obtained. These changes are shown in Fig. 17. Other modes of heat addition or removal yield corresponding shifts in the energy balance line.

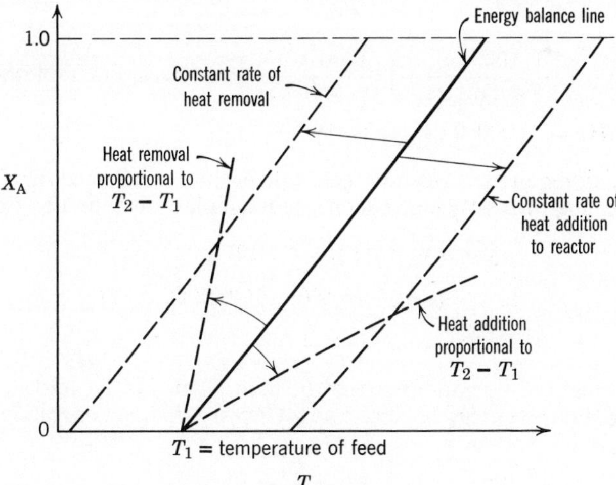

Fig. 17. Graphic representation of energy balance equation showing the shift in adiabatic line as a result of heat exchange with surroundings.

Comments. Figure 11 shows how the location and slope of energy balance line can be controlled by heat exchange, addition of inerts, etc. Figures 3, 4, and 5 show how reactor size and feed rate determine the location of the material balance curve. Examining the many combinations of variables available will show what designs can do a given job satisfactorily.

Extensions of these methods to reactor systems other than simple backmix have been developed by van Heerden (1953, 1958). Exploring the design of nonisothermal plug flow systems with various types and magnitudes of heat exchange invariably requires use of numerical methods for which high-speed computers are particularly suited. These will not be considered here. The reader is referred to Corrigan (1956), Smith (1955), Walas (1959), and Hougen and Watson (1947) for the development of these methods.

Example 6

For the reaction of the previous examples determine the hourly heat load required to operate, at their optimum conditions, (*a*) a single backmix reactor (*b*) two equal-sized backmix reactors in series processing 1000 gm moles A/hr. The feed enters at the following conditions:

$$C_{A0} = 2.5 \text{ gm moles A/liter}$$
$$T = 15^\circ\text{C}$$

In both cases the required conversion is $X_A = 0.60$.

Solution. (*a*) Based on a mole of entering limiting reactant A, we have from the data of Example 1

$$\mathbf{C}_p = \left(\frac{1000 \text{ cc}}{2.5 \text{ gm moles A}}\right)\left(\frac{1000 \text{ cal/}^\circ\text{C}}{1000 \text{ cc}}\right) = 400 \text{ cal/(gm mole A)(}^\circ\text{C)}$$
$$\Delta\mathbf{H}_r = -18{,}000 \text{ cal/gm mole A}$$

The heat load required to operate the single backmix reactor at 42°C, the optimum temperature for 60% conversion (see Example 3), is found by Eq. 26 to be

$$\begin{aligned}\mathbf{Q} &= (X_A)(\Delta\mathbf{H}_r) + \mathbf{C}_p\,\Delta T \\ &= (0.6)(-18{,}000) + (400)(42 - 15) \\ &= 0 \text{ cal/gm mole A}\end{aligned}$$

Therefore adiabatic operations should be used. This can be verified by noting that in Fig. E6 the energy balance line *ACD* for adiabatic operation, given by

$$X_A = \frac{\mathbf{C}_p\,\Delta T}{-\Delta\mathbf{H}_r} \tag{24}$$

intersects the material balance line at exactly the optimum point of operations.

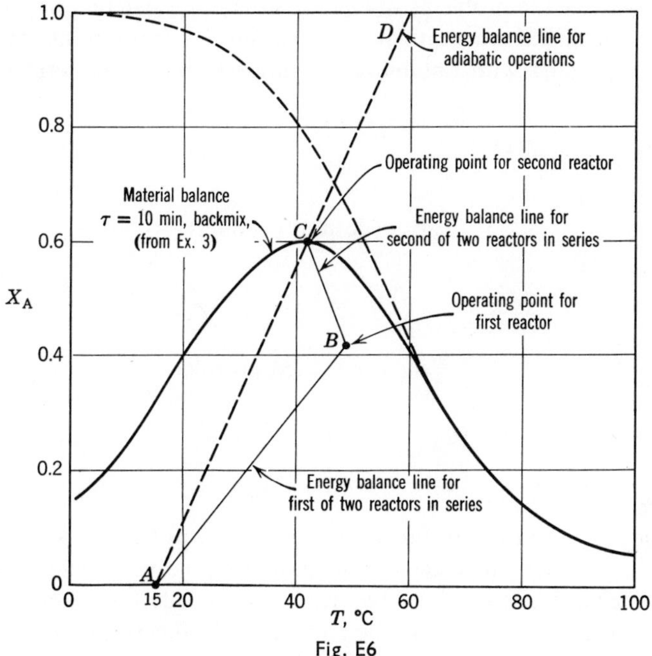

Fig. E6

(*b*) The heat load to the first of the two reactors should be such that the operating temperature is 49°C (see Example 5). Thus Eq. 26 gives

$$\begin{aligned}\mathbf{Q} &= X_A\,\Delta\mathbf{H}_r + \mathbf{C}_p\,\Delta T\\ &= (0.42)(-18{,}000) + (400)(49 - 15)\\ &= 6040 \text{ cal/gm mole A}\end{aligned}$$

or

$$\begin{aligned}Q &= (6040 \text{ cal/gm mole A})(1000 \text{ gm moles A/hr})\\ &\approx 6 \times 10^6 \text{ cal/hr}, \qquad \text{added to the first reactor}\end{aligned}$$

The heat load to the second reactor should be such that its temperature is 42°C. Thus from Eq. 26

$$\begin{aligned}\mathbf{Q} &= (X_{A,\text{out}} - X_{A,\text{in}})\,\Delta\mathbf{H}_r + \mathbf{C}_p(T_{\text{out}} - T_{\text{in}})\\ &= (0.60 - 0.42)(-18{,}000) + (400)(42 - 49)\\ &= -6040 \text{ cal/gm mole A}\end{aligned}$$

or $$Q \approx -6 \times 10^6 \text{ cal/hr}, \qquad \text{removed from second reactor}$$

Lines *AB* and *BC* of the figure show these quantities graphically.

MULTIPLE REACTIONS

As pointed out in the introduction to Chapter 7, in multiple reactions both reactor size and product distribution are influenced by the processing conditions. Since the problems of reactor size are no different in principle than those for single reactions and are usually less important than the problems connected with obtaining the desired product material, let us consider the latter.

Reactions in parallel

If the reactions

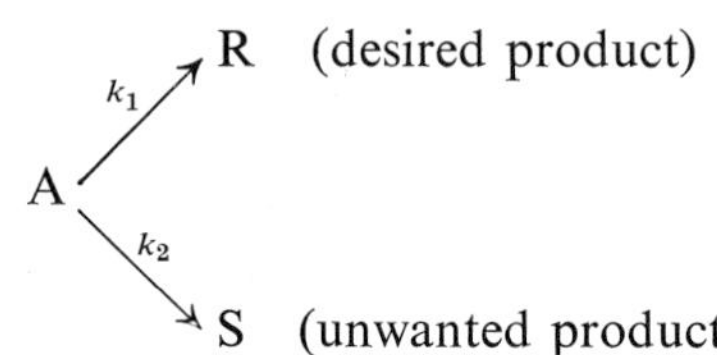

with kinetics

$$-r_1 = k_1 f_1(C), \qquad \text{with} \qquad k_1 = k_{01} e^{-E_1/RT}$$

$$-r_2 = k_2 f_2(C), \qquad \text{with} \qquad k_2 = k_{02} e^{-E_2/RT}$$

have different concentration functions, or $f_1 \neq f_2$, using appropriate high or low concentrations of reactants in the most suitable reactor type will maximize the yield of desired product R. These are questions considered in Chapter 7. If on the other hand the concentration functions are the same, the ratio of R to S formed is influenced neither by reactor type nor by reactant concentration, and the only way to change the product ratio is to vary the ratio of k values, or rate constants. This is done best by using a selective catalyst, however, if one cannot be found, the only other means available is to change the temperature of operations. In any case, whether the concentration functions are alike or not, the optimum temperature of operations should be used.

Let us examine this temperature dependency. For identical or unchanging concentration functions we have

$$\frac{dC_R}{dC_S} = \frac{k_{01} e^{-E_1/RT} f_1(C)}{k_{02} e^{\ E_2/RT} f_2(C)} = (\text{constant}) e^{(E_2 - E_1)/RT}$$

Since this function changes exponentially with a corresponding change in temperature, we may conclude that the ratio of R to S produced and k_1/k_2 both rise with an increase in temperature if the activation energy of the desired reaction is greater than that of the unwanted reaction. Thus

$$\text{if} \quad E_1 > E_2, \qquad \text{use a high } T$$

$$\text{if} \quad E_1 < E_2, \qquad \text{use a low } T$$

to increase production of R.

Reactions in series

Consider the elementary reactions

$$A \xrightarrow{k_1} R \xrightarrow{k_2} S$$

or

$$\left.\begin{aligned} A + B &\xrightarrow{k_1} R \\ R + B &\xrightarrow{k_2} S \end{aligned}\right\}$$

with an Arrhenius temperature dependency for the rate constants. As shown in Chapter 7, the maximum fractional yield of desired product R obtainable from any given type of reactor is determined by k_1/k_2. The variation of this ratio with temperature is given by

$$\frac{k_1}{k_2} = \frac{k_{01}e^{-E_1/RT}}{k_{02}e^{-E_2/RT}} = (\text{constant})e^{(E_2 - E_1)/RT}$$

Again if $E_1 > E_2$ a rise in temperature will increase k_1/k_2. Since large k_1/k_2 favors the production of intermediate R, we may conclude

$$\begin{aligned} &\text{if} \quad E_1 > E_2, \qquad \text{use a high } T \\ &\text{if} \quad E_1 < E_2, \qquad \text{use a low } T \end{aligned}$$

to increase production of R.

If S is the desired product, a high temperature should be used since this will cause both k_1 and k_2 to increase.

In general, the economics of the situation will determine the optimum temperature of operations. For example, although a lowering in temperature will favor the formation of R with respect to the formation of S (when $E_1 < E_2$), it has the opposite effect of slowing down the rates of both these reactions. Thus the optimum temperature of operations is found by balancing the increase in reactor cost for lower temperature operations with rising profits from increase in yield of product.

Extensions

For more complicated stoichiometry, temperature progressions may give optimum product yield. Consider for example the reaction

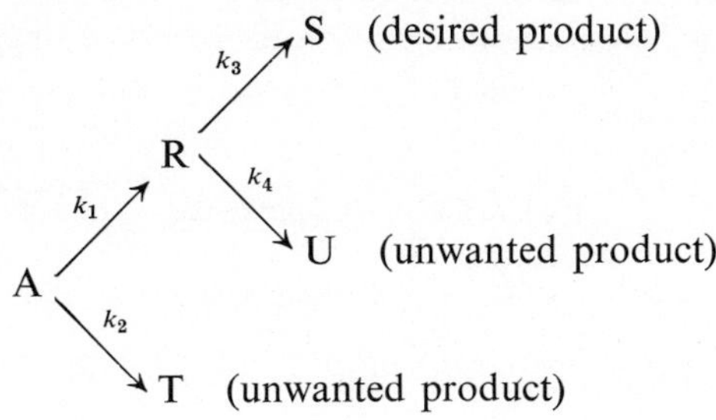

If $E_1 > E_2$ and $E_3 > E_4$, high temperatures should be used throughout. If $E_1 < E_2$ and $E_3 < E_4$, low temperatures should be used throughout. If, however, $E_1 > E_2$ but $E_3 < E_4$, high temperatures should be used for the decomposition of A but low temperatures should be used for the decomposition of R. Since A is present at the start in high concentrations whereas R reaches a maximum at later stages of reaction, it seems evident that the temperature should be high in the early stages of conversion and drop as reaction proceeds. Conversely, if $E_1 < E_2$ but $E_3 > E_4$, the temperature should start low, rising as reaction proceeds.

Denbigh (1958) treats this reaction in two backmix reactors, showing with an illustrative example how fractional yield can be more than doubled by using different temperatures in the two reactors.

One interesting point to be mentioned is that if $k_1 + k_2 \gg k_3 + k_4$, for all practical purposes A reacts away completely before R has a chance to decompose. Thus with proper size of backmix reactors the first reaction may be made to occur almost exclusively in the first of two reactors and the second primarily in the second reactor. The difference in temperature of the two tanks will be very great and will have a pronounced effect in improving yield. If $k_1 + k_2$ is not very much greater than $k_3 + k_4$, the reaction cannot be clearly separated among reactors, the difference in temperature between tanks will not be great, and the improvement in yield will not be very pronounced over isothermal operations.

Calculation of optimum temperature progression for plug flow or batch operations is difficult, though the general pattern of falling or rising temperatures can usually be found without too much difficulty from the activation energies of the participating reactions. Bilous and Amundson (1956) develop the necessary mathematics to treat this type of problem and illustrate this with the reaction

$$A \rightarrow R \rightarrow S$$

with any combination of first- and second-order kinetics.

Where the kinetics of the various participating reactions is not known, trial and error with different temperature progressions may result in substantial increase in yield of desired product.

Aris (1961) treats in detail optimization problems of single and multiple reactions and gives a survey of the pertinent literature.

RELATED READINGS

R. Aris, *The Optimal Design of Chemical Reactors*, Academic Press, New York, 1961.
P. H. Calderbank, *Chem. Eng. Progr.*, **49**, 585 (1953).
K. G. Denbigh, *Chem. Eng. Sci.*, **8**, 125 (1958).

K. Konoki, *Chem. Eng.* (*Japan*), **21,** 408, 780 (1957); **24,** 569 (1960); **25,** 31 (1961); **26,** 563 (1962).
H. Kubota, T. Akehata, and M. Shindo, *Chem. Eng.* (*Japan*), **23,** 506 (1959).
———, S. Namkoong, T. Akehata, and M. Shindo, *Can. J. Chem. Eng.*, **39,** 64 (1961).
C. van Heerden, *Ind. Eng. Chem.*, **45,** 1242 (1953).
———, *Chem. Eng. Sci.,* **8,** 133 (1958).

REFERENCES

R. Aris, *Can. J. of Chem. Eng.*, **40,** 87 (1962).
R. Aris, *The Optimal Design of Chemical Reactors*, Academic Press, New York, 1961, Ch. 1.
O. Bilous and N. R. Amundson, *Chem. Eng. Sci.*, **5,** 81 (1956).
T. E. Corrigan, *Chem. Eng.*, **63,** 221 (Aug. 1956); **63,** 211 (Sept. 1956).
K. G. Denbigh, *Chem. Eng. Sci.*, **8,** 125 (1958).
O. A. Hougen and K. M. Watson, *Chemical Process Principles*, Part III, John Wiley and Sons, New York, 1947.
J. M. Smith, *Chemical Engineering Kinetics*, McGraw-Hill, New York, 1956.
C. van Heerden, *Ind. Eng. Chem.*, **45,** 1242 (1953).
———, *Chem. Eng. Sci.,* **8,** 133 (1958).
S. Walas, *Reaction Kinetics for Chemical Engineers*, McGraw-Hill, New York, 1959.

PROBLEMS

1. The gases 20 cc A, 40 cc B, and 20 cc C measured at standard conditions (32°F, 1 atm) are forced into a 20-cc reaction vessel containing air at standard conditions. A, B, and C react according to the following stoichiometric equation

$$\tfrac{1}{2}\text{A} + \tfrac{3}{2}\text{B} \rightleftharpoons \text{C}$$

At 32°F equilibrium is attained when the pressure in the reaction vessel is 4 atm. Find the standard free-energy change ΔF° at 200 atm and 32°F for the reaction

$$2\text{C} \rightleftharpoons \text{A} + 3\text{B}$$

Assume that the perfect gas law holds throughout.

2. At 1000°K and 1-atm pressure substance A is 2 mole % dissociated according to the gas-phase reaction 2A $\rightleftharpoons$ 2B + C.

(*a*) Calculate the mole % dissociated at 200°K and 1 atm.

(*b*) Calculate the mole % dissociated at 200°K and 0.1 atm.

Data: Average C_p of A = 12 cal/(gm mole)(°C)
Average C_p of B = 9 cal/(gm mole)(°C)
Average C_p of C = 6 cal/(gm mole)(°C)

At 25°C and 1 atm 2000 cal are released when 1 mole A is formed from the reactants B and C.

3. Given the gas-phase reaction A $\rightleftharpoons$ B + C. Start with pure A. Suppose that 50% of the original A is dissociated at 1000°K and 10 atm as well as at 500°K and 0.1 atm.

(*a*) Calculate the per cent dissociation at 250°K and 1 atm.
(*b*) Calculate the per cent dissociation at 250°K and 0.01 atm.
Data: Average C_p of A = 12 cal/(gm mole)(°C)
Average C_p of B = 7 cal/(gm mole)(°C)
Average C_p of C = 5 cal/(gm mole)(°C)

4. Given the gas-phase reaction 2A ⇌ B + C. Start with 1 mole A and 2 moles B in 5 moles inert gas. Suppose that at 1000°K and 10 atm 66.7% of original A is dissociated and at 500°K and 0.1 atm 50% of original A is dissociated.
(*a*) Calculate the per cent dissociation at 250°K and 1 atm.
(*b*) Calculate the per cent dissociation at 250°K and 0.01 atm.
(*c*) Find $\Delta F°$ for the reaction A ⇌ $\frac{1}{2}$B + $\frac{1}{2}$C at 250°K and 1 atm.
(*d*) Find $\Delta F°$ for the reaction 2A ⇌ B + C at 250°K and 0.01 atm.
(*e*) Find $\Delta H_{r,298}$ for the reaction 2A ⇌ B + C.
Data: Average C_p of A = 7 cal/(gm mole)(°C)
Average C_p of B = 9 cal/(gm mole)(°C)
Average C_p of C = 5 cal/(gm mole)(°C)

5. At 1000°K and 1-atm pressure substance A is 2 mole % dissociated according to the following reaction

$$2A \rightleftharpoons 2B + C$$

(*a*) Calculate the mole % dissociated at 200°K and 1 atm.
(*b*) Calculate the mole % dissociated at 200°K and 0.1 atm.
Data: Average C_p of A = 8 cal/(gm mole)(°C)
Average C_p of B = 8 cal/(gm mole)(°C)
Average C_p of C = 8 cal/(gm mole)(°C)
At 25°C and 1 atm 2000 cal are released when 1 mole A is formed from the reactants B and C.

6. Given the following gas-phase reaction

$$A \rightleftharpoons B + C, \qquad \Delta H_{r,298} = 1000 \text{ cal/gm mole}$$

Start with 1 mole A in 4½ moles inert gas and suppose that 50% of the original A is dissociated at 1000°K and 100-atm total pressure.
(*a*) Find $\Delta F°$ at 500°K and 1 atm.
(*b*) Find $\Delta F°$ at 500°K and 0.01 atm.
(*c*) Find the per cent A dissociated at 500°K and 1 atm.
(*d*) Find the per cent A dissociated at 500°K and 0.01 atm.
Data:

		Critical Values	
Substance	Average C_p, cal/(gm mole)(°C)	T_c	p_c
A	13	1000	100
B	8	400	50
C	5	800	20

Assume that the system is an ideal solution:

$$f_A = y_A f_{A,\text{pure substance}} = y_A \pi \frac{f_{A,\text{pure substance}}}{\pi}$$

The last quantity is given by the Newton charts which may be found in most thermodynamics texts for chemical engineers.

7. Which reaction rate is more greatly influenced by a given change in (*a*) temperature, (*b*) total pressure?

Data: Both are gas-phase reactions with rates at 1028°C given by

$r_1 = 2.8 \times 10^2 C_A{}^2$, measured in cgs units
$r_2 = 4.1 \times 10^6 C_A^{0.5} C_B$, measured in British units with time in hours

8. The homogeneous gas-phase reaction $A + B \rightleftharpoons R + S$ yields 40% conversion of A in a given plug flow reactor when equimolar quantities of reactants are fed into the reactor at 2 atm and 25°C.

(*a*) At what temperature level should this reactor be operated so as to maximize conversion of reactant? Find this conversion.

(*b*) At this optimum temperature would it be possible to lower the pressure to slightly below atmospheric without drop in conversion? Such a change is desirable since possible leaks in the system would then not result in contamination of the atmosphere or loss in reactants.

Data: For the reaction as written and at 25°C

$$\Delta H_r = 1800 \text{ cal}$$
$$\Delta F^\circ = 0$$

Possible operating temperatures are between 0°C and 500°C, in which range

$$C_{pA} = 8 \text{ cal/(gm mole)(°C)}$$
$$C_{pB} = 10 \text{ cal/(gm mole)(°C)}$$
$$C_{pR} = 7 \text{ cal/(gm mole)(°C)}$$
$$C_{pS} = 5 \text{ cal/(gm mole)(°C)}$$

Assume the usual Arrhenius temperature dependency of the rate.

9. When operated isothermally at its optimum temperature the plug flow reactor of Example 2 yields 76% conversion of A to R.

(*a*) What conversion is possible if the optimum temperature progression is maintained through the reactor?

(*b*) Prepare a plot showing the temperature at 10% distance intervals through the reactor.

Note that the maximum allowable temperature is 65°C and the space time remains unchanged at 10 min.

10. Three equal-sized backmix reactors in series are available to process reactant of the examples in this chapter.

(*a*) If the space time for the three-reactor system is 10 min, calculate the temperatures that should be maintained in each of these reactors in order to maximize the conversion of A to R. Find this conversion.

(*b*) If the number of backmix reactors is increased indefinitely, keeping $\tau = 10$ min, what should the resulting conversion be?

11. Example 6*b* shows that the heat added to the first reactor equals exactly the heat removed from the second reactor, suggesting that the necessary heat interchange can be made between reacting streams without heat interchange with surroundings.

(*a*) Sketch one such scheme using countercurrent heat exchange among fluid streams flowing to or from the reactors (no heating or cooling coils within reactors). With $U = 50$ Btu/(hr)(ft^2 exchanger surface)(°F), find the size and number of exchangers needed.

(*b*) Repeat part *a* with the following modifications. Heat exchange is accomplished by passing the appropriate fluid streams through heating coils immersed in the backmix reactors. Use the same value for the over-all heat transfer coefficient U.

12. The aqueous-phase reactions

$$A + B \xrightarrow{k_1} R + T$$

$$R + B \xrightarrow{k_2} S + T$$

proceed with second-order kinetics. Find the optimum temperature of operation of a plug flow reactor, and find the corresponding maximum fractional yield of R obtainable, based on the amount of A consumed. R is the desired product, and any temperature level between 5 and 65°C may be used.

Data: Equimolar quantities of A and B are mixed and allowed to react in beakers at different temperatures. When all B is consumed, analysis shows that 75% A has reacted at 25°C, 60% A has reacted at 45°C.

13. The aqueous-phase reaction

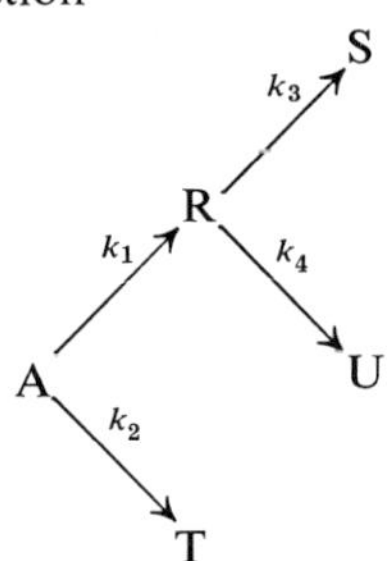

with elementary kinetics where

$$k_1 = 10^9 e^{-6000/T}$$
$$k_2 = 10^7 e^{-4000/T}$$
$$k_3 = 10^8 e^{-9000/T}$$
$$k_4 = 10^{12} e^{-12,000/T}$$

is to be run in two backmix reactors in series anywhere between 10 and 90°C.

(*a*) If both reactors are to be kept at the same temperature, what should that temperature be for maximum fractional yield of desired product S? Find this fractional yield.

(*b*) If the reactors may be kept at different temperatures, what should these temperatures be for maximum fractional yield of S? Find this fractional yield.

(*c*) For part *b*, what should the relative sizes of the two reactors be—approximately equal, first one larger, or first one smaller?

9

NONIDEAL FLOW

We have thus far restricted ourselves to the design of flow reactors in which flow followed one of two very specific idealized patterns, plug flow or backmix flow. Though real reactors never fully satisfy these requirements, a large number of designs so closely approximate these ideals that we can with negligible error consider them to be ideal. In other cases deviation from ideality can be considerable. This deviation can be caused by the channeling of fluid through the vessel, by the recycling of fluid within the vessel, or by the existence of stagnant regions of pockets of fluid in the vessel. Figure 1 shows a number of situations in which these nonideal flow patterns are likely to occur.

In all types of process equipment, such as shell and tube or finned-tube heat exchangers, packed absorption columns or chemical reactors channeling of fluid or the existence of stagnant pockets are to be guarded against since they always result in decrease in performance. Recycle flow is usually undesirable too, the exception to this rule being certain complex reactions and most autocatalytic and autothermal reactions.

The problems of nonideal flow are intimately tied to those of scale-up because the question of whether to pilot-plant or not rests in large part on whether we have knowledge of all the major variables involved in the process. If we do, there is no reason to pilot-plant. Often the factor that is uncontrolled in the design of chemical reactors is the magnitude of the nonideality of flow, and unfortunately this factor very often differs widely

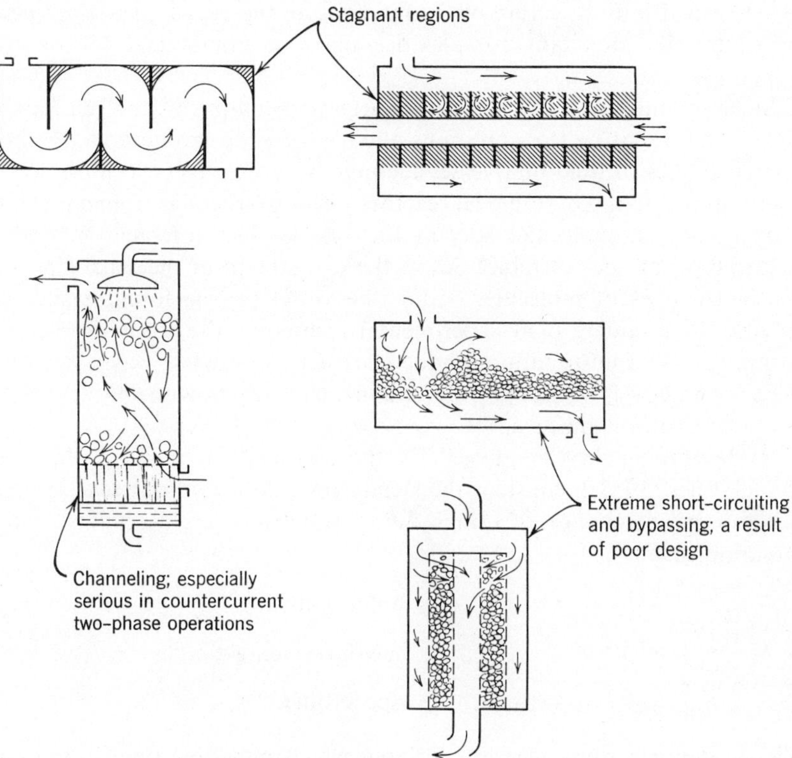

Fig. 1. Nonideal flow patterns which may exist in process equipment.

between large and small units. Therefore ignoring this factor may lead to gross errors in design.

In reality the flow of fluids is never ideal.

In this chapter we hope to consider enough about nonideal flow to acquire an intuitive feel for the magnitude of this phenomenon in reactors of various types, to know whether or not it has to be treated, and, when it does have to be treated, to approach its solution in a rational manner consistent with present-day knowledge of the subject.

RESIDENCE TIME DISTRIBUTION OF FLUID IN VESSELS

To predict the exact behavior of a vessel as a chemical reactor we must know what is happening in it. We must at least know how the fluid is passing through the vessel. And how can this be found? There is only one way, and that is to tag and follow each and every molecule as it passes through the vessel. This can be done essentially by having a complete velocity distribution picture of the fluid within the vessel. Though fine in principle, the attendant complexities make it impractical to use this approach.

Since we must set aside our goal of attaining complete knowledge about the system, let us be less ambitious and ask how we can describe the flow characteristics of fluid in a vessel adequately enough to yield information useful in the design of nonideal reactors. The approach is to find out how long individual molecules stay in the vessel. This information on the distribution of ages of molecules in the exit stream or the distribution of residence times of molecules within the vessel can be found easily and directly by a widely used experimental technique, the stimulus-response technique. This information can then be used in one of two ways to account for the nonideal flow behavior of fluid in a chemical flow reactor. We take up these questions in turn.

In developing the "language" for the treatment of nonideal flow [see Danckwerts (1953)], consider the steady-state flow, without reaction and without density change, of a single fluid through a vessel. Recalling for this situation that

$$\begin{aligned}\bar{t} = \tau = \frac{V}{v} &= \text{holding time}\\ &= \text{mean residence time}\\ &= \text{space time}\end{aligned}$$

we can define a dimensionless variable which measures time in units of mean residence time or holding time. This we call reduced time, or

$$\theta = \frac{t}{\bar{t}} = \frac{t}{\tau} = \frac{vt}{V} = \text{reduced time (dimensionless)} \tag{1}$$

I, the internal age distribution function for a fluid in a vessel

It is evident that in general different elements of fluid following different flow paths will take different periods of time to pass through the vessel. Let us at any instant record the distribution of ages of the fluid within the vessel as shown in Fig. 2, where the age of an element of fluid is measured from the time it enters the vessel. The symbol **I** is a measure of the distribution of ages of the fluid in the vessel defined in such a way that $\mathbf{I}\,d\theta$ is the fraction of the material with age between θ and $\theta + d\theta$. Since the sum of all the fractions of the material in the vessel is unity, this sum must also be the total area under the **I** versus θ curve. Thus

$$\int_0^\infty \mathbf{I}\,d\theta = 1$$

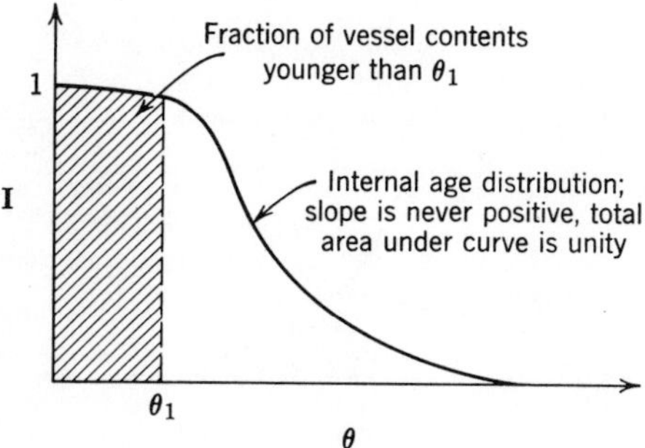

Fig. 2. A typical internal age distribution.

The fraction of the vessel's contents younger than age θ_1 is the shaded area of Fig. 2, or

$$\int_0^{\theta_1} \mathbf{I}\, d\theta$$

The fraction of the vessel's contents older than θ_1 is

$$\int_{\theta_1}^{\infty} \mathbf{I}\, d\theta = 1 - \int_0^{\theta_1} \mathbf{I}\, d\theta$$

E, the exit age distribution function of fluid leaving a vessel or the residence time distribution of fluid in a vessel

In a manner similar to the internal age distribution function, let **E** be the measure of the distribution of ages of all elements of the fluid stream leaving a vessel. Thus **E** is a measure of the distribution of residence times of the fluid within the vessel. Again the age is measured from the time the fluid elements enter the vessel. Let **E** be defined in such a way that $\mathbf{E}\, d\theta$ is the fraction of material in the exit stream with age between θ and $\theta + d\theta$. Referring to Fig. 3, we find the area under the **E** versus θ curve to be

$$\int_0^{\infty} \mathbf{E}\, d\theta = 1$$

The fraction of material in the exit stream younger than age θ_2 is

$$\int_0^{\theta_2} \mathbf{E}\, d\theta$$

whereas the fraction of material older than θ_2, the shaded area of Fig. 3, is

$$\int_{\theta_2}^{\infty} \mathbf{E}\, d\theta = 1 - \int_0^{\theta_2} \mathbf{E}\, d\theta$$

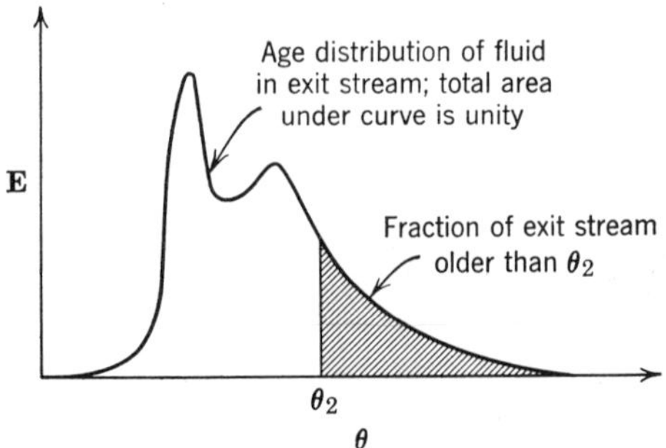

Fig. 3. A typical exit age distribution or distribution of residence times of fluid in vessel.

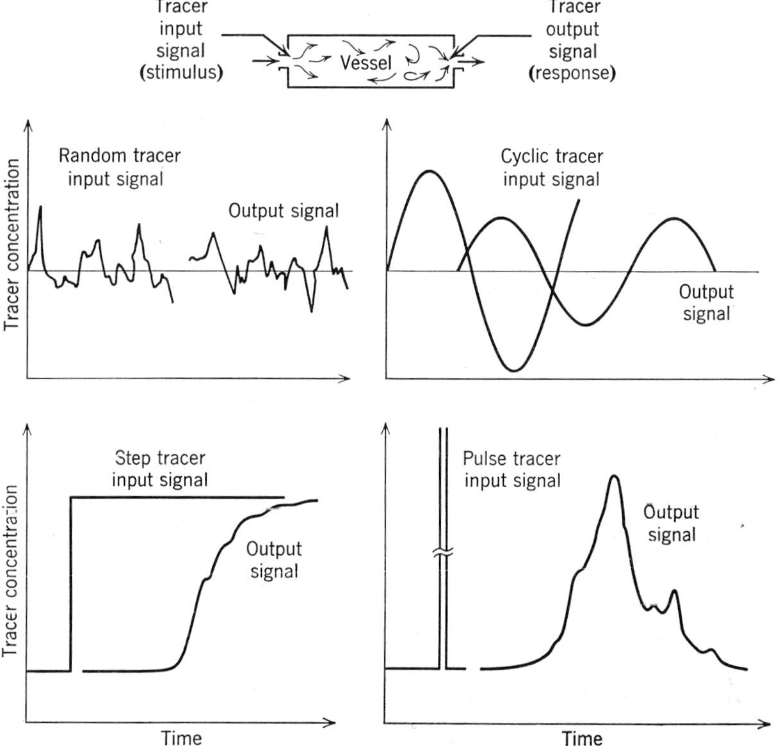

Fig. 4. Stimulus response techniques commonly used in the study of the behavior of systems.

Experimental methods

Since we plan to study nonideal flow reactors by means of the internal and exit age distribution functions, we should like to know how these functions can be found. Such measurements cannot be made directly, so we must resort to one of a number of experimental techniques, all of which may be classed as stimulus-response techniques. In all such experimentation we do something to the system and then see how the system reacts or responds to this stimulus. Analyzing the response gives the desired information about the system. This is a method of experimentation widely used in science.

In our problem the stimulus can well be a tracer input signal to the vessel, the response signal being the recording of tracer leaving the vessel. Any type of tracer input signal may be used—a random signal, a cyclic signal, a step or discontinuous signal, a pulse or discontinuous signal. Input signals of these types and typical response curves are shown in Fig. 4. For convenience, for ease of analysis, and because of the close similarity in shape between the output signal and the age distribution functions desired, only the last two modes of injection of tracer will be considered.

The F curve

With no tracer initially present in the entering fluid stream, let a step or jump tracer signal of concentration C_0 be imposed on the fluid stream entering the vessel. Then the concentration-time curve at the vessel outlet, measuring tracer concentration in terms of inlet tracer concentration and measuring time in reduced units, is called the **F** curve. As shown in Fig. 5 the **F** curve rises from 0 to 1.

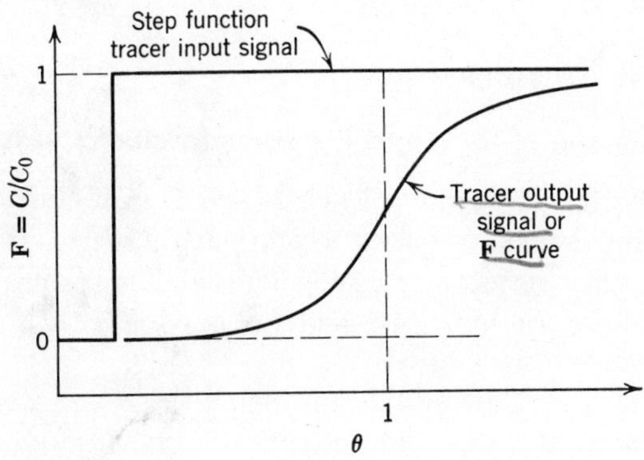

Fig. 5. Typical downstream signal, called the **F** curve, as a response to an upstream step input signal.

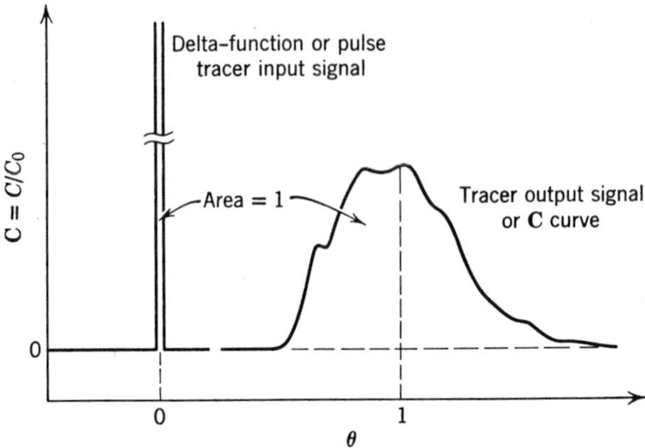

Fig. 6. Typical downstream signal, called the **C** curve, as a response to an upstream delta-function tracer input signal.

The C curve

The curve that describes the concentration-time function of tracer in the exit stream of a vessel in response to an idealized instantaneous or pulse tracer injection is called the **C** curve. Such an input is often called a delta-function input. As with the **F** curve, dimensionless coordinates are chosen. Concentrations are measured in terms of the initial concentration of injected tracer, C_0, if it is evenly distributed throughout the vessel, and time is measured in reduced units. With this choice the area under the **C** curve is always unity; hence

$$\int_0^\infty \mathbf{C}\, d\theta = \int_0^\infty \frac{C}{C_0}\, d\theta = 1 \quad \text{where} \quad C_0 = \int_0^\infty C\, d\theta = \frac{1}{\bar{t}} \int_0^\infty C\, dt \qquad (2)$$

A typical **C** curve is shown in Fig. 6.

Relation among the F, C, I, and E curves in closed vessels

Let us find the relation among **F**, **C**, **I**, and **E** in a closed vessel, the closed vessel being defined as one in which material passes in and out by bulk flow only. Thus diffusion or dispersion is absent at entrance and exit so that we do not, for example, have material moving upstream and out of the vessel entrance by swirls or eddies.

Consider steady-state flow of fluid through a vessel and a step function of tracer introduced into the fluid entering the vessel. Suppose that the tracer is simply a second fluid introduced into the vessel at time $t = 0$ in place of the original flowing fluid. Then at any time t or $\theta > 0$ a material balance for the vessel gives

$$\begin{pmatrix}\text{rate of}\\ \text{tracer}\\ \text{input}\end{pmatrix} = \begin{pmatrix}\text{rate of}\\ \text{tracer}\\ \text{output}\end{pmatrix} + \begin{pmatrix}\text{rate of tracer}\\ \text{accumulation}\\ \text{within vessel}\end{pmatrix}$$

or

$$\begin{pmatrix}\text{flow rate of}\\ \text{second fluid}\\ \text{into vessel}\end{pmatrix} = \begin{pmatrix}\text{flow rate}\\ \text{of fluid out}\\ \text{of vessel}\end{pmatrix}\begin{pmatrix}\text{fraction}\\ \text{of second fluid}\\ \text{in exit stream}\end{pmatrix} + \frac{d}{dt}\left[\begin{pmatrix}\text{volume of}\\ \text{vessel}\end{pmatrix}\begin{pmatrix}\text{fraction of second}\\ \text{fluid in vessel}\end{pmatrix}\right]$$

or in symbols

$$v\,\frac{\text{ft}^3}{\text{sec}} = v\mathbf{F}\,\frac{\text{ft}^3}{\text{sec}} + \frac{d}{dt}\left[V\int_0^\theta \mathbf{I}\,d\theta\right]\frac{\text{ft}^3}{\text{sec}} \tag{3}$$

Dividing by v and noting that $V/v = \bar{t}$ and $dt/\bar{t} = d\theta$, we have

$$1 = \mathbf{F} + \mathbf{I} \tag{4}$$

Also noting that at time θ

$$\begin{pmatrix}\text{fraction of}\\ \text{second fluid}\\ \text{in exit stream}\end{pmatrix} = \begin{pmatrix}\text{fraction of fluid}\\ \text{in exit stream}\\ \text{younger than } \theta\end{pmatrix}$$

we have

$$\mathbf{F} = \int_0^\theta \mathbf{E}\,d\theta \tag{5}$$

Similarly for a pulse tracer input we can show that

$$\mathbf{C} = \mathbf{E} \tag{6}$$

These expressions suffice to interrelate the **F**, **C**, **I**, and **E** functions at any time θ. Thus in summary

$$\begin{aligned}
&\mathbf{F} + \mathbf{I} = 1\\
&\mathbf{C} = \mathbf{E}\\
&\mathbf{F} = 1 - \mathbf{I} = \int_0^\theta \mathbf{E}\,d\theta = \int_0^\theta \mathbf{C}\,d\theta\\
&\mathbf{C} = \mathbf{E} = \frac{d\mathbf{F}}{d\theta} = -\frac{d\mathbf{I}}{d\theta}
\end{aligned} \tag{7}$$

These relationships show how stimulus-response experiments, using either step or pulse inputs, can conveniently give the age distribution of both the vessel contents and the fluid at the vessel outlet.

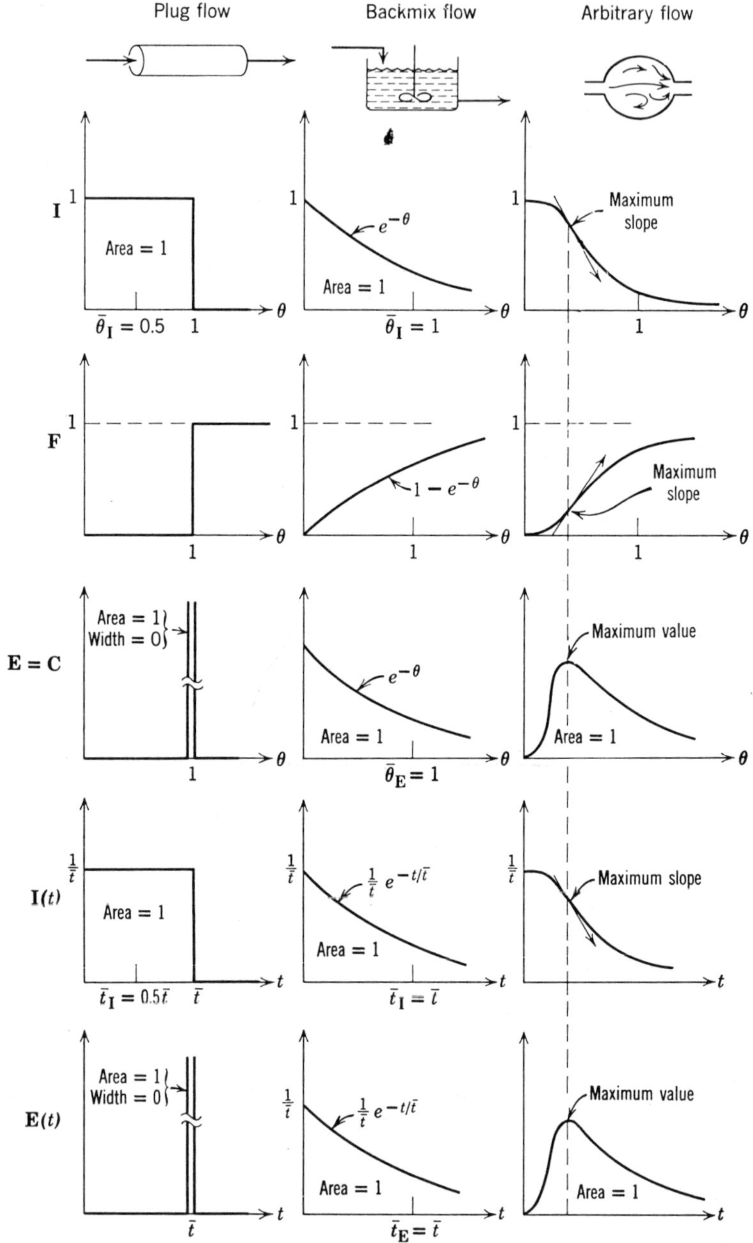

Fig. 7. Properties of the **F**, **C**, **I**, and **E** curves for various kinds of flow in closed vessels. The relationship between curves is given by Eqs. 7 and 8.

Age distribution functions may be expressed in ordinary time units rather than in dimensionless time units. They will be designated by $\mathbf{E}(t)$ and $\mathbf{I}(t)$. With this definition, $\mathbf{E}(t)\,dt$ becomes the fraction of material in the exit stream with age between t and $t + dt$, and we have

$$\mathbf{I} = \bar{t}\mathbf{I}(t),\ \mathbf{E} = \bar{t}\mathbf{E}(t), \qquad \text{with} \qquad \int_0^\infty \mathbf{E}(t)\,dt = 1$$

and

$$\bar{t}\mathbf{I}(t) = 1 - \int_0^t \mathbf{E}(t)dt \qquad \text{or} \qquad \mathbf{E}(t) = -\frac{\bar{t}d\mathbf{I}(t)}{dt} \tag{8}$$

and

$$\bar{t}\theta = t, \qquad \text{with} \qquad \bar{t} = \frac{V}{v} = \bar{t}_{\mathbf{E}} = \int_0^\infty t\mathbf{E}(t)\,dt$$

Figure 7 illustrates graphically the shapes of these curves for various flow conditions.

Mean and variance of a distribution

Associated with every age distribution $y = f(x)$ are two sets of parameters called the moments of the distribution. The kth moment about the origin, $k = 0, 1, 2, \ldots$, is defined by

$$M_k' = \frac{\int_0^\infty x^k f(x)\,dx}{\int_0^\infty f(x)\,dx}$$

and the kth moment about the mean or centroid μ of the distribution, $k = 0, 1, 2, \ldots$, is defined by

$$M_k = \frac{\int_0^\infty (x - \mu)^k f(x)\,dx}{\int_0^\infty f(x)\,dx}$$

The interesting property of the moments of a distribution is that they completely define the distribution; hence they can be used to compare distributions without comparing the actual curves themselves.

Two moments will be used frequently in this chapter; therefore we consider them briefly. The first moment about the origin, commonly called the mean or centroid of the distribution, is the location parameter of the distribution and is defined as

$$\mu = M_1' = \frac{\int_0^\infty x f(x)\,dx}{\int_0^\infty f(x)\,dx} \tag{9}$$

If the continuous distribution function is measured only at a number of equidistant points, then

$$\mu = \frac{\sum x_i f(x_i)\,\Delta x}{\sum f(x_i)\,\Delta x} = \frac{\sum x_i f(x_i)}{\sum f(x_i)} \tag{10}$$

The second moment about the mean, commonly called the variance, measures the spread of the distribution about the mean and is equivalent to the square of the radius of gyration of the distribution. It is defined for a continuous distribution as

$$\sigma^2 = M_2 = \frac{\int_0^\infty (x-\mu)^2 f(x)\,dx}{\int_0^\infty f(x)\,dx} \tag{11}$$

Again for measurements at a number of equidistant points this equation becomes in its equivalent forms

$$\sigma^2 = \frac{\sum (x_i-\mu)^2 f(x_i)\,\Delta x}{\sum f(x_i)\,\Delta x} = \frac{\sum x_i^2 f(x_i)}{\sum f(x_i)} - \mu^2 \tag{12}$$

When applied to the **C**, **E**, and **I** curves the denominators of many of these expressions, such as $\int \mathbf{E}\,d\theta$ and $\sum \mathbf{E}\,\Delta\theta$, are unity, in which case the expressions simplify somewhat. For example, in its various forms the mean age of material within a vessel is

$$\begin{aligned} \bar{\theta}_{\mathbf{I}} &= \int_0^\infty \theta\mathbf{I}\,d\theta = \frac{\sum \theta\mathbf{I}}{\sum \mathbf{I}} = \sum \theta\mathbf{I}\,\Delta\theta \\ \bar{t}_{\mathbf{I}} = \bar{t}\bar{\theta}_{\mathbf{I}} &= \int_0^\infty t\mathbf{I}(t)\,dt = \frac{\sum t\mathbf{I}(t)}{\sum \mathbf{I}(t)} = \sum t\mathbf{I}(t)\,\Delta t \end{aligned} \tag{13}$$

The mean age of the exit stream is

$$\bar{\theta}_{\mathbf{E}} = \bar{\theta}_{\mathbf{C}} = 1 = \int_0^\infty \theta\mathbf{E}\,d\theta = \frac{\sum \theta\mathbf{E}}{\sum \mathbf{E}} = \sum \theta\mathbf{E}\,\Delta\theta$$

or

$$\bar{t} = \bar{t}_{\mathbf{E}} = \bar{t}_{\mathbf{C}} = \int_0^\infty t\mathbf{E}(t)\,dt = \frac{\sum t\mathbf{E}(t)}{\sum \mathbf{E}(t)} = \sum t\mathbf{E}(t)\,\Delta t \tag{14}$$

The variance of the **E** or **C** distribution is

$$\begin{aligned} \sigma^2 &= \int_0^\infty (\theta-1)^2\mathbf{E}\,d\theta = \int_0^\infty \theta^2\mathbf{E}\,d\theta - 1 = \frac{\sum \theta^2\mathbf{E}}{\sum \mathbf{E}} - 1 \\ &= \sum \theta^2\mathbf{E}\,\Delta\theta - 1 \end{aligned}$$

or

$$\begin{aligned} \sigma_t^2 = \bar{t}^2\sigma^2 &= \int_0^\infty (t-\bar{t})^2\mathbf{E}(t)\,dt = \int_0^\infty t^2\mathbf{E}(t)\,dt - \bar{t}^2 \\ &= \frac{\sum t^2\mathbf{E}(t)}{\sum \mathbf{E}(t)} - \bar{t}^2 = \sum t^2\mathbf{E}(t)\,\Delta t - \bar{t}^2 \end{aligned} \tag{15}$$

We must keep in mind that these relationships have been shown to hold only for closed vessels. Where movement into or out of vessels can take place in ways other than by bulk flow, we usually have

$$\bar{t} = \frac{V}{v} \neq \bar{t}_C \neq \bar{t}_E$$

This fact is pointed out in Eqs. 23, 24, and 25 for a particular flow model.

Methods of using age distribution information

Tracer information is used either directly or in conjunction with flow models to predict performance of real flow reactors, the method used depending in large part on whether the reactor can be considered a linear system or whether it must be treated as a nonlinear system.

Linear and nonlinear processes. A process is linear if any change in stimulus results in a corresponding proportional change in response. Symbolically

$$\frac{\Delta(\text{response})}{\Delta(\text{stimulus})} = \frac{d(\text{response})}{d(\text{stimulus})} = k_1 = \text{constant}$$

or integrating

$$(\text{response}) = k_1(\text{stimulus}) + k_2$$

Processes that do not satisfy these conditions are not linear processes.

Linear processes have the following highly desirable property. If a number of independent linear processes are occurring simultaneously in a system, their over-all effect is also a linear process. In addition, the over-all effect of these individual linear processes occurring simultaneously in a system can be analyzed by studying each of the processes separately. This property of additivity does not extend to nonlinear processes. Hence nonlinear systems must be studied "in the total situation," and their over-all behavior cannot be predicted by knowledge of each of the contributing processes. Because of this property solutions to problems involving linear processes are relatively simple and are of wide generality. On the other hand solutions for nonlinear processes are much more difficult and are specific to each problem.

Linear systems without flow models. If the tracer has no unusual activity (adsorption at walls, disappearance by reaction), but simply passes through the vessel with the rest of the fluid, the stimulus-response experiment at steady state is linear in concentration. This linearity can be recognized if we note that the relationship between stimulus C_0 and response C can be expressed in dimensionless form in the **C** and **F** curves; thus C/C_0 is independent of concentration.

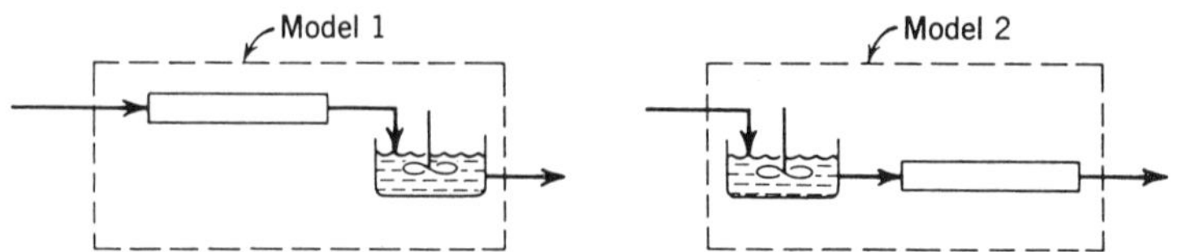

Fig. 8. Both models give identical tracer response signals and therefore act alike for reactions with linear rate equations but act differently for reactions with rates nonlinear in concentration.

Now by the additivity property of linear processes stimulus response information should be sufficient to account for the behavior of the nonideal flow vessel as a chemical reactor as long as the reaction rate is also linear in concentration. Reactions that fall into this category have defining rate equations of the general form

$$-r_A = k_1(C_A - k_2) = k_1C_A - k_3$$

From the physical standpoint C_A can never be negative; therefore we must restrict k_2 and k_3 to positive values. Thus the only reactions that can be used are of the form

$$-r_A = k_1(C_A - k_2) = k_1C_A - k_3, \qquad k_2, k_3 \geqslant 0 \tag{17}$$

This restriction rules out zero-order reactions. Therefore for reactions with rate given by Eq. 17 we can say

$$\begin{pmatrix}\text{tracer}\\ \text{information}\\ \text{for vessel}\end{pmatrix} + \begin{pmatrix}\text{kinetic data}\\ \text{for reaction}\\ \text{with rate linear}\\ \text{in concentration}\end{pmatrix} \rightarrow \begin{pmatrix}\text{behavior of}\\ \text{vessel as a}\\ \text{reactor}\end{pmatrix}$$

The main use of this method is with first-order reactions, both irreversible ($k_2 = 0$) and reversible ($k_2 > 0$).

Nonlinear systems with flow models. Unfortunately if the reaction occurring is not of the form of Eq. 17, and is therefore nonlinear, conversion cannot be found using age distribution information directly. To illustrate this point consider the two models of a flow reactor shown in Fig. 8. They both have identical tracer response curves and cannot be distinguished by tracer experiments. For reactions with the rate linear in concentration, however, it is not necessary to know which is the true flow pattern because both give identical conversions (see Problem 6.5). On the other hand, since conversions will differ in these two systems for nonlinear reactions (see Problem 6.7), the flow pattern which actually exists must be known before predictions of performance can be made.

In the absence of the needed point-to-point information the approach taken in finding conversions in nonlinear systems is to hypothesize what we consider to be reasonable models for the behavior of the fluid in the vessel and then calculate conversions on the basis of such postulated behavior. Naturally the closeness of predicted conversion to actual conversion will depend on how well the model mirrors reality.

Linear systems with flow models. In addition to predicting conversions in nonlinear reaction systems, flow models are often used to predict conversions in linear systems. This seemingly roundabout procedure is used because the parameters of these models often correlate with the variables of the system, such as Reynolds number, Schmidt number, etc. Such correlations can then be used to predict conversions without resorting to any experimentation. Such is the case with packed bed and tubular reactors. We take up the approach using models after considering the direct use of tracer data.

Example 1

The concentration readings in Table E1 represent a continuous response to a delta-function input into a closed vessel which is to be used as a chemical reactor. Tabulate the $\mathbf{E}(t)$ and $\mathbf{E}$ values; also plot the $\mathbf{E}$ distribution.

Table E1

Time t, min	Tracer Concentration, gm/ft^3 fluid
0	0
5	3
10	5
15	5
20	4
25	2
30	1
35	0

Solution. The area under the concentration versus time curve,

$$\Sigma C\,\Delta t = (3 + 5 + 5 + 4 + 2 + 1)5$$
$$= 100(\text{gm})(\text{min})/\text{ft}^3$$

gives the total amount of tracer added in the pulse input. To find $\mathbf{E}(t)$ this area must be unity; hence the concentration readings must each be divided by $\Sigma C\,\Delta t$, giving

$$\mathbf{E}(t) = \frac{C}{\Sigma C\,\Delta t}$$

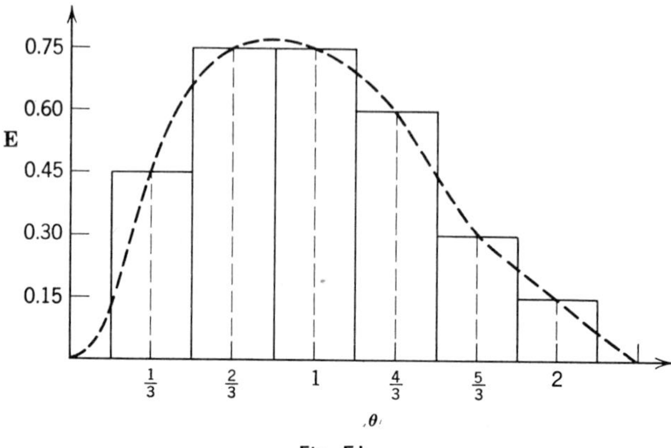

Fig. E1

This expression can be obtained directly by combining Eqs. 2, 7, and 8 to give

$$\mathbf{E}(t) = \mathbf{C}(t) = \frac{1}{\bar{t}}\frac{C}{C_0} = \frac{C}{\Sigma C\,\Delta t}$$

Thus we have

t, min	0	5	10	15	20	25	30
$\mathbf{E}(t) = \dfrac{C}{\Sigma C\,\Delta t}$, 1/min	0	0.03	0.05	0.05	0.04	0.02	0.01

To obtain **E**, change t to θ and $\mathbf{E}(t)$ to **E**. But to do this we first need the mean residence time in the vessel which is given by Eq. 10 as

$$\bar{t} = \frac{\Sigma tC}{\Sigma C}$$

From the tabulated data

$$\bar{t} = \frac{(5 \times 3) + (10 \times 5) + \cdots + (1 \times 30)}{3 + 5 + 5 + 4 + 2 + 1} = \frac{300}{20} = 15 \text{ min}$$

Hence from Eq. 8 the necessary conversions are

$$\theta = \frac{t}{\bar{t}} = \frac{t}{15}$$

$$\mathbf{E} = \bar{t}\mathbf{E}(t) = 15\mathbf{E}(t) = \frac{15C}{\Sigma C\,\Delta t}$$

and we find

θ	0	$\frac{1}{3}$	$\frac{2}{3}$	1	$\frac{4}{3}$	$\frac{5}{3}$	2
E	0	0.45	0.75	0.75	0.60	0.30	0.15

Figure E1 is a plot of this distribution.

Example 2

Tabulate and plot the internal age distribution **I** for the fluid in a vessel with flow characteristics of Example 1.

Solution. By writing Eq. 7 for measurements at a discrete number of points, **I** at any time can be found. Thus

$$\mathbf{I} = 1 - \int_0^\theta \mathbf{E}\, d\theta = 1 - \Sigma \mathbf{E}\, \Delta\theta$$

Table E2 and Fig. E2 show the details of the summation which is done by the trapezoidal rule.

Table E2

i	θ_i	$\mathbf{E}_i$	Area Present in the Interval between $i - 1$ and i, $\bar{\mathbf{E}}_i\, \Delta\theta = \dfrac{\mathbf{E}_i + \mathbf{E}_{i-1}}{2}(\theta_i - \theta_{i-1})$	Summing to θ_i $\overset{i}{\Sigma}\mathbf{E}\, \Delta\theta$	$\mathbf{I} = 1 - \Sigma\mathbf{E}\, \Delta\theta$
0	0	0	0	0	1
1	$\frac{1}{3}$	0.45	$\frac{0.45 + 0}{2} \cdot \frac{1}{3} = 0.075$	0.075	0.925
2	$\frac{2}{3}$	0.75	$\frac{0.75 + 0.45}{2} \cdot \frac{1}{3} = 0.200$	0.275	0.725
3	1	0.75	$\frac{0.75 + 0.75}{2} \cdot \frac{1}{3} = 0.250$	0.525	0.475
4	$\frac{4}{3}$	0.60	$\frac{0.60 + 0.75}{2} \cdot \frac{1}{3} = 0.225$	0.750	0.250
5	$\frac{5}{3}$	0.30	$\frac{0.30 + 0.60}{2} \cdot \frac{1}{3} = 0.150$	0.900	0.100
6	2	0.15	$\frac{0.15 + 0.30}{2} \cdot \frac{1}{3} = 0.075$	0.975	0.025
7	$\frac{7}{3}$	0	$\frac{0 + 0.15}{2} \cdot \frac{1}{3} = 0.025$	1.000	0

CONVERSION DIRECTLY FROM TRACER INFORMATION

Linear process. A variety of flow patterns can give the same tracer output curve. For linear processes, however, these all result in the same conversion. Consequently in such processes we may use any flow pattern

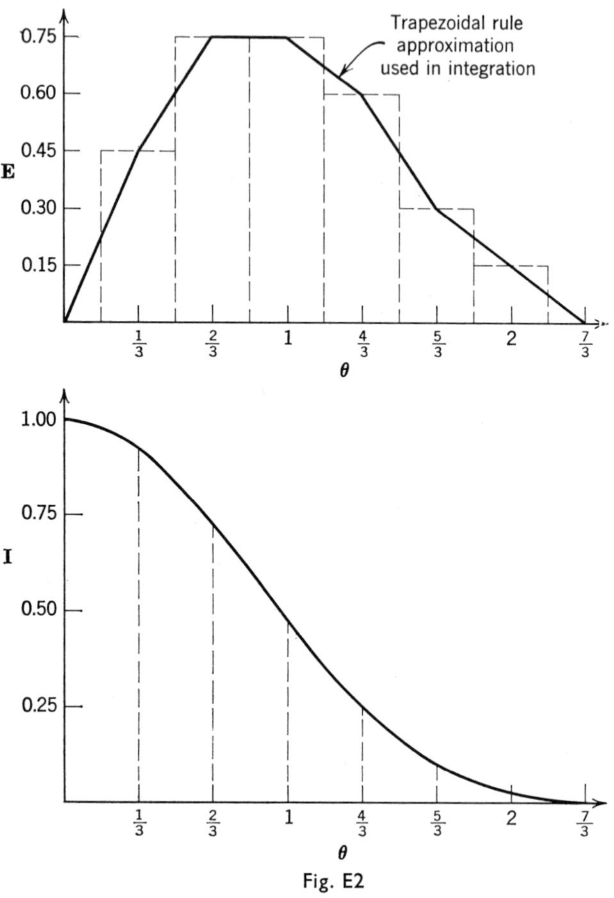

Fig. E2

we wish to determine conversions, as long as the pattern selected gives the same tracer response curve as the real reactor. The pattern invariably selected assumes that each element of fluid passes through the vessel with no intermixing with adjacent elements, the age distribution of material in the exit stream telling how long each of these individual elements have remained within the reactor. Thus for reactant A in the exit stream

$$\begin{pmatrix}\text{mean concentration}\\ \text{of reactant leaving}\\ \text{the reactor unreacted}\end{pmatrix} = \sum_{\substack{\text{all}\\ \text{elements}\\ \text{of exit}\\ \text{stream}}} \begin{pmatrix}\text{concentration of}\\ \text{reactant remaining}\\ \text{in an element of}\\ \text{age between } t\\ \text{and } t + dt\end{pmatrix}\begin{pmatrix}\text{fraction of exit}\\ \text{stream which}\\ \text{consists of}\\ \text{elements of age}\\ \text{between } t \text{ and}\\ t + dt\end{pmatrix}$$

or in symbols

$$\bar{C}_A = \int_{t=0}^{t=\infty} C_A \mathbf{E}(t)\, dt \tag{18}$$

For *first-order reactions* with rate $-r_A = kC_A$ and no density change

$$\ln \frac{C_A}{C_{A0}} = -kt \qquad \text{or} \qquad C_A = C_{A0}e^{-kt}$$

Hence Eq. 18 becomes

$$\frac{\bar{C}_A}{C_{A0}} = \int_0^\infty e^{-kt}\mathbf{E}(t)\,dt \tag{19}$$

For the reaction with *general form of linear rate equation* $-r_A = k_1(C_A - k_2)$, $k_2 \geqslant 0$, and no density change,

$$\ln \frac{C_A - k_2}{C_{A0} - k_2} = -k_1 t \qquad \text{or} \qquad C_A = e^{-k_1 t}(C_{A0} - k_2) + k_2 \tag{20}$$

Replacing in Eq. 18 we obtain

$$\bar{C}_A = \int_0^\infty [e^{-k_1 t}(C_{A0} - k_2) + k_2]\mathbf{E}(t)\,dt \tag{21}$$

Because we know $\mathbf{E}(t)$ from the experimentally determined **F** or **C** curves and have the kinetic information for the reaction in question, we can determine graphically or numerically from these equations the conversion in the nonideal reactor for reactions with linear rate equations.

Nonlinear processes. For reactions with nonlinear rate equations conversions cannot be calculated with tracer information alone. With Eq. 18, however, we can always calculate one of the two bounds, upper or lower, to the conversion in a given system. Now from Chapter 6 we may recall that when the flow pattern of fluid through a given reactor system is such that the reactant concentration stays as high as possible, conversions are highest for orders greater than unity but conversions are lowest for orders smaller than unity, zero order excluded. Since Eq. 18 assumes no intermixing of fluid elements, hence concentration of reactants as high as possible, it yields the upper bound to conversions for reactions with order greater than unity but yields the lower bound to conversions for reaction orders smaller than unity.

To calculate the other bound in each of these cases requires a rather involved treatment including definition of additional distribution functions concerning the life expectation of molecules already within the vessel. This problem is discussed in Chapter 10.

Example 3

The vessel of Example 1 is to be used as a reactor for a liquid-phase decomposition with rate

$$-r_A = kC_A, \qquad k = 0.307 \text{ min}^{-1}$$

Find the fraction of reactant unconverted in the real reactor and compare this with the fraction unconverted in a plug flow reactor of the same size. For both reactors use the space time of Example 1.

Solution. With negligible density change we have from Example 1 for both reactors

$$\tau = \bar{t} = 15 \text{ min}$$

For the plug flow reactor with $\varepsilon = 0$

$$\tau = C_{A0}\int_0^{X_A} \frac{dX_A}{-r_A} = -\frac{1}{k}\int_{C_{A0}}^{C_A} \frac{dC_A}{C_A} = \frac{1}{k}\ln\frac{C_{A0}}{C_A}$$

or

$$\frac{C_A}{C_{A0}} = e^{-k\tau} = e^{-(0.307)(15)} = e^{-4.6} = 0.01$$

Thus the fraction of reactant unconverted in a plug flow reactor equals 1.0%. For the real reactor the fraction unconverted, given by Eq. 19, is found as shown in Table E3.

Table E3

t	$\mathbf{E}(t)$	kt	e^{-kt}	$e^{-kt}\mathbf{E}(t)\,\Delta t$
5	0.03	1.53	0.2154	(0.2154)(0.03)5 = 0.0323
10	0.05	3.07	0.0464	0.0116
15	0.05	4.60	0.0100	0.0025
20	0.04	6.14	0.0021	0.0004
25	0.02	7.68	0.0005	0.0001
30	0.01	9.21	0.0001	0

$$\Sigma e^{-kt}\mathbf{E}(t)\,\Delta t = 0.0469$$

Hence the fraction of reactant unconverted in the real reactor, C_A/C_{A0}, equals 4.7%. From the table we see that the unconverted material comes in most part from the early portion of the $\mathbf{E}(t)$ curve. This suggests that channeling and short-circuiting can seriously hinder attempts to achieve high conversion in reactors.

MODELS FOR NONIDEAL FLOW

Many types of models can be used to characterize nonideal flow patterns within vessels. Some draw on the analogy between mixing in actual flow and a diffusional process. These are called *dispersion models.* Others visualize various flow regions connected in series or parallel. These are called *mixed models.* Some models are useful in accounting for the deviation of real systems, such as tubular vessels or packed beds, from plug flow; others describe the deviation of real stirred tanks from the ideal of backmix flow.

Models vary in complexity. For example, one-parameter models adequately represent packed beds or tubular vessels. On the other hand, two- to six-parameter models have been proposed to represent fluidized beds.

We first take up the dispersion model, then the *tanks in series model.* These adequately characterize flow in tubular and packed-bed reactors. This discussion is followed by one of mixed models which are used for reactors of all other types.

DISPERSION MODEL (DISPERSED PLUG FLOW)

Consider the plug flow of a fluid, on top of which is superimposed some degree of backmixing or intermixing, the magnitude of which is independent of position within the vessel. This condition implies that there exist no stagnant pockets and no gross bypassing or short-circuiting of fluid in the vessel. This is called the dispersed plug flow model; for brevity we simply call it the dispersion model. Figure 9 shows the conditions visualized. Note that with varying intensities of turbulence or intermixing performance for this model should range from plug flow at one extreme to backmix flow at the other. As a result the reactor volume required for the real reactor will lie between those calculated for plug and backmix flow.

We approach the problem of finding the equipment size for dispersed flow by calculating the size based on ideal plug flow and then making a correction to account for nonideality, or

$$V_{\text{actual}} = V_{\text{plug}} \begin{pmatrix} \text{correction} \\ \text{factor} \end{pmatrix}$$

where

$$\begin{pmatrix} \text{correction} \\ \text{factor} \end{pmatrix} = f \begin{pmatrix} \text{intensity of fluid mixing,} \\ \text{reactor geometry,} \\ \text{reaction rate} \end{pmatrix}$$

The first question posed is how to characterize quantitatively a mixing process in which elements of fluid overtake, slip by, or mix with one another to give a nonuniform residence time of fluid in the vessel. What parameter measures the magnitude of fluid backmixing in this situation?

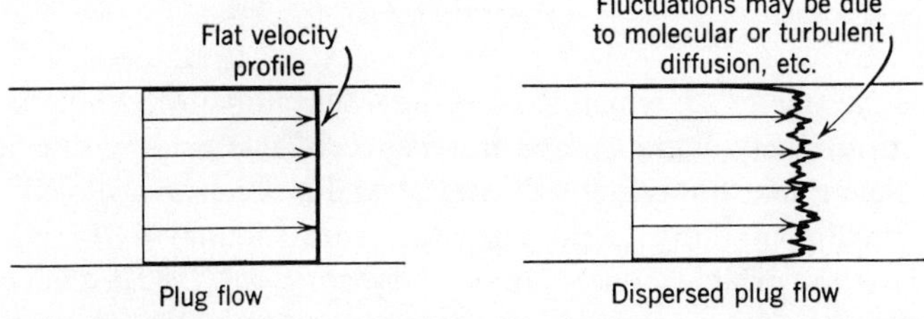

Fig. 9. Representation of the dispersion (dispersed plug flow) model.

To answer this let us digress briefly to a discussion of diffusional phenomena.

Many observed macroscopic or large-scale phenomena have an underlying mechanism which involves numerous fluctuations of small magnitude whose individual occurrences are unpredictable. We may at first expect that treatment of such phenomena is not possible. If these unpredictable tiny fluctuations are repeated a few times, however, an over-all pattern of behavior begins to emerge. As the number of occurrences of these tiny fluctuations increases, this pattern becomes sharper, and with it description and prediction of the over-all phenomenon become more and more exact. We say that these tiny fluctuations are statistical in nature. The treatment and explanation of such phenomena are one of the two cornerstones of physical science and, in fact, provide an understanding of why the second law of thermodynamics holds. It is only with such phenomena that we can tell the direction of time. Examples of such phenomena are conductive heat transfer and diffusion of matter, because the elementary mechanism in both involves the many collisions of individual molecules.

Now returning to the dispersion model, the mixing process involves a shuffling or redistribution of material either by slippage or eddies, and if this occurs a considerable number of times in the vessel, we can consider these disturbances to be statistical in nature, and therefore we may apply the equations for other statistical phenomena such as conductive heat transfer or molecular diffusion to this situation. For convenience let us use the latter. Now the molecular diffusion process in the x direction is well represented in most cases by Fick's law of diffusion,

$$\frac{\partial C}{\partial t} = \mathscr{D} \frac{\partial^2 C}{\partial x^2}$$

where $\mathscr{D}$, the coefficient of molecular diffusion, is a parameter which uniquely characterizes the diffusional process. In an analogous manner we may consider a dispersion model for backmixing of fluid flowing in the x direction, which is also well represented by Fick's law of diffusion. Hence with a uniform intensity of backmixing

$$\frac{\partial C}{\partial t} = D \frac{\partial^2 C}{\partial x^2} \tag{22}$$

where the parameter D, which we call the longitudinal or axial dispersion coefficient, uniquely characterized the degree of backmixing during flow. We use the terms "longitudinal" and "axial" because we wish to distinguish mixing in the direction of flow from mixing in the lateral or radial direction, which is not our primary concern. These two may be quite different in magnitude. For example, in streamline flow of fluids through pipes, axial mixing is mainly due to fluid velocity gradients whereas radial mixing is due to molecular diffusion alone.

Because the elementary process on which this model and its mathematical representation, Eq. 22, is based is viewed to be statistical in nature, hence usually taking place in relatively small regions of the reactor, this model usually represents quite satisfactorily flow that deviates not too greatly from plug flow. Real reactors of this type are packed-bed reactors and tubular reactors (long ones if flow is streamline).

Fitting the dispersion model to the real reactor

C curve. For a pulse or step tracer input into fluid in a dispersed plug flow, solution of Eq. 22 gives a family of **C** or **F** curves with the intensity of dispersion as the parameter. Actually the parameter which correctly characterizes the role played by dispersion is a dimensionless group D/uL which is called the vessel or reactor dispersion number. It varies from zero for plug flow to infinity for backmix flow and is the reciprocal of the axial Peclet number for mass transfer. Figures 10 and 11 show the general shape of these curves.

To characterize flow in a real vessel we need to select from the family of theoretical curves the curve that most closely fits the experimental **C** or **F** curve. From the D/uL of this fitted curve the behavior of the vessel as a reactor can then be predicted. Figure 10 shows that as D/uL rises the spread of the corresponding **C** curve, and therefore its variance, also increases. Variances of distribution are easy to calculate; therefore equating variances is probably the most convenient way of selecting a theoretical **C** curve to match an experimental **C** curve. The precise relationship between D/uL and variance of theoretical **C** curve, found by Levenspiel and Smith (1957) and Van der Laan (1958), depends on the end conditions of the vessels. For those setups most frequently encountered in experimentation these relationships are as follows,

Closed vessels. A closed vessel, shown in Fig. 12, is a finite vessel of length L, with tracer input at the vessel entrance and the output curve measured at the vessel outlet. We visualize that no material moves into or out of the vessel by dispersion ($D = 0$ at these points), and that entrance and exit effects are negligible (D is constant throughout the vessel). For the **C** curve in a closed vessel we find in dimensionless time units

$$\bar{\theta}_C = \frac{\bar{t}_C}{\bar{t}} = \frac{\bar{t}_C v}{V} = 1$$

and

$$\sigma^2 = \frac{\sigma_t^2}{\bar{t}^2} = 2\frac{D}{uL} - 2\left(\frac{D}{uL}\right)^2(1 - e^{-uL/D}) \tag{23}$$

Figures 10 and 11 represent the tracer curves for closed vessels.

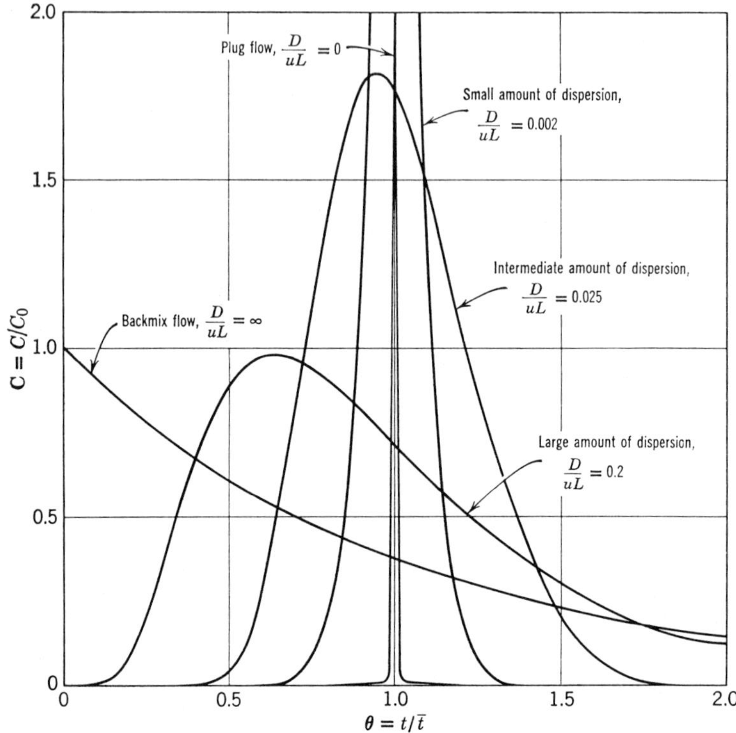

Fig. 10. **C** curves in closed vessels for various extents of backmixing as predicted by the dispersion model.

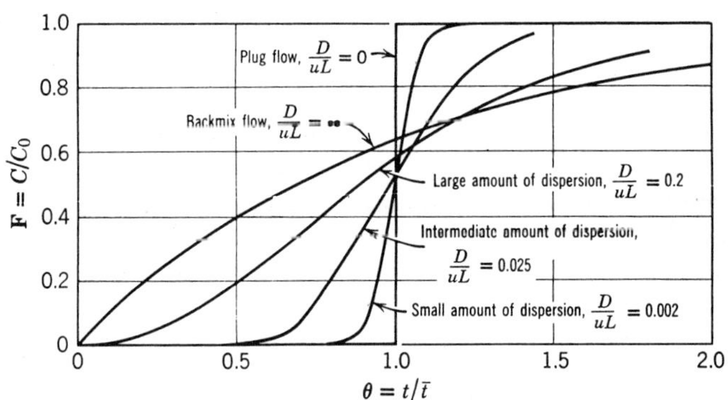

Fig. 11. **F** curves in closed vessels for various extents of backmixing as predicted by the dispersion model.

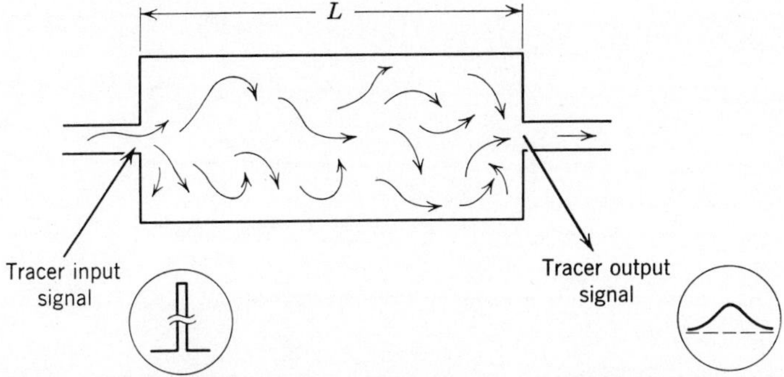

Fig. 12. Determination of dispersion in a closed vessel.

Open vessels. An open vessel, shown in Fig. 13, is essentially a vessel with no discontinuity in type of flow at the point of tracer injection or at the point of tracer measurement. The experimental section is simply a section of length L of the infinite vessel. For the **C** curve in an open vessel we find in dimensionless time units

$$\bar{\theta}_{\mathbf{C}} = \frac{\bar{t}_{\mathbf{C}}}{\bar{t}} = 1 + 2\frac{D}{uL}$$

and

$$\sigma^2 = \frac{\sigma_t^{\ 2}}{\bar{t}^2} = 2\frac{D}{uL} + 8\left(\frac{D}{uL}\right)^2 \qquad (24)$$

Open-closed vessels. The third case considered is shown in Fig. 14. It is the combination of the first two in which no dispersion occurs at

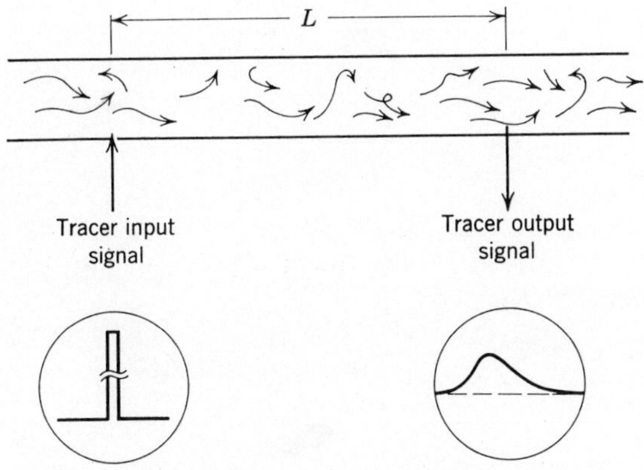

Fig. 13. Determination of dispersion in an open vessel.

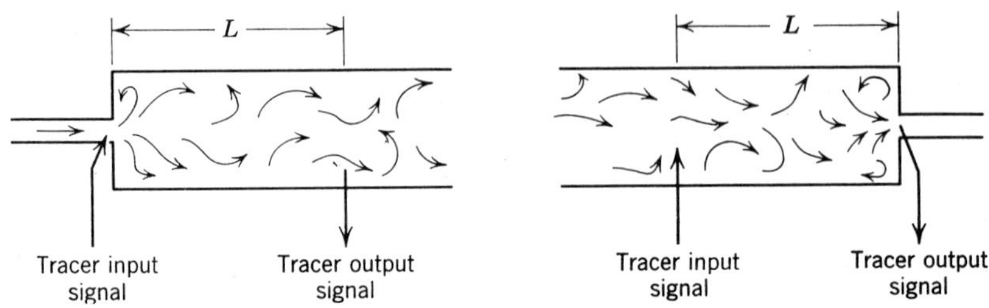

Fig. 14. Determination of dispersion in a closed-open and in an open-closed system.

either the tracer injection or recording point but not both. Here the **C** curve may be characterized by

$$\bar{\theta}_C = \frac{\bar{t}_C}{\bar{t}} = 1 + \frac{D}{uL}$$

and

$$\sigma^2 = \frac{\sigma_t^2}{\bar{t}^2} = 2\frac{D}{uL} + 3\left(\frac{D}{uL}\right)^2 \tag{25}$$

Small D/uL. For small deviations from plug flow, frequently encountered in real reactors, the **C** curves for all vessel end conditions approach each other, being well approximated by the normal, error, or Gaussian distribution:

$$\mathbf{C} = \frac{C}{C_0} = \frac{1}{2\sqrt{\pi(D/uL)}} \exp\left[-\frac{(1-\theta)^2}{4(D/uL)}\right]$$

for which the mean and variance are

$$\bar{\theta}_C = \frac{\bar{t}_C}{\bar{t}} = \frac{\bar{t}_C v}{V} = 1$$

and

$$\sigma^2 = 2\frac{D}{uL} \tag{26}$$

When $D/uL < 0.01$ the maximum error in this approximation for all vessels is less than $5(D/uL)$ or

$$5\% \quad \text{when } \frac{D}{uL} = 0.01$$

$$0.5\% \quad \text{when } \frac{D}{uL} = 0.001$$

Example 4

On the assumption that the vessel of Example 1, pg. 255, is well represented by the dispersion model, calculate the vessel dispersion number D/uL.

Solution. The variance of a continuous distribution measured at a finite number of equidistant locations is given by Eq. 12 as

$$\sigma^2 = \frac{\Sigma x_i^2 f(x_i)}{\Sigma f(x_i)} - \mu^2 = \frac{\Sigma x_i^2 f(x_i)}{\Sigma f(x_i)} - \left[\frac{\Sigma x_i f(x_i)}{\Sigma f(x_i)}\right]^2$$

Using the original tracer concentration time data given in Example 1, we find

$$\Sigma f(x_i) = \Sigma C_i = 3 + 5 + 5 + 4 + 2 + 1 = 20$$

$$\Sigma x_i f(x_i) = \Sigma t_i C_i = (5 \times 3) + (10 \times 5) + \cdots + (30 \times 1) = 300$$

$$\Sigma x_i^2 f(x_i) = \Sigma t_i^2 C_i = (25 \times 3) + (100 \times 5) + \cdots + (900 \times 1) = 5450$$

Therefore

$$\sigma_t^2 = \frac{5450}{20} - \left(\frac{300}{20}\right)^2 = 47.5$$

and

$$\sigma^2 = \frac{\sigma_t^2}{\bar{t}^2} = \frac{47.5}{(15)^2} = 0.211$$

Alternately, from the dimensionless distribution **E** versus θ of Example 1 we find from Eq. 12 or 15

$$\sigma^2 = \frac{\Sigma \theta^2 \mathbf{E}}{\Sigma \mathbf{E}} - 1 = \frac{(\frac{1}{9} \times 0.45) + (\frac{4}{9} \times 0.75) + \cdots + (4 \times 0.15)}{0.45 + 0.75 + 0.75 + 0.6 + 0.3 + 0.15} - 1$$

$$= 0.211$$

Now for a closed vessel we have from Eq. 23

$$\sigma^2 = 0.211 = 2\frac{D}{uL} - 2\left(\frac{D}{uL}\right)^2 (1 - e^{-uL/D})$$

Ignoring the second term on the right, we have as a first approximation

$$\frac{D}{uL} \approx 0.106$$

Correcting for the term ignored we find by trial and error

$$\frac{D}{uL} = 0.120$$

Example 5. Infinite Pipe, F curve

Von Rosenberg (1956) studied the displacement of benzene by *n*-butyrate in a $1\frac{1}{2}$-in.-diameter packed column 4 ft long. The fraction of *n*-butyrate in the exit stream was determined by refractive index measurements. When plotted,

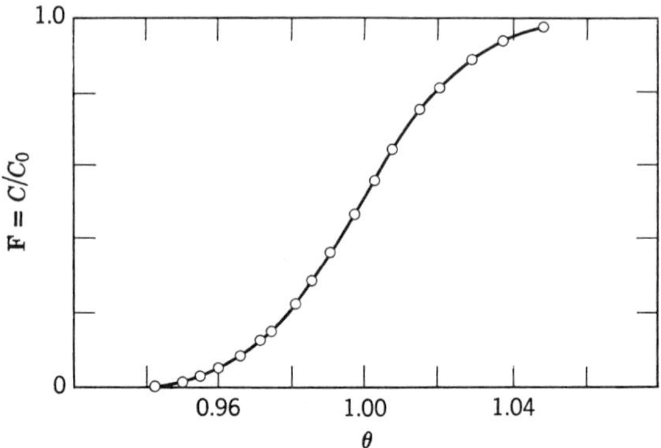

Fig. E5a. From von Rosenberg (1956).

the curve of time versus fraction *n*-butyrate was found to be S-shaped. For the run at the lowest flow rate, the velocity $u = 2.19 \times 10^{-5}$ ft/sec, which is about 2 ft/day. The **F** curve is shown in Fig. E5*a*.

Find the vessel dispersion number for this system.

Solution. Instead of finding the **C** curve by taking the slopes of the **F** curve and then determining the spread of this curve, let us illustrate a short cut which can be used when D/uL is small.

When D/uL is small the **C** curve approaches the normal curve of Eq. 26. When this is so the corresponding **F** curve, when plotted on probability paper, lies on a straight line. Plotting the original **F**-curve data on probability paper does actually result in an approximately straight line, as shown in Fig. E5*b*.

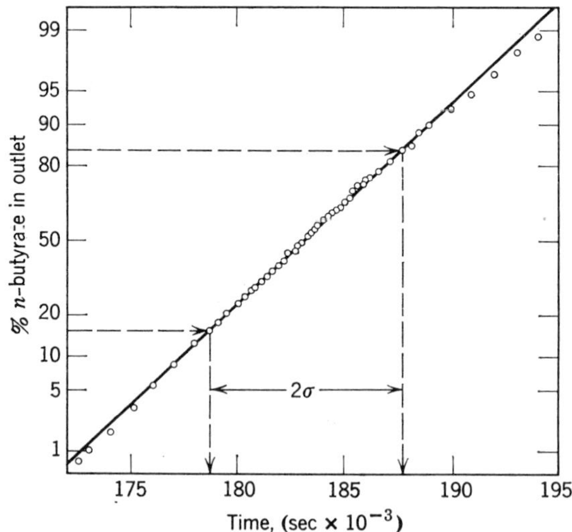

Fig. E5*b*. From Levenspiel and Smith (1957).

To find the variance, consequently the value of D/uL, from a probability graph is a simple matter if we observe the following property of a normal curve: that one standard deviation σ on either side of the mean of the curve includes 68% of the total area under the curve. Hence the 16th and 84th percentile points of the **F** curve are two standard deviations apart. The 84th percentile intersects the straight line through the data at 187,750 sec and the 16th percentile intersects it at 178,550 sec, so the difference, 9200 sec, is taken as the value of two standard deviations. Thus the standard deviation is

$$\sigma_t = 4600 \text{ sec}$$

We need this standard deviation in dimensionless time units if we are to find D. Therefore

$$\sigma = \frac{\sigma_t}{\bar{t}} = \sigma_t \frac{u}{L} = (4600 \text{ sec})\left(\frac{2.19 \times 10^{-5} \text{ ft/sec}}{4 \text{ ft}}\right) = 0.0252$$

Hence the variance

$$\sigma^2 = (0.0252)^2 = 0.00064$$

and from Eq. 26

$$\frac{D}{uL} = \frac{\sigma^2}{2} = 0.00032$$

Note that the value of D/uL is well below 0.01, justifying the use of the normal approximation to the **C** curve and this whole procedure.

Frequency response. Techniques other than the pulse or step tracer inputs can be used to investigate the dispersion model. Frequency response is one such technique. Here the phase lag and attenuation of a sinusoidal input signal as it passes through a vessel give the desired information on D/uL (see Fig. 15). Kramers and Alberda (1953) develop this method and show how it is used for closed vessels .

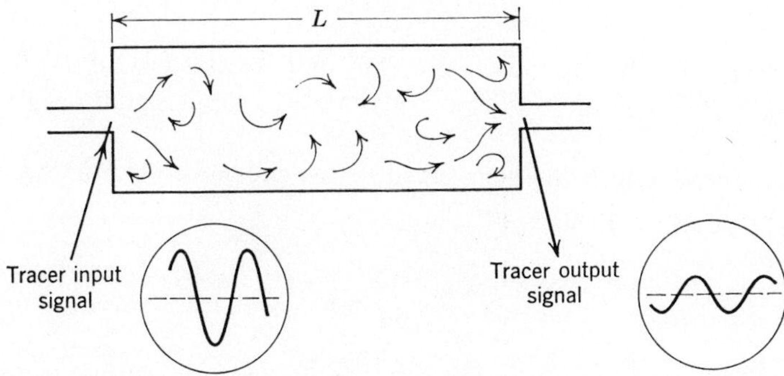

Fig. 15. Determination of dispersion in a closed vessel by means of sinusoidal tracer injection.

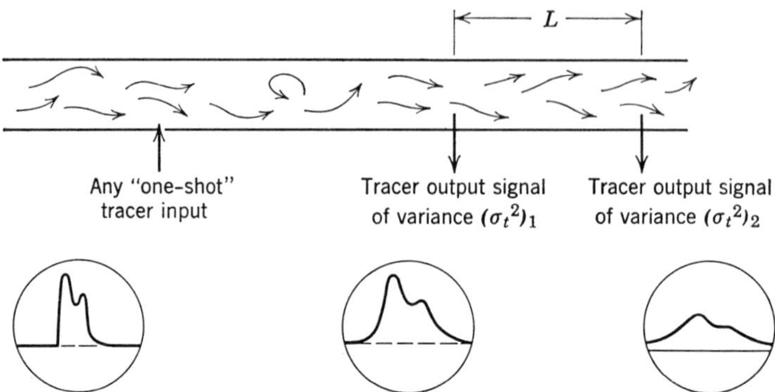

Fig. 16. Sketch of open-ended vessel showing location of dispersion measuring equipment.

Any "one-shot" tracer input. With a delta-function tracer input measurements need be taken at only one downstream point. From the resulting **C** curve D/uL can be found in a straightforward manner.

Obviously it is impossible to introduce tracer instantaneously but this limitation is not too serious if we can approximate the delta-function input fairly closely. Unfortunately in many cases this is often not practical, and the best we can do is not good enough. Most of the difficulty stems from the requirement that we add sufficient tracer to obtain reasonable **C**-curve readings, for the addition of these large amounts of tracer in a very short time can cause disturbances in flow patterns with spreading of tracer into the surrounding fluid by eddies.

When the inputs are far from ideal, in fact for any "one-shot" tracer input, we can still find D/uL by taking tracer readings at two downstream points. All that we need is the difference in variances of the concentration-time curves at these two points:

$$\Delta\sigma_t^2 = (\sigma_t^2)_2 - (\sigma_t^2)_1$$

This variance difference in dimensionless units is related to D/uL. For this procedure the location and shape of the tracer input signal need not be known.

Open vessels. For the open-ended vessel, shown in Fig. 16, the simple relationship given by Aris (1959),

$$\Delta\sigma^2 = \frac{\Delta\sigma_t^2}{\bar{t}^2} = 2\frac{D}{uL} \tag{27}$$

holds exactly, L and $\bar{t}$ referring to the region between the two measuring points.

Open-closed or closed vessels. For the three cases shown schematically in Fig. 17, the relation between the variances and the dispersion number is given by Bischoff (1960) as

$$\Delta\sigma^2 = \Delta\sigma_t^2\left(\frac{v}{V}\right)^2 = 2\frac{D}{uL} + \left(\frac{D}{uL}\right)^2\left(e^{-2uL/D} + 4e^{-uL/D} + 4\frac{uL}{D}e^{-uL/D} - 5\right) \tag{28}$$

Again L is the distance between the two measuring points, with the second point always located at the closed end of the vessel.

For most situations in which the dispersion model is applicable D/uL is very much smaller than unity, in which caes the second term of Eq. 28 is small with respect to the first term and may be neglected. Thus the simple expression of Eq. 27 which exactly characterizes the open-ended vessel becomes a good approximation for all the other vessel types. The magnitude of this approximation is seen by noting that when $D/uL = 0.1$, 0.01, 0.001, the error in using Eq. 27 instead of Eq. 28 is about 25%, 2.5%, and 0.25%.

Because this method does not restrict tracer input to delta functions, it is a powerful generalization which should be useful in experimentation. The following example illustrates the calculation procedure.

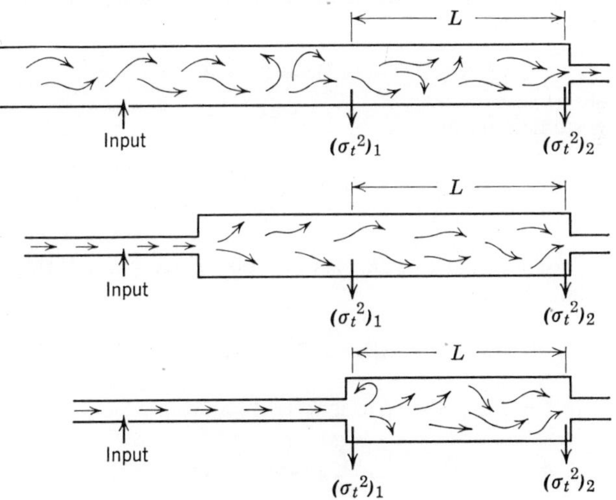

Fig. 17. Sketch of open-closed and closed vessels showing location of dispersion measuring equipment.

Example 6

The vessel dispersion number is to be found in a fixed-bed reactor packed with $\frac{1}{4}$-in. catalyst pellets. For this purpose tracer experiments are run in equipment shown in Fig. E6.

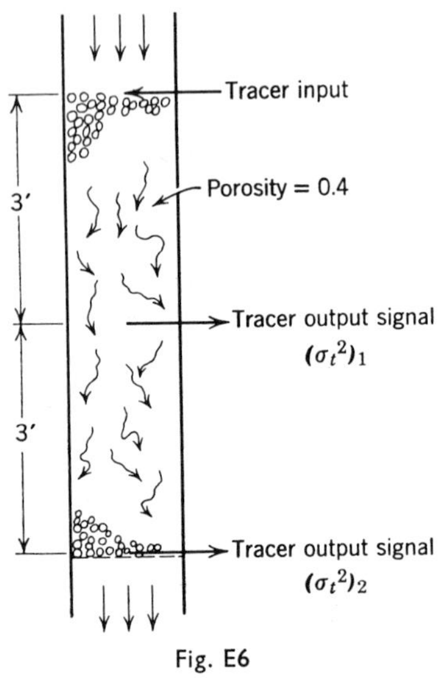

Fig. E6

Catalyst is laid down in a haphazard manner above a screen to a height of 6 ft in a vertical tube. Fluid flows downward through the packing, tracer is injected directly above the bed, and the output signals are recorded both at the screen and at the center of the bed.

(*a*) The following data apply to a specific experimental run. Bed porosity = 0.4, superficial velocity of fluid (based on an empty tube) = 0.04 ft/sec, and variances of output signals within and at the exit of the bed are found to be $(\sigma_t^2)_1 = 62$ sec² and $(\sigma_t^2)_2 = 87$ sec². Find D/uL.

(*b*) What error would be incurred if the calculation were based on the assumption of an open-ended (or section of infinite) vessel.

(*c*) Repeat part *a* for $(\sigma_t^2)_1 = 39$ sec² and $(\sigma_t^2)_2 = 64$ sec².

Assume that dispersion is absent at the packed-bed outlet.

Solution. (*a*) As the physical setup corresponds to the open-closed vessel, Eq. 28 applies. Thus

$$\Delta\sigma_t^2 = (\sigma_t^2)_2 - (\sigma_t^2)_1 = 87 - 62 = 25 \text{ sec}^2$$

and in dimensionless terms

$$\Delta\sigma^2 = \Delta\sigma_t^2\left(\frac{v}{V}\right)^2 = (25 \text{ sec}^2)\left[\frac{0.04 \text{ ft/sec}}{(3 \text{ ft})(0.4)}\right]^2 = \frac{1}{36}$$

Next D/uL is found from Eq. 28. As an approximation, ignoring the second term of Eq. 28, we find

$$\frac{D}{uL} = \frac{\Delta\sigma^2}{2} = \frac{1}{72}$$

With this value for D/uL, the term ignored becomes

$$\left(\frac{D}{uL}\right)^2\left(e^{-2uL/D} + 4e^{-uL/D} + 4\frac{uL}{D}e^{-uL/D} - 5\right)$$

$$= \left(\frac{1}{72}\right)^2\left(\frac{1}{e^{144}} + \frac{4}{e^{72}} + \frac{288}{e^{72}} - 5\right) = -0.000965$$

which amounts to 3.5% of $\frac{1}{36}$. Therefore the corrected value of D/uL is

$$\frac{D}{uL} = \left(\frac{1}{72}\right)(1.035) = 0.0144$$

(*b*) For the open-ended vessel Eq. 27 holds. This gives a value of $D/uL = \frac{1}{72}$ which is about 3.5% in error.

(*c*) For $(\sigma_t^2)_1 = 39\ \text{sec}^2$ and $(\sigma_t^2)_2 = 64\ \text{sec}^2$ we find

$$\Delta\sigma_t^2 = 64 - 39 = 25\ \text{sec}^2$$

which is identical with part *a*. Hence the solution is identical with that of part *a*.

Dispersion in a series of nonideal vessels. Dispersion characteristics of a vessel consisting of a number of regions in succession can be determined. Unavoidably, analysis is rather involved; however, when deviation from plug flow is small, we can use a relatively simple treatment based on the assumption that no dispersion occurs between flow regimes. For all practical purposes this assumption is satisfied if $D/uL < 0.01$ for each region of the vessel.

Consider a vessel consisting of j distinct flow regimes satisfying this assumption. From the additive properties of means and variances of independent distributions we have

$$\bar{t}_{\text{overall}} = \bar{t}_1 + \bar{t}_2 + \cdots + \bar{t}_j = \sum_{i=1}^{j} \bar{t}_i$$

and (29)

$$(\sigma_t^2)_{\text{overall}} = (\sigma_t^2)_1 + (\sigma_t^2)_2 + \cdots + (\sigma_t^2)_j = \sum_{i=1}^{j} (\sigma_t^2)_i$$

In a system consisting of a number of different flow regimes the dispersion characteristics of any one section can be found if the dispersion characteristics of all other sections are known, as well as that of the system as a whole. The method consists of the straightforward application of Eqs. 29 (see Fig. 18).

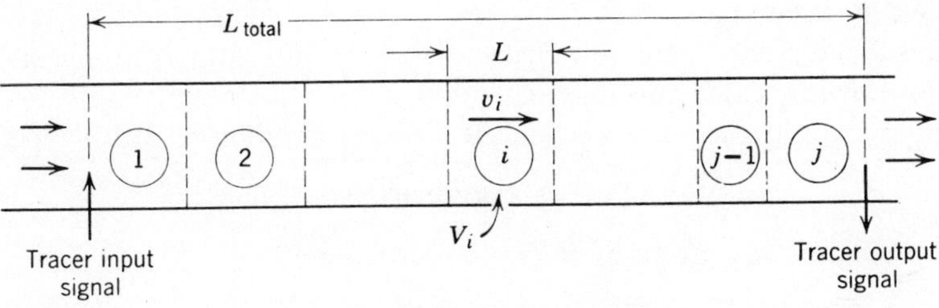

Fig. 18. Dispersion determination in one of a series of j vessels or j sections of an over-all system.

This may be a useful technique to apply when it is impractical or inconvenient to introduce tracer directly at the entrance of the experimental section or when the tracer output signal cannot be measured at the outlet of the experimental section.

Experimental findings on intensity of fluid mixing

The dispersed plug flow model satisfactorily describes the real flow of fluids in tubular vessels under certain conditions as well as in packed beds. Experimental findings for such vessels show that the intensity of dispersion measured by D/ud correlates well with the fluid and dynamic properties of the system. In the range of conditions usually of interest Fig. 19 is the correlation for packed beds and Figs. 20 and 21 are the correlations for tubular vessels. Note that in the streamline flow of fluids molecular diffusion plays a strong role; in addition, when the condition shown in Fig. 20 does not hold (pipe is not long enough), then the dispersion model is not a good description of streamline flow in pipes. More extended correlations are given by Bischoff and Levenspiel (1962).

No general correlations such as these are available at present for vessels other than packed beds and tubular vessels.

The vessel or reactor dispersion number is calculated from the intensity of dispersion, found from the charts, and the geometric factor for the reactor. Thus

$$\frac{D}{uL} = \begin{pmatrix}\text{intensity of}\\ \text{dispersion}\end{pmatrix}\begin{pmatrix}\text{geometric}\\ \text{factor}\end{pmatrix}$$

$$= \frac{D}{ud}\frac{d}{L}$$

where d is the characteristic length used in the charts.

Chemical reaction and dispersion

All previous discussion has led to the measure of dispersion by a dimensionless group D/uL. Let us now see how this is used to determine conversion by reaction.

Consider a steady-state-flow chemical reactor of length L through which fluid is flowing with a constant velocity u, and in which material is mixing axially with a dispersion coefficient D. Let the reaction be of the type

$$A \rightarrow \text{products}$$

with a reaction rate given by the nth-order reaction:

$$-r_A = -\frac{1}{V}\frac{dN_A}{dt} = -\frac{dC_A}{dt} = kC_A{}^n$$

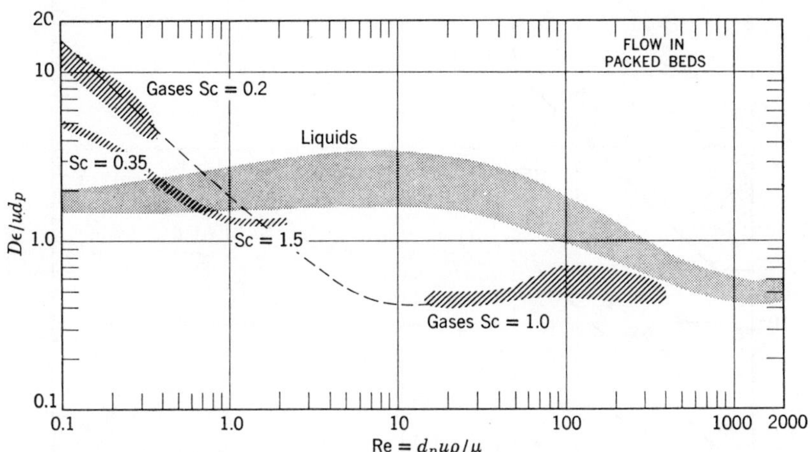

Fig. 19. Experimental findings on dispersion of fluids flowing with mean axial velocity u in packed beds; prepared in part from Bischoff (1961).

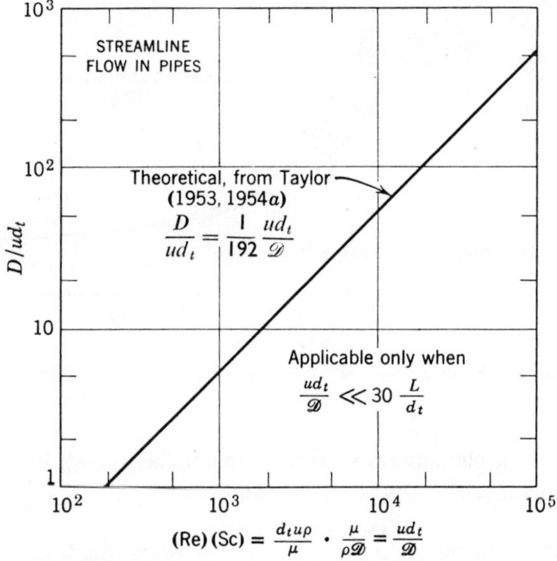

Fig. 20. Correlation for dispersion of fluids in streamline flow in pipes, from Levenspiel (1958).

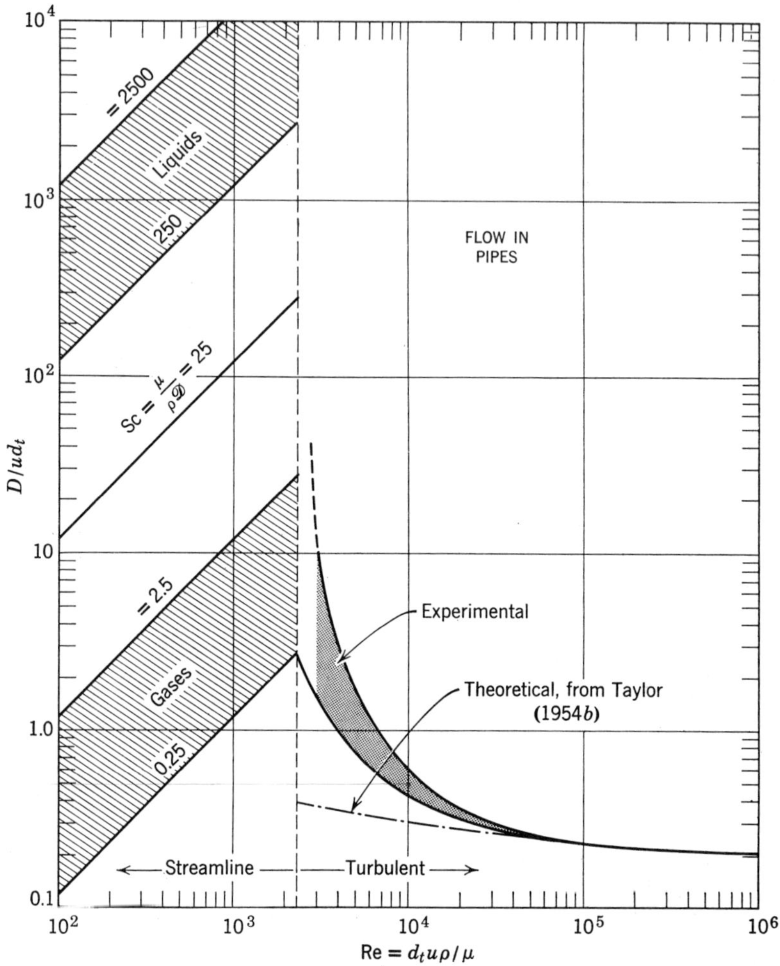

Fig. 21. Correlation for the dispersion of fluids flowing in pipes, adapted from Levenspiel (1958).

By referring to the elementary section of reactor as shown in Fig. 22, the basic material balance for any reaction component

$$\text{Input} = \text{Output} + \begin{matrix}\text{Disappearance}\\ \text{by reaction}\end{matrix} + \text{Accumulation} \tag{4.1}$$

becomes for component A

$$(\text{Out-in})_{\text{bulk flow}} + (\text{Out-in})_{\substack{\text{axial}\\ \text{dispersion}}} + \begin{matrix}\text{Disappearance}\\ \text{by reaction}\end{matrix} + \text{Accumulation} = 0 \tag{30}$$

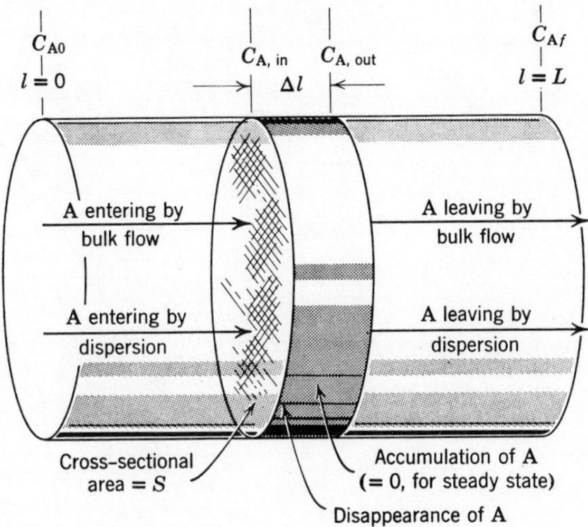

Fig. 22. Variables for a closed vessel in which reaction and dispersion are occurring.

The individual terms in moles A/time are as follows:
Entering by bulk flow

$$= \left(\frac{\text{moles A}}{\text{volume}}\right)\left(\begin{matrix}\text{volumetric}\\ \text{flow rate}\end{matrix}\right)$$

$$= \left(\frac{\text{moles A}}{\text{volume}}\right)\left(\begin{matrix}\text{flow}\\ \text{velocity}\end{matrix}\right)\left(\begin{matrix}\text{cross-sectional}\\ \text{area}\end{matrix}\right)$$

$$= C_{A,\text{in}} uS$$

Similarly, leaving by bulk flow

$$= C_{A,\text{out}} uS$$

Entering by axial dispersion, from the dispersion model,

$$\frac{dN_A}{dt} = -\left(DS\frac{dC_A}{dl}\right)_{\text{in}}$$

Similarly, leaving by axial dispersion,

$$\frac{dN_A}{dt} = -\left(DS\frac{dC_A}{dl}\right)_{\text{out}}$$

Disappearance by reaction

$$(-r_A)V = (-r_A)S\,\Delta l$$

Note that the difference between this material balance and that made for the ideal reactors of Chapter 5 is the inclusion of two extra terms, the

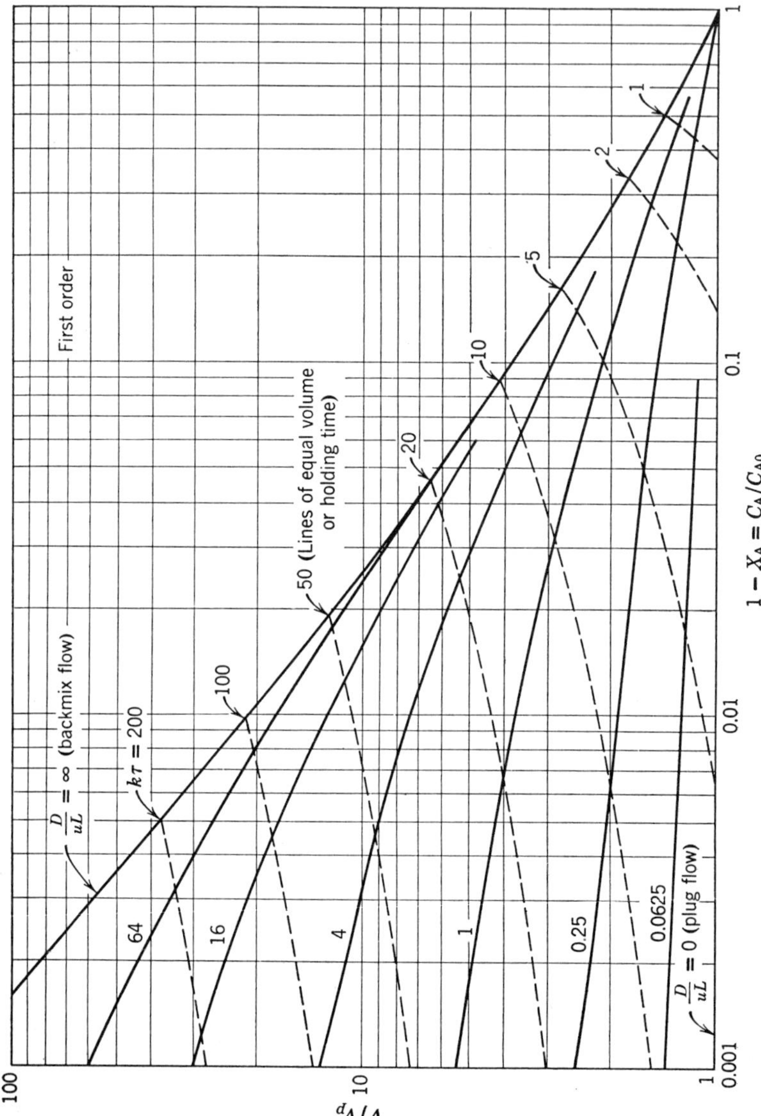

Fig. 23. Comparison of real and plug flow reactors for the first-order reaction $aA \rightarrow$ products, assuming negligible expansion; from Levenspiel and Bischoff (1959, 1961).

dispersion terms, because material enters and leaves the differential section not only by bulk flow but by dispersion as well. Entering all these terms in Eq. 30 and dividing by $S\,\Delta l$ gives

$$u\,\frac{(C_{A,\text{out}} - C_{A,\text{in}})}{\Delta l} - D\,\frac{\left[\left(\dfrac{dC_A}{dl}\right)_{\text{out}} - \left(\dfrac{dC_A}{dl}\right)_{\text{in}}\right]}{\Delta l} + (-r_A) = 0$$

Now the basic limiting process of calculus states that for any quantity Q which is a continuous function of l

$$\lim_{l_2 \to l_1} \frac{Q_2 - Q_1}{l_2 - l_1} = \lim_{\Delta l \to 0} \frac{Q_2 - Q_1}{\Delta l} = \frac{dQ}{dl}$$

So taking limits as $\Delta l \to 0$ we obtain

$$u\,\frac{dC_A}{dl} - D\,\frac{d^2C_A}{dl^2} + kC_A{}^n = 0 \qquad (31a)$$

In dimensionless form, by letting $z = l/L$ be the fractional length of reactor measured from the reactor entrance and letting $\tau = \bar{t} = L/u = V/v$, this expression becomes

$$\frac{D}{uL}\,\frac{d^2C_A}{dz^2} - \frac{dC_A}{dz} - k\tau C_A{}^n = 0 \qquad (31b)$$

or in terms of fractional conversion

$$\frac{D}{uL}\,\frac{d^2X_A}{dz^2} - \frac{dX_A}{dz} + k\tau C_{A0}^{n-1}(1 - X_A)^n = 0 \qquad (31c)$$

We see that the fractional conversion of reactant A in its passage through the reactor is governed by three dimensionless groups, a reaction rate group $k\tau C_{A0}^{n-1}$, the dispersion group D/uL, and the reaction order n.

First-order reaction. Equation 31 has been solved analytically by Wehner and Wilhelm (1956) for first-order reactions. For vessels with any kind of entrance and exit conditions the solution is

$$\frac{C_A}{C_{A0}} = 1 - X_A = \frac{4a \exp\left(\dfrac{1}{2}\dfrac{uL}{D}\right)}{(1 + a)^2 \exp\left(\dfrac{a}{2}\dfrac{uL}{D}\right) - (1 - a)^2 \exp\left(-\dfrac{a}{2}\dfrac{uL}{D}\right)} \qquad (32)$$

where $\qquad a = \sqrt{1 + 4k\tau(D/uL)}$

Figure 23 is a graphical representation of these results in useful form, prepared by combining Eqs. 32 and 5.12, and allows comparison of reactor sizes for plug and dispersed plug flow.

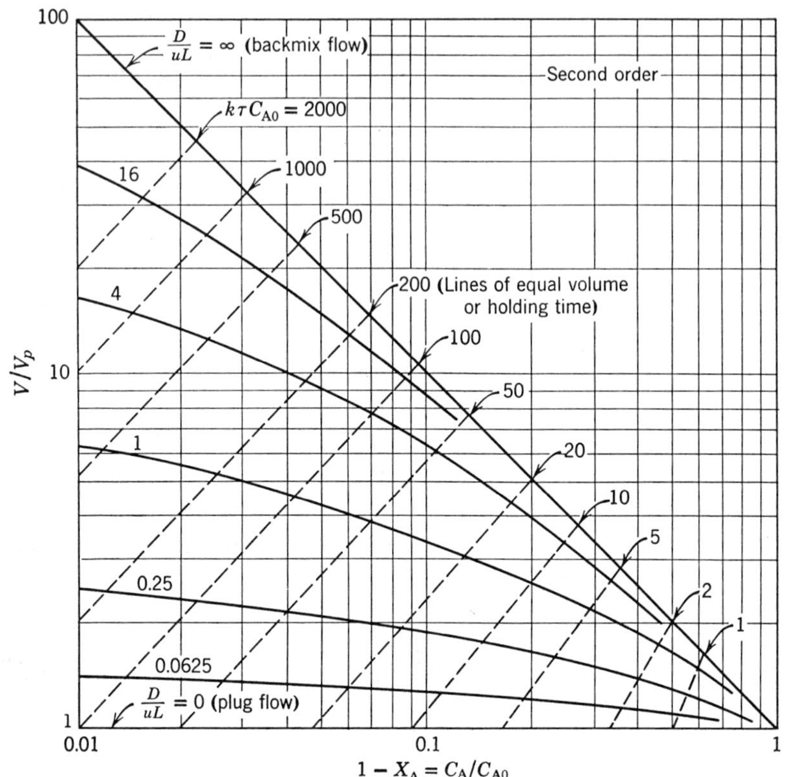

Fig. 24. Comparison of real and plug flow reactors for the second-order reactions

$$A + B \rightarrow \text{products}, \qquad C_{A0} = C_{B0}$$
$$2A \rightarrow \text{products}$$

assuming negligible expansion; from Levenspiel and Bischoff (1959, 1961).

For small deviations from plug flow, or for small D/uL, the comparison between real and plug flow reactors is as follows. For identical conversions in both reactors the size ratio becomes

$$\frac{L}{L_p} = \frac{V}{V_p} = \frac{\tau}{\tau_p} = 1 + k\tau \frac{D}{uL} = 1 + \frac{kD}{u^2} \tag{33}$$

For identical reactor size the ratio of reactant unconverted becomes

$$\frac{C_A}{C_{Ap}} = 1 + (k\tau)^2 \frac{D}{uL} \tag{34}$$

Second-order reactions. Figure 24 is the graphical representation of the solution of Eq. 31 for second-order reactions in closed vessels. It is used in a manner similar to the chart for first-order reactions.

Extensions. To estimate reactor performance for reactions of order different from one and two we may extrapolate or interpolate between Figs. 23 and 24. Alternately, the charts prepared by Fan and Bailie (1960) can be used. Note that backmixing does not affect performance for zero-order reactions.

For multiple reactions of the consecutive type we do not at present have a simple graphical representation of the effects of dispersion on product distribution and reactor size. Tichacek (1960) presents equations accounting for this effect and shows that for systems which deviate slightly from plug flow, say for $D/uL < 0.05$, the fractional decrease in the maximum amount of intermediate formed is closely approximated by the value of D/uL itself.

Where density changes produced by molar expansion are important, we may approximate this effect by considering it to be a multiplicative factor which can be dealt with by using Fig. 6.1.

Of the three reactor types generally used in industry, tubular, packed bed, and fluidized bed, only the first two exhibit marked nonisothermal behavior which need be considered in design. For these two reactor types the dispersion model, using axial and radial dispersion of both matter and heat, is the best way we now have for approximating the real situation. Bischoff and Levenspiel (1962) present and evaluate the various dispersion models which may be used here. They also present general correlations for axial and radial dispersion of matter in both packed beds and tubular reactors. Correlations for the radial and axial dispersion of heat in packed beds are given respectively in Yagi et al. (1961) and Kunii and Smith (1961). Additional discussions of the general problem are given by Froment (1959).

Example 7

Redo Example 3 on the assumption that the dispersion model is a good representation of flow in the reactor. Compare the calculated conversion by the two methods and comment.

Solution. Matching the experimentally found variance with that of the dispersion model, we find from Example 4

$$\frac{D}{uL} = 0.12$$

Conversion in the real reactor is found from Fig. 23. Thus moving along the $k\tau = (0.307)(15) = 4.6$ line from $C/C_0 = 0.01$ to $D/uL = 0.12$, we find that the fraction of reactant unconverted is approximately

$$\frac{C}{C_0} = 0.035, \qquad \text{or } 3.5\%$$

Figure E7 shows that except for a long tail the dispersion model curve has for the most part a greater central tendency than the actual curve. On the other

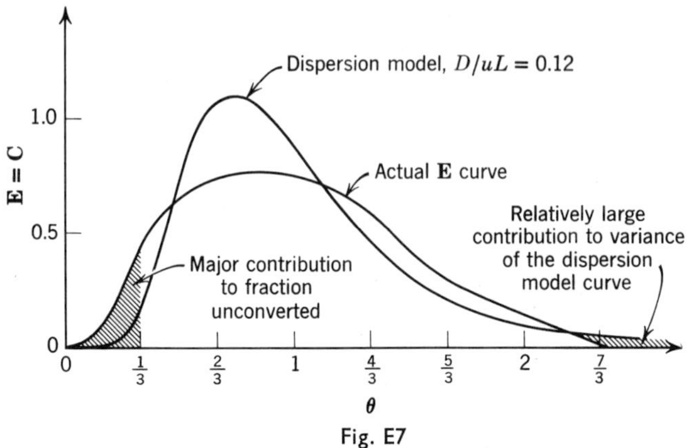

Fig. E7

hand, the actual curve has more short-lived material leaving the vessel. As this contributes most to the reactant remaining unconverted, the finding

$$\left(\frac{C}{C_0}\right)_{\text{actual}} = 4.7\% > \left(\frac{C}{C_0}\right)_{\substack{\text{dispersion}\\ \text{model}}} = 3.5\%$$

is expected.

TANKS IN SERIES MODEL

The tanks in series model is an alternate approach to the dispersion model for dealing with small deviations from plug flow. In this model we assume that the actual reactor can be represented by a series of j equal-sized backmix flow vessels. The output **C** curve for this model is somewhat similar to Fig. 10 of the dispersion model and can be shown to be

$$\mathbf{E} = \mathbf{C} = \frac{C}{C_0} = \frac{j^j \theta^{j-1}}{(j-1)!} e^{-j\theta} \tag{35}$$

with mean

$$\bar{\theta}_{\mathbf{C}} = 1 \tag{36}$$

and variance

$$\sigma_\theta^2 = \frac{1}{j} \tag{37}$$

From experimental variance measurements j can be found. Then performance of the real reactor can be found from Figs. 6 and 7 of Chapter 6.

Deans and Lapidus (1960) have extended the backmix reactors in series approach to handle the problem of nonisothermal nonideal flow in packed bed reactors. Their model uses a two-dimensional network of different-sized backmix reactors in place of the three-dimensional real reactor, and because concentration changes from tank to tank occur in discrete fashion, this model is claimed to be especially suited to the use of high-speed digital computers.

Comparison of tanks in series and dispersion models

As the dispersion model assumes a repeating random process, we would expect the two models to become identical for large j. This is so. But since the elementary processes visualized for these two models differ somewhat in that fluid cannot move upstream from tank to tank but can move upstream by dispersion, the **C** curves for these two models should differ more and more in shape with increasing deviation from plug flow. This also is so.

The correspondence between these two models is not clear-cut. Matching calculated variances gives

$$\sigma_\theta^2 = \frac{1}{j} = 2\frac{D}{uL} - 2\left(\frac{D}{uL}\right)^2(1 - e^{-uL/D}) \tag{38}$$

However, because the **C** curves differ in shape at fixed σ^2, the conversion predictions of these two models also differ. Figure 25 shows that the two

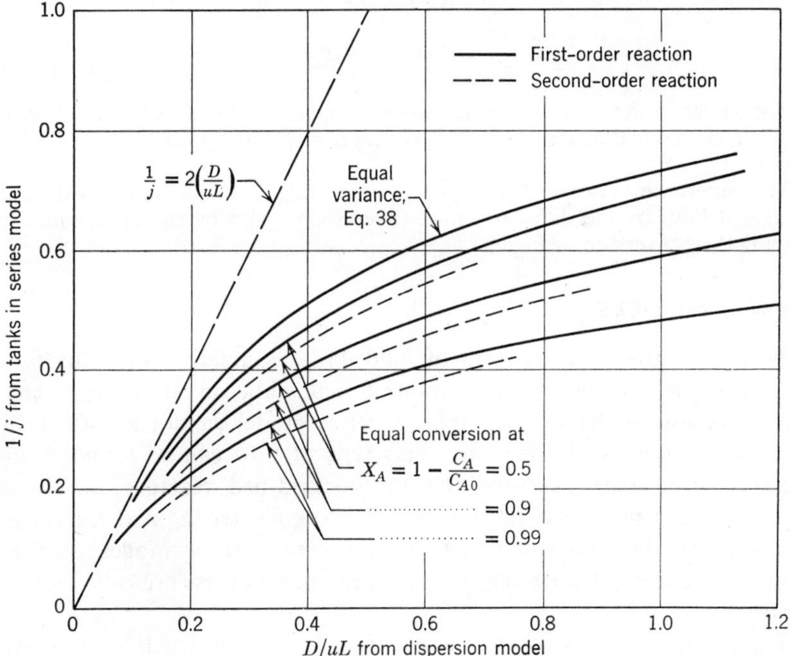

Fig. 25. Ways of comparing the tanks in series and dispersion models; adapted from Levenspiel (1962*b*).

methods of comparison, equality of variance and equality in performance as a reactor, vary increasingly with rise in reaction order and conversion.

The criterion we use in comparing models depends on the purpose of the comparison. Inasmuch as the purpose is primarily to compare performance of vessels as reactors, it is better to equate conversions rather than variances.

Example 8

Redo Example 3, assuming that the tanks in series model is a good representation of flow in the reactor. Compare the calculated conversion for this model with that of the dispersion model (3.5% from Example 7) and the direct method (4.7% from Example 3).

Solution. From the data we find (see Example 4)

$$\sigma^2 = 0.211$$

Matching variances we find from Eq. 37

$$j = \frac{1}{\sigma^2} = \frac{1}{0.211} = 4.76$$

Thus the real reactor behaves as a system of 4.76 equal-sized backmix reactors in series. Conversion for such a system is then given by Fig. 6.6 or can be calculated by Eq. 6.6. Thus for $k\bar{t} = (0.307)(15) = 4.6$ we find that the fraction unconverted is

$$\frac{C}{C_0} = 0.040 = 4.0\%$$

The explanation for this low value when compared to the direct-method value of 4.7% is identical to that given for the lower dispersion model value of 3.5% (see Example 7).

The difference between the tanks in series and dispersion model values is explained both by the difference in C-curve shapes and by the uncertainty in reading the conversion in Fig. 23.

MIXED MODELS

When the gross flow pattern of fluid deviates greatly from plug flow because of channeling or recirculation of fluid, eddies in odd corners, etc., the dispersion model or the tanks in series model cannot satisfactorily characterize flow in the reactor. This type of flow can be found in industrial stirred-tank reactors and in fluidized-bed reactors. In these situations it is probably the most fruitful to consider the real reactor as consisting of interconnected flow regions with various modes of flow between and around these regions. Models such as these are called *mixed models*.

The following kinds of regions are used in the construction of mixed models: *plug flow regions, backmix flow regions, dispersed plug flow regions, deadwater regions*.

The last mentioned region accounts for the portion of fluid in the vessel which is relatively slow moving and, for all practical purposes, stagnant. There are two ways to deal with deadwater regions: to assume their contents to be completely stagnant or to view a slow interchange of their contents with the fluid passing through the vessel. In the first approach the treatment is quite simple; the second approach more closely approximates real situations but requires rather involved analyses [see Adler and Hovorka (1961)]. We shall consider only this first approach.

In attempting to represent flow in a real vessel by mixed models containing completely stagnant fluid, we meet with difficulties. For example, the existence of completely stagnant fluid cannot be reconciled with the assumption of steady-state flow through the vessel. Again, with this definition the mean age of the vessel contents would not be useful in matching models because, even if a deadwater region consisted of only one molecule, the calculated mean age of the vessel contents would still be infinite.

The following definition of deadwater regions from Levenspiel (1962*a*) overcomes these difficulties while still maintaining a concept of these regions which is useful in matching models with real situations;

> In a vessel the deadwater regions are the relatively slow moving portions of the fluid which we chose to consider to be completely stagnant. Deadwater regions contribute to the vessel volume; however, we ignore these regions in determining the various age distributions.

The cutoff point in residence time between what we chose to consider as active fluid and what we choose to consider as stagnant fluid depends on the accuracy of predictions of vessel performance. In most cases material that stays in a vessel twice the mean residence time can, with negligible error, be taken as stagnant. As a case in point, consider Example 3. If we take $1.5\bar{t}$ as the cutoff point, 15% of the fluid is involved (see Example 2); however, the error that results from ignoring this 15% of the fluid amounts to 0.0001/0.0469, or less than 0.3% of the predicted conversion.

In addition to these regimes, mixed models may use the following kinds of flow:

Bypass flow, where a portion of the fluid bypasses the vessel or a particular flow region.

Recycle flow, where a portion of the fluid leaving the vessel or leaving a flow region is recirculated and returned to mix with fresh fluid.

Cross flow, where interchange but no net flow of fluid occurs between different flow regions.

With these as the components of mixed models the problem is then to find the volumes of the various regions and the rate of each type of flow occurring such that the response curves of the model match as closely as

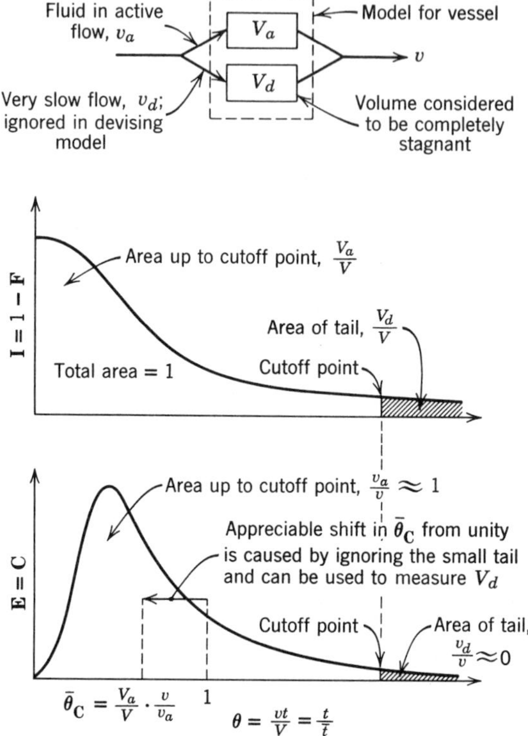

Fig. 26. Particular features of age distribution curves for mixed models which include deadwater regions; adapted from Levenspiel (1962a, 1963).

possible the response curves for the real vessel. The following suggestions may be helpful in this search.

Existence of deadwater regions. Select a reasonable cutoff point, say $\theta = 2$, and find the mean of the **C** curve up to that point. If no deadwater regions are present, then

$$\bar{\theta}_C = \frac{\text{measured } \bar{t}_C}{V/v} \approx 1$$

If deadwater regions are present, then

$$\bar{\theta}_C < 1$$

The fraction of vessel consisting of deadwater regions is given by the deviation of $\bar{\theta}_C$ from unity. Hence

$$\bar{\theta}_C = \frac{\bar{t}_C}{\bar{t}} = \frac{(V/v)_a}{V/v} = \frac{V_a}{V} \cdot \frac{v}{v_a} \quad \text{or} \quad \frac{V_d}{V} = 1 - \frac{v_a}{v}\,\bar{\theta}_C \tag{39}$$

Alternatively the area under the **I** curve will give V_d. Figure 26 summarizes these results.

Existence of bypass flow. In bypass flow we may look at the incoming fluid as splitting into two parallel streams, the fraction passing through the vessel being v_1, the fraction bypassing it instantaneously being v_2. Figure 27 shows characteristics of typical response curves when bypass flow occurs. From the rapid initial drop in the **I** curve, from the shift in mean value for the main portion of the **E** curve, or from the area of the main portion of the **E** curve, the magnitude of such short-circuiting can

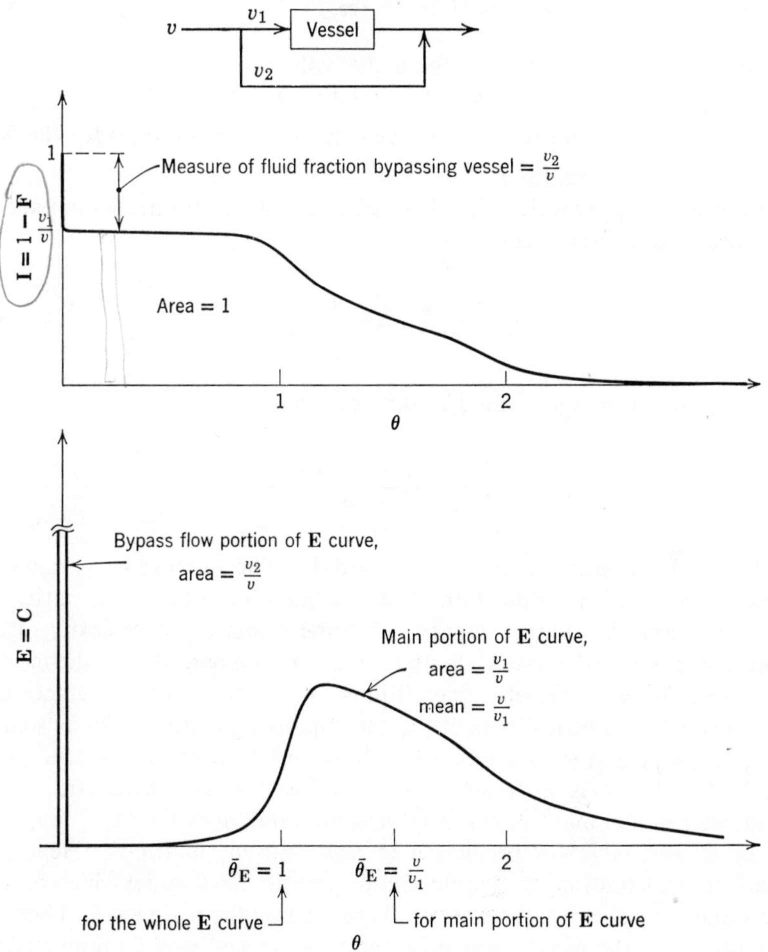

Fig. 27. Particular features of age distribution curves for models which include bypass flow; from Levenspiel (1962*a*).

be estimated. Probably the role of bypass flow can be evaluated more easily from **F** or **I** curves than from the **C** or **E** curves.

Regions in series. For flow regions 1, 2, . . . connected in series the mean age of vessel contents is

$$\bar{t}_{\mathrm{I}} = \bar{t}_{\mathrm{I1}}\frac{V_1}{V} + (\bar{t}_{\mathrm{E1}} + \bar{t}_{\mathrm{I2}})\frac{V_2}{V} + (\bar{t}_{\mathrm{E1}} + \bar{t}_{\mathrm{E2}} + \bar{t}_{\mathrm{I3}})\frac{V_3}{V} + \cdots \tag{40}$$

whereas the mean age of fluid in the exit stream is

$$\bar{t}_{\mathrm{E}} = \bar{t}_{\mathrm{E1}} + \bar{t}_{\mathrm{E2}} + \cdots \tag{41}$$

Here $V_1, V_2, \ldots$ refer only to the active volumes
V refers to the total vessel volume
$\bar{t}_1, \bar{t}_2, \ldots$ refer to the separately measured mean times for the flow regions 1, 2, ...

Regions in parallel. For flow regions 1, 2, . . . connected in parallel the mean age of vessel contents is

$$\bar{t}_{\mathrm{I}} = \bar{t}_{\mathrm{I1}}\frac{V_1}{V} + \bar{t}_{\mathrm{I2}}\frac{V_2}{V} + \cdots \tag{42}$$

whereas the mean age of fluid in the exit stream is

$$\bar{t}_{\mathrm{E}} = \frac{V_1 + V_2 + \cdots}{v} \tag{43}$$

Number of parameters in a model. The number of parameters used in a model is an indication of its flexibility in fitting a wide variety of situations and in addition suggests to some extent the complexity of the accompanying mathematics. With more and more parameters, the models are able to fit wider variety of conditions. We must, however, balance this gain against the unwieldiness of the accompanying mathematics as well as the possibility that such a model may have very little correspondence with fact. The latter is a serious objection because an unrealistic many-parameter model may closely fit all present data "after the fact," but may be quite unreliable for prediction in new untried situations. Hence, in fitting a real situation, we should aim for the simplest model which fits the facts and whose various regions are suggested by the real vessel. Then the parameters of the model have physical meaning and may be predicted by independent methods. This question is of concern in fitting models to fluidized beds. The tanks-in-series and dispersion models are one-parameter models. In general, the number of parameters in a mixed model is

$$\begin{aligned}\begin{matrix}\text{Number of}\\ \text{parameters}\end{matrix} &= \sum\begin{pmatrix}\text{flow regions in}\\ \text{excess of one}\end{pmatrix} + \sum\begin{pmatrix}\text{flow paths in}\\ \text{excess of one}\end{pmatrix} + \sum\begin{pmatrix}\text{zones of}\\ \text{cross flow}\end{pmatrix}\\ &\quad + \sum\begin{pmatrix}\text{flow regions}\\ \text{with dispersion}\end{pmatrix} - \sum\begin{pmatrix}\text{arbitrary restrictions}\\ \text{on flow, volume, etc.}\end{pmatrix} \end{aligned} \tag{44}$$

Figure 28 illustrates some simple mixed models and their tracer response curves. In these models V_b, V_p, and V_d stand for the volume of backmix, plug flow, and deadwater regions. If V is the volume of vessel, we then have

$$V = \sum V_b + \sum V_p + \sum V_d$$

The flow rates of streams in parallel are designated by $v_1, v_2, \ldots$. If v is the flow rate of fluid to the vessel, then with $v_d = 0$ we have

$$v = v_1 + v_2 + \cdots$$

Varying the relative sizes of the flow regions as well as the flow rate of parallel streams allows great flexibility in matching the response curves of these models to that for the real vessel. Eguchi (1961) presents the mixed models which have been used to date to represent flow in various kinds of vessels.

The following brief discussion shows how mixed models can be used to characterize flow in and predict conversion from two broad classes of process equipment, real stirred tanks, and fluidized beds.

Application to stirred-tank reactors

The first attempt to describe the behavior of a real stirred-tank reactor under various conditions of agitation with a mixed model was made by Cholette and Cloutier (1959). By matching **F** curves and rejecting numerous alternative models, they found that their data were best fitted by a model consisting of a backmix region and of a deadwater region with a portion of the fluid bypassing the vessel. The internal age distribution function for this model is

$$\mathbf{I} = 1 - \mathbf{F} = \frac{v_1}{v}\exp\left(-\frac{v_1}{v}\frac{V}{V_b}\theta\right)$$

or

$$\mathbf{I}(t) = \frac{1}{\bar{t}_a}\frac{V_b}{V}e^{-t/\bar{t}_a} \tag{45}$$

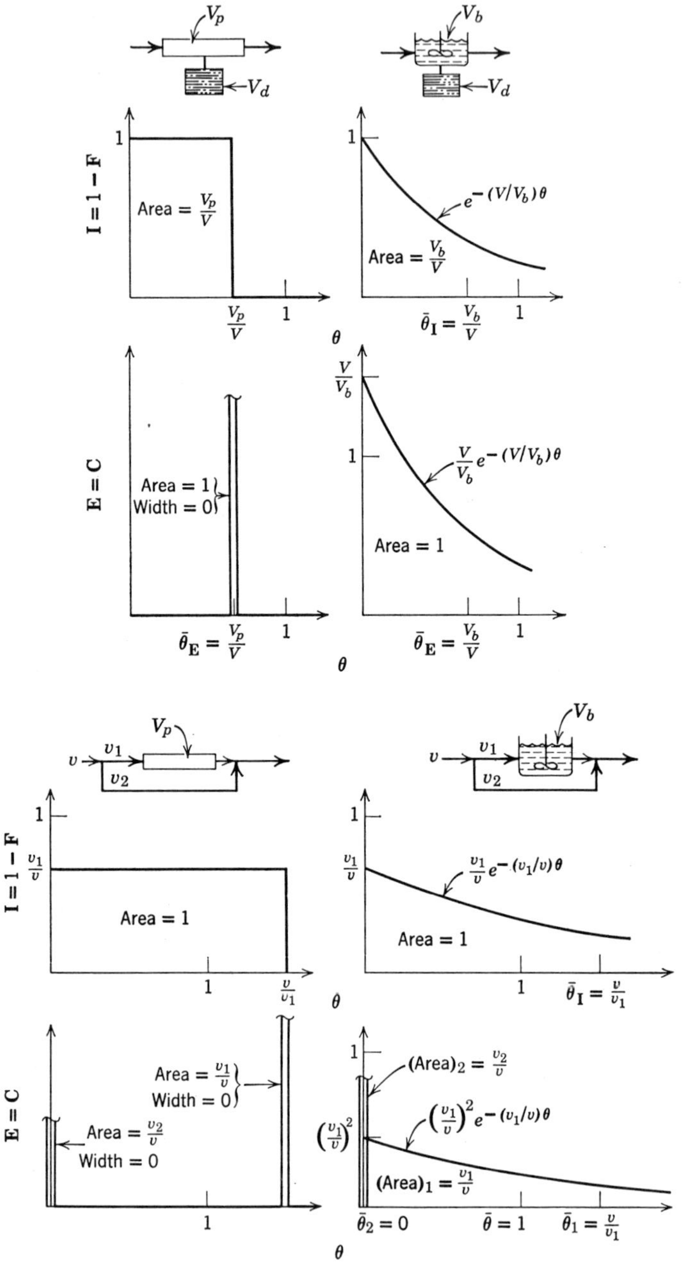

Fig. 28. Simple mixed models and their age distribution functions; in part from Levenspiel (1962*a*).

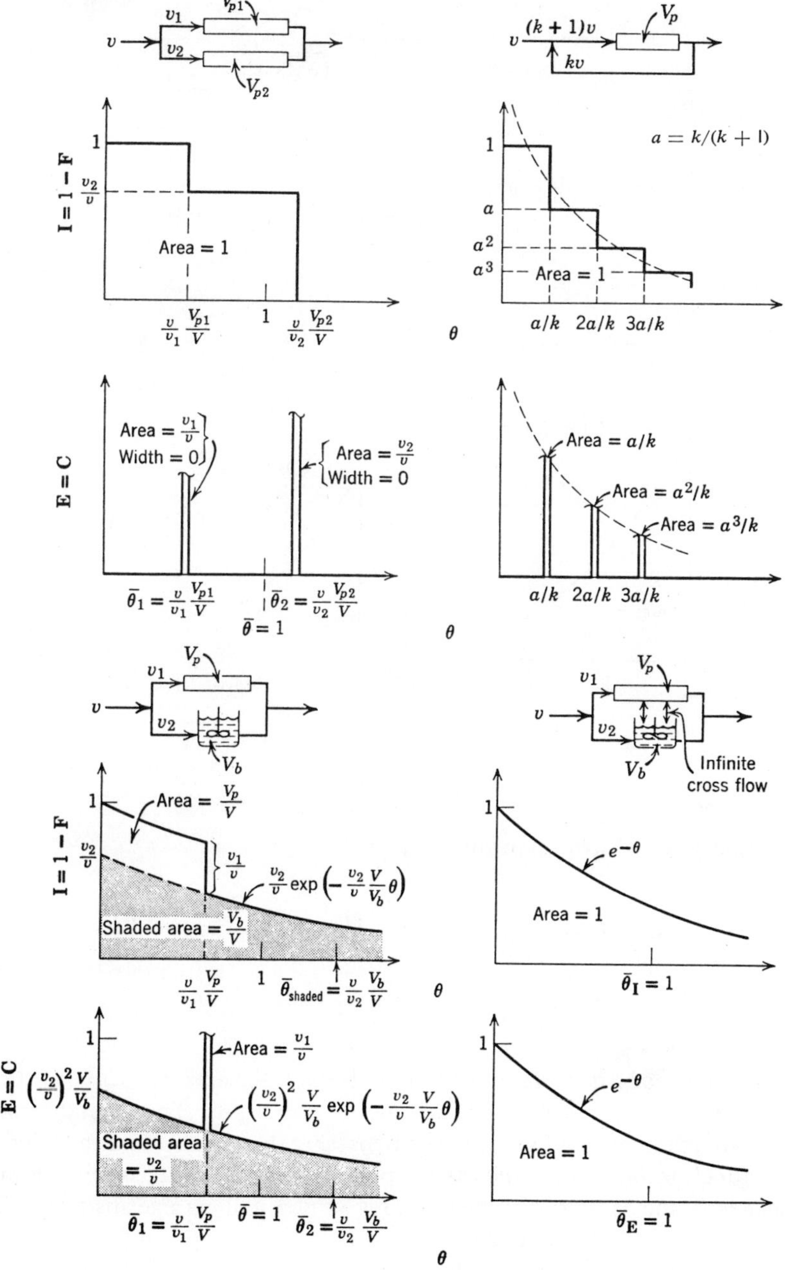

Fig. 28 (continued).

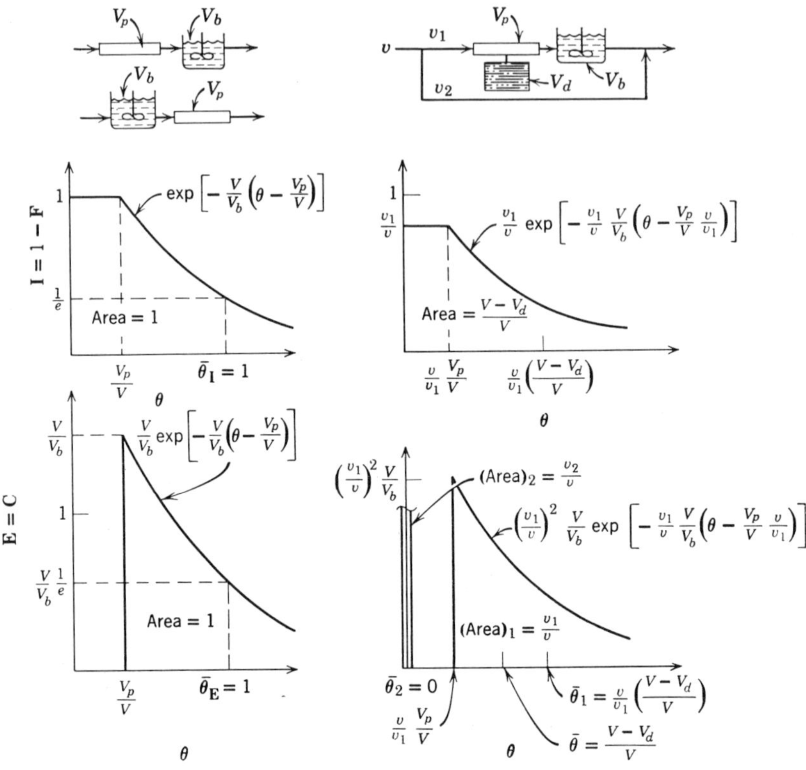

Fig. 28 (continued).

and the exit age distribution function is

$$\mathbf{E} = \mathbf{C} = \left(\frac{v_1}{v}\right)^2 \frac{V}{V_b} \exp\left(-\frac{v_1}{v}\frac{V}{V_b}\theta\right) + \frac{v_2}{v}\,\delta(\theta = 0)$$

or

$$\mathbf{E}(t) = \frac{1}{\bar{t}_a}\frac{v_1}{v}\exp\left(-\frac{t}{\bar{t}_a}\right) + \frac{v_2}{v}\,\delta(t = 0) \tag{46}$$

The first term of Eq. 46 represents flow through the active portion of the vessel. This has a mean residence time of $\bar{t}_a = V_b/v_1$. The second term of Eq. 46 represents the fluid which is bypassing the vessel. Here the Dirac delta function $\delta(t = 0)$ stands for a pulse of unit quantity occurring at time $t = 0$ and is zero elsewhere. This model and its age distribution functions are shown in Fig. 29.

Cholette and Cloutier also found that agitation rate influenced the parameters of this model. This is shown in Fig. 30. As we may expect,

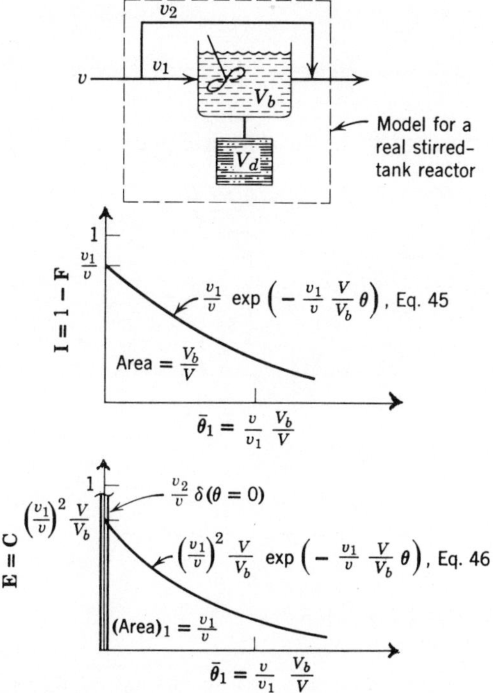

Fig. 29. Model and age distribution functions for a real stirred-tank reactor.

increased agitation decreases both the bypassing rate and size of dead-water regions, and, if agitation is vigorous enough, above 300 rpm for their experimental setup, backmix flow is achieved.

Although the quantitative findings of Fig. 30 may be expected to hold only for their vessel geometry, still, until evidence is presented to the contrary, we may expect this flow model to describe flow in stirred-tank reactors.

Conversion from this model is found by noting that the exit stream $\bar{C}_A$ consists of reacted fluid C_A from the active backmix region mixed with unreacted bypassing fluid C_{A0}. By material balance then

$$(v_1 + v_2)\bar{C}_A = v_1 C_A + v_2 C_{A0}$$

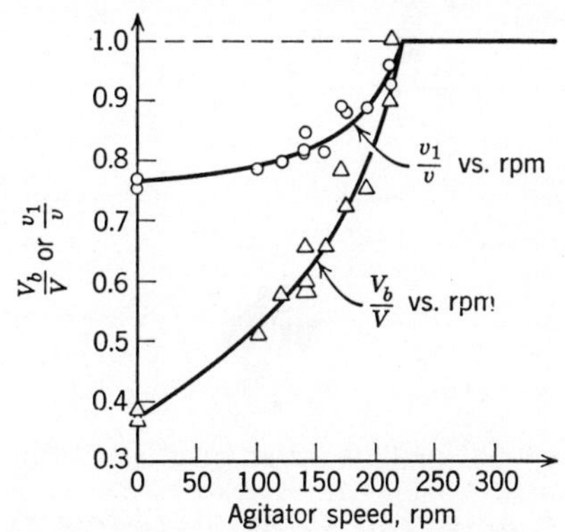

Fig. 30. Effect of agitation on the parameters of the model for a stirred tank, from Cholette and Cloutier (1959).

or

$$\frac{\bar{C}_A}{C_{A0}} = \frac{v_1}{v}\frac{C_A}{C_{A0}} + \frac{v_2}{v} \tag{47}$$

where C_A/C_{A0} is found from the design equation for backmix reactors,

$$\bar{t}_a = \frac{C_{A0} - C_A}{-r_A} \tag{5.9}$$

For *zero-order reactions* Eq. 47 reduces to

$$\frac{\bar{C}_A}{C_{A0}} = \frac{v_1}{v}\left(1 - \frac{k\bar{t}_a}{C_{A0}}\right) + \frac{v_2}{v} \tag{48}$$

For *first-order reactions* Eq. 47 reduces to

$$\frac{\bar{C}_A}{C_{A0}} = \frac{v_1}{v}\frac{1}{1 + k\bar{t}_a} + \frac{v_2}{v} \tag{49}$$

For *second-order reactions* Eq. 47 reduces to

$$\frac{\bar{C}_A}{C_{A0}} = \frac{v_1}{v}\frac{-1 + \sqrt{1 + 4kC_{A0}\bar{t}_a}}{2kC_{A0}\bar{t}_a} + \frac{v_2}{v} \tag{50}$$

In an alternate manner the exit age distribution function for this model can be used directly to find the conversion for the linear processes of Eq. 17. Thus by combining Eqs. 18 and 46 the expression to be solved is

$$\frac{\bar{C}_A}{C_{A0}} = \frac{1}{\bar{t}_a}\frac{v_1}{v}\int_0^\infty \left(\frac{C_A}{C_{A0}}\right)_{\text{batch}} e^{-t/\bar{t}_a}\,dt + \frac{v_2}{v}\int_0^\infty \left(\frac{C_A}{C_{A0}}\right)_{\text{batch}} \delta(t = 0)\,dt$$

Since $\delta(t = 0)$ is simply unit quantity at time $t = 0$ and is zero elsewhere, the second integral is unity (see pg. xv); thus we have

$$\frac{\bar{C}_A}{C_{A0}} = \frac{1}{\bar{t}_a}\frac{v_1}{v}\int_0^\infty \left(\frac{C_A}{C_{A0}}\right)_{\text{batch}} e^{-t/\bar{t}_a}\,dt + \frac{v_2}{v} \tag{51}$$

which for first-order reactions reduces to Eq. 48.

Application to fluidized-bed reactors

Mixed models are presently being used in an attempt to characterize flow in fluidized-bed reactors. These reactors, widely used in industry today, are heterogeneous gas-solid or liquid-solid systems. Consequently their treatment must account for the following: streams of two materials, solid and fluid, move through the vessel; reaction may be homogeneous, heterogeneous or both; in some cases it is primarily the solid that is being treated, whereas in others it is the gas with the solid acting as catalyst or as a heat reservoir.

Despite these added complications, it is worthwhile at this point to consider fluidized beds briefly, for they best illustrate the use of fairly involved mixed models to characterize reactors of industrial importance.

Fig. 31. Typical cross section through a fluidized bed showing the vigorous action and the two phases, the lean or bubble phase and the dense or emulsion phase.

Characteristics of a fluidized bed. In a fluidized bed gas is passed upward through a bed of solids at a rate high enough so that all the particles are suspended. By examination we see that the bed is not homogeneous. It bubbles, it boils, and solids move about in jerky turbulent motion. Gas percolates through the solid and also bubbles up through the bed with little contacting of solids. We can imagine the violent action occurring in an industrial unit 150 ft high and 30 ft in diameter. Figure 31 shows a typical cross section through a fluidized bed.

The fluidized bed has three characteristics that make it a very attractive reactor system.

1. The violent motion and rapid redistribution of solids result in a remarkably temperature-stable system without hot spots. This makes for good control of the reaction.

2. The large gas-solid contact area, as well as the good contacting of phases, makes this an efficient system for effecting catalytic and noncatalytic gas-solid reactions.

3. The solids can be handled very conveniently by pneumatic systems when in the fluidized state. In the noncatalytic system the solid is the material to be treated; in catalytic reactions the solid catalyst must be periodically cleaned or regenerated. In both systems solids must be introduced and then removed. In fluidized reactors the usual costly materials-handling equipment is not needed, for solid can be pumped into and out of the system like a fluid.

The undesirable characteristics of a fluidized reactor happen to be those associated with nonideal flow. Thus for reactions of all types the reactor size increases very rapidly at high conversions, much more so than for a plug flow reactor. In addition, in multiple reactions optimum product distribution cannot be attained.

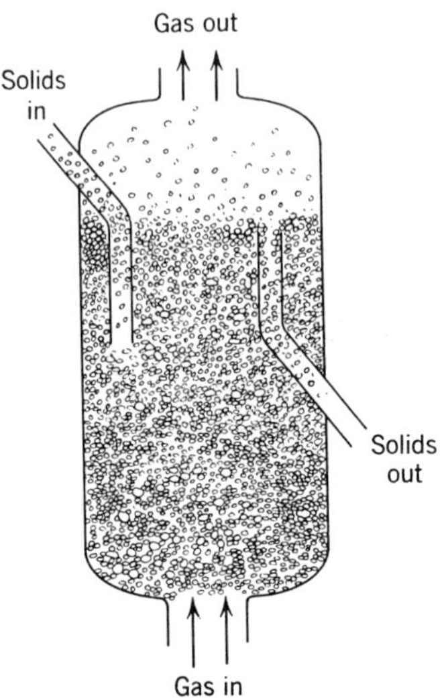

Fig. 32. A fluidized bed with continuous feed and discharge of solids.

Now the extent of deviation from plug flow must be known for adequate design of such units—therefore the intensive efforts that have been concentrated on the problem of characterizing the nonideal behavior of fluidized beds.

Residence time distribution of solids in a fluidized bed. In noncatalytic gas-solid reactions, say in the roasting of sulfide ore, it is the solid that is being treated; therefore it is of primary importance to know the residence time distribution of solids in the reactor. For a steady-state fluidized bed with continuous feed and discharge of solids as shown in Fig. 32 the following have been found.

1. If the feed consists of a single size of solid, the bed may be considered to be completely mixed. Thus we may consider that we have backmix flow of solids.

2. If the feed consists of a wide size distribution, each particle size may be considered to be uniformly distributed within the bed. In other words, each size can be considered to be in backmix flow within the bed.

These conclusions are not strictly correct; however, since the length of stay of solids within reactors is relatively long, they become reasonable approximations.

In noncatalytic gas-solid reactions in which the conversion of solid is of primary interest, information on how the contacting gas passes through the bed is not critical, for the concentration of reactant in the gas does not usually change greatly in passing through the reactor. In such reactions the residence time distribution information for solids alone is adequate for design. Chapter 12 considers this whole problem in detail.

Residence time distribution of a gas in a fluidized bed. In solid-catalyzed gas-phase reactions the residence time distribution of the gas in the bed is of primary importance in determining performance—hence the need for this information. Early studies relied on the dispersion model; however, the inability of this approach to yield broad predictive

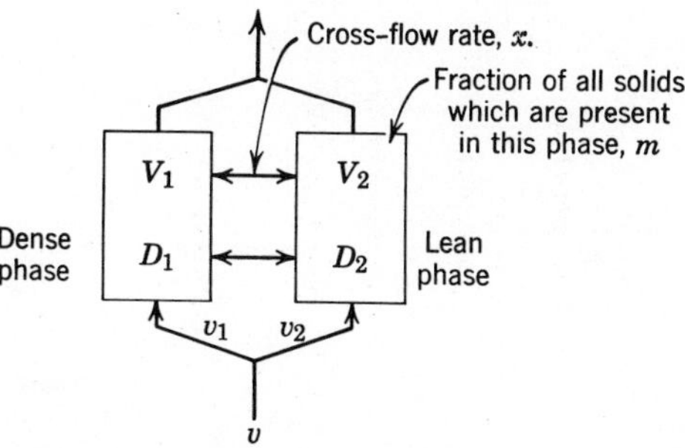

Fig. 33. General two-region model of a fluidized bed. Fluid is in dispersed plug flow in both regions. The six model parameters are m, x, V_1, v_1, D_1, D_2.

correlations, in particular with solid-catalyzed gas-phase reactions, seems to point out that this one-parameter model can only crudely explain fluidized-bed behavior.

A different approach was needed, and this was found in mixed models. The two-compartment model was an obvious choice, with each of the two compartments corresponding to one of the two "phases" in a fluidized bed, the "bubble" or lean phase and the "emulsion" or dense phase. A number of such models have been proposed. These are all special cases of the general two-region, six-parameter model shown in Fig. 33. This general model has not as yet been used for two reasons, the difficulty in interpreting experimental data in the evaluation of the model parameters, and the fact that a simpler version could probably represent reality just as well. Many different sets of restrictions have been proposed to reduce the general model to more tractable form with fewer parameters. The restrictions used are the following.

1. Fix the dispersion coefficients at infinity or zero to obtain backmix or plug flow in the individual regions.
2. Assume that no solids are present in the lean phase.
3. Assume that there is no net gas flow upward through the dense phase.
4. Assume that the volume of, the fraction solids within, and the gas flow through the dense phase remains the same at all gas velocities, in which case the lean phase alone expands and contracts to account for the variation in total volume of fluidized bed with change in gas flow rate. The dense-phase characteristics are given by the conditions at incipient fluidization.

Table 1 shows the restrictions that must be placed on this general model

Table I. Models for fluidized beds

Model	Restrictions on General Model of Fig. 33		Model Parameters for		Reference
	Dense Phase	Lean Phase	Homogeneous Reactions	Heterogeneous Reactions, Catalytic	
M1	$D_1 = 0$ (plug flow) v_1, V_1 fixed[a]	$D_2 = 0$ (plug flow) no solids, $m = 0$	x	x	Shen and Johnstone (1955) Gomezplata and Shuster (1960)
M2	$D_1 = \infty$ (backmix) v_1, V_1 fixed[a]	$D_2 = 0$ (plug flow) no solids, $m = 0$	x	x	Shen and Johnstone (1955)
M3	$D_1 = 0$ (plug flow) v_1, V_1 fixed[a]	$D_2 = 0$ (plug flow)	m, x	m, x	Mathis and Watson (1956)
M4	$D_1 = 0$ (plug flow) $v_1 = 0$	$D_2 = 0$ (plug flow)	V_1, m, x	m, x	Lewis et al (1959)
M5	$D_1 = \infty$ (backmix) $v_1 = 0$	$D_2 = 0$ (plug flow)	V_1, m, x	m, x	Lewis et al (1959)
M6		$D_2 = 0$ (plug flow) no solids, $m = 0$	V_1, v_1, x, D_1	v_1, x, D_1	May (1959)
M7	no cross flow, $x = 0$	no solids, $m = 0$	V_1, v_1, D_1, D_2	v_1, D_1, D_2	Van Deemter (1960)
M8	$D_1 = 0$ (plug flow)	$D_2 = 0$ (plug flow)	V_1, v_1, m, x	v_1, m, x	Lanneau (1960)

x = cross-flow rate of gas.
m = fraction of all solids present in lean phase at any time. Solids are free to move between phases.
[a] As given by conditions of incipient fluidization.
Note: $V = V_1 + V_2$ and $v = v_1 + v_2$ are known and are not parameters of the models.

to obtain each of the special cases studied. Also shown are the number of parameters for each of the models.

What is now needed is an evaluation of these models: to find the models that satisfactorily fit the fluidized bed in its wide range of behavior, and then to select from these the simplest model of good fit. Unfortunately, practically every one of these models is flexible enough to correlate the data of any one investigation. Consequently, a proper evaluation would require putting these models to the test under the extremely wide variety of operating conditions of the different investigators. This is not a simple matter and, although it has not been done, it needs doing if we wish to be able to identify the simplest good representation of a fluidized bed.

It is interesting to note that the form of the conversion equations and the method of analysis for these models depend on whether homogeneous or heterogeneous reactions are occurring. This fact becomes clear if we note that no heterogeneous reaction can take place in a phase, no matter what its volume, if that phase contains no solid, whereas the extent of homogeneous reaction does depend on the volume of the phase. Thus for homogeneous reacting systems the volume ratio of phases is a parameter of the model, but in catalytic systems it is not. This fact is shown by the number of parameters tabulated for the models of Table 1.

For lack of applications, conversion expressions for these two-region models have not been developed for homogeneous systems. For heterogeneous systems the appropriate expressions can be found in the works of the individual investigators.

Table 2

Performance Predicted by Use of	Reaction with Rate Linear in Concentration, $-r_A = k_1C_A - k_2$, with $k_2 > 0$	Reaction with Nonlinear Rate Equation
Tracer measurement directly	Always good	Not valid;[a] however, either upper or lower bound to conversion can be calculated.
Flow models	Good if model predicts correctly the age distribution of material	Good if actual flow pattern throughout the reactor and that predicted by the model correspond (if model actually reflects reality)

[a] In the special case of a macrofluid (see Chapter 10), performance predictions are good.

SUMMARY

Tracer experimentation is the most convenient tool for determining when deviations from ideal flow are serious and for handling these deviations.

Conversion in a reactor with nonideal flow can be determined either directly from tracer data or by use of a flow model. We should note that each and every flow model predicts a flow pattern for the fluid through the vessel as well as the associated age distribution functions. Table 2 summarizes the conditions for the validity of these two approaches.

Single-parameter models have been developed to account for relatively small deviations from plug flow. These models are good representations of the performance of tubular and packed-bed reactors.

Models with two or more parameters have had but little use to date. In fact, treating nonideal flow in any of its aspects is a relatively recent development.

RELATED READING

O. Levenspiel and K. B. Bischoff, *Advances in Chemical Engineering*, **4**, 95 Academic Press, New York, (1963).

REFERENCES

R. J. Adler and R. B. Hovorka, Preprint 3, Second Joint Automatic Control Conference, Denver, Colo., June 1961.
R. Aris, *Chem. Eng. Sci.*, **9**, 266 (1959).
K. B. Bischoff, *Chem. Eng. Sci.*, **12**, 68 (1960).
———, Ph. D. thesis, Illinois Institute of Technology, 1961.
——— and O. Levenspiel, *Chem. Eng. Sci.*, **17**, 245, 257 (1962).
A. Cholette and L. Cloutier, *Can. J. Chem. Eng.*, **37**, 105 (1959).
P. V. Danckwerts, *Chem. Eng. Sci.*, **2**, 1 (1953).
H. A. Deans and L. Lapidus, *A.I.Ch.E. Journal*, **6**, 656, 663 (1960).
W. Eguchi, *Proc. 25th Anniv. Congress, Soc. Chem. Eng.* (*Japan*), Nov. 1961.
L. T. Fan and R. C. Bailie, *Chem. Eng. Sci.*, **13**, 63 (1960).
G. F. Froment, *Ind. chim. belge*, **24**, 619 (1959).
A. Gomezplata and W. W. Shuster, *A.I.Ch.E. Journal*, **6**, 454 (1960).
H. Kramers and G. Alberda, *Chem. Eng. Sci.*, **2**, 173 (1953).
D. Kunii and J. M. Smith, *A.I.Ch.E. Journal*, **7**, 29 (1961).
K. P. Lanneau, *Trans. Inst. Chem. Eng.* (*London*), **38**, 125 (1960).
O. Levenspiel, *Ind. Eng. Chem.*, **50**, 343 (1958).
———, *Can. J. Chem. Eng.*, **40**, 135 (1962*a*), **41**, 132 (1963).
———, *Chem. Eng. Sci.*, **17**, 576 (1962*b*).
——— and K. B. Bischoff, *Ind. Eng. Chem.*, **51**, 1431 (1959); **53**, 313 (1961).
——— and W. K. Smith, *Chem. Eng. Sci.*, **6**, 227 (1957).
W. K. Lewis, E. R. Gilliland, and W. Glass, *A.I.Ch.E. Journal*, **5**, 419 (1959).
J. F. Mathis and C. C. Watson, *A.I.Ch.E. Journal*, **2**, 518 (1956).

W. G. May, *Chem. Eng. Progr.*, **55**, 12, 49 (1959).
C. Y. Shen and H. F. Johnstone, *A.I.Ch.E. Journal*, **1**, 349 (1955).
G. I. Taylor, *Proc. Roy. Soc.* (*London*), **219A,** 186 (1953); **225A,** 473 (1954*a*).
———, *Proc. Roy. Soc.* (*London*), **223A,** 446 (1954*b*).
L. J. Tichacek, *A.I.Ch.E. Journal*, **9,** 394 (1963).
J. J. Van Deemter, *Chem. Eng. Sci.*, **13,** 143 (1960).
E. Th. Van der Laan, *Chem. Eng. Sci.*, **7,** 187 (1958).
D. U. von Rosenberg, *A.I.Ch.E. Journal*, **2,** 55 (1956).
J. F. Wehner and R. H. Wilhelm, *Chem. Eng. Sci.*, **6,** 89 (1956).
S. Yagi, D. Kunii, and N. Wakao, Paper A-10, International Heat Transfer Conference, Denver, Colo., Aug. 1961.

PROBLEMS

1. From the New York Times Magazine, December 25, 1955, comes the following noteworthy news item: "The United States Treasury reported that it costs eight-tenths of a cent each to print dollar bills, and that of the billion and a quarter now in circulation, a billion have to be replaced annually." Assume that the bills are put into circulation at a constant rate and continuously; that the bills are withdrawn from circulation without regard to their condition, in a random manner; that there is no change in the total number of bills in circulation.

(*a*) Determine the age distribution of a representative batch of bills being taken out of circulation.
(*b*) Determine the age distribution of all bills in circulation.
(*c*) Find the average age of bills in circulation.
(*d*) Find the average life of a dollar bill.
(*e*) What fraction of the bills is used for over 4 years?
(*f*) At any time how many bills in circulation are over 21 years old?

2. Referring to the previous problem, suppose a new series of dollar bills is put into circulation at a given instant in place of the original series.

(*a*) What is the fraction of new bills in circulation at any time?
(*b*) Plot this equation.
(*c*) What is the rate of withdrawal of the new bills?
(*d*) Plot this equation.

3. Referring to problems 1 and 2, suppose that during a working day a gang of counterfeiters put into circulation one million dollars in one-dollar bills.

(*a*) If not detected, what will be the number in circulation as a function of time?
(*b*) After 10 years, how many of these bills are still in circulation?
(*c*) What assumptions in addition to those already made are required to solve this problem?

4. Given the output curve Fig. P4 for a delta-function input to a closed vessel. Assuming no deadwater, find the **C** curve for this system and the exit age distribution functions **E** and **E**(t). Present your results in the forms of sketches of these functions with coordinates of important points labeled.

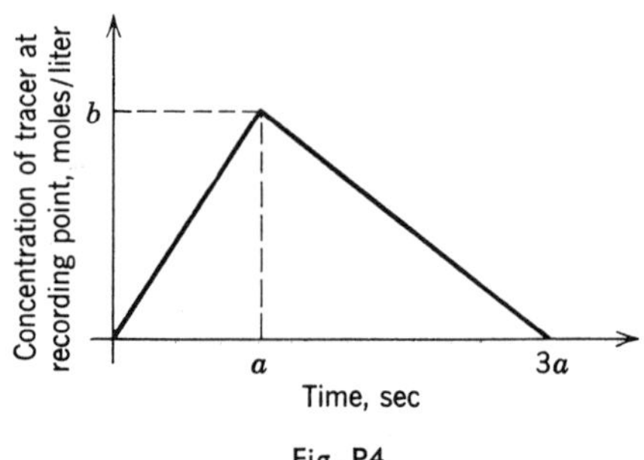

Fig. P4

5. The output tracer curve in Fig. P5 is obtained from a delta-function tracer input into the system. Assuming no deadwater, find in both t and θ units the internal and exit age distribution curves as well as the mean ages of material within the vessel and in the exit stream. Present your results in the form of four curves, labeling all important features.

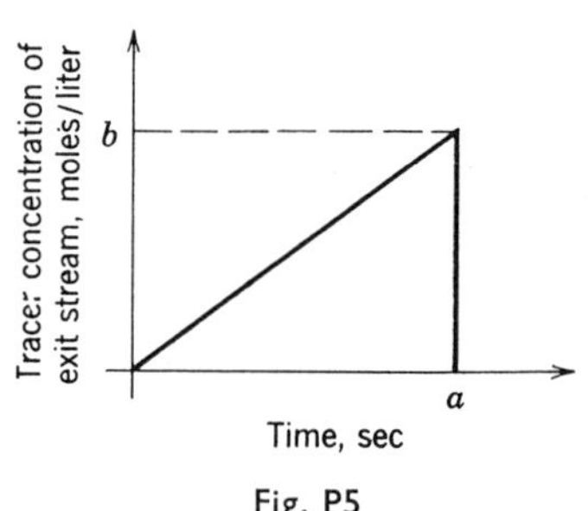

Fig. P5

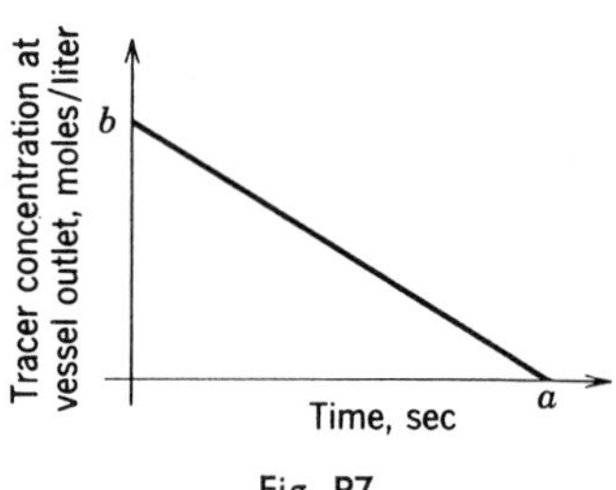

Fig. P7

6. Find **F**, **C**, **I**, and **E** curves for the steamline flow of fluids in pipes, assuming no molecular diffusion. *Caution:* Where radial variations in flow rate occur, the **F** curve is defined as the volumetric flow rate of second or tracer fluid divided by the total flow rate of fluid.

7. Find the variance in both t and θ units for the tracer output curve (Fig. P7) obtained from a delta-function tracer input.

8.(*a*) Consider a system in which a number of processes are occurring at the same time. If each of the processes occurring is linear and is not influenced by the other processes, the system as a whole acts as a linear process. With this fact accepted, show for any type of flow that a flow reactor in which a reaction with rate $-r_A = k_1C_A - k_2$, $k_2 > 0$, is taking place is a linear process.

(*b*) Repeat for the elementary reaction $A \underset{k_2}{\overset{k_1}{\rightleftharpoons}} R$.

(*c*) Repeat for the elementary reaction $A \xrightarrow{k_1} R \xrightarrow{k_2} S$.

9. Can we use tracer data directly to calculate conversion for a first-order reaction with expansion? If so, how must Eq. 19 be modified to account for this expansion.

10. For reactions with rate equations approximated by $-r_A = kC_A^{-n}$, does Eq. 18 give the upper or lower bound to conversion?

11. A specially designed vessel is to be used as a reactor for a first-order liquid-phase reaction. Since flow in this vessel is suspected to be nonideal, tracer methods are used to estimate the magnitude of this effect, the following concentration readings representing a continuous response at the vessel outlet to a delta-function tracer input to the vessel inlet. What conversion can we expect in this reactor if conversion in a backmix reactor employing the same space time is 82.18%.

Time t, sec	10	20	30	40	50	60	70	80
Tracer concentration (arbitrary reading)	0	3	5	5	4	2	1	0

We suspect that the dispersion or tanks in series models are poor representations of the flow pattern.

12. Often a pipeline must transport more than one material. These materials are then transported successively, and switching from one to another forms a zone of contamination between the two flowing fluids. Let A refer to the leading fluid and let B refer to the following fluid in a 12-in.-i.d. pipe.

(*a*) If the average Reynolds number of the flowing fluids is 10,000, find the 10%–90% contaminated width 10 miles downstream from the point of feed.

(*b*) Find the 10%–99% contaminated width at this location (10%–99% contamination means allowing up to 10% of B in A but only allowing 1% of A in B).

(*c*) Find the 10%–90% contaminated width 160 miles downstream from the point of feed.

(*d*) For a given flow rate, how does contaminated width vary with length of pipe.

See *Petroleum Refiner*, **37**, 191 (March 1958).

13. A pipeline 100 km long will be constructed to transport wine from a wine-producing center to the distribution point. Red and white wine are to flow in turn through this pipeline. Naturally, in switching from one to the other, a region of *vin rosé* is formed. The quantity of *vin rosé* is to be minimized since it is not popular and does not fetch a good price on the market.

(*a*) How does the pipeline size at given Reynolds number affect the quantity of *vin rosé* formed in the switching operation?

(*b*) For fixed volumetric flow rate in the turbulent flow region, what pipe size minimizes the *vin rosé* formed during the switching operation?

(*c*) Assuming that the pipeline is operating at present, what flow rate should we select to minimize the formation of *vin rosé*?

14. A 30-ft length of pipe is packed with 20 ft of 1/4-in. material, 2 ft of 1/64-in. material, and 8 ft of 1/8-in. material.

(*a*) What is the variance in output **C** curve for this packed section if the fluid takes 3 min to flow through the section.

(*b*) With what size of material must a 10-ft length of pipe be packed if it is to give a dimensionless tracer response curve identical to that of the original pipe at the same flow rate of fluid.

Assume a constant porosity of packing and a constant intensity of dispersion given by an average value of $D/ud_p = 2$.

15. Show for small deviations from plug flow that Eq. 32 reduces to Eqs. 33 and 34.

16. Tubular reactors for thermal cracking are designed on the assumption of plug flow. On the suspicion that nonideal flow may be an important factor now being ignored, let us make a rough estimate of its role. For this assume isothermal operations in a 1-in.-i.d. tubular reactor, using a Reynolds number of 10,000 for flowing fluid. The cracking reaction is approximately first order. If calculations show that 99% decomposition can be obtained in a plug flow reactor 10 ft long, how much longer must the reactor be if nonideal flow is taken into account?

17. Suppose we are told that a reactor behaves like three equal-sized backmix reactors in series. If we want to use the dispersion model to represent the system, what value of vessel dispersion number should we use if the basis of comparison is taken to be (*a*) the variance, (*b*) identical performance as a reactor when a second-order reaction is taking place.

18. Derive the expression

$$\mathbf{E} = \mathbf{C} = \frac{C}{C_0} = \frac{\theta^{j-1} j^j}{(j-1)!} \exp(-j\theta) \tag{35}$$

for the j equal-sized tanks in series model. To do this make a material balance about the first, second, . . . , jth tank and relate V_i, θ_i, and C_{0i} for each tank with V, θ, and C_0 based on the system as a whole.

19. Derive an expression for the **F** curve for the tanks in series model, using as starting point the **C** curve, Eq. 35.

20. Show that the mean and variance of the **C** curve of the tanks in series model are given by

$$\bar{\theta}_{\mathbf{C}} = 1 \tag{36}$$

and

$$\sigma_\theta^2 = \frac{1}{j} \tag{37}$$

21. For no backmixing (plug flow, $j = \infty$) the tanks in series model predicts for the **C** curve of a vessel that $\sigma^2 = 0$, whereas for infinite backmixing (backmix flow, $j = 1$) it predicts that $\sigma^2 = 1$. For the dispersion model show that the end conditions for closed vessels are the only ones for which the variance matches these extremes.

Note: This result shows that the closed vessel is the one to be used in comparing the dispersion with the tanks in series model, the correspondence being given by Eq. 38.

22. Let us introduce a term called the length of a dispersion unit, and let this be the length of vessel which provides the mixing equivalent to one stirred tank in backmix flow.

(*a*) For a vessel long enough so that deviation from plug flow is small, Eq. 38 becomes with negligible error

$$\frac{1}{j} = 2\frac{D}{uL}$$

Find the length of a dispersion unit.

(*b*) Find the length of a dispersion unit for water flowing in a pipe at Reynolds numbers of 2, 200, and 200,000.

(*c*) Find the length of a dispersion unit for water and air flowing in a packed bed at a particle Reynolds number of 100.

(*d*) What does the answer of part *c* suggest for a model for the actual mixing process occurring in a packed bed.

23. A reactor has flow characteristics given by the non-normalized **C** curve in Table P23, and by the shape of this curve we feel that the dispersion or tanks in series models should satisfactorily represent flow in the reactor.

Table P23

Time	Tracer Concentration
1	9
2	57
3	81
4	90
5	90
6	86
8	77
10	67
15	47
20	32
30	15
41	7
52	3
67	1

(*a*) Find the conversion expected in this reactor, assuming that the dispersion model holds.
(*b*) Find the number of tanks in series which will represent the reactor and the conversion expected, assuming that the tanks in series model holds.
(*c*) Find the conversion by direct use of the tracer curve.
(*d*) Comment on the difference in these results, and state which one you think is the most reliable.
(*e*) Assuming that the dispersion model is the correct model, find the corresponding number of tanks and conversion for the tanks in series model.

Data: The elementary liquid-phase reaction taking place is $A + B \rightarrow$ products, with a large enough excess of B so that the reaction is essentially first order. In addition, if plug flow existed, conversion would be 99% in the reactor.

24. Repeat the previous problem with the following modifications. The elementary liquid-phase reaction taking place is $A + B \rightarrow$ products, with equimolar quantities of A and B fed into the reactor. If plug flow existed, conversion would be 99% in the reactor.

25. Figure 28 shows that in a model consisting of a plug flow and a backmix region in series, precisely $1/e$ of the material in the exit stream of the vessel is of age greater than $\bar{t}$, no matter what the relative sizes of the plug flow and backmix regions are. Show that this is so.

26. A population with 56% women has a mortality rate of 18 deaths per year per 1000 population. Per 100 deaths, 48 are women. Assuming that the population is at steady state, determine the life expectancy of males and females.

27. We suspect that the reactor with the accurate **C** curve shown in Table P27 behaves like two backmix reactors in parallel.
(*a*) In the manner of Fig. 29 develop the **E** curve for this model.
(*b*) Fit the real reactor with this flow model.

The **C** curve was obtained in the 100-gal reactor using a flow rate of 20 gal fluid/min.

Table P27

θ	C
0.1	1.4
0.4	0.80
0.8	0.38
1.5	0.12
1.8	0.080
2.5	0.040
3.7	0.020
4.4	0.015
5.6	0.010
7.1	0.006

28. Find a flow model which will give the normalized response curve of Fig. P28.

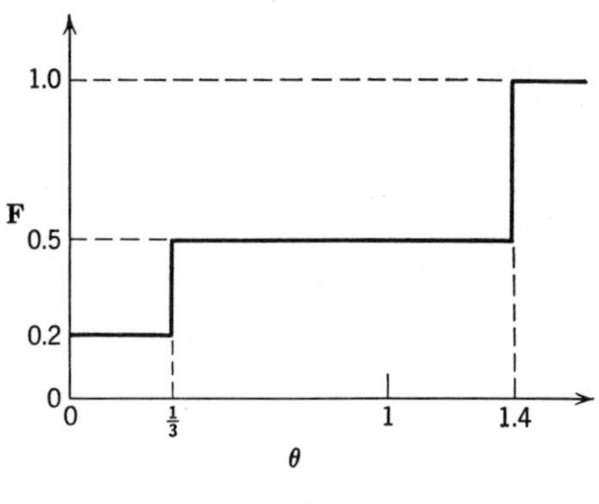

Fig. P28

29. Derive the response curves for a model consisting of two backmix regions in series, their sizes not necessarily equal.

30. Misfortune has befallen us. We planned to repaint our reactor; however, just as the last speck of old paint was scraped off by the two chemical engineering students in our summer trainee program, the whole unit collapsed into little flakes of rust. Fortunately there was little damage, though it is a pity that those two nice boys disappeared completely. I always suspected that that stuff was corrosive. Leaving sentiment aside, I wish to point out that shutdowns are costly, so we don't want this to happen again.

Table P30

Time, min	Concentration of Ink at Reactor Outflow
0–20 sec	Rapid fluctuations with jumps up to 5000
10	90
20	55
30	35
40	20
50	10
60	7
80	3
100	1

We are not operating on a shoestring any longer and can afford to replace this reactor by a commercial unit for which backmix flow is guaranteed. I am sure, however, that it does not have to be as large as our last unit. Ours may have been somewhat inefficient since we used a salvaged gasoline tank for the reactor and an outboard motor for the mixer, and had the inlet and overflow pipes close to each other. What volume of commercial unit should we order so that the product will be identical to that in the old unit?

Here is all the information available on the unit, including results of the experiments by those two nice boys made with gallon bottles of India ink, a flashlight, and a photographer's exposure meter (see Table P30). Perhaps you can figure out what they were up to.

Data;

Reactor: Cylindrical tank about 8 ft diameter, 18 ft long with $800 ft^3$ of usable volume.

Reaction: Elementary second order, equimolar feed, 60% conversion.

Flow rate: 20 ft^3 feed/min.

A gallon of India ink evenly distributed throughout the reactor gives a concentration reading of 100.

10

MIXING OF FLUIDS

The problem associated with the mixing of reactant fluids is broad enough to justify its treatment in a separate chapter. This problem may occur with extremely fast reactions in homogeneous systems as well as in all heterogeneous systems and concerns the actual mode of mixing of reactants, whether it occurs on the microscopic scale (mixing of individual molecules) or whether it occurs on the macroscopic scale (mixing of clumps, groups, or aggregates of molecules).

To distinguish between these two modes of mixing, let liquid A be available in two forms. In the first, shown in Fig. 1, the liquid is as we normally visualize it, with individual molecules free to move about the liquid, to collide and intermix with all other molecules of the liquid. Let us call such a liquid a *microfluid*, and let this type of mixing be called *micromixing*. In the second form, also shown in Fig. 1, A is available in a large number of small sealed packets, each containing a large number, say

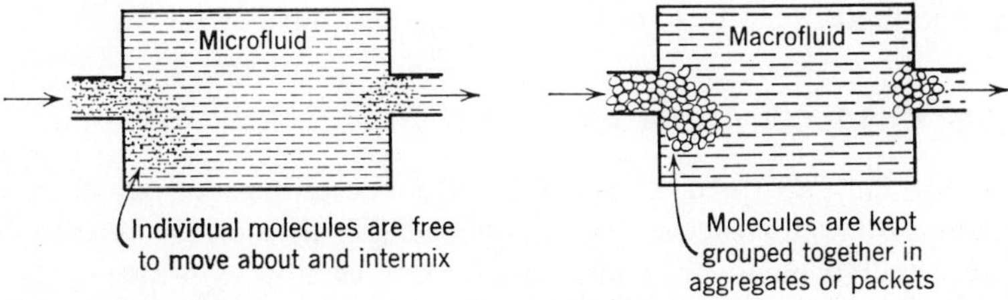

Fig. 1. Flow of idealized microfluid and macrofluid. Tracer measurements cannot distinguish between them; however, for chemical reactions these fluids may behave differently.

about 10^{12}, molecules. In addition, suppose the boundary of each packet to be chemically inert, its only role being to preserve the individuality of each packet of molecules. Let us call this state of the liquid *macrofluid* and the mixing of such a fluid *macromixing*.

A fluid that does not exhibit these extremes in behavior is called a *partially segregated* fluid. A microfluid exhibits no segregation and a macrofluid exhibits complete segregation, but a real fluid exhibits segregation to a lesser or greater extent, depending on its properties and the kind of system in which mixing is taking place.

Since the degree of segregation can influence the performance of homogeneous or heterogeneous reacting systems, both with respect to product distribution and capacity, we should like to be able to estimate the role played by this factor. To do this we need a quantitative definition of the degree of segregation as well as an experimental method of finding the degree of segregation in real systems. Though a definition has been proposed by Danckwerts (1958*b*), the experimental determination of the degree of segregation for homogeneous systems is not a simple matter. The stimulus-response methods of Chapter 9 are of no use, and the methods suggested to date involve analyzing concentration changes and fluctuations in extremely small regions of reacting fluid or following the actual conversions of reactions with nonlinear and known kinetics [see Danckwerts (1958*a*, *b*)].

In this chapter we do not deal with the quantitative aspects of partial segregation but consider simply what happens in the extremes when we have micromixing or macromixing. We determine how these forms of mixing influence the progress of reactions. This will tell us which form of mixing is advantageous and which is not, which to promote and which to depress. Finally we examine various designs to see which one can best promote the type of mixing desired.

Let us now examine the difference in behavior of reacting microfluids and macrofluids in various reactor systems. We concern ourselves at first with systems in which a single fluid is reacting and then with systems in which two fluids must be contacted for reaction to occur.

SELF-MIXING OF A SINGLE FLUID

The normally accepted state is that of a microfluid, and all previous discussions on homogeneous reactions have been based on the assumption that the fluid behaves as a microfluid. Let us now consider a single reacting macrofluid being processed in turn in batch, plug flow, and backmix reactors, and let us see how this state of aggregation can result in behavior different from that of a microfluid.

Batch reactor

Let the batch reactor be filled with a macrofluid containing reactant A. Since each aggregate or packet of this macrofluid acts as its own little batch reactor, conversion is the same in all aggregates and is in fact identical to what would be obtained if the reactant fluid were a microfluid. Thus for batch operations the state of aggregation is not a variable and does not affect conversion or product distribution. This conclusion holds, no matter what reaction is occurring, as long as the aggregates contain a large enough number of molecules.

Plug flow reactor

Since plug flow can be visualized as a flow of small batch reactors passing through the equipment in succession, the conclusion for batch operations extends to plug flow operations.

Backmix reactor

When a microfluid containing reactant A is treated in a backmix reactor, as shown in Fig. 2, all the reactant drops to the low concentration prevailing in the reactor. No clumps of molecules retain their high initial concentration of A. We may characterize this by saying that each molecule loses its identity and has no determinable past history. In other words, by examining its neighbors we cannot tell whether a molelule is a newcomer or an old-timer in the reactor.

For a backmix reactor processing a microfluid, the conversion of reactant is found by the usual methods for homogeneous reactions, or

$$X_A = \frac{(-r_A)V}{F_{A0}} \tag{5.9}$$

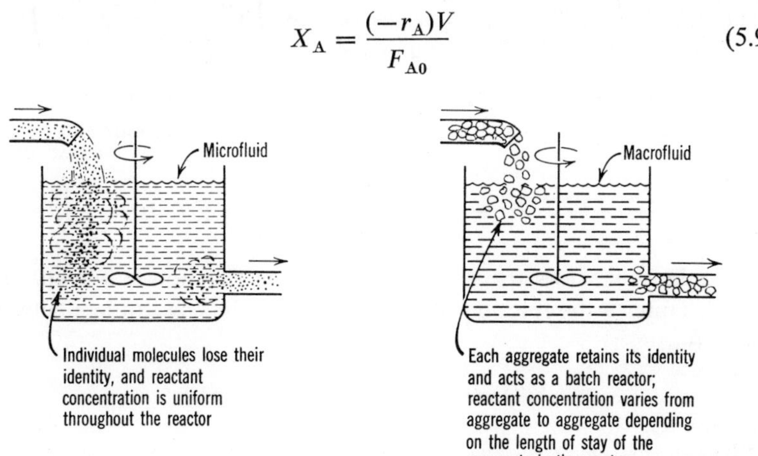

Fig. 2. Difference in behavior of microfluids and macrofluids in backmix reactors.

or, with no density changes,

$$\frac{C_A}{C_{A0}} = 1 - \frac{(-r_A)\bar{t}}{C_{A0}} \tag{1}$$

where $\bar{t}$ is the mean residence time of fluid in the reactor.

When a macrofluid enters a backmix reactor, the reactant concentration in the aggregates does not drop immediately to a low value but decreases in the same way as does the concentration in a batch reactor. Thus a molecule in a macrofluid does not lose its identity, its past history is not unknown, and its age can be estimated by examining its neighboring molecules.*

Because the concentration of A in the macrofluid does not drop immediately to a low concentration, the performance of a backmix reactor processing macrofluid differs from one processing microfluid. Visualize the millions upon millions of little equal-sized aggregates of macrofluid, batch reactors all, churning about in the vessel. The extent of reaction in each aggregate is dependent only on the length of stay of the aggregate in the reactor and the kinetics of the reaction. This also holds for any aggregate of the exit stream. Thus the fraction of reactant unconverted in the exit stream is obtained by determining the extent of reaction in all the aggregates of the exit stream. Thus we may write for the exit stream of the macrofluid as a whole

$$\begin{pmatrix}\text{fraction of}\\ \text{reactant}\\ \text{unreacted}\end{pmatrix} = \sum_{\substack{\text{all aggregates}\\ \text{in the exit}\\ \text{stream}}} \begin{pmatrix}\text{fraction of}\\ \text{reactant}\\ \text{remaining in}\\ \text{an aggregate}\\ \text{of age between}\\ t \text{ and } t + \Delta t\end{pmatrix} \begin{pmatrix}\text{fraction of exit}\\ \text{stream consisting}\\ \text{of aggregates}\\ \text{of age between}\\ t \text{ and } t + \Delta t.\end{pmatrix} \tag{2}$$

Since the distribution of residence time of the aggregates in the reactor is given by the exit age distribution function as defined in Chapter 9, Eq. 2 becomes

$$1 - \bar{X}_A = \frac{\bar{C}_A}{C_{A0}} = \int_0^\infty \left(\frac{C_A}{C_{A0}}\right)_{\text{batch}} \mathbf{E}(t)\, dt \tag{3}$$

For backmix reactors the exit age distribution function is known. Thus from Chapter 9 the fraction of the exit stream that has an age between t and $t + dt$ is

$$\mathbf{E}(t)\, dt = \frac{v}{V} e^{-vt/V}\, dt = \frac{e^{-t/\bar{t}}}{\bar{t}}\, dt \tag{4}$$

* Incidentally, the laws of behavior of these two systems provide an interesting illustration of the distinction between two broad types of processes, the probabilistic and the stochastic processes.

Replacing Eq. 3 in Eq. 4, we obtain

$$1 - \bar{X}_A = \frac{\bar{C}_A}{C_{A0}} = \int_0^\infty \left(\frac{C_A}{C_{A0}}\right)_{\text{batch}} \frac{e^{-t/\bar{t}}}{\bar{t}}\, dt \tag{5}$$

This is the general equation for determining conversion of macrofluid in a backmix reactor and may be solved once the kinetics of the reaction is given. Consider various reaction orders.

For a *first-order reaction*, the expression for batch operations, found in Chapter 3,

$$\left(\frac{C_A}{C_{A0}}\right)_{\text{batch}} = e^{-kt} \tag{6}$$

is applicable to the conversion in any single aggregate. When Eq. 6 is replaced in Eq. 5 for backmix operations, we obtain

$$\frac{\bar{C}_A}{C_{A0}} = \frac{1}{\bar{t}} \int_0^\infty e^{-kt} e^{-t/\bar{t}}\, dt$$

which on integration gives

$$\frac{\bar{C}_A}{C_{A0}} = \frac{1}{1 + k\bar{t}} \tag{7}$$

This equation is identical with that obtained for a first-order reaction of a microfluid; for example, see Eq. 6.5. Thus we find that the degree of segregation has no effect on conversion for first-order reactions.

For a *second-order reaction* of a single reactant the conversion equation for batch operations is found from Eq. 3.14*b* to be

$$\frac{C_A}{C_{A0}} = \frac{1}{1 + C_{A0}kt} \tag{8}$$

Replacing Eq. 8 in Eq. 5 gives the conversion of a macrofluid in a backmix reactor:

$$\frac{\bar{C}_A}{C_{A0}} = \frac{1}{\bar{t}} \int_0^\infty \frac{e^{-t/\bar{t}}}{1 + C_{A0}kt}\, dt$$

By letting $\alpha = 1/C_{A0}k\bar{t}$ and converting into reduced time units $\theta = t/\bar{t}$, this expression becomes

$$\frac{\bar{C}_A}{C_{A0}} = \alpha e^{\alpha} \int_\alpha^\infty \frac{e^{-(\alpha+\theta)}}{\alpha + \theta}\, d(\alpha + \theta) = \alpha e^{\alpha}\, \text{ei}(\alpha) \tag{9}$$

This integral, represented by ei(α) or $-$Ei($-\alpha$), is called the *exponential integral*. It is a function alone of α, and its value is tabulated in a number of tables of integrals. Thus the conversion of a macrofluid, given by Eq. 9, may be compared to that for microfluid in a backmix reactor:

$$\frac{C_A}{C_{A0}} = \frac{1}{1 + C_A k\bar{t}} \tag{10}$$

For an *nth-order reaction* the conversion in a plug flow reactor can be found by the methods of Chapter 3 to be

$$\frac{C_A}{C_{A0}} = [1 + (n-1)C_{A0}^{n-1}kt]^{1/(1-n)} \tag{11}$$

Combining this expression with Eq. 5 gives the conversion for an nth-order reaction of a macrofluid which can then be compared with the conversion for microfluids.

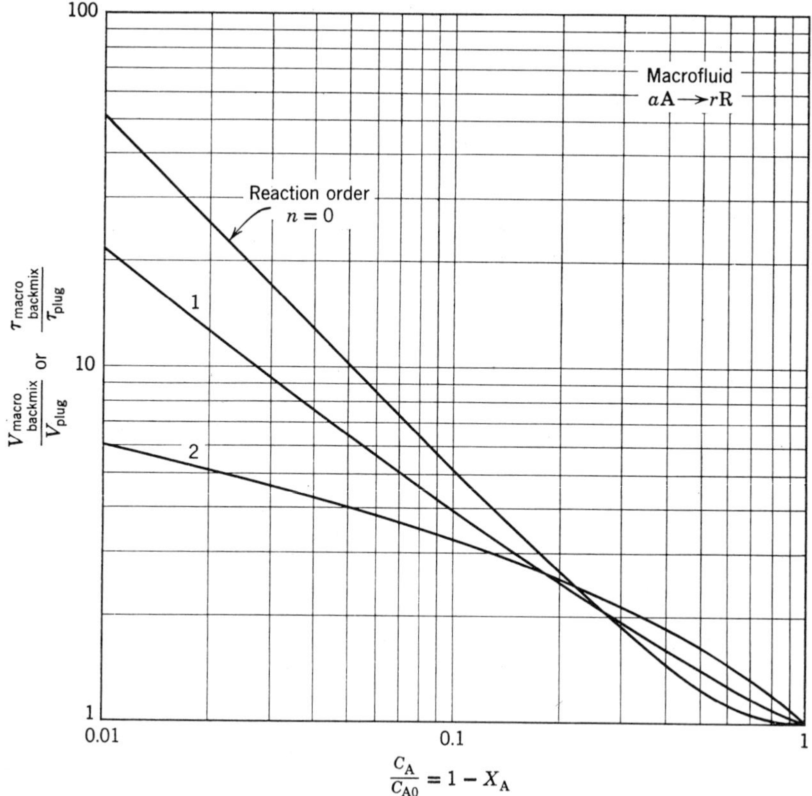

Fig. 3. Comparison of performance of a backmix reactor with a plug flow reactor, both treating a macrofluid with nth-order kinetics and $\varepsilon_A = 0$.

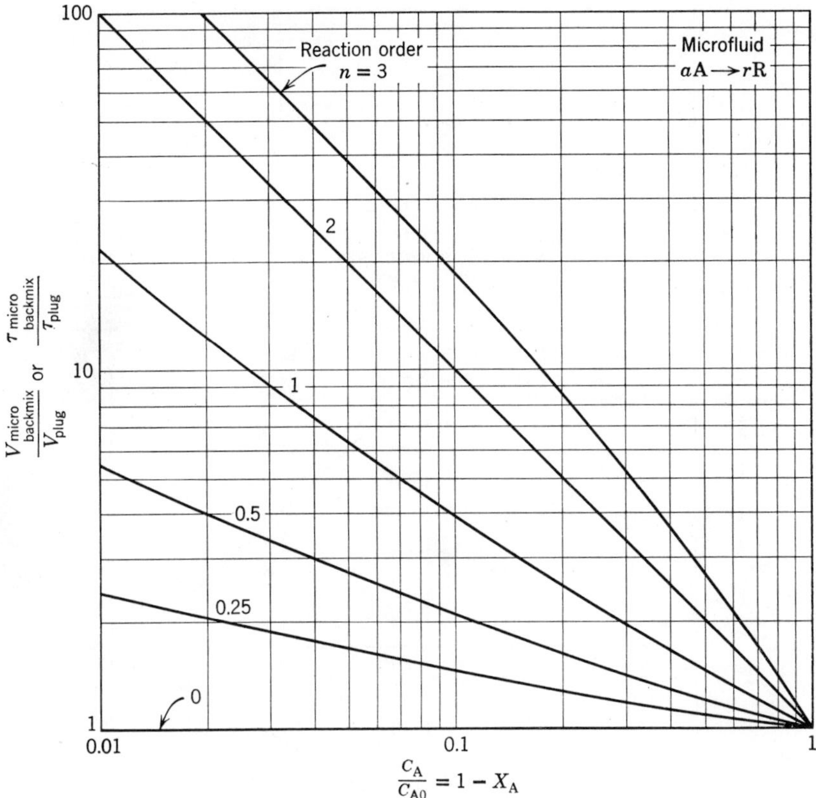

Fig. 4. Comparison of performance of a backmix reactor with a plug flow reactor, both treating a microfluid with nth-order kinetics and $\varepsilon_A = 0$.

Figures 3, 4, and 5 graphically illustrate the difference in performance of macrofluids and microfluids in backmix reactors and shows clearly that a rise in segregation improves reactor performance for reaction orders greater than unity but lowers performance for reaction orders smaller than unity. Table 1 summarizes the relationships used in preparing these charts. Greenhalgh et al. (1959) give an alternate presentation of these charts.

Flow with arbitrary exit age distribution E

Each flow pattern of fluid through a vessel has associated with it a definite clearly defined residence time distribution or exit age distribution function **E**. The converse is not true, however. Each exit age distribution function does not define a specific flow pattern. Here we would like to know what range in fluid behavior, flow patterns, and conversion are

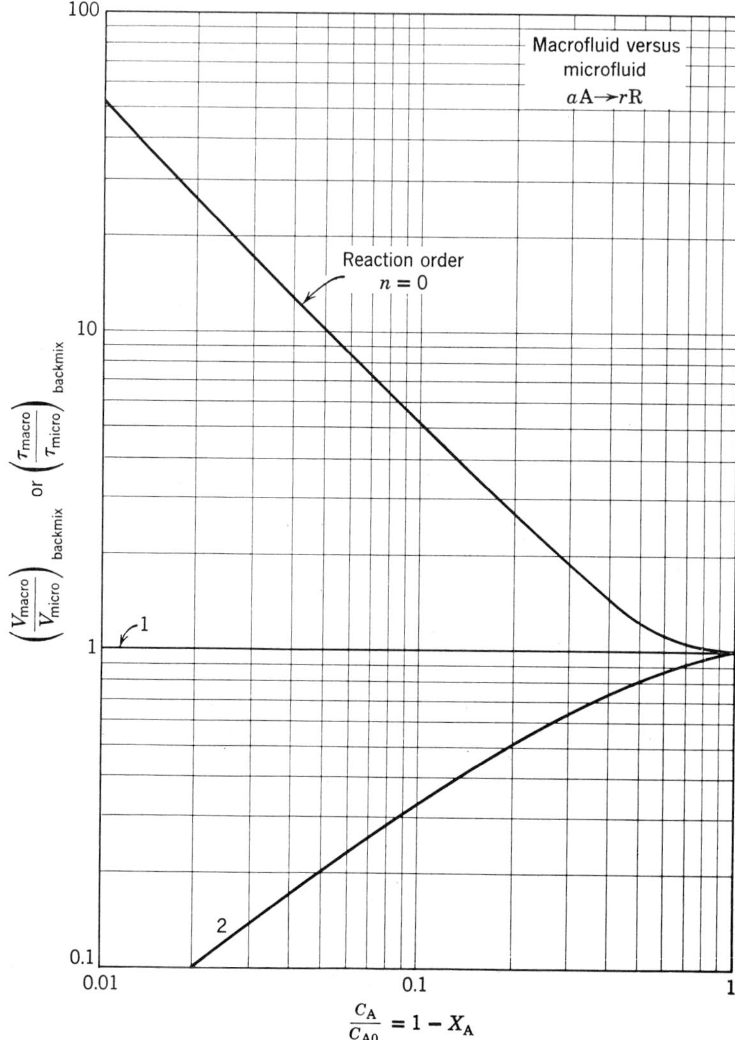

Fig. 5. Comparison of performance of backmix reactors treating macrofluids and microfluids with nth-order kinetics and $\varepsilon_A = 0$.

possible given any particular exit age distribution function. We start with a number of special exit age distributions and then consider any arbitrary distribution and its associated flow patterns.

Let a fluid pass in steady-state flow through a vessel. What can we infer about the possible flow patterns of this fluid if we are told that each of its molecules stays in the vessel for exactly 1 min, this being the particular **E**

Table I. Conversion equations for macrofluids and microfluids with $\varepsilon = 0$ in ideal reactors

	Plug Flow	Backmix Flow	
	Microfluid or Macrofluid	Microfluid	Macrofluid
General kinetics	$\tau = -\int_{C_0}^{C} \frac{dC}{-r}$	$\tau = \frac{C_0 - C}{-r}$	$\frac{\overline{C}}{C_0} = \frac{1}{\tau}\int_0^{\infty}\left(\frac{C}{C_0}\right)_{\text{batch}} e^{-t/\tau}\, dt$
nth-order reaction ($R = C_0^{n-1}k\tau$)	$\frac{C}{C_0} = [1 + (n-1)R]^{1/(1-n)}$ $R = \frac{1}{n-1}\left[\left(\frac{C}{C_0}\right)^{1-n} - 1\right]$	$\left(\frac{C}{C_0}\right)^n R + \frac{C}{C_0} - 1 = 0$ $R = \left(1 - \frac{C}{C_0}\right)\left(\frac{C_0}{C}\right)^n$	$\frac{\overline{C}}{C_0} = \frac{1}{\tau}\int_0^{\infty}[1 + (n-1)C_0^{n-1}kt]^{1/(1-n)}e^{-t/\tau}\, dt$
Zero-order reaction $\left(R = \frac{k\tau}{C_0}\right)$	$\frac{C}{C_0} = 1 - R, \quad R \leqslant 1$ $C = 0, \quad R \geqslant 1$	$\frac{C}{C_0} = 1 - R, \quad R \leqslant 1$ $C = 0, \quad R \geqslant 1$	$\frac{\overline{C}}{C_0} = 1 - R + Re^{-1/R}$
First-order reaction ($R = k\tau$)	$\frac{C}{C_0} = e^{-R}$ $R = \ln\frac{C_0}{C}$	$\frac{C}{C_0} = \frac{1}{1+R}$ $R = \frac{C_0}{C} - 1$	$\frac{\overline{C}}{C_0} = \frac{1}{1+R}$ $R = \frac{C_0}{C} - 1$
Second-order reaction ($R = C_0k\tau$)	$\frac{C}{C_0} = \frac{1}{1+R}$ $R = \frac{C_0}{C} - 1$	$\frac{C}{C_0} = \frac{-1 + \sqrt{1+4R}}{2R}$ $R = \left(\frac{C_0}{C} - 1\right)\frac{C_0}{C}$	$\frac{\overline{C}}{C_0} = \frac{e^{1/R}}{R}\,\text{ei}\left(\frac{1}{R}\right)$

$R = C_0^{n-1}k\tau$, reaction rate group for nth-order reaction
$\tau = \bar{t}$ since $\varepsilon = 0$ throughout.

distribution selected? One possible flow pattern is that of plug flow with no intermixing in the vessel of fluid elements of different ages. Are any other flow patterns possible? For example could not the incoming fluid mix homogeneously with the contents of the vessel as in a backmix reactor, with but one difference, that after a residence time of 1 min each and every molecule somehow separates itself from the mixture and moves to the exit of the vessel? This flow pattern, or more generally any flow pattern for which a certain amount of mixing (of fluid of different ages) is followed by the same amount of unmixing, would give a residence time distribution identical to plug flow. However, these patterns are not permitted since the unmixing process clearly violates the second law of thermodynamics. Thus the only pattern permitted for this age distribution is one with no intermixing of fluid of different ages, and as a consequence it is immaterial whether we have a macrofluid or microfluid.

Next consider the exponential decay exit age distribution of backmix flow. Here mixing of the incoming fluid with the vessel contents must be immediate (no other pattern can give such a distribution); however, we may still retain the aggregates of a macrofluid. Thus different conversion is possible in backmix flow.

Now consider the exit age distribution function **E** given in Fig. 6 and the four flow patterns that are consistent with it (others are possible). In all these patterns we see that there is a period of intermixing and a period with no intermixing. This intermixing of fluids of different ages may occur early as in patterns *a* and *c*, or it may occur late as in patterns *b* and *d*. Both this earliness or lateness factor as well as the possible segregated character of the fluid can influence performance of a reactor system of given size.

What inferences can be drawn from this discussion?

1. During flow, fluid elements of different ages can intermix. However, this is not a reversible process; once mixed the fluid cannot unmix.

2. Plug flow and backmix flow represent the two extremes in intermixing of fluid—no intermixing for plug flow, complete intermixing for backmix flow.

3. All other flow patterns represent flow with some intermediate extent of intermixing.

4. Given an arbitrary **E** value, intermixing may occur in the early stages of passage of fluid through a vessel or in later stages (see Fig. 6), and this may result in different reactor performance.

5. Thus besides the kinetic aspects, two additional factors influence the performance of a reactor with given residence time distribution of fluid: the *earliness* or *lateness* at which mixing occurs, the *macrofluid* or *microfluid* properties of the fluid.

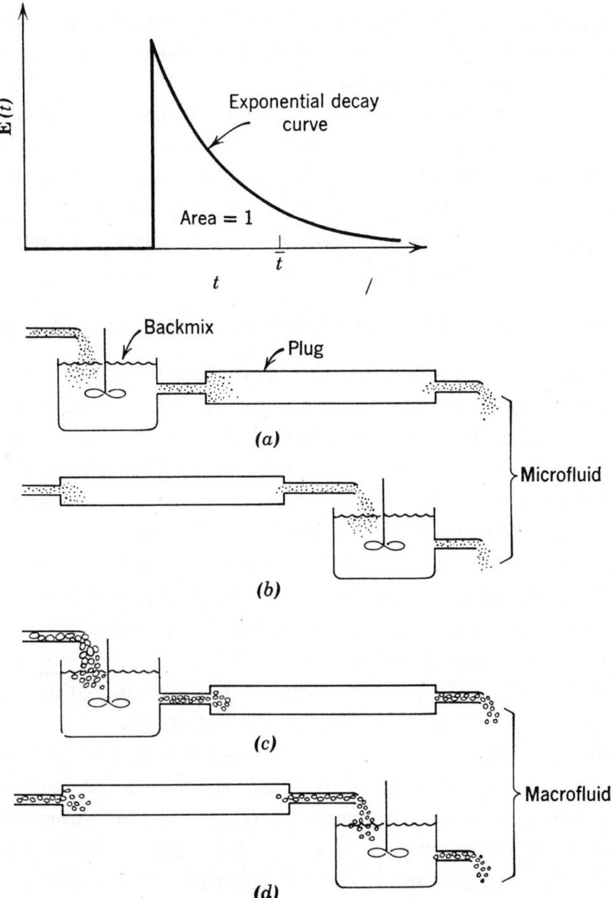

Fig. 6. Some of the possible flow patterns which could give the exit age distribution function shown.

6. The extremes in behavior for a given **E** occur when intermixing is as early or as late as possible.

Let us consider the conversion obtained for these extremes. In late (hence minimum) intermixing the concentration of reactants stays as high as possible throughout the passage of fluid through the reactor. This condition is satisfied by the segregated flow of a macrofluid since the fluid aggregates do not intermix and react to an extent dependent only on their lengths of stay in the reactor. Thus the general expression for the conversion of macrofluids in any reactor, Eqs. 2 and 3, apply, and we have

$$\frac{\bar{C}_A}{C_{A0}} = \int_0^\infty \left(\frac{C_A}{C_{A0}}\right)_{\text{batch}} \mathbf{E}(t)\, dt \tag{3}$$

Reaction kinetics gives $(C_A/C_{A0})_{batch}$, tracer experiments give $\mathbf{E}(t)$; hence both types of information are needed to determine conversion of macrofluids in flow through any reactor.

In the other extreme the mixing required by the given residence time distribution occurs as early as possible. This extreme is sometimes called *maximum-mixedness* flow. Zwietering (1959) treated this situation by introducing a new distribution function, the life expectation distribution function which measures how much longer a molecule still has to stay in the vessel. Thus for any molecule in the vessel

$$\text{Total residence time} = \text{Present age} + \text{Life expectation}$$

For maximum-mixedness flow, molecules that eventually leave the reactor at the same time (or have the same life expectation) will mix with each other as early as possible. This analysis allows determination of conversions for a state of maximum mixedness, given the restriction of an arbitrary exit age distribution for the fluid flow. Conversions so calculated will yield the other extreme from that found for macromixing.

The maximum-mixedness model is of interest only for homogeneous systems. Because of its somewhat sophisticated treatment and because models presented in Chapter 9 frequently approximate the nonideal behavior in homogeneous systems more closely, we will not go into the details of this model. On the other hand Eq. 3 for macrofluids characterizes heterogeneous systems and finds much use there.

By examining early and late mixing in backmix and plug flow reactors (micromixing and macromixing in these reactors), we may draw the following inferences for reactors with arbitrary residence time distribution.

1. When the **E** function is close to the **E** function for plug flow, early or late mixing is unimportant. When **E** approaches the exponential decay curve of backmix flow, the difference between early and late mixing becomes great. The maximum possible difference in performance is given by Figs. 3, 4, and 5 for backmix flow.

2. Conversions for late mixing or macromixing can be calculated from Eq. 3. Late mixing increases conversions for reaction order greater than unity but depresses conversions for reaction orders smaller than unity. Thus the assumption of macromixing gives conservative conversion predictions for reaction orders smaller than unity but may be too high for reaction orders greater than unity.

3. Reactions of first order are unaffected by early or late, macro- or micromixing.

Example 1

Consider a second-order reaction occurring in a reactor whose residence time distribution is given by the two-vessel model of Fig. 6, where backmix and plug flow units are of equal size. With $\tau = 1$ for each unit calculate the conversion obtained for the four flow schemes of Fig. 6 and verify the statements just made that the late mixing of the macrofluids of Figs. 6*c* and *d* gives maximum conversion whereas early mixing of microfluids as shown in Fig. 6*a* gives minimum conversion. For simplicity let $k = 1$ and let $C_0 = 1$.

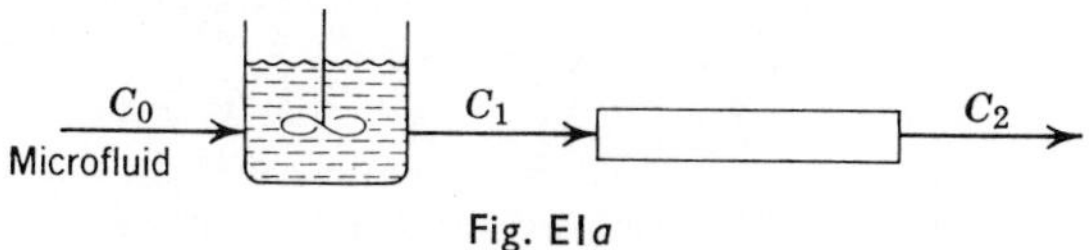

Fig. E1*a*

Solution. *Scheme a.* Referring to Fig. E1*a*, we have for the backmix reactor

$$\tau = 1 = \frac{C_0 - C_1}{kC_1^2} = \frac{1 - C_1}{C_1^2}$$

or

$$C_1 = \frac{-1 + \sqrt{1 + 4}}{2} = 0.618$$

For the plug flow reactor

$$\tau = 1 = -\int_{C_1}^{C_2} \frac{dC}{kC^2} = \frac{1}{k}\left(\frac{1}{C_2} - \frac{1}{C_1}\right)$$

or

$$C_2 = \frac{C_1}{C_1 + 1} = \frac{0.618}{1.618} = 0.382$$

Scheme b. Referring to Fig. E1*b* we have for the plug flow reactor

$$\tau = 1 = -\int_{C_0}^{C_1'} \frac{dC}{kC^2} = \frac{1}{C_1'} - 1$$

or

$$C_1' = 0.5$$

For the backmix reactor

$$\tau = 1 = \frac{C_1' - C_2'}{kC_2'^2} = \frac{0.5 - C_2'}{C_2'^2}$$

or

$$C_2' = 0.366$$

Schemes c and d. From Fig. 9.28 the exit age distribution function for the two equal-sized reactor system is

$$\mathbf{E} = 2e^{1-2\theta}, \qquad \text{when } \theta > \tfrac{1}{2}$$
$$= 0, \qquad \text{when } \theta < \tfrac{1}{2}$$

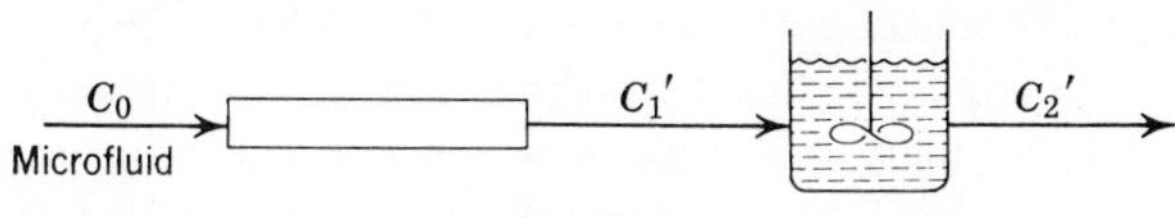

Fig. E1*b*

or

$$\mathbf{E}(t) = \frac{2}{\bar{t}} e^{1-2t/\bar{t}}, \qquad \text{when } \frac{t}{\bar{t}} > \tfrac{1}{2}$$

$$= 0, \qquad \text{when } \frac{t}{\bar{t}} < \tfrac{1}{2}$$

Thus Eq. 3 becomes

$$C = \int_{\bar{t}/2}^{\infty} \frac{1}{1 + C_0 kt} \cdot \frac{2}{\bar{t}} e^{1-2t/\bar{t}}\, dt$$

With the mean residence time in the two-vessel system $\bar{t} = 2$ min, this becomes

$$C = \int_1^{\infty} \frac{e^{1-t}}{1 + t}\, dt$$

and replacing $1 + t$ by x we obtain the exponential integral

$$C = \int_2^{\infty} \frac{e^{2-x}}{x}\, dx = e^2 \int_2^{\infty} \frac{e^{-x}}{x}\, dx = e^2 \,\mathrm{ei}(2)$$

From a table of integrals we find ei(2) = 0.04890 from which

$$C = 0.362$$

Though not proved here, scheme *a* actually represents the extreme of early mixing, or maximum mixedness. The results of this example confirm the statements made in the text, that macromixing gives higher conversions than micromixing for reaction orders greater than unity. The difference is small here because the conversion levels are low; however, this difference becomes more important as conversion approaches unity.

Applications and extensions

In general, homogeneous systems behave as microfluids, the exceptions being very viscous fluids or systems in which very fast reactions are taking place. These may exhibit partial segregation. Treatment of segregation in homogeneous systems is scarce.

Consideration of macromixing and micromixing is important in heterogeneous systems because one of the two phases of such systems usually approximates a macrofluid. For example, the solid phase of fluid-solid systems can be treated exactly as a macrofluid because each particle of solid is a distinct aggregate of molecules. For such systems, then, Eq. 3 with the appropriate kinetic expression is the starting point for design. This we shall see in the chapters to follow. As another example, the dispersed phase of a liquid-liquid system is partially segregated. This segregation is increased with rise in interfacial tension, for then coalescence of droplets is depressed.

Rietema (1958) considered reaction in noncoalescing drops (macrofluid extreme) and pointed out that zero-order kinetics in the dispersed phase can closely approximate real diffusion-controlled reacting systems. Curl (1963) then extended this treatment to the continual coalescence and

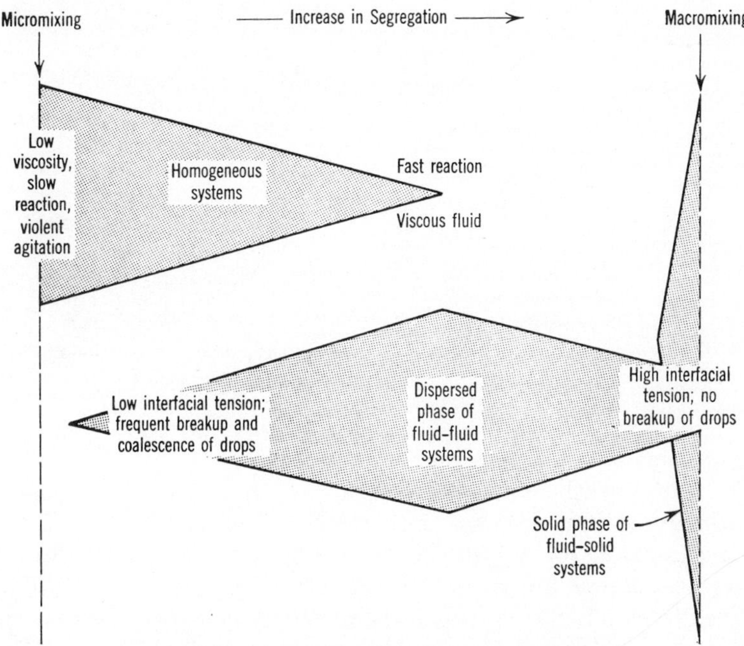

Fig. 7. Extent of segregation in different systems.

breakup of drops. As expected, he found that a rise in frequency of collision results in an approach to microfluid behavior. These findings can be shown to give a family of lines in Fig. 5, with frequency of coalescence as parameter, and indicate that the frequency of collision needed to approach microfluid behavior rises greatly at high conversion. For example, to approach halfway to microfluid behavior on Fig. 5 requires 10 collisions per mean residence time at 80% conversion but 50 collisions per mean residence time at 95% conversion. Experimental findings on frequency of collisions of droplets and applications to real liquid systems are reported by Madden and Damerell (1962) and Miller et al. (1963).

Figure 7 shows graphically how real systems behave with respect to macromixing and micromixing. Unfortunately, we have very little useful information at present on behavior intermediate between these two extremes.

MIXING OF TWO MISCIBLE FLUIDS

Here we consider one topic, the role of the mixing process when two completely miscible reactant fluids A and B are brought together. The mixing of two fluids, when these are immiscible, is a proper subject for

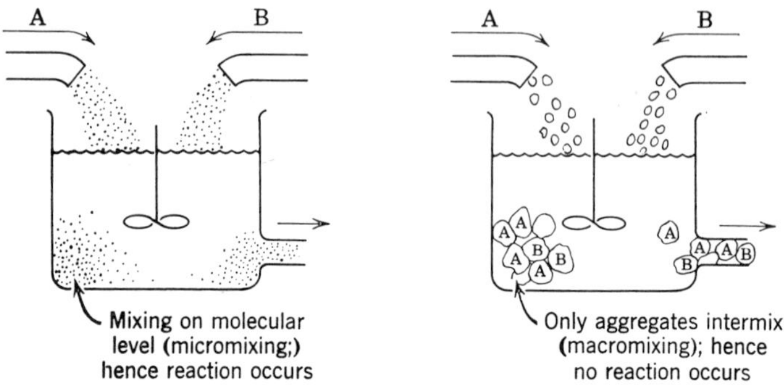

Fig. 8. Difference in behavior of microfluids and macrofluids in the reaction of A and B.

study in the chapters on heterogeneous reactions; therefore discussion of such systems will be left for the following chapters.

When two miscible fluids A and B are mixed, we normally assume that they first form a homogeneous mixture which then reacts. However, when the time required for A and B to become homogeneous is not short with respect to the time for reaction to take place, reaction occurs during the mixing process. In this situation the problem of mixing becomes important. Such is the case for very fast reactions or with very viscous reactant fluids.

To help understand what occurs when two real reactant fluids A and B are brought together and mixed, let us imagine that we have available A and B, each in both microfluid and macrofluid states. In one beaker mix micro A with micro B and in another beaker mix macro A with macro B and let them react. What do we find? When in microfluid state, A and B behave in the expected manner, and reaction occurs. However, when they are in the macrofluid state, no reaction takes place because molecules of A cannot contact molecules of B. These two situations are illustrated in Fig. 8 for the backmix reactor; however, the conclusions hold for any reactor type and any reaction as long as individual aggregates contain only one or the other of the reactants. So much for the treatment of the two extremes in behavior.

Now a real system acts as shown in Fig. 9 with regions of A-rich fluid and regions of B-rich fluid.

Though partial segregation requires an increase in reactor size, this is not the only consequence. For example, when reactants are viscous fluids, their mixing in a stirred tank or batch reactor often places layers or "streaks" of one fluid next to the other. Reaction takes place at different rates throughout the reactor, and the resulting product has different properties from point to point. This may make it commercially unacceptable. Such is the case in polymerization reactions in which monomer must be intimately mixed with a catalyst. For reactions such as this the problem of mixing is of primary importance and often the rate of reaction and product uniformity correlate well with the mixing energy input to the fluid.

For fast reactions the increase in reactor size from segregation is unimportant; however, other side effects become important. For example, if the product of reaction is a solid precipitate, the size of the precipitate particles may be influenced by the rate of intermixing of reactants, a fact that is well known from the analytical laboratory. As another example, hot gaseous reaction mixtures may contain appreciable quantities of a desirable compound because of favorable thermodynamic equilibrium at such temperatures. To reclaim this component the gas may have to be cooled. But, as is often the case, a drop in temperature causes an unfavorable shift in equilibrium with essentially complete disappearance of desired material. To avoid this and to "freeze" the composition of hot gases, cooling must be very rapid. When the method of quenching used involves mixing the hot gases with an inert cold gas, the success of such a procedure is primarily dependent on the rate at which segregation can be destroyed. Finally the length, type, and temperature of a burning flame, the combustion products obtained, the noise levels of jet engines, and the physical properties of polymers as they are affected by the molecular weight distribution of the material are some of the many phenomena or end results of phenomena that are closely tied to and influenced by the rate and intimacy of fluid mixing.

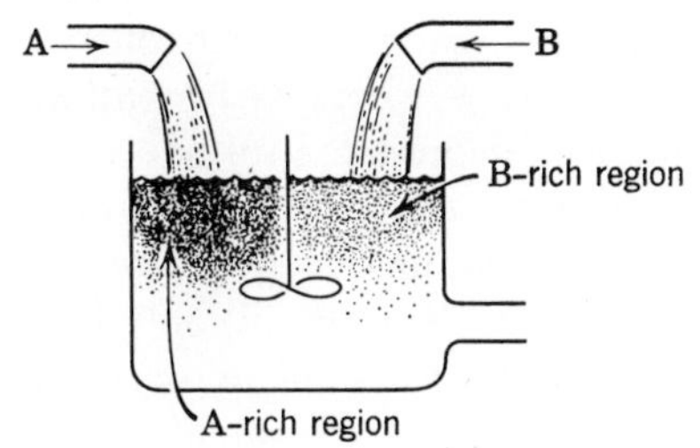

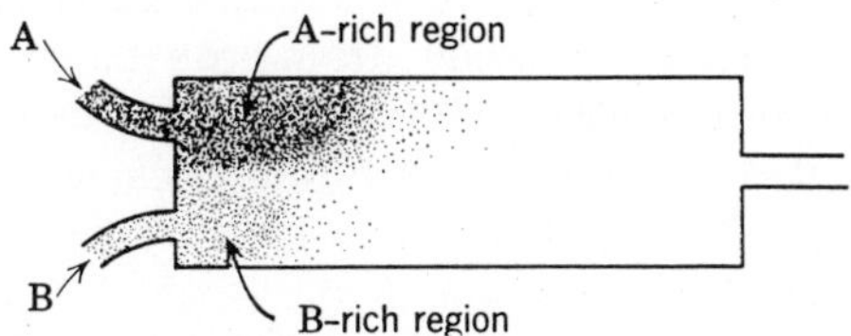

Fig. 9. Partial segregation in the mixing of two miscible fluids in a reactor.

Product distribution in multiple reactions

When multiple reactions take place on mixing two reactant fluids and when these reactions proceed to an appreciable extent before homogeneity is attained, segregation is important and can affect product distribution.

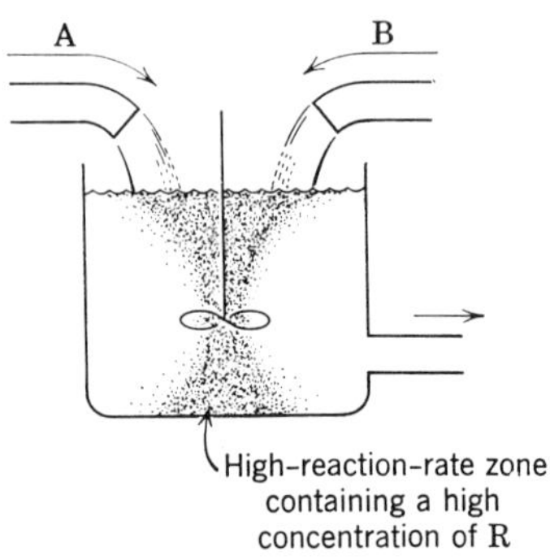

Fig. 10. When reaction rate is very high, zones of nonhomogeneity exist in a reactor. This condition is detrimental to obtaining high yields of intermediate R from the reactions

$$A + B \rightarrow R$$
$$R + B \rightarrow S$$

Consider the homogeneous-phase competitive consecutive reactions

$$A + B \xrightarrow{k_1} R$$
$$R + B \xrightarrow{k_2} S$$

occurring when A and B are poured into a batch reactor. If the reactions are slow enough so that the contents of the vessel are uniform before reaction takes place, the maximum amount of R formed is governed by the k_2/k_1 ratio. This situation, treated in Chapter 7, is one in which we may assume micromixing of fluids. If, however, the fluids are very viscous or if the reactions are fast enough, they will occur in the narrow zones between regions of high A concentration and high B concentration. This is shown in the batch reactor of Fig. 10. The zone of high reaction rate will contain a higher concentration of R than the surrounding fluid. But from the qualitative treatment of this reaction in Chapter 7 we know that any nonhomogeneity in A and R will depress formation of R. Thus partial segregation of reactants will depress the formation of intermediate.

For increased reaction rate, the zone of reaction narrows, and in the limit, for an infinitely fast reaction, becomes a boundary surface between the A-rich and B-rich regions. Now R will only be formed at this plane. What will happen to it? Consider a single molecule of R formed at the reaction plane. If it starts its random wanderings (diffusion) into the A zone and never moves back into the B zone, it will not react further. However, if it starts off into the B zone or if at any time during its wanderings it moves through the reaction plane into the B zone, it will be attacked by B to form S. Interestingly enough, from probabilities associated with a betting game treated by Feller (1957), we can show that the odds in favor of a molecule of R escaping from the B zone become smaller and smaller as the number of diffusion steps taken by a molecule gets larger and larger. This conclusion holds, no matter what pattern of wanderings is chosen for the molecules of R. Thus no R is formed. Looked at from

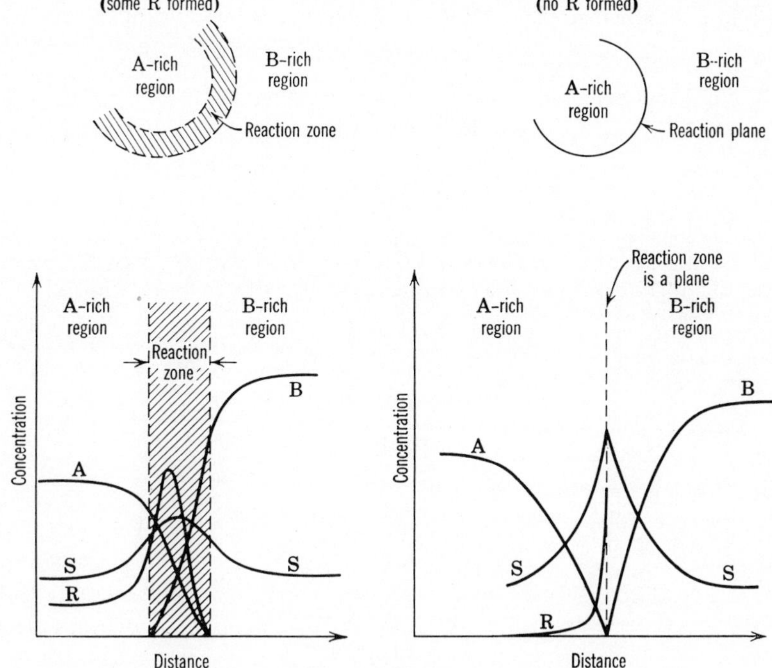

Fig. 11. Concentration profiles of the components of the reactions

$$A + B \rightarrow R$$

$$R + B \rightarrow S$$

at a representative spot in the reactor between A-rich and B-rich fluid for a very fast and for an infinitely fast reaction.

the point of view of Chapter 7, an infinitely fast reaction gives a maximum nonhomogeneity of A and R in the mixture, resulting in no R being formed. Figure 11 shows the concentration of materials at a typical reaction interface and illustrates these points.

Application to design

These observations on the extremes in behavior serve as a guide to the selection and design of equipment favoring the formation of intermediate when reaction is very fast. The important point is to achieve homogeneity in A and R throughout the reaction mixture by making the reaction zone as widespread as possible, or by dispersing B in as fine a form in A rather than dispersing A in B. As an example, let us compare the relative worths of various experimental setups, all treating the same amounts of A and B and designed to produce R. The reaction is fast and of the type

$$A + B \xrightarrow{k_1} R$$

$$R + B \xrightarrow{k_2} S$$

Example 2. Batch Reactor

The methods shown in Fig. E2 are progressively better because the reaction zone becomes larger. Thus there is less chance of A diffusing into B and less chance of a high R concentration occurring locally. For a slow reaction all three setups would be equally good.

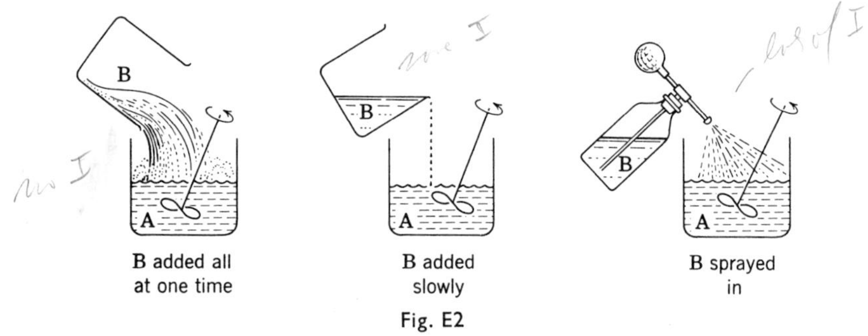

Fig. E2

Example 3. Long versus Short Tubular Flow Reactor

For a fast reaction the size of reactor plays no role after a certain length, the length that is necessary for A and B to be well mixed (Fig. E3). For very viscous materials or for streamline flow of fluids this length may be considerable, but, in general, satisfactory mixing is obtained within a length of several pipe diameters.

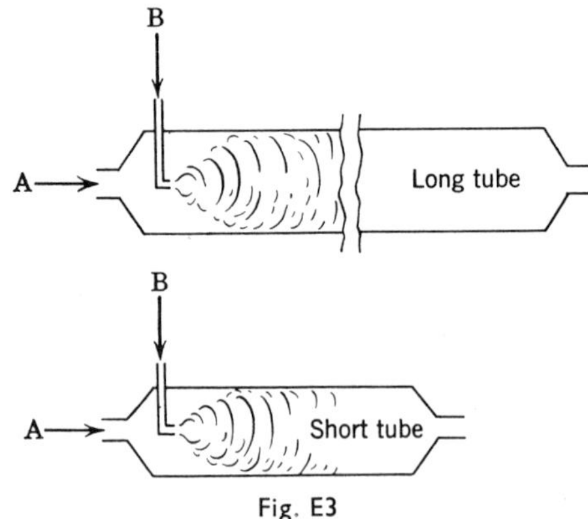

Fig. E3

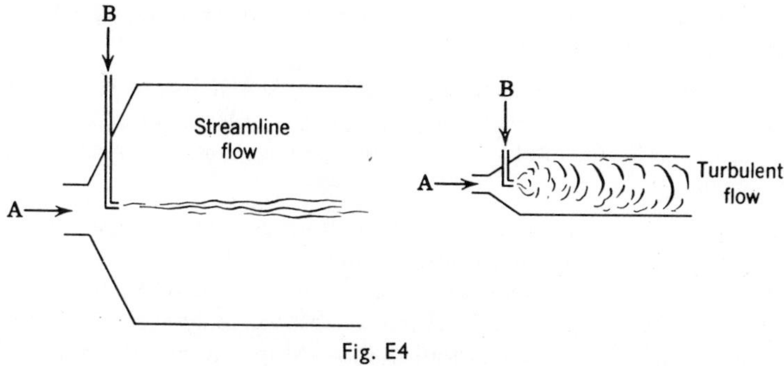

Fig. E4

Example 4. Streamline versus Turbulent Flow

For the same treatment rates the Reynolds number must be greater in the second setup (Fig. E4). With turbulent flow we have more intense mixing and a more widespread reaction zone; therefore the second setup is to be preferred.

With these examples we may propose the following rules for design for homogeneous systems involving fast reactions.

1. Induce rapid and early mixing of reactants.
2. Slow down the reaction by any means possible, such as having it occur in many locations in the reactor, diluting the reactants, employing a negative catalyst, or changing the temperature.

Many ways of contacting A and B are possible, and the selection of a setup depends on the properties of the system at hand.

REFERENCES

R. L. Curl, *A.I.Ch.E. Journal*, **9,** 175 (1963).
P. V. Danckwerts, *Chem Eng. Sci.*, **7,** 116 (1958*a*).
———, *Chem. Eng. Sci.*, **8,** 93 (1958*b*)
W. Feller, *An Introduction to Probability Theory and its Applications*, Vol. I, second edition, John Wiley and Sons, New York, 1957, p. 254.
R. E. Greenhalgh, R. L. Johnson, and H. D. Nott, *Chem. Eng. Progr.,* **55** no. 2, 44 (1959).
A. J. Madden and G. L. Damerell, *A.I.Ch.E. Journal*, **8,** 233 (1962).
R. S. Miller, J. L. Ralph, R. L. Curl and G. D. Towell, *A.I.Ch.E. Journal*, **9,** 196 (1963).
K. Rietema, *Chem. Eng. Sci.*, **8,** 103 (1958).
Th. N. Zwietering, *Chem. Eng. Sci.,* **11,** 1 (1959).

PROBLEMS

1. Derive the expression given in Table 1 for the zero-order reaction of a macrofluid in a backmix reactor. Zero-order reactions are of importance since they often approximate reactions in the dispersed phase of liquid-liquid systems where the kinetics is diffusion-controlled.

2. Find the conversion of a macrofluid in two equal-sized backmix reactors in series (*a*) for zero-order kinetics, (*b*) for first-order kinetics, (*c*) for second-order kinetics. (*d*) Qualitatively, how do these conversions compare with that of a microfluid?

3. Reactant A in one test tube is carefully poured into another test tube containing B (5 sec operation) and is violently shaken (3 sec operation); the resulting mixture is then analyzed. Though B is absent, A, R, and S are found. When the process is reversed, or B poured into A, analysis shows that different amounts of A, R, and S are present in the mixture whereas B is still absent.

(*a*) Briefly explain this result.

(*b*) In which case is the concentration of A, of R, of S higher?

(*c*) How should A and B be contacted to find a reliable value of k_2/k_1?

Data: The reaction is

$$\mathrm{A + B} \xrightarrow{k_1} \mathrm{R}$$

$$\mathrm{R + B} \xrightarrow{k_2} \mathrm{S}$$

with elementary second-order kinetics.

4. Show that the conversion of macrofluid in a real stirred-tank reactor which is represented by the Cholette and Cloutier model of Chapter 9 is as follows.

(*a*) For zero-order reactions

$$X_A = \frac{v_1}{v} R(1 - e^{-1/R}), \qquad R = k\bar{t}_a/C_{A0}$$

(*b*) For first-order reactions

$$X_A = \frac{v_1}{v}\left(\frac{R}{1 + R}\right), \qquad R = k\bar{t}_a$$

(*c*) For second-order reactions

$$X_A = \frac{v_1}{v}\left[1 - \frac{e^{1/R}\,\mathrm{ei}(1/R)}{R}\right], \qquad R = kC_{A0}\bar{t}_a$$

(*d*) Qualitatively, how do these conversions compare with that of microfluids?

5. For an infinitely fast reaction

$$\mathrm{A + B} \xrightarrow{k_1} \mathrm{R}$$

$$\mathrm{R + B} \xrightarrow{k_2} \mathrm{S}$$

select any model for the diffusion of R from the reaction surface between A-rich and B-rich regions and show what fraction of a given batch of molecules of R formed at the interface still remain unreacted after 5, 10, and 15 diffusion steps. Plot this curve. Does the result seem to confirm the statement, made in this chapter, that in the limit, for an infinitely fast reaction, no intermediate R is obtained.

6. In the presence of a catalyst, reactant A decomposes with first-order kinetics as follows:

$$A \xrightarrow[\text{catalyst}]{k_1} R \xrightarrow[\text{catalyst}]{k_2} S$$

Reactant A and catalyst are introduced separately into a backmix reactor; A forms the dispersed phase while the catalyst is introduced in the continuous phase.

(*a*) Assuming a uniform composition within each droplet of dispersed phase, no movement of A or R into the continuous phase, and identical concentration of catalyst within all the droplets, determine how the reaction proceeds and determine the expected $C_{R,\,max}$.

(*b*) How does this compare with the setup in which reactant A forms the continuous phase while catalyst forms the dispersed phase.

7. Repeat the previous problem with the following change. The catalyst is replaced by reactant B and the reaction is

$$A + B \xrightarrow{k_1} R$$

$$R + B \xrightarrow{k_2} S$$

with elementary second-order kinetics.

8. Reactant A is 57% converted in 6 min in a batch reactor. The reaction is first-order reversible, $A \rightleftharpoons R$, with an equilibrium conversion of 60%. Find the conversion of this reactant in a real stirred-tank reactor which is approximated by the Cholette and Cloutier model of Chapter 9 (active volume = 60%, bypass flow = 10%) (*a*) if the reacting materials are in the dispersed phase (macrofluid), (*b*) if the reacting materials are in the continuous phase (microfluid). In both cases the space time of the active phase is 6 min.

9. Repeat the previous problem if the reaction is to take place in two equal-sized backmix reactors with a space time of the active phase of 3 min in each unit.

11

INTRODUCTION TO REACTOR DESIGN FOR HETEROGENEOUS SYSTEMS

These final four chapters treat the kinetics and design of chemical reactors for heterogeneous systems of various kinds, each chapter considering a different system (see Chapter 1 for discussions of heterogeneous and homogeneous systems). For these systems there are two complicating factors that must be accounted for beyond what is normally considered in homogeneous systems.

1. *The complications of the rate equation.* Since more than one phase is present, the movement of material from phase to phase must be considered in the rate equation. Thus the rate expression in general will incorporate the mass transfer terms in addition to the usual chemical kinetics term of homogeneous reactions. These mass transfer terms are different in type and numbers in the different kinds of heterogeneous systems; hence no single rate expression has general application.

2. *The contacting patterns for two-phase systems.* In homogeneous systems we considered two ideal flow patterns of the reacting fluid, plug and backmix flow. In ideal contacting of heterogeneous systems, each fluid may be in plug or backmix flow. Thus many combinations of contacting patterns are possible. For example, if both phases are in plug flow we can have concurrent, countercurrent, or crosscurrent flow of the two phases. On top of this, if one of the phases is discontinuous, as are droplets or solid particles, its macrofluid characteristics may have to be considered. Just as with the plug and backmix flow of a single-phase system, each of the many methods of contacting of two phases has associated with it a specific form of design equation which must be developed for that contacting pattern.

In comparing the two broad types of heterogeneous noncatalytic two-phase systems, the fluid-solid and fluid-fluid systems, we find by and large that the forms of the rate equations are quite different; in addition, some of the many contacting patterns are used primarily with one rather than the other of the systems. As a result design procedures for each of these systems will have features particular to that system. Because of this, these two systems are treated separately in the following two chapters. In the rest of this chapter we consider some of the aspects of these two factors, rate and contacting pattern, as they affect the treatment of heterogeneous systems of all types.

Rate equation for heterogeneous reactions

In general the rate equation for a heterogeneous reaction accounts for more than one process. This leads us to ask how such processes, some involving transport phenomena, others chemical reactions, can be incorporated into one over-all rate expression. The problem of combining rates for different processes is met in conductive heat transfer through layers of different materials, in convective heat and mass transfer from one liquid to another through stagnant boundary films, and also in complex reactions. In all these situations, however, the over-all rate combines processes of the same kind. Let us consider the general problem of combining rates for processes of different kinds.

Let $r_1, r_2, \ldots, r_n$ be the rates of change for the individual processes that are to be accounted for by an over-all rate. If the change can take place by more than one path, called parallel paths, the over-all rate will be greater than the rate for any of the individual paths. In fact, if the various parallel paths are independent of each other, the over-all rate will be simply the sum of all the individual rates, or

$$r_{\text{over-all}} = \sum_{i=1}^{n} r_i$$

On the other hand, if the over-all change requires that a number of steps take place in succession, then at steady state each step will proceed at the same rate. Thus

$$r_{\text{over-all}} = r_1 = r_2 = \cdots = r_n$$

In certain heterogeneous systems, such as fluid-solid noncatalytic reactions, resistance to reaction can be considered to occur in series. In other systems, such as catalytic fluid-solid reactions, more involved series-parallel relationships exist.

Two points should be mentioned here. First, when rates are to be compared or combined, they should be defined in the same manner,

Because the rate of mass transfer is determined by the flux of material or the flow normal to a surface of area S or

$$Q_g = \frac{1}{S}\frac{dN}{dt}$$

then if we wish to consider chemical reaction concurrently, the form of rate equation that must be used is the one based on unit area rather than unit volume which was used in homogeneous systems. Thus in heterogeneous reactions the form of rate equation frequently found is

$$Q_s = r'' = \frac{1}{S}\frac{dN}{dt}$$

Second, some property of the system must be selected as a measure of the rate of change. This factor is often called the driving force for the change and is usually suggested by thermodynamics as the displacement from equilibrium. Driving forces commonly used are temperature difference for heat transfer, concentration difference for mass transfer, and displacement from equilibrium for chemical reaction. Thus for heterogeneous reactions involving mass transfer steps and chemical reaction steps in series, we may write

$$r = f(\text{concentration})$$

Usually we do not know the concentrations of materials at intermediate positions, but only the over-all concentration difference across a number of processes, so it will be convenient to express the rate in terms of the over-all concentration difference. This can easily be done if the rate expressions for all the steps of the process are linear in concentration (first power in concentrations or concentrations differences). If the functional relationships are not all linear, the expression becomes quite unwieldy. The following example will illustrate these points.

Example 1

The irreversible reaction

$$\text{A (gas)} + \text{B (solid)} \rightarrow \text{R (gas)}$$

takes place as shown in Fig. E1. Dilute A diffuses through a stagnant film onto a plane surface consisting of B. Then A and B react to yield gaseous product R which diffuses back through the film into the main gas stream. By diffusion the flux of A to the surface is given by

$$Q_g = \frac{1}{S}\frac{dN}{dt} = -\mathscr{D}\frac{\Delta C}{\Delta x} = -\frac{\mathscr{D}}{\Delta x}(C_g - C_s) = -k_g(C_g - C_s) \qquad \text{(i)}$$

The rate of reaction based on unit surface is

$$Q_s = \frac{1}{S}\frac{dN}{dt} = -k_s C_s^n \tag{ii}$$

where k_s is the reaction rate constant based on unit surface and n is the reaction order with respect to A.

At steady state write the over-all rate of reaction in terms of k_g, k_s and the concentration of A in the main gas stream C_g, noting that the concentration of A on the surface C_s cannot be measured and should not appear in the final expression. Do this for a reaction which is (*a*) first order with respect to A, (*b*) second order with respect to A.

Solution. (*a*) *For a reaction which is first order with respect to* A, $n = 1$. At steady state the flow rate to the surface is equal to the reaction rate at the surface (processes in series). Thus

$$Q_g = Q_s$$

or from Eqs. i and ii

$$k_g(C_g - C_s) = k_s C_s$$

Therefore

$$C_s = \frac{k_g}{k_g + k_s} C_g \tag{iii}$$

Replacing Eq. iii in either Eq. i or Eq. ii eliminates the surface concentration which cannot be measured. Thus

$$Q_g = Q_s = \frac{1}{S}\frac{dN}{dt} = -\frac{1}{1/k_g + 1/k_s} C_g = -k_{\text{over-all}} C_g \tag{iv}$$

Comment. This result shows that $1/k_g$ and $1/k_s$ are additive resistances. The addition of resistances to obtain an over-all resistance is permissible only when the rate is a linear function of the driving force and when the processes occur in series.

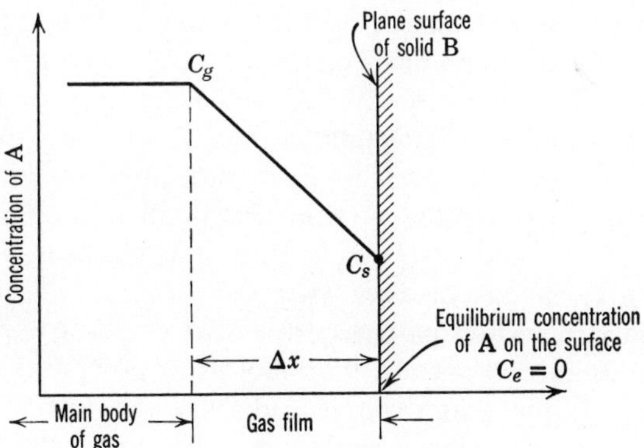

Fig. E1

(*b*) *For a reaction which is second order with respect to* A, $n = 2$. Again at steady state

$$Q_g = Q_s$$

or

$$k_g(C_g - C_s) = k_s C_s^2$$

which is a quadratic in C_s. Solving, we obtain

$$C_s = \frac{-k_g + \sqrt{k_g^2 + 4k_s k_g C_g}}{2k_s} \tag{v}$$

Eliminating C_s in either Eq. i or ii with the value found in Eq. v, we find

$$Q_g = Q_s = -\frac{k_g}{2k_s}\left(2k_s C_g + k_g - \sqrt{k_g^2 + 4k_s k_g C_g}\right) \tag{vi}$$

Comment. Comparing Eqs. iv and vi, we see clearly that unless the various driving forces are linear functions of the system variable, combining rates does not yield simple expressions. This fact influences the treatment of reaction rates for heterogeneous systems. When the chemical reaction is of first order, this rate can be combined with the mass transfer steps without trouble; however, when the reaction is of an order different from one and the rates must be combined, it is common practice to select experimental conditions where the chemical step with little error can be considered to be first order.

Now chemical reaction rates change very rapidly with temperature and also widely from reaction to reaction; hence we often find that the chemical step contributes either the major resistance or hardly any resistance to reaction. When one step contributes the major resistance to the over-all change, this step is called the *rate-controlling* step and may well be considered alone as the only step that influences the rate of reaction. Because one step does usually contribute major resistance to change, much of our treatment in the succeeding chapters is developed on the assumption that one or the other of the many steps is rate controlling.

Contacting patterns for two-phase systems

There are many ways that two phases can be contacted, and for each the design equation will be unique. If the rate expression is also particular to that heterogeneous system, its peculiarities will be incorporated into the design equation. Thus we may say that the design equation is tailored to fit the rate expression and contacting pattern.

With ideal flow of both phases, we have eight principal ways to contact the phases. Figure 1 shows these. Note that no distinction need be made between macrofluids and microfluids when the phase is in plug flow; however, this may have to be done when the material is in backmix flow.

In fluid-solid systems flow patterns *g* and *d* are the more important, since these represent fluidized beds and continuous-belt processing of solids. In fluid-fluid systems, flow patterns *g*, *a*, and *b* are of primary interest since they approximate single mixer-settler, cascade, and tower operations. These are the flow patterns we shall take up in the following chapters.

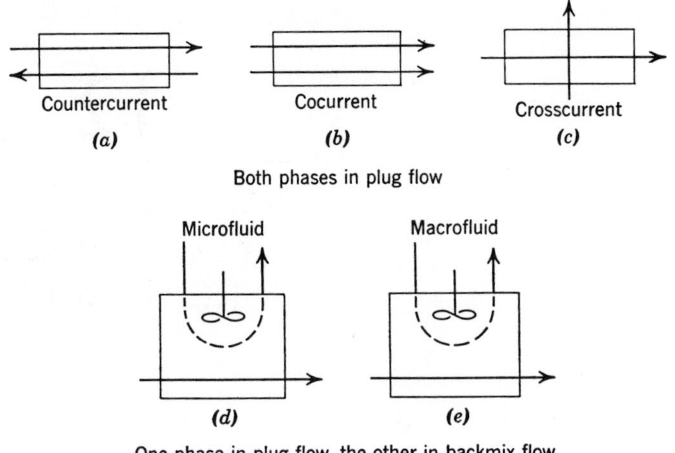

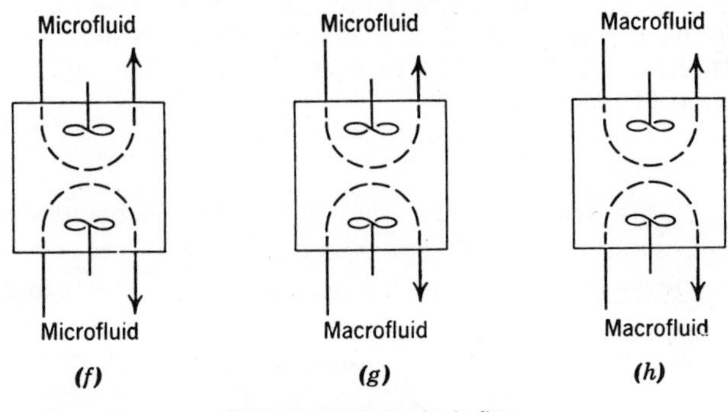

Both phases in backmix flow

Fig. 1. Contacting patterns for immiscible phases in ideal flow. Note that the state of segregation is important only for backmix flow.

Design equations for these ideal flow patterns may be developed without too much difficulty. However, when real flow deviates considerably from these, we can do one of two things: we may develop models to mirror actual flow closely, or we may calculate performance with ideal patterns which "bracket" actual flow.

Fortunately, most real reactors for heterogeneous systems can be satisfactorily approximated by one of the eight ideal flow patterns of Fig. 1. This can be seen by comparing these patterns with the sketches of typical reactors for fluid-solid and fluid-fluid systems (Figs. 12.13, 13.5, and 14.17). Notable exceptions are the reactions taking place in fluidized beds.

12
NONCATALYTIC FLUID-SOLID REACTIONS

In this chapter we consider the class of heterogeneous reactions in which a gas or liquid contacts a solid and reacts with it, causing it to be transformed into product material. Such reactions may be represented by

$$\text{A(fluid)} + b\text{B(solid)} \rightarrow \text{fluid products} \tag{1}$$

$$\rightarrow \text{solid products} \tag{2}$$

$$\rightarrow \text{fluid and solid products} \tag{3}$$

As shown in Fig. 1, solid particles remain unchanged in size during reaction when they contain large amounts of impurities which remain as a nonflaking ash or if they form a firm product material by the reactions of Eq. 2 or Eq. 3. Particles shrink in size during reaction when a flaking ash or product material is formed or when pure B is used in the reaction of Eq. 1.

Fluid-solid reactions are numerous and of great industrial importance. Those in which the solid does not appreciably change in size during reaction are as follows.

1. The roasting (or oxidation) of sulfide ores to yield the metal oxides. For example, in the preparation of zinc oxide the sulfide ore is mined, crushed, separated from the gangue by flotation, and then roasted in a

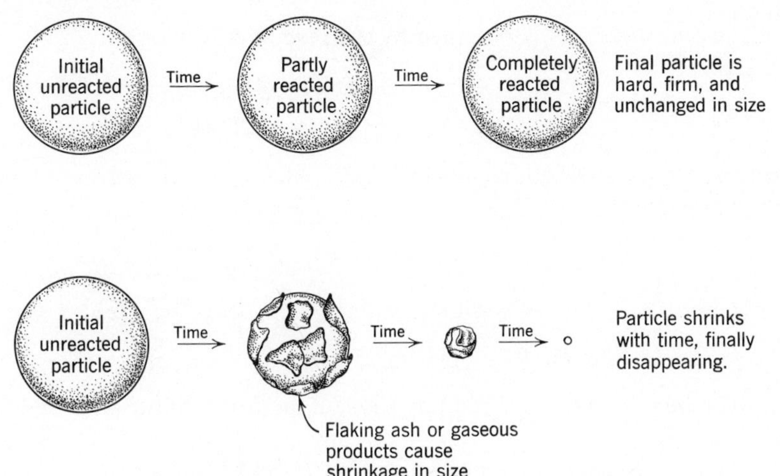

Fig. 1. Range in behavior of solid while reacting with surrounding fluid.

reactor to form hard white zinc oxide particles according to the reaction

$$2ZnS(s) + 3O_2(g) \rightarrow 2ZnO(s) + 2SO_2(g)$$

Similarly iron pyrites react as follows:

$$4FeS_2(s) + 11O_2(g) \rightarrow 8SO_2(g) + 2Fe_2O_3(s)$$

2. The preparation of metals from their oxides by reaction in reducing atmospheres. For example, iron is prepared from crushed and sized magnetite ore in continuous-countercurrent, three-stage, fluidized-bed reactors according to the reaction

$$Fe_3O_4(s) + 4H_2(g) \rightarrow 3Fe(s) + 4H_2O(g)$$

3. The nitrogenation of calcium carbide to produce cyanamide:

$$CaC_2(s) + N_2(g) \rightarrow CaCN_2(s) + C(\text{amorphous})$$

4. The protective surface treatment of solids such as the plating of metals.

The most common examples of fluid-solid reactions in which the size of solid changes are the reactions of carbonaceous materials such as coal briquettes, wood, etc., with low ash content to produce heat or heating fuels. For example, with an insufficient amount of air producer gas is formed by the reactions

$$C(s) + O_2(g) \rightarrow CO_2(g)$$

$$2C(s) + O_2(g) \rightarrow 2CO(g)$$

$$C(s) + CO_2(g) \rightarrow 2CO(g)$$

With steam, water gas is obtained by the reactions

$$C(s) + H_2O(g) \rightarrow CO(g) + H_2(g)$$
$$C(s) + 2H_2O(g) \rightarrow CO_2(g) + 2H_2(g)$$

Other examples of reactions in which solids change in size are as follows.

1. The manufacture of carbon disulfide from the elements:

$$C(s) + 2S(g) \xrightarrow{750-1000\,^\circ C} CS_2(g)$$

2. The manufacture of sodium cyanide from sodium amide:

$$NaNH_2(l) + C(s) \xrightarrow{800^\circ C} NaCN(l) + H_2(g)$$

3. The manufacture of sodium thiosulfate from sulfur and sodium sulfite:

$$Na_2SO_3(\text{solution}) + S(s) \rightarrow Na_2S_2O_3(\text{solution})$$

Other examples are the dissolution reactions, the attack of metal chips by acids, and the rusting of iron.

In Chapter 11 we pointed out that treatment of heterogeneous reaction required the consideration of two factors in addition to those normally encountered in homogeneous reactions, the first being the modification of the kinetic expressions resulting from the mass transfer between phases, the second being the contacting patterns of the reacting phases.

Let us now develop the rate expressions for fluid-solid reactions. These will then be used in design.

SELECTION OF A MODEL

In asking the question "How do we obtain an expression for the rate of reaction of a solid particle?" we must realize that any such expression is simply the mathematical representation of a conceptual model or picture which is selected beforehand. If the model corresponds closely to what really takes place, the rate expression derived from the model will closely predict and describe the actual kinetics; if the model widely differs from reality, the derived kinetic expressions will be useless. We must remember that the most elegant and high-powered mathematical analysis based on a model which does not correspond with reality is simply a mathematical exercise which is worthless for the engineer who must make design predictions. What we say here about a model holds not only in deriving kinetic expressions but in all areas of engineering.

The requirement for a model from which to develop the kinetic equations is that it be the closest representation of the actual phenomenon which can reasonably be treated without undue mathematical complexities. It is of

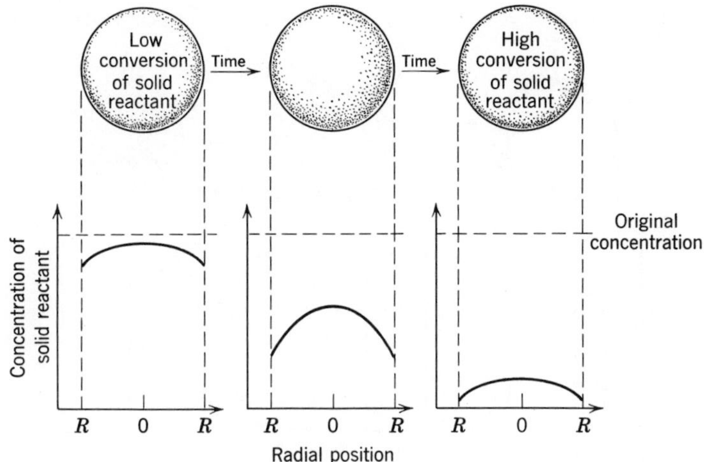

Fig. 2. According to the progressive-conversion model, reaction proceeds continuously throughout the solid particle.

little use to select a model which very closely mirrors reality but which is so complicated that we cannot do anything with it. Unfortunately, this all too often happens.

For the noncatalytic reactions of solid particles with the surrounding fluid, we consider two rather simple idealized models, the continuous-reaction model and the unreacted-core model.

Continuous-reaction model

Here we visualize that reactant gas enters and reacts throughout the solid particle at all times, most likely at different rates at different locations within the particle. Thus, solid reactant is converted continuously and progressively throughout the particle as shown in Fig. 2.

Unreacted-core model

Here we visualize that reaction occurs first at the outer skin of the solid particle. The zone of reaction then moves into the solid, leaving behind completely converted material and inert solid. We refer to these as "ash." Thus, at any time during reaction, there exists an unreacted core of material which shrinks in size during reaction as shown in Fig. 3.

Comparison of models with real situations

In slicing and examining the cross section of partly reacted solid particles, we usually find unreacted solid material surrounded by a layer of ash. The boundary of this unreacted core may not always be sharply defined as the model shows it; nevertheless, evidence from a wide variety

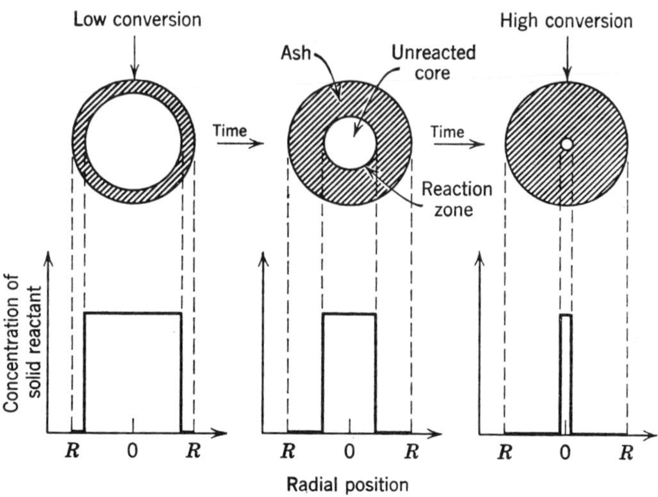

Fig. 3. According to the unreacted-core model, reaction proceeds at a narrow front which moves into the solid particle. Reactant is completely converted as the front passes by.

of situations indicates that the unreacted-core model approximates reality more closely in most cases than the progressive-conversion model. Observations with burning coal, wood, briquettes, and tightly wrapped newspapers also lend weight to the unreacted-core model.

We may object to this model on the basis of observations of the slow heating and subsequent boiling of an egg or the baking of a cake; here the reaction proceeds throughout the whole mass. This objection is overcome if we note that these are not heterogeneous reactions such as those shown in Eqs. 1, 2, and 3, requiring the contacting of a solid with a fluid for the reaction to proceed. These are reactions promoted by heat, and it is immaterial whether the heat is introduced by contact with a hot fluid phase or by radiant energy.

Sometimes the progressive-conversion model fits facts better than the unreacted-core model, such as the slow reaction of a very porous solid. An example of this is the slow poisoning of a catalyst pellet.

Since the shrinking unreacted-core model seems to represent reality more closely in a wide variety of situations, we develop the kinetic equations for it in the following section. However, we should like to point out that others, for example, Walker et al. (1959), drawing on the ideas of catalytic gas-solid reaction, have used the continuous-reaction model to develop kinetic equations for heterogeneous noncatalytic reactions.

In the treatment to follow we consider the fluid phase to be a gas, but, this is done only for convenience since the treatment applies equally well to all fluids, both gases and liquids.

RATE OF REACTION FOR SPHERICAL PARTICLES OF UNCHANGING SIZE

In the unreacted-core model we visualize five steps occurring in succession during reaction (see Fig. 4).

Step 1. Diffusion of gaseous reactant A through the film surrounding the particle to the surface of the solid.

Step 2. Penetration and diffusion of A through the blanket of ash to the surface of the unreacted core, the reaction surface.

Step 3. Chemical reaction of the gaseous reactant A with solid.

Step 4. Diffusion of gaseous products through the ash back to the surface of the solid.

Step 5. Diffusion of gaseous reaction products through the gas film back into the main body of the fluid.

Very often certain of these steps do not exist. For example, if no gaseous products are formed or if the reaction is irreversible, steps 4 and 5 do not contribute directly to the resistance to reaction.

Since these steps must occur successively for reaction to take place, we

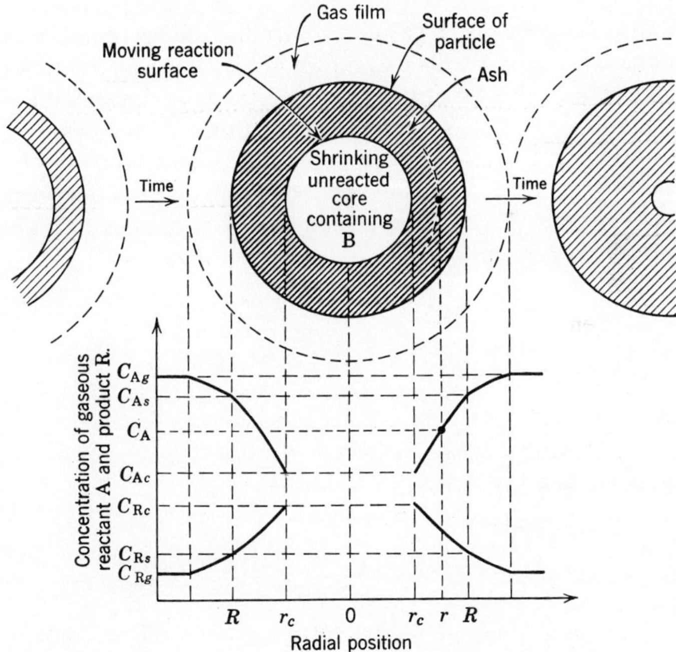

Fig. 4. Representation of concentrations of reactants and products for the reaction $A(g) + bB(s) \rightleftharpoons rR(g) + sS(s)$ for a particle of unchanging size.

consider them to offer resistances in series. Because of this, whenever one of the steps offers the major resistance, that step may be considered alone as the rate-controlling step.

Resistances of the different steps can and usually do vary greatly from each other; therefore in the treatment of the kinetics we can usually consider one of these five steps as rate controlling. We should like to know which step controls in a given situation. Moreover, when operating conditions are changed, we should like to know when the controlling resistance changes.

In this treatment we consider the chemical reaction to be elementary and irreversible and represented kinetically by Eqs. 1, 2, or 3, in which case steps 4 and 5 do not apply. In addition, we consider the particle to be spherical. Extension of this analysis to particles of other simple geometrical shapes such as long cylinders or flat plates (end effects ignored) is straightforward; however, for irregular-shaped particles analysis is difficult. So let us now determine the rate at which an individual spherical particle reacts when mass transfer of reactant through the boundary film, diffusion through ash, and chemical reaction in turn control.

Gas film diffusion controls

With the resistance of the gas film controlling, the concentration profile for gas-phase reactant A will be as shown in Fig. 5. From this figure we see that no reactant is present at the surface; hence the concentration driving force $C_{Ag} - C_{As} = C_{Ag}$ is constant at all times during reaction of the particle. Since it is convenient to derive the kinetic equations based on available surface, focus attention on the unchanging exterior surface of a particle S_{ex}. Noting from the stoichiometry of Equations 1, 2, and 3 that $dN_B = b\,dN_A$, we write

$$-\frac{1}{S_{ex}}\frac{dN_B}{dt} = -\frac{1}{4\pi R^2}\frac{dN_B}{dt} = -\frac{b}{4\pi R^2}\frac{dN_A}{dt}$$

$$= bk_g(C_{Ag} - C_{As}) = bk_gC_{Ag} = \text{constant} \quad (4)$$

If we let ρ_B be the molar density of B in the solid and V be the volume of a particle, the amount of B present in a particle is

$$N_B = \rho_B V = \left(\frac{\text{moles B}}{\text{ft}^3 \text{ solid}}\right)(\text{ft}^3 \text{ solid})$$

The decrease in volume or radius of unreacted core accompanying the disappearance of dN_B moles of solid reactant or $b\,dN_A$ moles of fluid reactant is then given by

$$-dN_B = -b\,dN_A = -\rho_B\,dV = -\rho_B\,d(\tfrac{4}{3}\pi r_c^3) = -4\pi\rho_B r_c^2\,dr_c \quad (5)$$

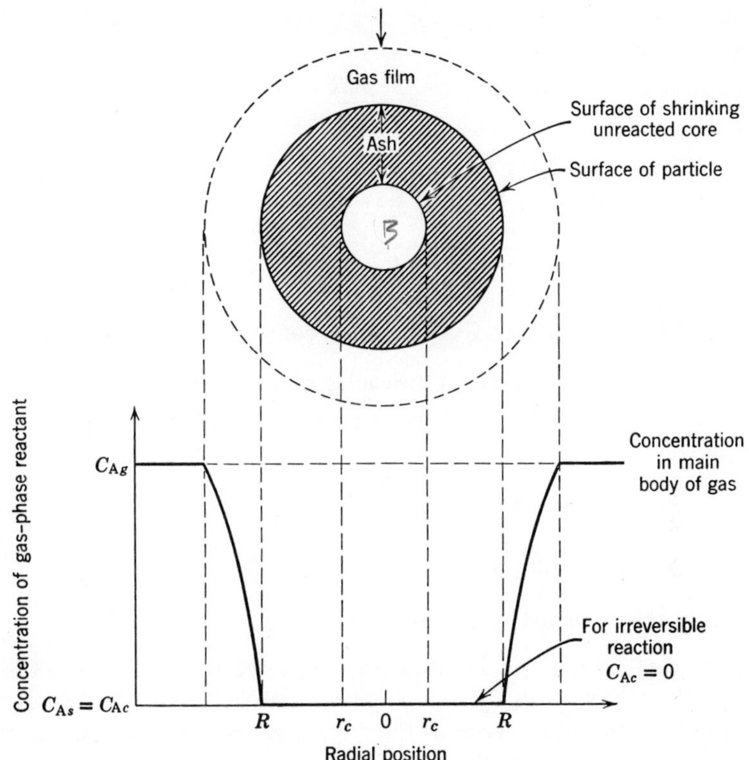

Fig. 5. Representation of a reacting particle when gas film diffusion is the controlling resistance, the reaction being A(g) + bB(s) → products.

Replacing Eq. 5 in 4 gives the rate of reaction in terms of the shrinking radius of unreacted core, or

$$-\frac{1}{S_{\text{ex}}}\frac{dN_{\text{B}}}{dt} = -\frac{\rho_{\text{B}}r_c^{\,2}}{R^2}\frac{dr_c}{dt} = bk_gC_{\text{A}g}$$

Rearranging and integrating, we find how the unreacted core shrinks with time. Thus

$$-\frac{\rho_{\text{B}}}{R^2}\int_R^{r_c} r_c^{\,2}\,dr_c = bk_gC_{\text{A}g}\int_0^t dt$$

$$t = \frac{\rho_{\text{B}}R}{3bk_gC_{\text{A}g}}\left[1 - \left(\frac{r_c}{R}\right)^3\right] \tag{6}$$

Let the time for complete reaction of a particle be τ. By taking $r_c = 0$ in Eq. 6, we find

$$\tau = \frac{\rho_B R}{3bk_g C_{Ag}} \tag{7}$$

The radius of unreacted core in terms of fractional time for complete conversion is given by combining Eqs. 6 and 7, or

$$\frac{t}{\tau} = 1 - \left(\frac{r_c}{R}\right)^3$$

This can be written in terms of fractional conversion by noting that

$$1 - X_B = \left(\frac{\text{volume of unreacted core}}{\text{total volume of particle}}\right) = \frac{\frac{4}{3}\pi r_c^{\,3}}{\frac{4}{3}\pi R^3} = \left(\frac{r_c}{R}\right)^3 \tag{8}$$

Therefore

$$\frac{t}{\tau} = 1 - \left(\frac{r_c}{R}\right)^3 = X_B \tag{9}$$

which is shown graphically in Figs. 9 and 10 (pp. 353 and 354).

Diffusion through ash controls

Figure 6 illustrates the situation in which the resistance to diffusion through the ash controls the rate of reaction. To develop an expression between time and radius, such as Eq. 6 for film resistance, requires a two-step analysis. First we examine a typical partially reacted particle, writing the flux relationships for this condition. Then we apply this type of relationship for all values of r_c, in other words we integrate r_c between R and 0.

Consider a partially reacted particle as shown in Fig. 6. Both reactant A and boundary of unreacted core move inward toward the center of the particle. But the rate of shrinkage of unreacted core is smaller than the rate of movement of A toward the unreacted core by a factor of about 1000, which is roughly the ratio of densities of solid to gas. Because of this it is reasonable for us to assume, as far as the concentration gradient of A in the ash at any time is concerned, that the unreacted core is stationary. This assumption of quasi steady-state conditions for diffusing A at any time for any radius of unreacted core allows great simplification in the mathematics which follows. With this assumption the rate of reaction of reactant A at any instant is given by its rate of diffusion into the particle through a shell of any radius r in the ash, or

$$-\frac{dN_A}{dt} = 4\pi r^2 Q_A = 4\pi R^2 Q_{As} = 4\pi r_c^{\,2} Q_{Ac} = \text{constant} \tag{10}$$

For convenience, let the flux of A within the ash layer be expressed by Fick's law for equimolar counterdiffusion, though other forms of this diffusion equation will give the same result (see Problem 12.1). Then noting that both Q_A and dC_A/dr are positive, we have

$$Q_A = \mathscr{D}\frac{dC_A}{dr} \tag{11}$$

Combining Eqs. 10 and 11, we obtain for any r

$$-\frac{dN_A}{dt} = 4\pi r^2\,\mathscr{D}\frac{dC_A}{dr} = \text{constant} \tag{12}$$

Integrating across the ash layer from R to r_c we obtain

$$-\frac{dN_A}{dt}\int_R^{r_c}\frac{dr}{r^2} = 4\pi\mathscr{D}\int_{C_{Ag}=C_{As}}^{C_{Ac}=0} dC_A$$

or

$$-\frac{dN_A}{dt}\left(\frac{1}{r_c} - \frac{1}{R}\right) = 4\pi\mathscr{D}C_{Ag} \tag{13}$$

This expression represents the conditions of a reacting particle at any time.

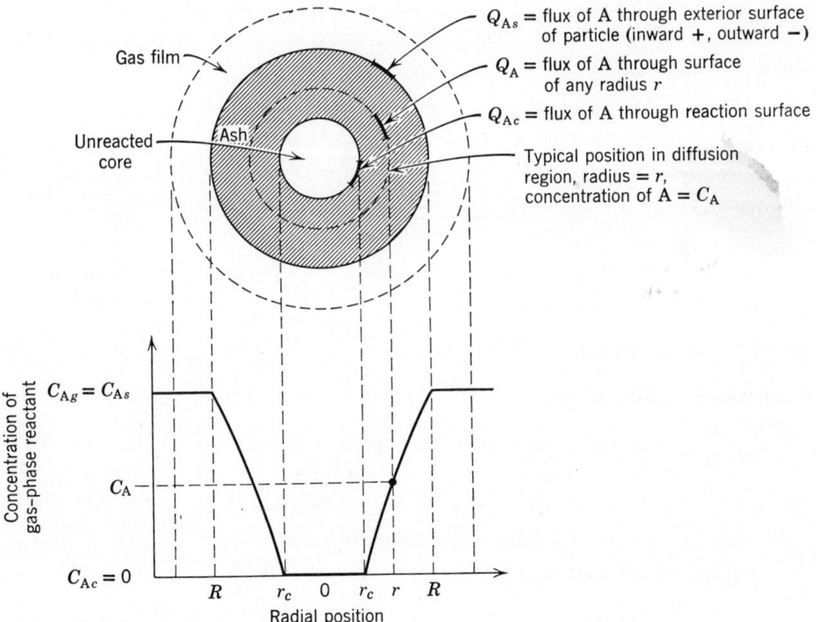

Fig. 6. Representation of a reacting particle when ash diffusion is the controlling resistance, the reaction being A(g) + bB(s) → products.

In the second part of the analysis we let the size of unreacted core change with time. For a given size of unreacted core, dN_A/dt is constant; however, as the core shrinks the ash layer becomes thicker, causing a decrease in the rate of diffusion of A. Consequently, integration of Eq. 13 with respect to time and other variables should yield the required relationship. But we note that this equation contains three variables, t, N_A, and r_c, one of which must be eliminated or written in terms of the other variables before integration can be performed. As with film diffusion, let us express N_A in terms of r_c. This relationship is given by Eq. 5. Replacing Eq. 5 in Eq. 13, separating variables and integrating, we obtain

$$-\rho_B \int_{r_c=R}^{r_c} \left(\frac{1}{r_c} - \frac{1}{R}\right) r_c^2 \, dr_c = b\mathscr{D}C_{Ag} \int_0^t dt$$

or

$$t = \frac{\rho_B R^2}{6b\mathscr{D}C_{Ag}} \left[1 - 3\left(\frac{r_c}{R}\right)^2 + 2\left(\frac{r_c}{R}\right)^3\right] \tag{14}$$

For complete reaction of a particle, $r_c = 0$ and the time required is

$$\tau = \frac{\rho_B R^2}{6b\mathscr{D}C_{Ag}} \tag{15}$$

The radius of unreacted core based on the time required for complete conversion is found by dividing Eq. 14 by Eq. 15, or

$$\frac{t}{\tau} = 1 - 3\left(\frac{r_c}{R}\right)^2 + 2\left(\frac{r_c}{R}\right)^3 \tag{16}$$

which in terms of fractional conversion, as given in Eq. 8, becomes

$$\frac{t}{\tau} = 1 - 3(1 - X_B)^{2/3} + 2(1 - X_B) \tag{17}$$

These results are presented graphically in Figs. 9 and 10, pp. 353 and 354.

Chemical reaction controls

Figure 7 illustrates concentration gradients within a particle when chemical reaction controls. Since the progress of the reaction is independent of the presence of any ash layer, the quantity of material reacting is proportional to the available surface of unreacted core. Thus, based on unit surface of unreacted core, the rate of reaction for the stoichiometry of Eqs. 1, 2, and 3 is

$$-\frac{1}{4\pi r_c^2}\frac{dN_B}{dt} = -\frac{b}{4\pi r_c^2}\frac{dN_A}{dt} = bk_s C_{Ag} \tag{18}$$

Writing N_B in terms of the shrinking radius, as given in Eq. 5, we obtain

$$-\frac{1}{4\pi r_c^2}\rho_B 4\pi r_c^2 \frac{dr_c}{dt} = -\rho_B \frac{dr_c}{dt} = bk_s C_{Ag}$$

which on integration becomes

$$-\rho_B \int_R^{r_c} dr_c = bk_s C_{Ag} \int_0^t dt$$

or

$$t = \frac{\rho_B}{bk_s C_{Ag}}(R - r_c) \tag{19}$$

The time $\boldsymbol{\tau}$ required for complete reaction is given when $r_c = 0$, or

$$\boldsymbol{\tau} = \frac{\rho_B R}{bk_s C_{Ag}} \tag{20}$$

The decrease in radius or increase in fractional conversion of the particle

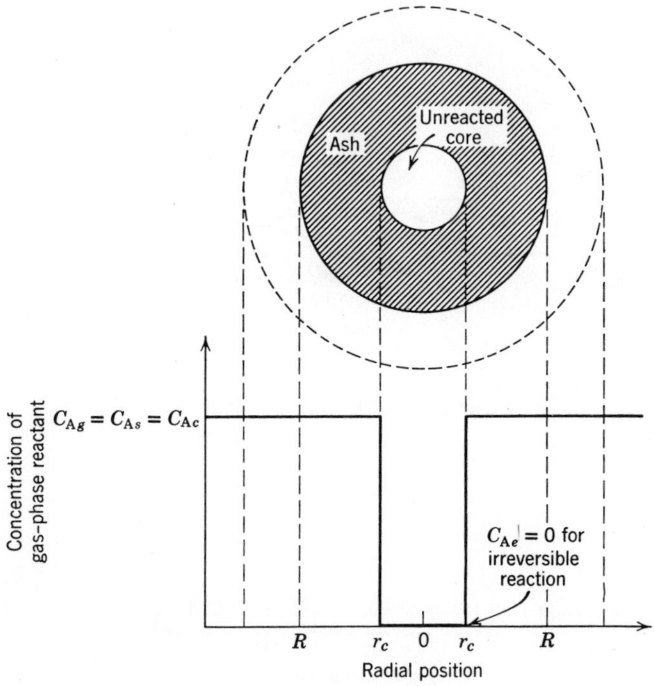

Fig. 7. Representation of a reacting particle when chemical reaction is the controlling resistance, the reaction being $A(g) + bB(s) \rightarrow$ products.

in terms of τ is found by combining Eqs. 19 and 20. Thus

$$\frac{t}{\tau} = 1 - \frac{r_c}{R} = 1 - (1 - X_B)^{1/3} \tag{21}$$

This result is plotted in Figs. 9 and 10, pp. 353 and 354.

RATE OF REACTION FOR SHRINKING SPHERICAL PARTICLES

When no ash forms, as in the burning of pure carbon in air, the reacting particle shrinks during reaction, finally disappearing. This process is illustrated in Fig. 8. For a reaction of this kind we visualize the following three steps occurring in succession.

Step 1. Diffusion of reactant A from the main body of the gas through the gas film to the surface of the solid.

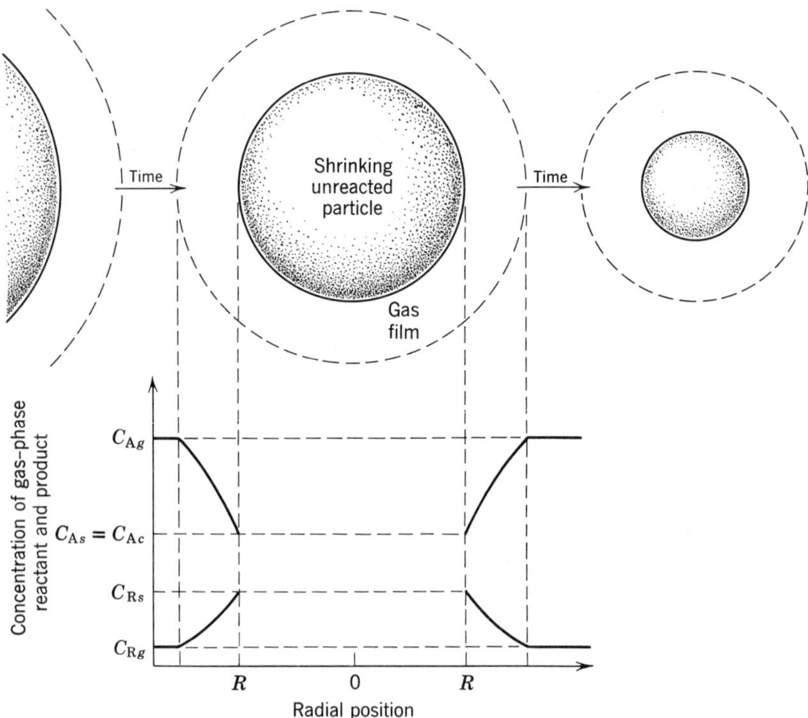

Fig. 8. Representation of concentration of reactants and products for the reaction $A(g) + bB(s) \rightarrow rR(g)$ between a shrinking solid particle and gas.

Step 2. Reaction on the surface between reactant A and solid.

Step 3. Diffusion of reaction products from the surface of the solid through the gas film back into the main body of gas.

Note that ash is absent and cannot contribute any resistance.

As with particles of constant size, let us see what rate expressions result when one or the other of the resistances controls. Again consider an irreversible reaction.

Chemical reaction controls

When chemical reaction controls, the behavior is identical to that of particles of unchanging size; therefore Fig. 7 and Eqs. 19 or 21 will represent the time-conversion behavior of single particles, both shrinking and of constant size.

Gas film diffusion controls

Film resistance at the surface of a particle is dependent on numerous factors, such as the relative velocity between particle and fluid, size of particle, and fluid properties. These have been correlated on the basis of experimental evidence by semiempirical dimensionless equations, each of which correlates the variables only for a specific method of contacting of fluid with solid, such as packed beds, fluidized beds, and solids in free fall. One such example for the mass transfer of a component of mole fraction y in a fluid to free-falling solids is given by Froessling (1938):

$$\frac{k_g d_p y}{\mathscr{D}} = 2.0 + 0.6(\mathrm{Sc})^{1/3}(\mathrm{Re})^{1/2}$$

$$= 2.0 + 0.6\left(\frac{\mu}{\rho\mathscr{D}}\right)^{1/3}\left(\frac{d_p u \rho}{\mu}\right)^{1/2} \tag{22}$$

During reaction particles shrink in size, and when these are in free fall the relative velocity between gas and solid also varies because the terminal settling velocity of particles is itself dependent on the size of the particles. These changes cause the film resistance, measured by k_g, to vary during reaction. Now time versus size relationship for such particles can be developed; however, a different relationship would be obtained every time a different correlation of the type shown in Eq. 22 is used. All such relationships would be cumbersome and limited in generality; therefore they will not be considered here.

Nevertheless, the general trend of film resistance with change in particle size and gas velocity is as follows. Film resistance drops with decrease in particle size but rises with decrease in gas velocity, particle size being the primary influence. As an example, Fig. 12 (p. 356) and Eq. 22 show that

$$\begin{aligned} k_g &\sim \frac{1}{d_p}, \qquad \text{for } (\mathrm{Sc})^{1/3}(\mathrm{Re})^{1/2} \ll 3.3 \\ k_g &\sim \frac{u^{1/2}}{d_p^{1/2}}, \qquad \text{for } (\mathrm{Sc})^{1/3}(\mathrm{Re})^{1/2} \gg 3.3 \end{aligned} \tag{23}$$

COMBINATION OF RESISTANCES FOR SPHERICAL PARTICLES

First consider the progressive reaction of a spherical particle of unchanging size. The relative importance of the resistances in the gas film and ash layer to chemical reaction will vary as conversion progresses. This can be seen by noting that the gas film resistance remains unchanged throughout, the resistance to reaction increases as the surface of unreacted core decreases, and ash diffusion resistance is nonexistent at the start when no ash is present but becomes progressively more and more important as the ash layer builds up. As a result of these changing resistances, a proper estimate of their relative roles is obtained only by considering the complete reaction of a particle.

Thus in terms of the mean rate as averaged over the time necessary for complete reaction, eliminating all intermediate concentrations as shown in the example of Chapter 11, we have

$$-\frac{1}{S_{\mathrm{ex}}}\overline{\frac{dN_{\mathrm{A}}}{dt}} = \bar{k}_s C_{\mathrm{A}} = \frac{1}{\dfrac{1}{k_g} + \dfrac{1}{k_d} + \dfrac{3}{k_s}} C_{\mathrm{A}} \tag{24}$$

where $k_d = 2\mathscr{D}/R$ is the measure of the conductance through the ash layer, $R/2$ being the average thickness of this layer.

For ash-free particles which shrink with reaction, only two resistances, gas film and surface reaction, need be considered. Since these are both based on the exterior surface of particles, we may combine them to give at any instant

$$-\frac{1}{S_{\mathrm{ex}}}\frac{dN_{\mathrm{A}}}{dt} = \bar{k}_s C_{\mathrm{A}} = \frac{1}{\dfrac{1}{k_g} + \dfrac{1}{k_s}} C_{\mathrm{A}} \tag{25}$$

DETERMINATION OF THE RATE-CONTROLLING STEP

The kinetics and rate-controlling steps of a fluid-solid reaction are found by following the progressive conversion of solid particles and noting

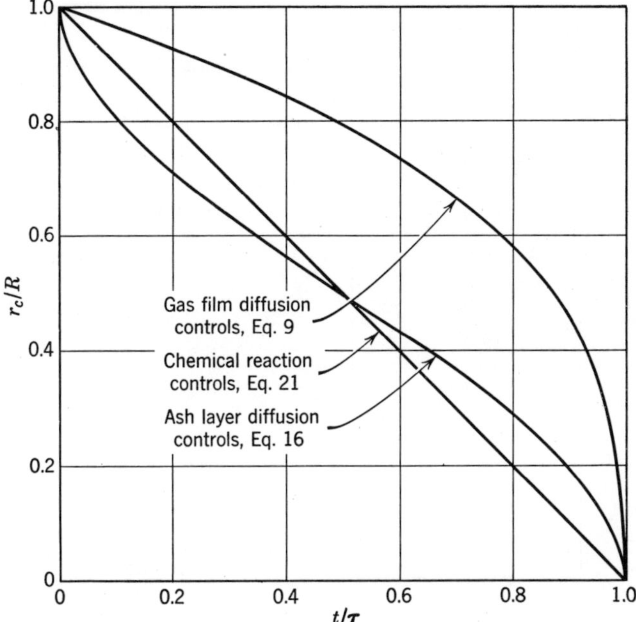

Fig. 9. Progress of reaction of a single solid particle with surrounding fluid measured in terms of time for complete reaction. From Yagi and Kunii (1955).

how particle size and operating temperature influence this conversion. This information can be obtained by any one of a number of experimental programs. The one actually selected will depend on the facilities available and the materials at hand. The following observations based on the rate information of the previous sections are a guide to a rational plan of experimentation and to the proper interpretation of experimental results.

Temperature. The chemical step is usually much more temperature sensitive than the physical steps are. Hence performing the experiment at different temperatures should easily distinguish between ash or film diffusion on the one hand and chemical reaction on the other hand as the controlling step.

Time. Figures 9 and 10 show the progress of a reaction in a particle of unchanging size when chemical reaction, film diffusion, and ash diffusion in turn control. Results of kinetic runs for various periods compared with these predicted curves should indicate the rate-controlling step. Unfortunately, the difference between ash diffusion and chemical reaction as controlling steps is not great and may be masked by the scatter in experimental data.

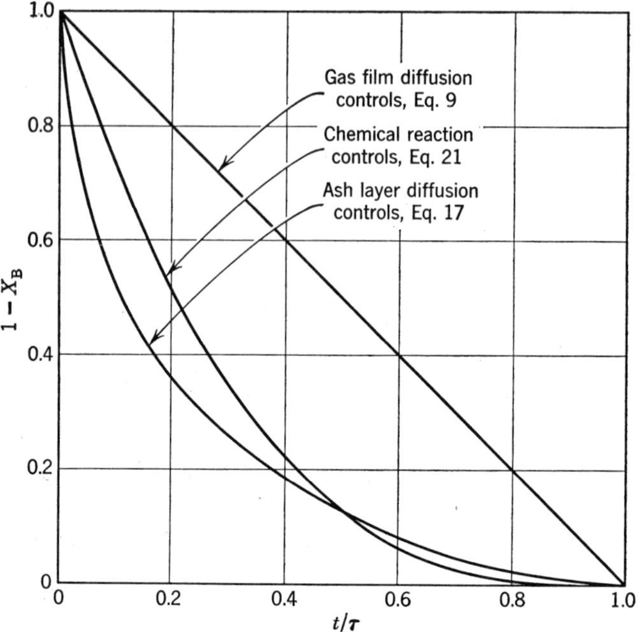

Fig. 10. Progress of reaction of a single solid particle with surrounding fluid measured in terms of time for complete conversion.

Particle size. Equations 15 and 20 and Eq. 7 with 23 show that the time needed to achieve the same fractional conversion for particles of different but unchanging sizes is given by

$$\frac{t_2}{t_1} = \frac{\tau_2}{\tau_1} \approx \left(\frac{R_2}{R_1}\right)^{1.5\text{ to }2.0}, \qquad \text{for film diffusion controlling (for a rise in the Reynolds number the power on } R_2/R_1 \text{ drops)} \tag{26}$$

$$\frac{t_2}{t_1} = \frac{\tau_2}{\tau_1} = \left(\frac{R_2}{R_1}\right)^2, \qquad \text{for ash diffusion controlling} \tag{27}$$

$$\frac{t_2}{t_1} = \frac{\tau_2}{\tau_1} = \frac{R_2}{R_1}, \qquad \text{for chemical reaction controlling} \tag{28}$$

Thus kinetic runs with different sizes of particles can distinguish between reactions in which the chemical and physical steps control.

Ash versus film resistance. When a hard solid ash is formed during reaction, resistance to the passage of gas-phase reactant is usually much greater through this ash than through the gas film surrounding the particle. Hence in the presence of a nonflaking ash layer, film resistance can safely

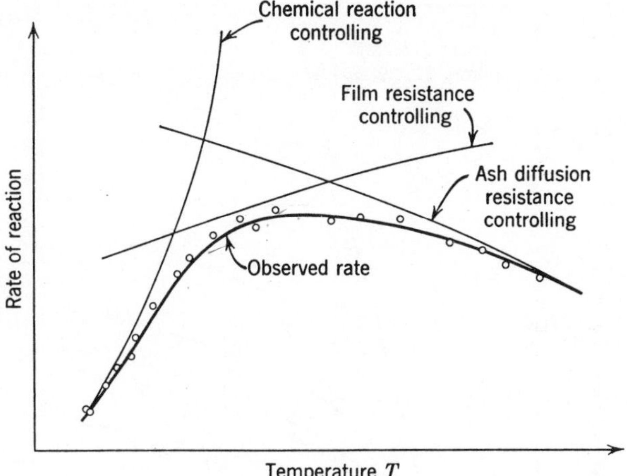

Fig. 11. Because of the series relationship among the resistances to reaction, the net or observed rate is never higher than for any of the individual steps acting alone.

be ignored. In addition, ash resistance alone is unaffected by changes in gas velocity.

Predictability of film resistance. The magnitude of film resistance can be estimated from dimensionless correlations such as Eq. 22. Thus an observed rate approximately equal to the calculated rate suggests that film resistance controls.

Over-all versus individual resistance. If a plot of individual rate coefficients is made as a function of temperature as shown in Fig. 11, the over-all coefficient given by Eq. 24 or 25 cannot be higher than any of the individual coefficients.

With these observations we can usually discover with a small carefully planned experimental program which is the controlling mechanism.

Let us illustrate the interplay of resistance with the well-studied gas-solid reaction of pure carbon particles with oxygen:

$$C + O_2 \rightarrow CO_2$$
$$[B(s) + A(g) \rightarrow \text{gaseous products}]$$

with rate equation

$$-\frac{1}{S_{ex}}\frac{dN_B}{dt} = -\frac{1}{4\pi R^2} 4\pi R^2 \rho_B \frac{dR}{dt} = -\rho_B \frac{dR}{dt} = \bar{k}_s C_A$$

Since no ash is formed at any time during reaction, we have here a case of kinetics of shrinking particles for which two resistances at most, surface

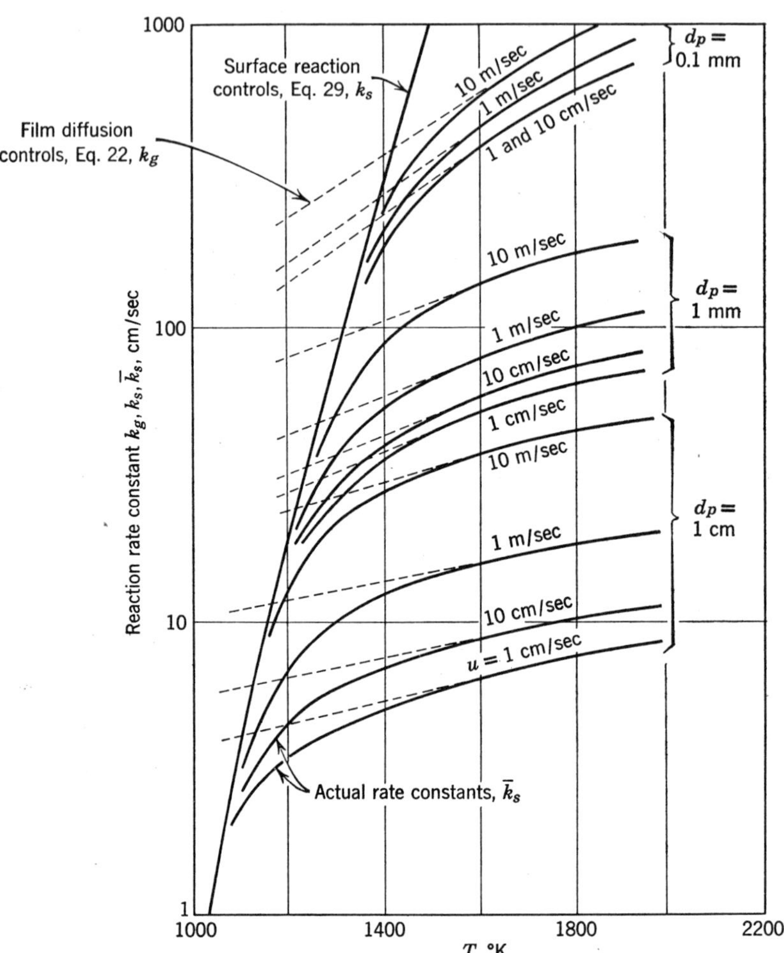

Fig. 12. Rate of combustion of pure carbon particles, adapted from Yagi and Kunii (1955).

reaction and gas film, may play a role. In terms of these, the over-all rate constant at any instant from Eq. 25 is

$$\frac{1}{\bar{k}_s} = \frac{1}{k_s} + \frac{1}{k_g}$$

For surface reaction controlling, Parker and Hottel (1936) found that the rate is represented by

$$-\frac{1}{S_{\text{ex}}}\frac{dN_{\text{B}}}{dt} = \frac{4.32 \times 10^{11}\, C_{\text{A}g}}{\sqrt{T}}\, e^{-44{,}000\ \text{cal}/RT} = k_s C_{\text{A}g} \tag{29}$$

where T is in degrees Kelvin and C_{Ag} is in gram moles per liter. For film diffusion controlling, Eq. 22 holds. Figure 12 shows all this information in convenient graphical form and allows determination of $\bar{k}_s$ for different values of the system variables. Note that when film resistance controls, the reaction is rather temperature insensitive but is dependent on particle size and relative velocity between solid and gas. This is shown by the family of lines, close to parallel and practically horizontal.

In extrapolating to new untried operating conditions, we must know when to be prepared for a change in controlling step and when we may reasonably expect the rate-controlling step not to change. For example, for particles with nonflaking ash a rise in temperature, and to a lesser extent an increase in particle size, may cause the rate to switch from reaction to diffusion controlling, the critical temperature being a function of particle size, solid porosity, and reaction kinetics. For reactions in which ash is not present, a rise in temperature will again cause the reaction to switch from reaction to gas film resistance controlling.

Finally we should note that the relative importance of the various resistances changes during the reaction of particles. These effects have been considered, however, and have been accounted for to give a proper mean estimate of their relative rates in Eq. 24.

APPLICATION TO DESIGN

Three factors primarily control the design of a fluid-solid reactor, the reaction kinetics for single particles, the size distribution of these solids being treated, and the flow patterns of both solids and fluids in the reactor. Where the kinetics are complex and not well known, where the products of reaction form a blanketing fluid phase, where temperatures within the system vary greatly from position to position, analysis of the situation becomes difficult and present design is based largely on the experiences gained by many years of operations, innovation, and small changes made on existing reactors. The blast furnace for producing iron is probably the most important industrial example of such a system.

Though some real industrial reactions may never yield to simple analyses, this should not deter us from studying idealized systems. These satisfactorily represent many real reacting systems and in addition may be taken as the starting point for more involved analyses. Here we consider only the greatly simplified idealized systems in which the reaction kinetics, flow characteristics, and size distribution of solids are known.

Referring to Fig. 13, let us discuss briefly how the various types of flow may be classified in gas-solid operations.

Solid and gas both in plug flow. When solids and gas pass through the

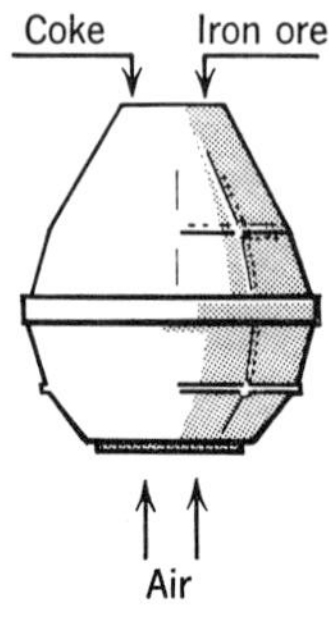

(*a*) Blast furnace

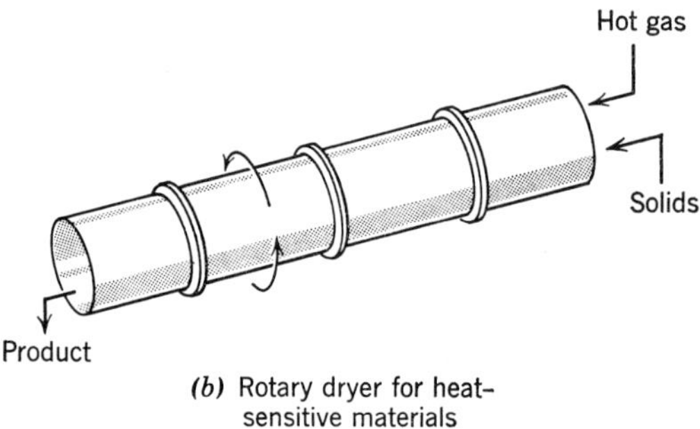

(*b*) Rotary dryer for heat-sensitive materials

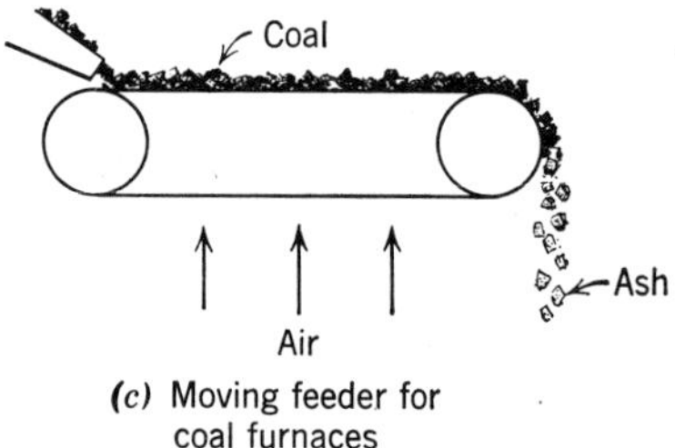

(*c*) Moving feeder for coal furnaces

Fig. 13. Various contacting patterns in fluid-solid reactors: (*a*) countercurrent plug flow; (*b*) cocurrent plug flow; (*c*) crosscurrent plug flow; (*d*) mixed plug flow; (e) mixed operations, gas—intermediate, solids—backmix; (*f*) semibatch operations.

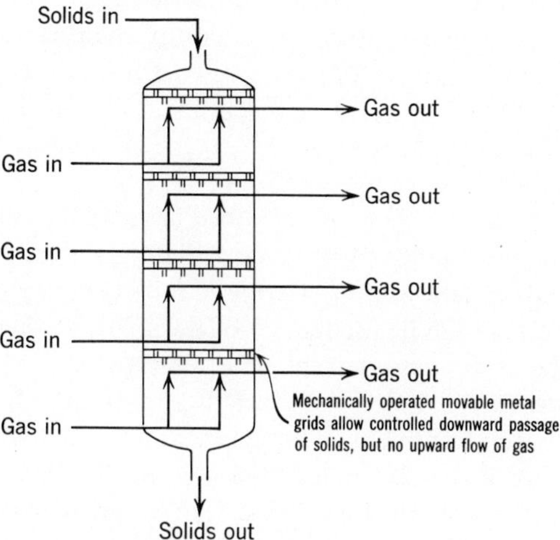

(d) Moving-bed reactor

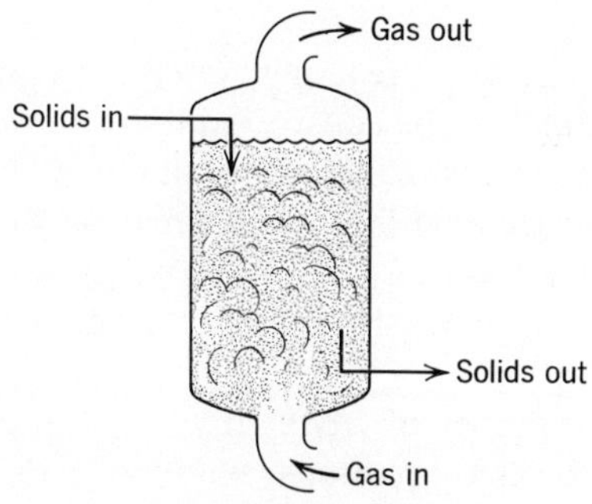

(e) Fluidized-bed reactor

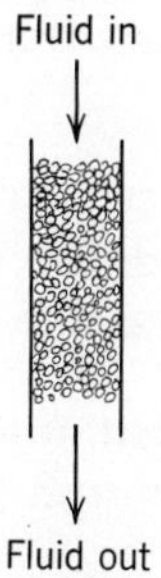

(f) Ion exchange bed

reactor in plug flow, their compositions will change during passage. In addition, such operations are usually nonisothermal.

The contacting of phases may be accomplished in many ways: by countercurrent flow as in blast furnaces and cement kilns (Fig. 13*a*), by cocurrent flow as in polymer driers (Fig. 13*b*), by cross flow as in moving belt feeders for furnaces (Fig. 13*c*), or by some combination of these as in moving bed reactors [see Vener (1955)], (Fig. 13*d*).

Solids in backmix flow. The fluidized bed (Fig. 13*e*) is the best example of a reactor with backmix flow of solids. The gas flow in such reactors is difficult to characterize and is intermediate between backmix and plug flow. Because of the high heat capacity of the solid, isothermal conditions can frequently be safely assumed in such operations.

Semibatch operations. The ion exchange column of Fig. 13*f* is an example of the batch treatment of solids in which the flow of fluid closely approximates plug flow. In an ordinary home fireplace, another semibatch operation, the flow of fluid deviates more greatly from plug flow.

Batch operations. The dissolution and reaction of a given quantity of solid in a batch of fluid such as the acid attack of a solid are a common example of batch operations.

Analysis and design of fluid-solid reacting systems are greatly simplified if the composition of the fluid can be considered to be uniform throughout the reactor. Since this is a reasonable approximation where fractional conversion of fluid-phase reactants is not too great or where fluid backmixing is considerable, as in fluidized beds, this assumption can frequently be used without deviating too greatly from reality. We use this assumption in all the analyses which follow.

Let us now consider a number of frequently met contacting patterns, and let us develop their design equations, employing in every case the assumption of uniform gas composition within the reactor.

Particles of a single size, plug flow of solids, uniform gas composition

The contact time or reaction time needed for any specific conversion of solid is found in a straightforward manner from the equations derived earlier for film, ash, or chemical resistance controlling, Eq. 9, 17, or 21.

Mixture of particles of different but unchanging sizes, plug flow of solids, uniform gas composition

Consider a solid feed consisting of a mixture of different-sized particles. The size distribution of this feed can be represented by a continuous size distribution function analogous to those presented in Chapter 9 for the age distributions **I** and **E** of fluids. On the other hand, it can be represented as

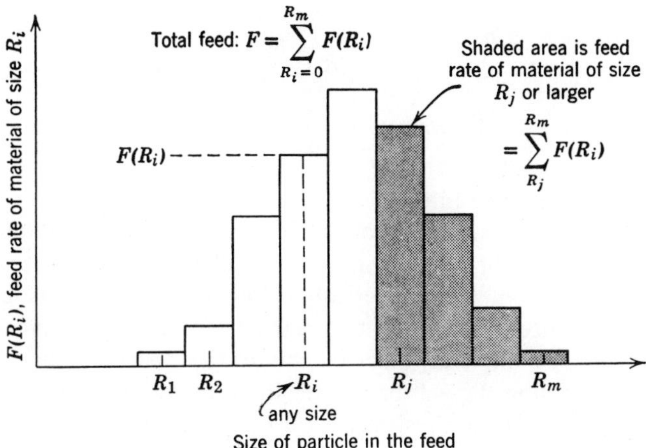

Fig. 14. Representation of the feed rate of a mixture of particles.

a discrete distribution. We use the latter representation since actual determination of size distribution is made in terms of discrete distributions, the screen analyses. Even if these discrete distributions are transformed into continuous distributions, these must later be converted back to discrete distributions before they can be treated.

Let F be the quantity of solid being treated in unit time. Since the density of solid may change during reaction, F is defined as the volumetric feed rate of solid in the general case. Where density change of the solid is negligible, F becomes the mass feed rate of solid as well. In addition, let $F(R_i)$ be the quantity of material of size R_i fed to the reactor. If R_m is the largest particle size in the feed, we have for particles of unchanging size

$$F = \sum_{R_i=0}^{R_m} F(R_i)$$

Figure 14 shows the general characteristics of a discrete distribution.

When in plug flow all solids stay in the reactor for the same length of time t_p. From this and the kinetics for whatever resistance controls the conversion $X_B(R_i)$ for any size of particle R_i can be found. Then the mean conversion $\bar{X}_B$ of the solids leaving the reactor can be obtained by properly summing to find the over-all contribution to conversion of all sizes of particles. Thus

$$\begin{pmatrix}\text{mean value for}\\ \text{the fraction of}\\ \text{B unconverted}\end{pmatrix} = \sum_{\text{all sizes}} \begin{pmatrix}\text{fraction of reactant}\\ \text{unconverted in solids}\\ \text{of size } R_i\end{pmatrix} \begin{pmatrix}\text{fraction of feed}\\ \text{which is of size } R_i\end{pmatrix} \tag{30}$$

or in symbols

$$1 - \bar{X}_B = \sum_{R_i=0}^{R_m} [1 - X_B(R_i)] \frac{F(R_i)}{F}, \qquad 0 \leqslant X_B \leqslant 1$$

or

$$1 - \bar{X}_B = \sum_{R(t_p=\tau)}^{R_m} [1 - X_B(R_i)] \frac{F(R_i)}{F} \tag{31}$$

where $R(t_p = \tau)$ is the radius of the largest particle completely converted in the reactor. These two forms of Eq. 31, actually identical, require some discussion. First of all, we know that the smaller a particle the shorter the time required for complete conversion. However, since all particles have the same residence time t_p in the reactor, some, those smaller than $R(t_p = \tau)$, will be completely reacted. But for these particles the calculated fractional conversion X_B will be greater than unity, indicating more than 100% conversion, which physically is meaningless. Thus in the first form of Eq. 31 X_B must not be allowed to take on values greater than unity. In the second form this condition is incorporated into the lower limit of the summation because particles smaller than $R(t_p = \tau)$ are completely converted and do not contribute to the fraction unconverted, $1 - \bar{X}_B$.

The terms $R(t_p = \tau)$ and $1 - X_B(R_i)$ in Eq. 31 are given by the kinetic expressions for the appropriate controlling resistances and when known allow evaluation of the mean conversion for a mixed feed. The following example illustrates the procedure.

Example 1

A feed consisting

30% of 50-μ-radius particles
40% of 100-μ-radius particles
30% of 200-μ-radius particles

is to be fed continuously in a thin layer onto a moving grate crosscurrent to a flow of reactant gas. For the planned operating conditions the time required for complete conversion is 5, 10, and 20 min for the three sizes of particles in the solid feed. Find the conversion of solids for a residence time of 8 min in the reactor.

Solution. From the statement of the problem we may consider the solids to be in plug flow with $t_p = 8$ min and the gas to be uniform in composition. Hence for a mixed feed Eq. 31 is applicable, or

$$1 - \bar{X}_B = [1 - X_B(50\ \mu)] \frac{F(50\ \mu)}{F} + [1 - X_B(100\ \mu)] \frac{F(100\ \mu)}{F} + \cdots \tag{31}$$

where

$$\frac{F(50\ \mu)}{F} = 0.30 \quad \text{and} \quad \tau(50\ \mu) = 5 \text{ min}$$

$$\frac{F(100\ \mu)}{F} = 0.40 \quad \text{and} \quad \tau(100\ \mu) = 10 \text{ min}$$

$$\frac{F(200\ \mu)}{F} = 0.30 \quad \text{and} \quad \tau(200\ \mu) = 20 \text{ min}$$

Since for the three sizes of particles

$$R_1:R_2:R_3 = \tau_1:\tau_2:\tau_3$$

we see from Eq. 28 that chemical reaction controls and the conversion-time characteristics for each size is given by Eq. 21 or

$$[1 - X_B(R_i)] = \left(1 - \frac{t_p}{\tau(R_i)}\right)^3$$

Replacing in Eq. 31 we obtain

$$1 - \bar{X}_B = \underbrace{\left(1 - \frac{8 \text{ min}}{10 \text{ min}}\right)^3 (0.4)}_{\text{for } R=100\mu} + \underbrace{\left(1 - \frac{8}{20}\right)^3 (0.3)}_{\text{for } R=200\mu}$$

$$= 0.0032 + 0.0648 = 0.068$$

Hence the fraction of solid converted equals 93.2%.

Note that the smallest size of particles is completely converted and does not contribute to the summation of Eq. 31.

Particles of a single unchanging size, backmix flow of solids, uniform gas composition

Consider the reactor of Fig. 13*e* with constant flow rates of both solids and gas into and out of the reactor. With the assumption of uniform gas concentration and backmix flow of solids, this model represents a fluidized-bed reactor in which there is no carryover of solids.

The conversion X_B of reactant in a single particle depends on its length of stay in the bed, and for the appropriate controlling resistance is given by Eq. 9, 17, or 21. However, the length of stay is not the same for all particles in the reactor; hence we must calculate a mean conversion $\bar{X}_B$ of material. Recognizing that the solid behaves as a macrofluid, this can be done by the methods of Chapter 10. Thus in terms of the fraction of solid reactant unconverted we may write for the solids leaving the reactor

$$\begin{pmatrix}\text{mean value for}\\ \text{the fraction of}\\ \text{B unconverted}\end{pmatrix} = \sum_{\substack{\text{particles}\\ \text{of all}\\ \text{ages}}} \begin{pmatrix}\text{fraction of reactant}\\ \text{unconverted for}\\ \text{particles staying in}\\ \text{the reactor for time}\\ \text{between } t \text{ and } t+dt\end{pmatrix} \begin{pmatrix}\text{fraction of}\\ \text{exit stream}\\ \text{which has}\\ \text{stayed in the}\\ \text{reactor for a}\\ \text{time between}\\ t \text{ and } t+dt\end{pmatrix} \tag{32}$$

or in symbols

$$1 - \bar{X}_B = \int_0^\infty (1 - X_B)\mathbf{E}(t)\, dt$$

Again, when a particle remains in the reactor for a time longer than that required for complete conversion of that particle, the calculated conversion is greater than 100%, or $X_B > 1$. Since this has no physical significance, X_B should remain at unity for particle residence times greater than $\boldsymbol{\tau}$. To guarantee that such particles do not contribute to the fraction unconverted, we modify this equation to read

$$1 - \bar{X}_B = \int_0^{\tau} (1 - X_B)\mathbf{E}(t)\, dt \tag{33}$$

where $\mathbf{E}(t)$ is the exit age distribution of the solids in the reactor expressed in time units (see Chapter 9).

For backmix flow of solids with mean residence time $\bar{t}$ in the reactor we find from Chapter 9

$$\mathbf{E}(t) = \frac{e^{-t/\bar{t}}}{\bar{t}} \tag{34}$$

Thus for backmix flow of the single size of solid which is completely converted in time $\boldsymbol{\tau}$, we obtain

$$1 - \bar{X}_B = \int_0^{\tau} (1 - X_B)\frac{e^{-t/\bar{t}}}{\bar{t}}\, dt \tag{35}$$

This may be integrated for the various controlling resistances.

For *film resistance controlling* Eq. 9 with Eq. 35 yields

$$1 - \bar{X}_B = \int_0^{\tau} \left(1 - \frac{t}{\tau}\right)\frac{e^{-t/\bar{t}}}{\bar{t}}\, dt \tag{36}$$

which on integration by parts gives

$$\bar{X}_B = \frac{\bar{t}}{\tau}(1 - e^{-\tau/\bar{t}})$$

or in equivalent expanded form, useful for large $\bar{t}/\boldsymbol{\tau}$, (37)

$$1 - \bar{X}_B = \frac{1}{2}\frac{\tau}{\bar{t}} - \frac{1}{3!}\left(\frac{\tau}{\bar{t}}\right)^2 + \frac{1}{4!}\left(\frac{\tau}{\bar{t}}\right)^3 - \cdots$$

For *chemical reaction controlling* Eq. 21 replaced in Eq. 35 gives

$$1 - \bar{X}_B = \int_0^{\tau} \left(1 - \frac{t}{\tau}\right)^3 \frac{e^{-t/\bar{t}}}{\bar{t}}\, dt \tag{38}$$

Integrating by parts using the recursion formula, found in any table of integrals, we obtain

$$\bar{X}_B = 3\frac{\bar{t}}{\tau} - 6\left(\frac{\bar{t}}{\tau}\right)^2 + 6\left(\frac{\bar{t}}{\tau}\right)^3(1 - e^{-\tau/\bar{t}})$$

or in equivalent form, useful for large $\bar{t}/\boldsymbol{\tau}$, (39)

$$1 - \bar{X}_B = \frac{1}{4}\frac{\tau}{\bar{t}} - \frac{1}{20}\left(\frac{\tau}{\bar{t}}\right)^2 + \frac{1}{120}\left(\frac{\tau}{\bar{t}}\right)^3 - \cdots$$

For *ash resistance controlling* replacement of Eq. 17 in Eq. 35 followed by integration leads to a cumbersome expression which on expansion yields [see Kunii (1958), Yagi and Kunii (1961)]

$$1 - \bar{X}_B = \frac{1}{5}\frac{\tau}{\bar{t}} - \frac{19}{420}\left(\frac{\tau}{\bar{t}}\right)^2 + \frac{41}{4620}\left(\frac{\tau}{\bar{t}}\right)^3 - 0.00149\left(\frac{\tau}{\bar{t}}\right)^4 + \cdots \quad (40)$$

Figures 15 and 16 present these results for solids in backmix flow in convenient graphical form. Figure 16 shows clearly at high conversion of solids that the backmix reactor requires a much larger holding time for solids than does a plug flow reactor.

Extensions of these expressions to multistage operations are straightforward and are considered in problems 16 and 17.

Example 2

Yagi et al. (1951) roasted pyrrhotite (iron sulfide) particles dispersed in asbestos fibers and found that the time for complete conversion was related to particle size as follows:

$$\tau \propto R^{1.5}$$

Particles remained as hard solids during reaction.

A fluidized-bed reactor is planned to convert pyrrhotite ore to the corresponding oxide. The feed is to be uniform in size, $\tau = 20$ min, with mean residence time $\bar{t} = 60$ min in the reactor. What fraction of original sulfide ore remains unconverted?

Solution. Since a hard product material is formed during reaction, film diffusion can be ruled out as the controlling resistance. For chemical reaction controlling Eq. 28 shows that

$$\tau \propto R$$

whereas for ash diffusion controlling Eq. 27 shows that

$$\tau \propto R^2$$

As the experimentally found diameter dependency lies between these two values, it is reasonable to expect that both these mechanisms offer resistance to conversion. Using in turn ash diffusion and chemical reaction as the controlling resistance should then give the upper and lower bound to the conversion expected.

The solids in a fluidized bed approximate backmix flow; hence for chemical reaction controlling Eq. 39, with $\tau/\bar{t} = 20\text{ min}/60\text{ min} = \frac{1}{3}$, gives

$$1 - \bar{X}_B = \frac{1}{4}\left(\frac{1}{3}\right) - \frac{1}{20}\left(\frac{1}{3}\right)^2 + \frac{1}{120}\left(\frac{1}{3}\right)^3 - \cdots = 0.078$$

For ash diffusion controlling Eq. 40 gives

$$1 - \bar{X}_B = \frac{1}{5}\left(\frac{1}{3}\right) - \frac{19}{420}\left(\frac{1}{3}\right)^2 + \frac{41}{4620}\left(\frac{1}{3}\right)^3 - \cdots = 0.062$$

Hence the fraction of sulfide remaining is between 6.2% and 7.8%, or on averaging

$$1 - \bar{X}_B = 0.07, \qquad \text{or } 7.0\%$$

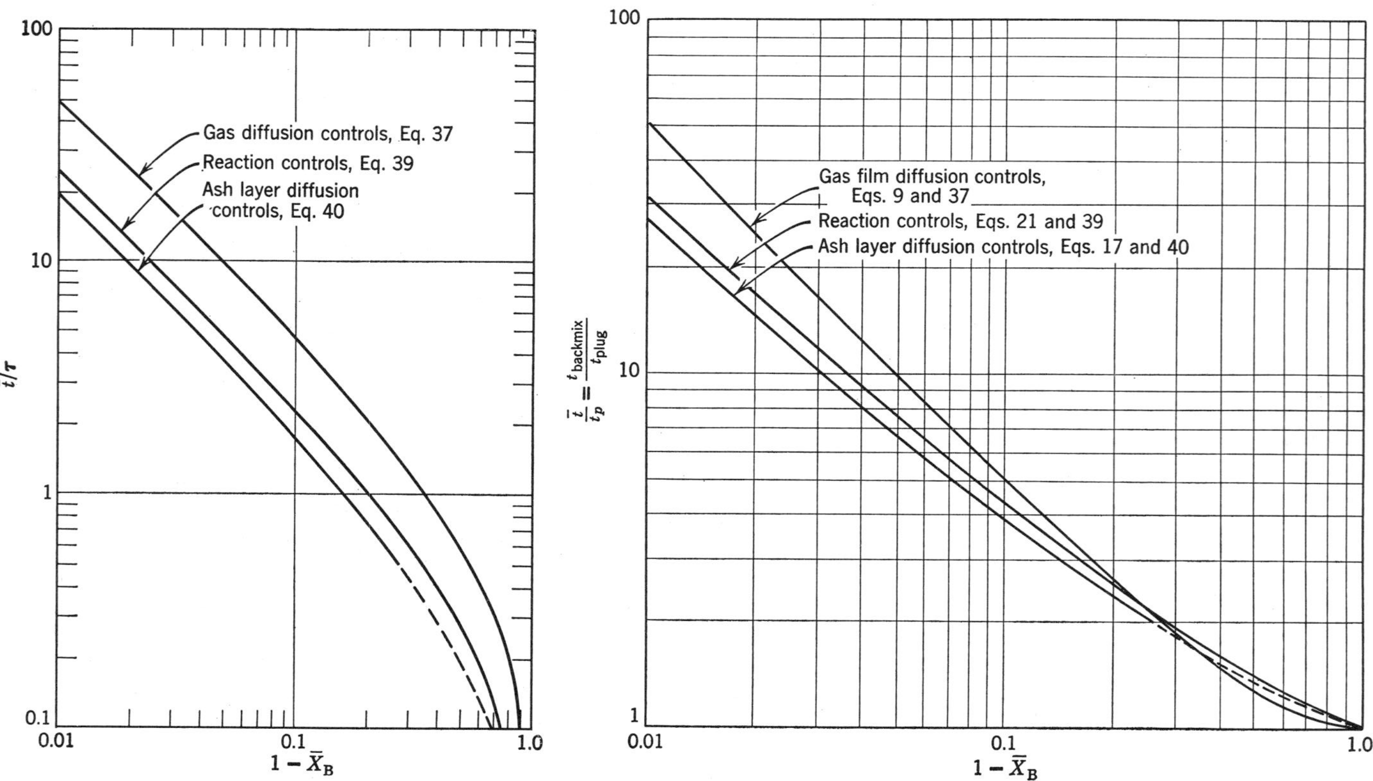

Fig. 15. Mean conversion versus mean residence time in a backmix reactor, single size of solid.

Fig. 16. Comparison of holding times needed to effect a given conversion for backmix and plug flow of a single size of solid.

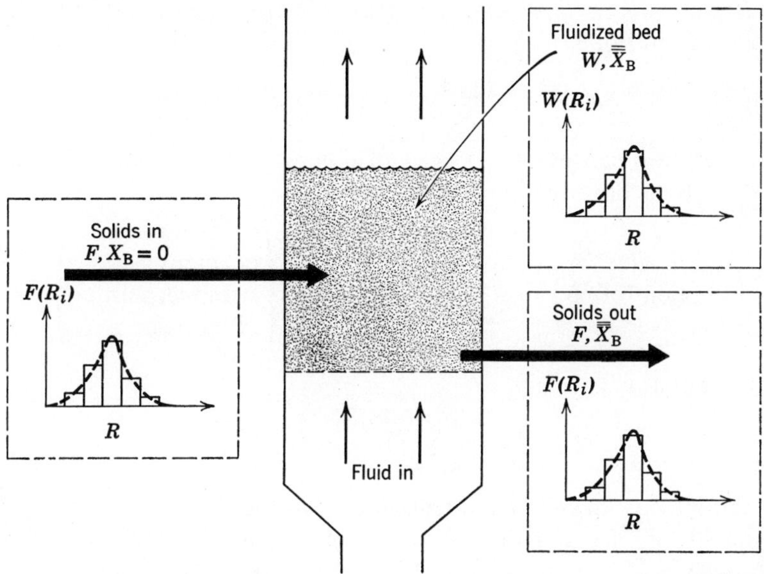

Fig. 17. Representation of a backmix reactor with mixed feed and single exit stream. Note that size distribution of flow streams and the bed are alike.

Mixture of particles of different but unchanging size, backmix flow of solids, uniform gas composition

Often a spectrum of particle sizes is used as feed to a backmix reactor. For such a feed and a single exit stream (no carryover) the methods leading to Eqs. 31 and 35, when combined, should yield the required conversion.

Let us now consider such a reacting system which is shown in Fig. 17. Since the particles remain unchanged in size and since the exit stream is representative of the bed conditions, we conclude that the size distributions of the bed, feed, and exit streams are all alike, or

$$\frac{F(R_i)}{F} = \frac{W(R_i)}{W} \tag{41}$$

where W is the quantity of material in the reactor and where $W(R_i)$ is the quantity of material of any size R_i in the reactor. In addition, for this flow the mean residence time $\bar{t}(R_i)$ of material of any size R_i is equal to the mean residence time of solid in the bed, or

$$\bar{t} = \bar{t}(R_i) = \frac{W}{F} = \frac{\begin{pmatrix}\text{weight of solid in} \\ \text{the reactor}\end{pmatrix}}{\begin{pmatrix}\text{feed rate of solids} \\ \text{to the reactor}\end{pmatrix}} \tag{42}$$

Letting $\bar{X}_B(R_i)$ be the mean conversion of particles of size R_i in the bed, we have from Eq. 33

$$1 - \bar{X}_B(R_i) = \int_0^{\tau(R_i)} [1 - X_B(R_i)] \frac{e^{-t/\bar{t}}}{\bar{t}} \, dt \tag{43}$$

However, feed consists of particles of different sizes; hence the over-all mean of B unconverted in all these sizes is

$$\begin{pmatrix}\text{mean value for}\\ \text{fraction of B}\\ \text{unconverted}\end{pmatrix} = \sum_{\substack{\text{all}\\ \text{sizes}}} \begin{pmatrix}\text{fraction un-}\\ \text{converted in}\\ \text{particles of}\\ \text{size } R_i\end{pmatrix} \begin{pmatrix}\text{fraction of exit}\\ \text{or entering}\\ \text{stream consisting}\\ \text{of particles of}\\ \text{size } R_i\end{pmatrix} \tag{44}$$

or in symbols

$$1 - \bar{\bar{X}}_B = \sum_{R=0}^{R_m} [1 - \bar{X}_B(R_i)] \frac{F(R_i)}{F}$$

Combining Eqs. 43 and 44 and replacing the former expression with Eq. 37, 39, or 40 for each size of particle, we obtain in turn, for *film diffusion controlling*,

$$1 - \bar{\bar{X}}_B = \sum^{R_m} \left\{ \frac{1}{2} \frac{\tau(R_i)}{\bar{t}} - \frac{1}{3!} \left[\frac{\tau(R_i)}{\bar{t}} \right]^2 + \cdots \right\} \frac{F(R_i)}{F} \tag{45}$$

for *chemical reaction controlling*,

$$1 - \bar{\bar{X}}_B = \sum^{R_m} \left\{ \frac{1}{4} \frac{\tau(R_i)}{\bar{t}} - \frac{1}{20} \left[\frac{\tau(R_i)}{\bar{t}} \right]^2 + \cdots \right\} \frac{F(R_i)}{F} \tag{46}$$

for *ash diffusion controlling*,

$$1 - \bar{\bar{X}}_B = \sum^{R_m} \left\{ \frac{1}{5} \frac{\tau(R_i)}{\bar{t}} - \frac{19}{420} \left[\frac{\tau(R_i)}{\bar{t}} \right]^2 + \cdots \right\} \frac{F(R_i)}{F} \tag{47}$$

where $\tau(R_i)$ is the time for complete reaction of particles of size R_i. The following example illustrates the use of these expressions.

Example 3

A feed consisting

30% of 50-μ-radius particles
40% of 100-μ-radius particles
30% of 200-μ-radius particles

is to be reacted in a fluidized-bed steady-state flow reactor constructed from a 4-ft length of 4-in. pipe. The fluidizing gas is the gas-phase reactant, and at the planned operating conditions the time required for complete conversion is 5, 10, and 20 min for the three sizes of feed. Find the conversion of solids in the reactor for a feed rate of 1 kg solids/min if the bed contains 10 kg solids.

Additional information:
The solids are hard and unchanged in size and weight during reaction.
A cyclone separator is used to separate and return to the bed any solids that may be entrained by the gas.
The change in gas-phase composition across the bed is small.

Solution. From the statement of the problem we may treat the fluidized bed as a backmix reactor. For mixed feed Eq. 44 is applicable, and since chemical reaction controls (see Example 1), this equation reduces to Eq. 46 where from the problem statement

$$F = 1000 \text{ gm/min} \qquad \bar{t} = \frac{W}{F} = \frac{10{,}000 \text{ gm}}{1000 \text{ gm/min}} = 10 \text{ min}$$
$$W = 10{,}000 \text{ gm}$$

$$\begin{aligned} F(50\ \mu) &= 300 \text{ gm/min} \quad \text{and} \quad \tau(50\ \mu) = 5 \text{ min} \\ F(100\ \mu) &= 400 \text{ gm/min} \quad \text{and} \quad \tau(100\ \mu) = 10 \text{ min} \\ F(200\ \mu) &= 300 \text{ gm/min} \quad \text{and} \quad \tau(200\ \mu) = 20 \text{ min} \end{aligned}$$

Replacing in Eq. 46 we obtain

$$1 - \bar{\bar{X}}_B = \underbrace{\left[\frac{1}{4}\left(\frac{5 \text{ min}}{10 \text{ min}}\right) - \frac{1}{20}\left(\frac{5}{10}\right)^2 + \cdots\right]\frac{300 \text{ gm/min}}{1000 \text{ gm/min}}}_{\text{for } R = 50\ \mu}$$

$$+ \underbrace{\left[\frac{1}{4}\left(\frac{10 \text{ min}}{10 \text{ min}}\right) - \frac{1}{20}\left(\frac{10}{10}\right)^2 + \cdots\right]\frac{400}{1000}}_{\text{for } R = 100\ \mu}$$

$$+ \underbrace{\left[\frac{1}{4}\left(\frac{20 \text{ min}}{10 \text{ min}}\right) - \frac{1}{20}\left(\frac{20}{10}\right)^2 + \cdots\right]\frac{300}{1000}}_{\text{for } R = 200\ \mu}$$

$$= \left(\frac{1}{8} - \frac{1}{80} + \cdots\right)\frac{3}{10} + \left(\frac{1}{4} - \frac{1}{20} + \frac{1}{120} - \cdots\right)\frac{4}{10}$$

$$+ \left(\frac{1}{2} - \frac{1}{5} + \frac{1}{15} - \frac{2}{110} + \cdots\right)\frac{3}{10}$$

$$= 0.034 + 0.083 + 0.105 = 0.222$$

The mean conversion of solids is then

$$\bar{\bar{X}}_B = 77.8\,\%$$

Application to a fluidized bed with both carryover and underflow of solids

Carryover of fines may occur in a fluidized bed for a feed consisting of a wide size distribution of solids. When this happens we have a reactor as shown in Fig. 18 with one feed stream and two exit streams. Let subscripts 0, 1, 2 refer to the feed, underflow, and carryover streams respectively.

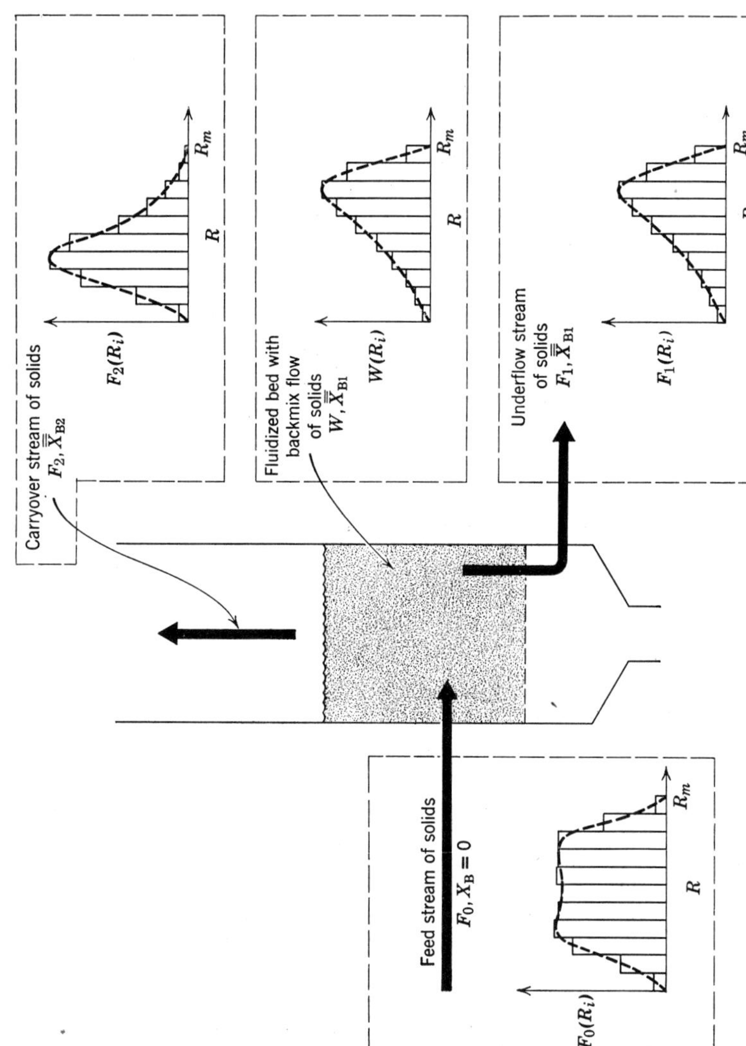

Fig. 18. Representation of a fluidized bed with carryover of solids.

Then by material balances, for the whole streams and for particles of size R_i, we find

$$F_0 = F_1 + F_2 \tag{48}$$

and

$$F_0(R_i) = F_1(R_i) + F_2(R_i) \tag{49}$$

Since backmix flow is still assumed, the composition of the underflow stream is still representative of the composition within the bed, or

$$\frac{F_1(R_i)}{F_1} = \frac{W(R_i)}{W} \tag{50}$$

For this bed the mean residence time of material of different sizes need not be the same. In fact, since small particles are more likely to be blown out of the bed, intuition suggests that they stay in the bed for a shorter time than the larger particles. The mean residence time in the bed of particles of size R_i is then, on combining with Eq. 49 and 50,

$$\bar{t}(R_i) = \frac{\begin{pmatrix}\text{weight of particles}\\ \text{of size } R_i \text{ in the bed}\end{pmatrix}}{\begin{pmatrix}\text{flow rate of such particles}\\ \text{into and out of the bed}\end{pmatrix}}$$

$$= \frac{W(R_i)}{F_0(R_i)} = \frac{W(R_i)}{F_1(R_i) + F_2(R_i)} = \frac{1}{\dfrac{F_1}{W} + \dfrac{F_2(R_i)}{W(R_i)}} \tag{51}$$

This expression shows that the mean residence time, hence conversion, of particles of any given size is the same in the underflow and carryover stream.

The mean conversion of particles of size R_i from Eq. 33 is then

$$1 - \bar{X}_B(R_i) = \int_0^{\tau(R_i)} [1 - X_B(R_i)] \frac{e^{-t/\bar{t}(R_i)}}{\bar{t}(R_i)}\, dt \tag{52}$$

and for a feed consisting of a mixture of particles we have, as with Eq. 44,

$$\begin{pmatrix}\text{mean value for}\\ \text{fraction of B}\\ \text{unconverted}\end{pmatrix} = \sum_{\text{all sizes}} \begin{pmatrix}\text{fraction un-}\\ \text{converted in}\\ \text{particles of}\\ \text{size } R_i\end{pmatrix} \begin{pmatrix}\text{fraction of feed}\\ \text{or combined exit}\\ \text{streams consist-}\\ \text{ing of particles}\\ \text{of size } R_i\end{pmatrix}$$

or

$$1 - \bar{\bar{X}}_B = \sum^{R_m} [1 - \bar{X}_B(R_i)] \frac{F_0(R_i)}{F_0} \tag{53}$$

Equations 53 and 52 combined in turn with Equations 37, 39, and 40 give for *film diffusion controlling*,

$$1 - \overline{\overline{X}}_B = \sum^{R_m} \left\{ \frac{1}{2} \frac{\tau(R_i)}{\bar{t}(R_i)} - \frac{1}{3!} \left[\frac{\tau(R_i)}{\bar{t}(R_i)} \right]^2 + \cdots \right\} \frac{F_0(R_i)}{F_0} \tag{54}$$

for *chemical reaction controlling*,

$$1 - \overline{\overline{X}}_B = \sum^{R_m} \left\{ \frac{1}{4} \frac{\tau(R_i)}{\bar{t}(R_i)} - \frac{1}{20} \left[\frac{\tau(R_i)}{\bar{t}(R_i)} \right]^2 + \cdots \right\} \frac{F_0(R_i)}{F_0} \tag{55}$$

for *ash diffusion controlling*,

$$1 - \overline{\overline{X}}_B = \sum^{R_m} \left\{ \frac{1}{5} \frac{\tau(R_i)}{\bar{t}(R_i)} - \frac{19}{420} \left[\frac{\tau(R_i)}{\bar{t}(R_i)} \right]^2 + \cdots \right\} \frac{F_0(R_i)}{F_0} \tag{56}$$

Comparison with Eqs. 45 to 47 shows that it is simply the variation of the mean residence time with particle size which distinguishes the conversion in fluidized beds with carryover from the ordinary backmix reactor equations in which $\bar{t}(R_i) = \bar{t} =$ constant. For a feed of a single size, $\tau(R_i) = \tau =$ constant, and these expressions reduce even further to Eq. 37, 39, and 40.

To determine $\bar{t}(R_i)$ requires finding the size distribution of the various streams (see Eq. 51), and since we normally know only the size distribution of the feed, these equations are not useful as they stand for predictive purposes and design. We may overcome this difficulty by making use of independent information on the rate at which particles are blown out of fluidized beds.

Elutriation experiments show that the number of marked particles of a given size blown out of a fluidized bed of given height is proportional to the number of such particles present in the bed, or

$$-\frac{d\,(\text{number of marked particles})}{dt} = \kappa\,(\text{number of marked particles}) \tag{57}$$

where κ, called the elutriation velocity constant, has the units of reciprocal time and is a function of the properties of the system. Yagi and Kunii (1962) and Wen and Hashinger (1960) present generalized relationships for κ which correlate data obtained in a wide variety of physical systems.

Figure 19, illustrating typical elutriation experiments, shows how particle size, gas velocity, and bed depth influence κ. In fluidization of small particles which are to some extent blown out of the bed, the interrelationship between these variables is approximated by

$$\kappa \sim \frac{(\text{gas velocity})^4}{(\text{bed height})(\text{particle size})^{2\text{ to }3}} \tag{58}$$

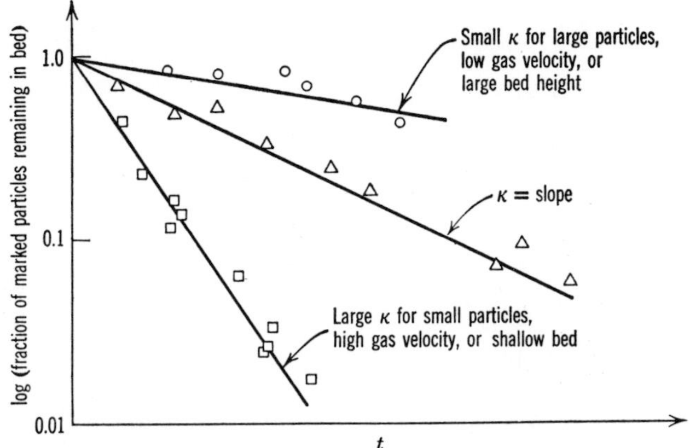

Fig. 19. Typical results of elutriation experiments showing the dependency of κ on the fluidization variables. Adapted from Yagi and Kunii (1961).

Equation 58 should not be extrapolated to larger particles which are not blown out of the bed because it predicts a nonzero value for κ, whereas for such particles κ is actually zero. Figure 20 shows this effect.

For particles of size R_i in a bed of specified height

$$\kappa(R_i) = \frac{\begin{pmatrix}\text{rate of carryover of} \\ \text{particles of size } R_i\end{pmatrix}}{\begin{pmatrix}\text{weight of such particles} \\ \text{present in the bed}\end{pmatrix}} = \frac{F_2(R_i)}{W(R_i)} \tag{59}$$

With $\kappa(R_i)$ available from independent experiments, we have with Eq. 51

$$\bar{t}(R_i) = \frac{W(R_i)}{F_0(R_i)} = \frac{1}{F_1/W + \kappa(R_i)} \tag{60}$$

One last term F_1 is still to be evaluated before $\bar{t}(R_i)$ can be predicted. When the $\bar{t}(R_i)$ values are known, the conversion can be calculated from Eqs. 54, 55, and 56. Now F_1 is found by combining Eq. 60 with Eq. 50 and rearranging to give

$$F_1(R_i) = \frac{F_0(R_i)}{1 + (W/F_1)\kappa(R_i)} \tag{61}$$

which on summing over all particle sizes gives the composition and flow rate of the underflow stream. Thus

$$\begin{aligned} F_1 &= F_1(R_1) + F_1(R_2) + \cdots F_1(R_m) \\ &= \sum^{R_m} \frac{F_0(R_i)}{1 + (W/F_1)\kappa(R_i)} \end{aligned} \tag{62}$$

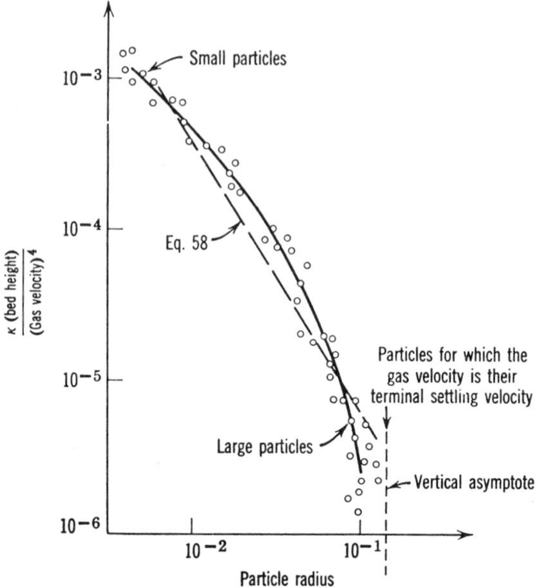

Fig. 20. Interrelationship of variables in elutriation experiments with a bed of mixed particles. Adapted from Kunii (1958).

Knowing the feed, size of bed, and κ for all particle sizes allows us to solve for F_1 by trial and error as follows. Choose a value for F_1, evaluate $F_1(R_i)$ from Eq. 61, sum up all the $F_1(R_i)$, and see whether this matches the F_1 selected.

Finally, the most involved problem we may encounter in design is to find the size of reactor for a specified conversion $\overline{\overline{X}}_B$ of feed F_0 of known size distribution. The solution is as follows.

1. Select a value of W and find the corresponding $\kappa(R_i)$ for the gas velocity and bed height to be used. Note that $\kappa(R_i)$ is inversely proportional to bed height, hence inversely proportional to W.
2. Find $F_1(R_i)$ and F_1 by the trial and error solution of Eq. 62.
3. Determine $\bar{t}(R_i)$ from Eq. 60.
4. Calculate the conversion by Eq. 54, 55, or 56.
5. See whether the calculated conversion matches the required conversion. If it is too low, use a larger value of W and repeat the process.

Example 4

Solve Example 3 with the following modifications. The cyclone separator is removed and higher gas flow rates are used; therefore solids are entrained by the fluidizing gas. The elutriation velocity constant for the operating conditions

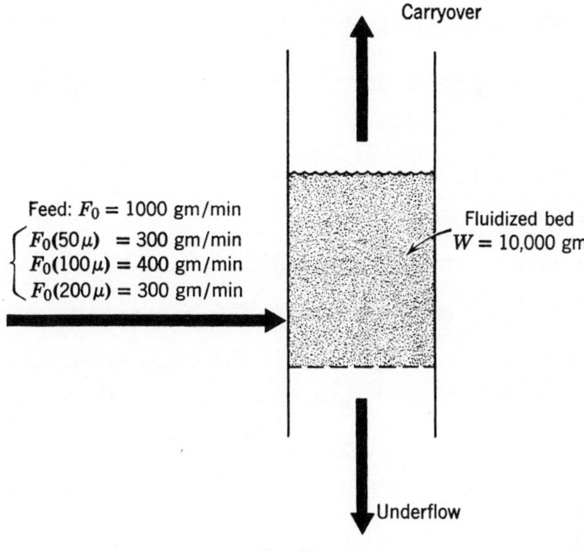

Fig. E4*a*

and bed height is estimated to be

$$\kappa = (2000\ \mu^2/\text{min})\ d_p^{-2}$$

where d_p is the particle diameter in microns.

Solution. From Example 3 and by solving for $\kappa(R_i)$ we have

$$F_0 = 1000\ \text{gm/min}, \qquad \bar{t} = \frac{W}{F_0} = 10\ \text{min}$$
$$W = 10{,}000\ \text{gm}$$
$$\kappa(50\ \mu) = 0.2/\text{min} \qquad \tau(50\ \mu) = 5\ \text{min}$$
$$\kappa(100\ \mu) = 0.05/\text{min} \qquad \tau(100\ \mu) = 10\ \text{min}$$
$$\kappa(200\ \mu) = 0.0125/\text{min} \qquad \tau(200\ \mu) = 20\ \text{min}$$
$$F_0(50\ \mu) = 300\ \text{gm/min}$$
$$F_0(100\ \mu) = 400\ \text{gm/min}$$
$$F_0(200\ \mu) = 300\ \text{gm/min}$$

Figure E4*a* shows quantities of all streams known at this point. The procedure will be as follows.

Step a. Find F_1 by trial and error solution of Eq. 62.
Step b. Determine $\bar{t}(R_i)$ from Eq. 60.
Step c. Calculate the conversion from Eq. 55, since chemical reaction controls.
Step a. Guess $F_1 = 625$ gm/min; then the value of F_1 calculated by Eq. 62 is

$$F_1 = \underbrace{\frac{300\ \text{gm/min}}{1 + \dfrac{10{,}000\ \text{gm}}{625\text{gm/min}}(0.2/\text{min})}}_{R\,=\,50\ \mu} + \underbrace{\frac{400}{1 + \dfrac{10{,}000}{625}(0.05)}}_{R\,=\,100\ \mu} + \underbrace{\frac{300}{1 + \dfrac{10{,}000}{625}(0.0125)}}_{R\,=\,200\ \mu}$$

$= 71.4$ gm of 50-μ material $+ 222.2 + 250$
$= 543.6$ gm, too low

Guess $F_1 = 400$ gm/min. Then by calculation

$$F_1 = \frac{300}{1 + \dfrac{10{,}000}{400}(0.2)} + \frac{400}{1 + \dfrac{10{,}000}{400}(0.05)} + \frac{300}{1 + \dfrac{10{,}000}{400}(0.0125)}$$

$$= 50 + 177.7 + 228.5$$

$$= 456.2 \text{ gm/min}, \qquad \text{too high}$$

Guess $F_1 = 500$ gm. Then by calculations similar to those just given we find

$$F_1 = 60 + 200 + 240 = 500 \text{ gm}, \qquad \text{check}$$

Thus we have

$$F_1 = 500 \text{ gm/min} \qquad \text{and} \qquad \left.\begin{aligned} F_1(50\ \mu) &= 60 \text{ gm/min} \\ F_1(100\ \mu) &= 200 \text{ gm/min} \\ F_1(200\ \mu) &= 240 \text{ gm/min} \end{aligned}\right\}$$

Step b. From Eq. 60 the mean residence times of the various sizes of particles are

$$\bar{t}(50\ \mu) = \frac{1}{F_1/W + \kappa(50\ \mu)} = \frac{1}{\dfrac{500 \text{ gm/min}}{10{,}000 \text{ gm}} + 0.2 \text{ min}} = 4 \text{ min}$$

$$\bar{t}(100\ \mu) = \frac{1}{500/10{,}000 + 0.05} = 10 \text{ min}$$

$$\bar{t}(200\ \mu) = \frac{1}{500/10{,}000 + 0.0125} = 16 \text{ min}$$

Step c. From Eq. 55 we then find the mean over-all conversion. Thus

$$1 - \bar{\bar{X}}_B = \underbrace{\left[\frac{1}{4}\left(\frac{5 \text{ min}}{4 \text{ min}}\right) - \frac{1}{20}\left(\frac{5}{4}\right)^2 + \frac{1}{120}\left(\frac{5}{4}\right)^3 - \cdots\right]\frac{300 \text{ gm/min}}{1000 \text{ gm/min}}}_{R = 50\ \mu}$$

$$+ \underbrace{\left[\frac{1}{4}\left(\frac{10 \text{ min}}{10 \text{ min}}\right) - \frac{1}{20}\left(\frac{10}{10}\right)^2 + \cdots\right]\frac{400}{1000}}_{R = 100\ \mu}$$

$$+ \underbrace{\left[\frac{1}{4}\left(\frac{20 \text{ min}}{16 \text{ min}}\right) - \frac{1}{20}\left(\frac{20}{16}\right)^2 + \cdots\right]\frac{300}{1000}}_{R = 200\ \mu}$$

$$= 0.075 + 0.083 + 0.075 = 0.233$$

The mean conversion of solids is then

$$\bar{\bar{X}}_B = 76.7\%$$

The composition of the bed and of the various streams, obtained by material balance, is shown in Fig. E4*b*.

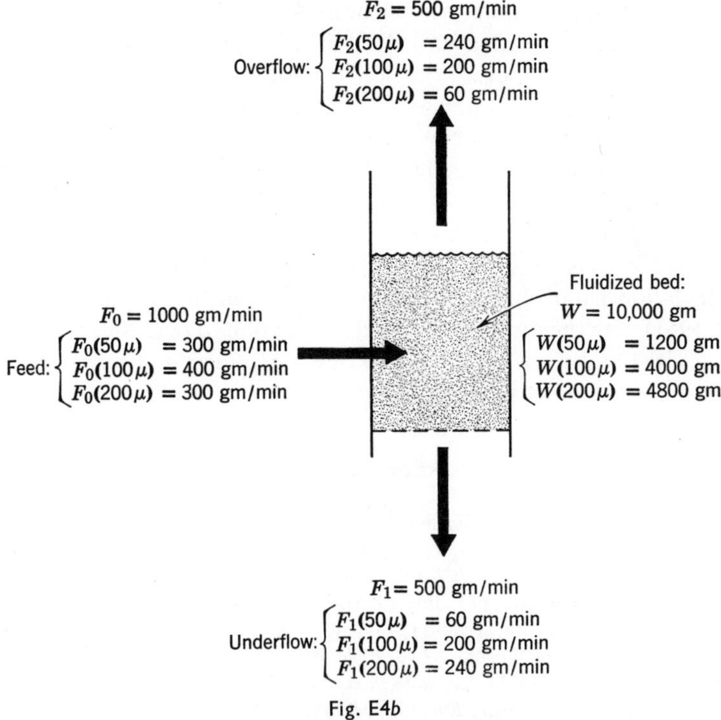

Fig. E4*b*

Comparing the solutions for Examples 3 and 4 we see that conversion is not lowered appreciably by the elutriation of fines from the bed. Actually, as shown in the problems at the end of the chapter, conversion can sometimes be increased by allowing solids to be blown out of the bed.

This may seem surprising at first, but the reason becomes clear when we realize that the elutriation of fines which are converted in a short time allows the larger sizes of particles to remain in the bed for longer periods, hence increasing their conversion.

The predominance of larger particles in the bed can be seen in Fig. E4*b*.

Comments

We have examined a number of contacting patterns for the fluid-solid phases and have presented the design procedure for them. In doing so we have made a number of assumptions, the major ones being:

1. No appreciable change in size of particles during reaction.
2. Ideal flow of the phases. For fluidized beds this means uniformity in composition at all points within the bed.
3. Steady-state operations.

In addition, to obtain numerical answers we used rate expressions such as Eqs. 9, 17, and 21 which entailed additional assumptions. We may feel that with these rather severe restrictive assumptions our models have but few applications. This is not so, for models such as those presented here have represented satisfactorily a large number of systems of industrial importance and have been used for their actual design; see Yagi and Kunii (1961) and Kunii (1958).

Modification of these methods to account for varying composition within fluidized beds is considered by Yagi and Kunii (1961) and Kunii (1958), and deviation from plug flow in moving bed reactors is treated by Yagi et al. (1961) with the dispersion model. Extension to reactions of shrinking particles is straightforward if the feed rate is expressed in terms of numbers of particles of various sizes fed to the reactor.

REFERENCES

N. Froessling, *Gerlands Beitr. Geophys.*, **52,** 170 (1938).
D. Kunii, Ph.D. thesis, University of Tokyo, 1958.
A. L. Parker and H. C. Hottel, *Ind. Eng. Chem.*, **28,** 1334 (1936).
R. E. Vener, *Chem. Eng.*, **62,** 175 (July 1955).
P. L. Walker, Jr., F. Rusinko, Jr., and L. G. Austin, *Advances in Catalysis,* **11,** 133 (1959).
C. Y. Wen and R. F. Hashinger, *A.I.Ch.E. Journal*, **6,** 220 (1960).
S. Yagi and D. Kunii, *5th Symposium (International) on Combustion.* Reinhold, New York, 1955, p. 231; *Chem. Eng. (Japan)*, **19,** 500 (1955).
——— and ———, *Chem. Eng. Sci.*, **16,** 364, 372, 380, (1961).
———, ———, K. Nagahara, and H. Naito, *Chem. Eng. (Japan)*, **25,** 469 (1961).
———, K. Takagi, and S. Shimoyama, *J. Chem. Soc. (Japan), Ind. Chem. Sec.*, **54,** 1 (1951).

PROBLEMS

1. Equation 11

$$Q_A = \mathscr{D}\frac{dC_A}{dr}$$

only applies for an equimolar diffusion of gas-phase reactant into the ash layer of a reacting particle and gaseous product out of it. When no gaseous product is formed, we have diffusion of a single component through stagnant fluid, for which the flux equation becomes

$$Q_A = \frac{\mathscr{D}\pi}{p_{\text{inert}}}\frac{dC_A}{dr}$$

For this situation and ash diffusion controlling, find the expression for t/τ and compare it with Eq. 17. Comment.

2. By combining resistances as suggested in this chapter, derive Eq. 24 for the complete reaction of particles of unchanging size.

3. A large stockpile of coal is burning. Every part of its surface is in flames. In a 24-hr period the linear size of the pile, as measured by its silhouette against the horizon, seems to decrease by about 5%.

(*a*) How should the burning mass decrease in size?
(*b*) When should the fire burn itself out?
(*c*) State the assumptions on which your estimation is based.

4. A solid feed consisting

50 wt % of $\frac{1}{16}$-in. particles and smaller
25 wt % of $\frac{1}{8}$-in. particles
25 wt % of $\frac{1}{4}$-in. particles

is to be passed through an inclined rotating tubular reactor, somewhat like a cement kiln, in which it reacts with gas of uniform composition. The reaction is $A(g) + B(s) \rightarrow R(s)$ which proceeds with a well-defined unreacted core leaving a hard nonfriable solid product.

To determine the design specifications of the reactor (length, diameter, angle of incline, rate of rotation), the residence time of the solid must be known. For this two small samples of solids are introduced into an environment identical to that planned for the reactor and are kept there for an hour. Under these conditions $\frac{1}{8}$-in. particles are 87.5% converted, $\frac{1}{4}$-in. particles are 58.0% converted.

Find the residence time needed in the tubular reactor, assuming plug flow of solids, for (*a*) 98% conversion of B, and (*b*) 95% conversion of B.

5. In a uniform environment $\frac{1}{4}$-in. solid particles are 87.5% converted to product in 5 min. The solids are unchanged in size during reaction, and the chemical reaction step is known to be rate controlling. What must be the mean residence time of solids to achieve the same mean conversion of reactant in a fluidized-bed reactor operating with the same environment as before, using a feed consisting of equal quantities of $\frac{1}{8}$-in. and $\frac{1}{16}$-in. particles?

6. In a uniform environment $\frac{1}{4}$-in. solid particles are 87.5% converted to product in 5 min. The solids are unchanged in size during reaction, and the ash diffusion step is known to be controlling. What mean conversion is obtainable in a fluidized-bed reactor operating with the same environment but using a feed consisting of equal weights of $\frac{1}{8}$-in. and $\frac{1}{16}$-in. particles. The mean residence time of solids in this reactor is 30 min.

7. A fluidized-bed reactor is planned for the continuous conversion of solid reactant B to solid product R. To find the mean residence time of solids in this flow reactor the following data are obtained in a batch-fluidized unit.

At 1-min intervals, solids are removed from the batch reactor and are analyzed for B and R by an analytical technique which can find the 50% conversion point of B to R. The following results are found.

Size of particles in the batch reactor	$\frac{1}{8}$ in.	$\frac{3}{8}$ in.
Temperature of the run	1020°F	1090°F
Time for 50% conversion	15 min	2 hr

What mean residence time is necessary to achieve 98% conversion of B to R if the flow reactor is to be operated at 1020°F with a feed of $\frac{1}{16}$-in. particles?

Note: The particles are unchanged in size during reaction; therefore it is safe to ignore gas film resistance.

8. (*a*) Particles of a single size are fed to a fluidized bed at a rate of 2 lb/min. The bed contains 60 lb solids. What is the mean residence time of solid if carryover is absent?

(*b*) With the same solid feed rate the gas flow rate is increased with the result that the bed expands, thus containing only 50 lb solids. Another effect is that 0.86 lb solid/min is blown over. What is the mean residence time of solids under these conditions?

9. Steady-state experiments on the elutriation rates of solids are conducted in the simple apparatus consisting of a fluidized bed followed by a cyclone which serves to separate and return to the bed all entrained solids (Fig. P9).

In a typical experiment a specially prepared batch of narrowly sized titanium oxide composed of 400 gm of uniform 50-μ-diameter particles, 600 gm of uniform 100-μ-diameter particles is introduced with 5000 gm of larger material, approximately 300-μ diameter, and is fluidized with gas at a fixed velocity. When steady state is achieved, the carryover rate is 22 gm/min consisting of 27.3% of 100-μ particles, the rest being 50-μ particles. As the amount of solid in the recycle system at any instant is small, about 10 gm, it may be neglected in computing the composition of the bed.

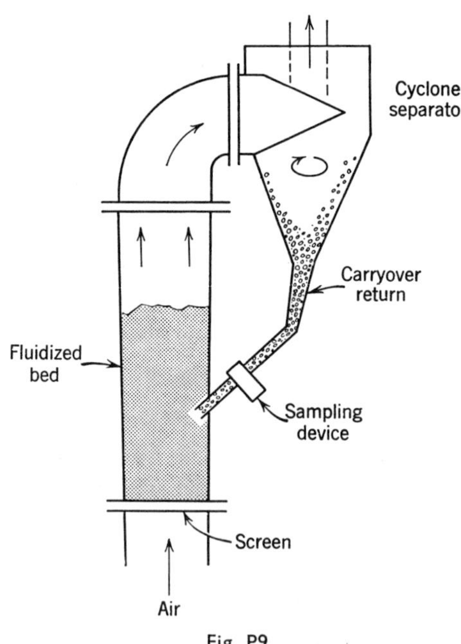

Fig. P9

Find the elutriation velocity constant as a function of radius of particles (in centimeters), assuming the following type of relationship to hold: $\kappa(R) = \alpha R^{\beta}$. What are the dimensions of α and β?

10. (*a*) A mixed solid feed with size distribution $F(R_i)$ and reaction-controlled kinetics with $\tau(R_i)$ known is to be contacted with fluid of fixed composition in a raining solids (or falling solids) reactor of length L. If the solids are small enough, then Re < 0.1 and Stokes law holds. Assuming that by the time the solids enter the reactor they have attained their terminal settling velocity,

$$v_t = \frac{2\Delta\rho}{9\mu} R^2 = MR^2$$

derive and develop as far as possible the expression which gives the fractional conversion of solids leaving the reactor as a function of the pertinent variables of the system.

Assume no change in weight or size of particle with reaction, hence unchanging velocity of fall.

(*b*) Repeat with gas film resistance controlling.

11. Glass beads were batch-fluidized in a 4-in.-i.d. column with 70°F 1-atm air at 4.02 ft/sec, and the quantities of the various sizes of solids blown out in a 2-min interval were determined by Wen and Hashinger (1960) as shown in the following table.

Particle Diameter, in.	Quantity Initially Present, gm	Quantity Removed, gm
0.0028	450	414
0.0039	450	291
0.0058	450	148
0.0110	4050	0

Determine the elutriation velocity constant as a function of particle size for the three small sizes of glass beads.

12. Solve Example 3 with the following modification: the kinetics of the reaction is ash diffusion controlled with $\tau(R = 100\ \mu) = 10$ min.

13. Solve Example 4 with the following modification: the kinetics of the reaction is ash diffusion controlled with $\tau(R = 100\ \mu) = 10$ min.

14. A pilot plant is to be built to explore the fluidized-bed technique as a means of roasting zinc blende. The reactor is to have an internal diameter of 10 cm and an underflow pipe 18 cm from the bottom of the bed. Feed to the experimental reactor is to be 35.5 gm/min consisting 40% of 20-μ-diameter particles, 60% of 80-μ-diameter particles. For the optimum gas velocity through the bed, the following bed characteristics can be estimated from values in the literature.

$$\kappa(10\ \mu) = 0.4/\text{min}$$

From elutriation data: $\kappa(40\ \mu) = 0.01/\text{min}$

From bed porosity data: $W = 1100$ gm
For the temperature selected and ore to be processed, $\tau(10\ \mu) = 2.5$ min, $\tau(40\ \mu) = 10$ min.

(*a*) What conversion of ZnS may be expected in this reactor?

(*b*) The installation of a cyclone to separate and return to the reactor any solids entrained by the fluidizing gas is being considered as a possible means of increasing the sulfide conversion. Find the effect on conversion of such a device.

15. A commercial-sized reactor (bed diameter = 3 ft, bed height = 6 ft) is to be built to treat 1500 lb/hr of feed of the previous problem. Assuming no change in bed density and gas velocity, find the conversion of sulfide to oxide in such a unit.

16. When reaction is the rate-controlling step, the conversion of solid in a two-stage fluidized-bed reactor (assume backmix flow in equal-sized stages) can be found to be

$$1 - \bar{X}_B = 1 - \frac{6}{y} + \frac{18}{y^2} - \frac{24}{y^3} + \left(\frac{6}{y^2} + \frac{24}{y^3}\right)e^{-y}$$

where $y = \tau/\bar{t}_i$, and $\bar{t}_i$ is the holding time of solids per stage.

(*a*) When $\bar{t}_i > \tau$ show that this conversion expression reduces to

$$1 - \bar{X}_B = \frac{y^2}{20}\left(1 - \frac{y}{3} + \frac{y^2}{14} - \frac{y^3}{84} + \cdots\right)$$

(*b*) Selecting $y = 2$, 1, 0.5, and 0.25, prepare the appropriate line on Fig. 16 for two-stage fluidized-bed reactors.

(*c*) From this line find the new treatment rate of solid if a second identical stage is placed in series with a single-stage fluidized-bed reactor. Conversion of solid is to remain at 99%.

(*d*) Present the general expression for conversion in an equal-sized *j*-stage fluidized-bed reactor.

Note: For ash diffusion controlling, expressions analogous to these are difficult to obtain. These expressions may be used as a close approximation, however, because the progress of reaction of individual particles is rather similar in the two cases (see Fig. 10).

17. Solid is being converted in a *j*-stage fluidized-bed reactor (assume backmix flow in equal-sized stages) under conditions in which the resistance of the gas film is the rate-controlling step.

(*a*) Present the conversion versus holding time expression for this operation.

(*b*) For a two-stage fluidized bed show that this general expression reduces to

$$1 - \bar{X}_B = 1 - \frac{2}{y} + \left(1 + \frac{2}{y}\right)e^{-y}$$

where $y = \tau/\bar{t}_i$, and $\bar{t}_i$ is the holding time of solids per stage; or for $\bar{t}_i > \tau$

$$1 - \bar{X}_B = y^2\left(\frac{1}{6} - \frac{y}{12} + \frac{y^2}{40} - \frac{y^3}{180} + \cdots\right)$$

(*c*) Selecting $y = 4, 2, 1,$ and 0.5, prepare the appropriate line on Fig. 16 for two-stage fluidized-bed reactors.

(*d*) From this line find the new treatment rate of solid if a second identical stage is placed in series with a single-stage fluidized-bed reactor. Conversion of solid is to remain at 99%.

18. The Lavender Hill Philanthropic Society is a worthy organization dedicated to the preservation of important historical monuments and buildings.

Like all the other members of this close knit group, you expect, in compensation for your efforts, only the satisfaction of seeing a job well done—plus a small token commission on each project. You have worked up steadily in the organization and at present have charge of the disposal team.

Now the latest venture, and by far the boldest and grandest one ever undertaken by this group, is to save Fort Knox from sinking completely out of sight because of the excessive and unplanned for overload on the foundations. The solution to this weighty problem is obvious; eliminate the overload.

Advanced design and planning estimate that the foundation overload can be sufficiently lightened by removing 20 tons of long cylindrical 1-in.-diameter gold bars worth about $40,000,000. These will be delivered to you at 8:00 p.m. on *the* day. It is up to you to dispose of them as soon as possible, but certainly before 8:00 a.m. the next day, when visiting dignitaries of the various constabularies may be expected. After weighing the various alternatives, you hit on the ingenious plan of dumping the bars in the employees' swimming pool, which will be filled for that occasion with aqua regia.

A literature search produces no useful rate data for this reaction, so an experiment is devised with the only sample of gold available, a $\frac{1}{2}$-in.-diameter gold marble. The following results are obtained, using the same fluid as in the pool.

Size of Marble, diameter in inches	Time, min
0.5	0
0.4	42
0.3	87
0.2	130
0.1	172
0	216

(*a*) At what time can the bars be expected to disappear, and can the 8 a.m. deadline be met?

(*b*) Certainly the earlier the bars dissolve the safer the project is from unforeseen contingencies. With the thought that agitation may speed up the reaction, the Project Director helpfully suggests that the group's psychologist, and not too reliable member, Harry, with a slight push or prod, may volunteer his services in agitating the pool. Would Harry's services be needed?

Note: Naturally the employees' swimming pool is large enough so that the acid strength is not appreciably lowered during reaction.

13
HETEROGENEOUS FLUID-FLUID REACTIONS

Heterogeneous fluid-fluid reactions are made to take place for one of two reasons. First the product of reaction of immiscible reactants may be a desired material. Such reactions are numerous and can be found in practically all areas of the chemical industry where organic syntheses are employed. An example of liquid-liquid reactions is the nitration of organics with a mixture of nitric and sulfuric acids to form materials such as nitroglycerin. The chlorination of liquid benzene and other hydrocarbons with gaseous chlorine is an example of gas-liquid reactions. In the inorganic field we have the manufacture of sodium amide, a solid, from gaseous ammonia and liquid sodium:

$$NH_3(g) + Na(l) \xrightarrow{250^\circ C} NaNH_2(s) + \tfrac{1}{2}H_2$$

Fluid-fluid reactions may also be made to take place to facilitate the removal of an unwanted component from a fluid. Thus the absorption of a solute gas by water may be accelerated by adding a suitable reagent to the water which will react with the solute being absorbed. Table 1 shows the reagents used for various solute gases.

The following factors will determine the design method used for fluid-fluid systems.

The over-all rate expression. Since materials in the two separate phases must contact each other before reaction can occur, both mass transfer and rate of chemical reaction will enter the over-all rate expression for the reaction.

Equilibrium solubility. The solubility of the reacting components will limit their movement from phase to phase. This factor will certainly

Table I. Absorption systems with chemical reaction[a]

Solute Gas	Reagent
CO_2	Carbonates
CO_2	Hydroxides
CO_2	Ethanolamines
CO	Cuprous amine complexes
CO	Cuprous ammonium chloride
SO_2	$Ca(OH)_2$
SO_2	Ozone–H_2O
SO_2	$HCrO_4$
SO_2	KOH
Cl_2	H_2O
Cl_2	$FeCl_2$
H_2S	Ethanolamines
H_2S	$Fe(OH)_3$
SO_3	H_2SO_4
C_2H_4	KOH
C_2H_4	Trialkyl phosphates
Olefins	Cuprous ammonium complexes
NO	$FeSO_4$
NO	$Ca(OH)_2$
NO	H_2SO_4
NO_2	H_2O

[a] Adapted from Teller (1960).

influence the form of the rate equation since it will determine whether the reaction takes place in one or both phases.

The contacting scheme. In gas-liquid systems semibatch and countercurrent contacting schemes predominate. In liquid-liquid systems backmix flow (mixer-settlers) and batch contacting are used in addition to counter and cocurrent contacting.

Many possible permutations of rate, equilibrium, and contacting pattern can be visualized; however, only some of these are important in the sense that they are widely used on the technical scale. We treat only these cases.

THE RATE EQUATION

For convenience let us call the two phases the gas and liquid phases: let A be the reactant in the gas phase, B the reactant in the liquid phase. If we are actually dealing with two liquids rather than a gas and liquid, we simply let the gas phase of this treatment be the second liquid phase and make the appropriate change in terminology.

Consider the contacting of gas containing reactant A with liquid containing reactant B. The over-all rate expression will account for the resistances provided by the mass transfer step between phases and by the chemical reaction step. The relative magnitudes of these two processes can vary greatly. At one extreme we may have so fast a reaction that only the resistance to mass transfer need be considered in the rate expressions. At the other extreme the reaction may be so much slower than mass transfer that nonuniformities in composition within a phase do not exist, materials are uniformly distributed within a phase, and reaction alone influences the over-all rate of the process. Between these extremes the rate equation must account for both these phenomena.

Starting with a reaction that is very fast compared with mass transfer and ending with the other extreme, let us consider the various forms of over-all rate expressions for the reaction of A and B, each initially present in a distinct fluid phase.

Mass transfer controls (reaction is infinitely fast)

The concept that the resistance to mass transfer and reaction occurs in two films on either side of the interface between phases [see Lewis and Whitman (1924)] has been successfully used in chemical engineering, influencing the design procedures for fluid-fluid mass transfer operations. For example, the rate of physical absorption of a gas-phase component by a liquid is expressed by

$$-r_A'' = -\frac{1}{S}\frac{dN_A}{dt} = \frac{1}{1/k_{Ag} + H_{Ai}/k_{Al}}(p_A - H_{Ai}C_A)$$

$$= \frac{1}{1/k_{Ag}H_{Ai} + 1/k_{Al}}\left(\frac{p_A}{H_{Ai}} - C_A\right) = \begin{pmatrix}\text{over-all}\\\text{rate co-}\\\text{efficient}\end{pmatrix}\begin{pmatrix}\text{over-all}\\\text{driving}\\\text{force}\end{pmatrix} \qquad (1)$$

where k_{Ag} and k_{Al} are the individual mass transfer coefficients in gas and liquid film, or reciprocal measures of the resistances afforded by these films, and H_{Ai} is the equilibrium distribution coefficient between phases.

Using the two-film model with an infinitely fast reaction of any order with the stoichiometry

$$\text{A (in gas phase)} + b\text{B (in liquid phase)} \rightarrow \text{products}$$

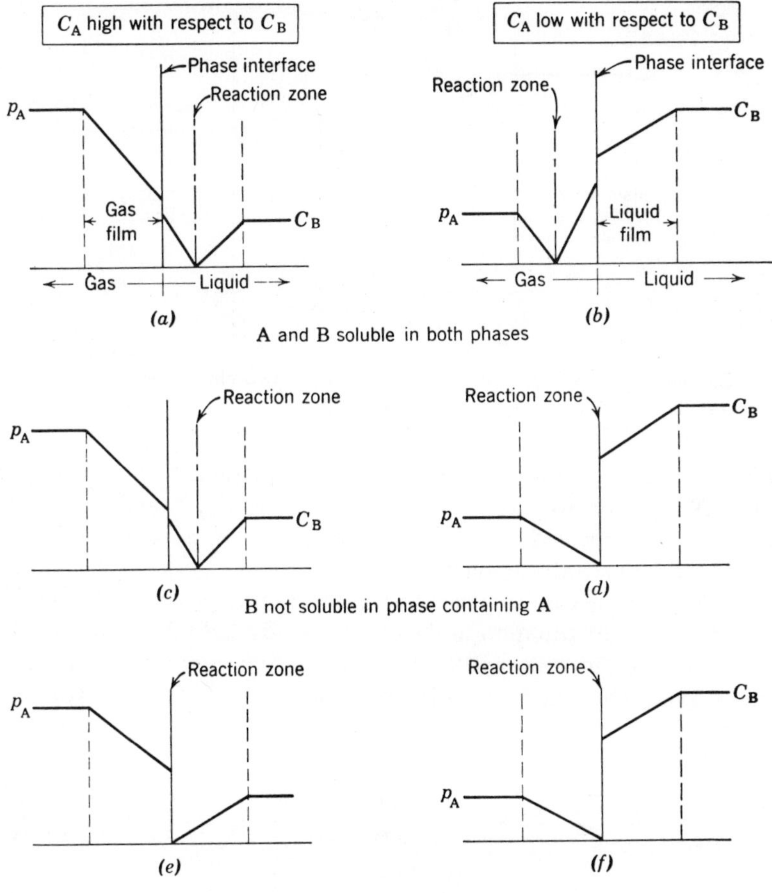

Fig. 1. Concentration profiles of reactants in films between phases for an infinitely fast irreversible reaction of any order

$$A\begin{pmatrix}\text{gas}\\\text{phase}\end{pmatrix} + bB\begin{pmatrix}\text{liquid}\\\text{phase}\end{pmatrix} \rightarrow \text{products}$$

Concentration and solubilities of reactants determine location of reaction zone and the form of rate equation. In *a*, *b*, and *c*, both reactants influence rate; in *d*, e, and *f*, only one or the other of the reactants influences rate.

we find that a number of situations, shown in Fig. 1, may occur. In all these the reaction takes place within the film, the reactants diffusing toward the reaction zone which is a sharply defined surface between A-rich and B-rich regions. Because the reaction is assumed to be infinitely fast, no A and B can exist simultaneously at any one place.

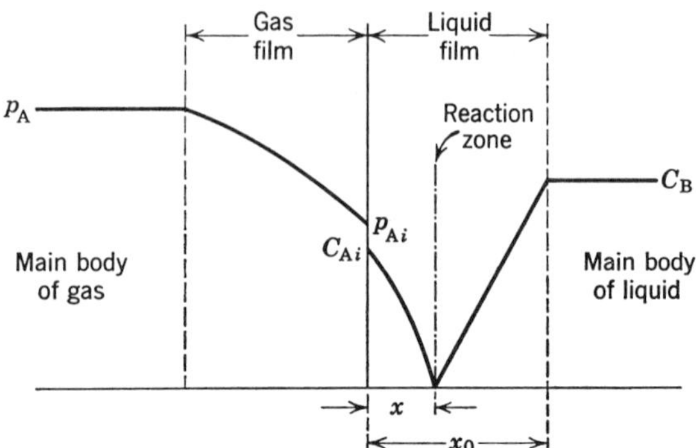

Fig. 2. Concentrations of reactants as visualized by the two-film theory for an infinitely fast irreversible reaction of any order, A + bB → products.

With regard to the development of a rate equation, Fig. 1 shows that essentially we have two cases; that shown in Figs. 1*a*, *b*, and *c* where the reaction zone is located within a film and Figs. 1*d*, *e*, and *f* where the reaction takes place at the interface itself.

Consider first the case in which the reaction takes place within the film. Figure 2 shows this situation in detail. At steady state the flow rate of B toward the reaction zone will be b times the flow rate of A toward the reaction zone. Thus the rate of disappearance of A and B at steady state is given by

$$-r_A'' = -\frac{r_B''}{b} = -\frac{1}{S}\frac{dN_A}{dt} = \underbrace{k_{Ag}(p_A - p_{Ai})}_{\text{A in gas film}}$$

$$= \underbrace{k_{Al}(C_{Ai} - 0)\frac{x_0}{x}}_{\text{A in liquid film}} = \underbrace{\frac{k_{Bl}}{b}(C_B - 0)\frac{x_0}{x_0 - x}}_{\text{B in liquid film}} \tag{2}$$

where k_{Ag} and k_{Al}, k_{Bl} are the mass transfer coefficients in gas and liquid phases. These are the coefficients given in the literature for straight mass transfer without chemical reaction and are therefore based on flow through the whole fluid film.

At the interface the relationship between p_A and C_A is given by the distribution coefficient, which is called Henry's law constant in gas-liquid systems. Thus we have

$$\frac{p_{Ai}}{C_{Ai}} = H_{Ai} \tag{3}$$

In addition, since the movement of material within a laminar film is visualized to occur by diffusion alone, then for A and B moving through the same section of film we have*

$$\frac{k_A}{k_B} = \frac{\mathscr{D}_A/\Delta x}{\mathscr{D}_B/\Delta x} = \frac{\mathscr{D}_A}{\mathscr{D}_B} \tag{4}$$

Eliminating the unknown values x, x_0, p_{Ai}, C_{Ai} in Eqs. 2, 3, and 4, we obtain

$$-r_A'' = -\frac{r_B''}{b} = -\frac{1}{S}\frac{dN_A}{dt} = -\frac{1}{bS}\frac{dN_B}{dt} = \frac{\dfrac{\mathscr{D}_{Bl}}{\mathscr{D}_{Al}}\dfrac{C_B}{b} + \dfrac{p_A}{H_{Ai}}}{\dfrac{1}{k_{Al}} + \dfrac{1}{H_{Ai}k_{Ag}}} \tag{6}$$

The constant b is given by the reaction stoichiometry, and the values for $\mathscr{D}_{Bl}/\mathscr{D}_{Al}$, k_{Ag}, and k_{Al} can be found or estimated from the literature. The only term still to be found is the distribution coefficient H_{Ai} for the partial pressure of A at the interface of B-free liquid. Since this partial pressure is not known, H_{Ai} is approximated by H_A, the distribution coefficient for the partial pressure in the main body of gas. This is a reasonable approximation since the variation in H is usually quite small for the partial-pressure differences involved.

With all terms known Eq. 6 can then be used directly in design for the situations shown in Figs. 1*a*, *b*, and *c*.

Now if the concentration of one of the components, say B, is increased, the reaction zone moves into the gas film. However, if B is not soluble in the gas, the reaction zone will remain at the interface between phases. Situations of this kind are shown in Figs. 1*d*, *e*, and *f*. Consider Fig. 1*d* in which B is the insoluble component. When C_B is high relative to p_A or more specifically when

$$k_{Ag}p_A \leqslant \frac{k_{Bl}}{b}C_B \tag{7}$$

this condition in Eq. 2 requires that the reaction zone move to and remain (since B is insoluble) at the interface. When this happens, the resistance

* Alternative models [Higbie (1935), Danckwerts (1950, 1955)] showing the continual replacement of fluid at the interface with fresh fluid have also been used. These surface renewal theories all predict that

$$\frac{k_A}{k_B} = \left(\frac{\mathscr{D}_A}{\mathscr{D}_B}\right)^{1/2} \tag{5}$$

and evidence indicates that this relationship is more closely correct than Eq. 4.

Though these unsteady-state theories are rather different from the two-film theory, and from a physical point of view are probably more correct, still all these models give essentially the same results. Because of this and because the two-film theory is so much easier to develop and use than the others, we shall deal with it exclusively.

of the gas phase controls, and the rate is not affected by any further increase in concentration of B. In addition, Eq. 6 simplifies to

$$-r_A'' = -\frac{r_B''}{b} = -\frac{1}{S}\frac{dN_A}{dt} = k_{Ag}p_A \tag{8}$$

To determine which of the two forms of rate expressions, Eq. 6 or Eq. 8, to use in any specific situation requires knowledge of the concentrations of reactants and of the physical properties of the fluids being used. Nevertheless, we can make a rough, order of magnitude, estimation as follows. For mass transfer of a constituent through a liquid

$$\mathscr{D}_l \approx 10^{-5}\ \text{cm}^2/\text{sec}$$

and

$$x_0 \approx 10^{-2}\ \text{cm}$$

hence

$$k_l = \frac{\mathscr{D}_l}{x_0} \approx 10^{-3}\ \text{cm/sec} \tag{9}$$

For a gas phase on the other hand

$$\mathscr{D}_g \approx 0.1\ \text{cm}^2/\text{sec}$$

and

$$x_0 \approx 10^{-2}\ \text{cm}$$

hence for driving forces in concentration units

$$k_g' = k_g RT = \frac{\mathscr{D}_g}{x_0} \approx 10\ \text{cm/sec} \tag{10}$$

Replacing these values in Eq. 7 shows that when

$$\frac{p_A}{RT} = C_{Ag} < \frac{10^{-4}C_{Bl}}{b} \tag{11}$$

the simple form of rate expression, Eq. 8, may be used. We should bear in mind that Eq. 11 is only an order of magnitude estimate.

In the special case where reactant B, insoluble in gas phase, is not dissolved in an inert liquid but is the liquid itself, no liquid film exists and the rate is determined completely by the gas film resistance. Here Eq. 8 should naturally be used.

Note that these expressions are applicable to reactions with any kinetics because this treatment assumes that resistance to reaction is negligible compared to the resistance of mass transfer. What is important, however, in determining the form of the rate equation is the stoichiometry of the reaction.

Example 1 (p. 404) illustrates the use of these forms of kinetic equations.

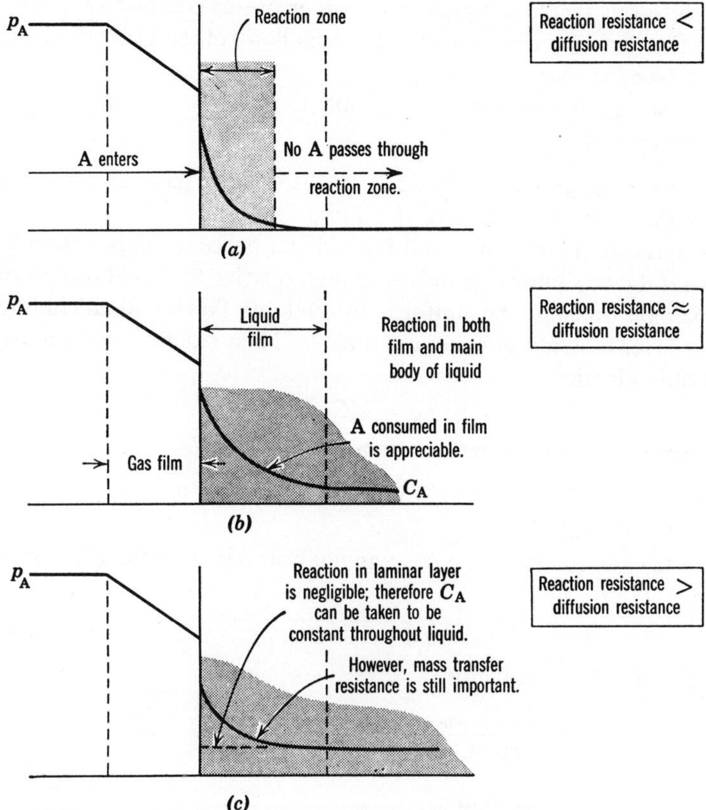

Fig. 3. Graphical representation of the three possible situations in which both reaction and mass transfer enter into the over-all rate expression. The concentration profile for reactant A diffusing from gas and reacting with B in liquid is shown. It is assumed that C_B is high and unchanging throughout, and that B is insoluble in gas.

Mass transfer and reaction both important

Three subcases may be recognized here, depending on the relative importance of the mass transfer and reaction resistances. These are graphically represented in Fig. 3. Let us examine these starting with the infinitely fast irreversible reaction treated earlier, allowing the rate of the chemical step to become progressively slower.

Reaction rate is fast compared with mass transfer. As the infinitely fast reaction is made to slow down, we visualize the surface of reaction between A-rich and B-rich fluid broadening into a diffuse zone of finite width located completely within the laminar layer. Both reactants diffuse into this reaction region, but neither passes completely through it; thus neither reactant can pass into the main body of the other fluid without reacting (see Fig. 3*a*).

Only one case here yields rather simply to analysis, and this involves the following assumptions.

1. Reactant B, present in the liquid, is insoluble in gas. This assumption restricts the zone of reaction to the liquid film.

2. The reaction between A and B is a linear process. This assumption is satisfied if the concentration of B is so high relative to A that its concentration may be taken to be uniform throughout the liquid, including the laminar layer where it is being consumed. Then reactions with *n*th-order irreversible kinetics

$$-r_A = k'C_A C_B^{n-1}$$

reduce to pseudo first-order reactions

$$-r_A = kC_A \qquad \text{where} \qquad k = k'C_B^{n-1}$$

which are linear processes.

The rate equation resulting from an analysis based on these assumptions is

$$-r_A'' = \frac{1}{1/k_{Ag} + H_{Ai}\mathscr{E}/k_{Al}} p_A \tag{12}$$

where the effectiveness factor

$$\mathscr{E} = \frac{(k_{Al})_{\text{without reaction}}}{(k_{Al})_{\text{with reaction}}} = \frac{\tanh x_0\sqrt{k/\mathscr{D}_{Al}}}{x_0\sqrt{k/\mathscr{D}_{Al}}}$$

$$= \frac{\tanh mx_0}{mx_0} < 1 \tag{13}$$

With the parameters of the system k_{Al}, k_{Ag}, k, $\mathscr{D}_A$, $x_0 = \mathscr{D}_{Al}/k_{Al}$, and H_{Ai} known or estimable, the rate of reaction can be found.

Consider $H_{Ai} = p_{Ai}/C_{Ai}$. Does it make sense to talk of an equilibrium if entering molecules of A are rapidly combining with the molecules of B present in the liquid? Is this not a dynamic situation with one process trying to achieve equilibrium, the other opposing it? To answer, note that the movement of molecules resulting in collision between A and B are relatively rare compared to molecular movement in general, consequently the process tending to equilibrium is by far the more rapid of the two. Thus H_{Ai} should be unaffected by reaction of A. Another objection may be raised in that the liquid is not the same in the two cases. In one case we have pure solvent; in the other, foreign material such as reactant B and products of reaction. Certainly this should change H_{Ai}. Fortunately, for aqueous solutions the effect of such solutes can be estimated by finding how similar but unreacting materials affect H_{Ai}; see van Krevelens and Hoftyzer (1948a).

The question of how to relax the above assumptions and still obtain useful results is presently receiving much attention.

Reaction rate is intermediate compared with mass transfer. When the reaction rate is further slowed, the reaction zone occupies the whole width of the laminar layer and reactant A is able to pass completely through this layer without reaction into the main body of the other fluid. Thus reaction takes place both in the laminar layer and also within the main body of the fluid. In general, the relatively high concentration of reactant A in the laminar layer results in an appreciable fraction of reactant being consumed in this layer.

Hatta (1932) analyzed this situation using the same assumptions as those for the previous case, namely that B is not soluble in gas, C_B is high and constant throughout the liquid, and the reaction is essentially of first order (see Fig. 3*b*). The over-all rate expression in terms of the partial pressure of A in the main gas stream is cumbersome to use and again requires evaluation of the distribution coefficient of reactant A in B-rich solution. The difficulty of performing this evaluation when reaction is fast enough to allow an appreciable amount of reaction to take place within the laminar layer has already been noted.

The general form of the rate expression obtained has not yet been used in design.

Reaction rate is slow compared with mass transfer. When the reaction rate is slow compared to mass transfer, most of reactant A is able to pass through the laminar layer into the main body of liquid without reacting. Thus we view the laminar layer to provide a resistance to the over-all process, but with the restriction that the fraction of A reacting within this laminar layer is small enough so that we may take the concentration of A to be uniform throughout the liquid, including the laminar layer (see Fig. 3*c*).

According to Hatta (1932) the fraction of entering component A which reaches the main body of liquid is

$$\frac{C_{Al}\cosh x_0\sqrt{k/\mathscr{D}_{Al}} - C_{Ai}}{C_{Al} - C_{Ai}\cosh x_0\sqrt{k/\mathscr{D}_{Al}}} = \frac{C_{Al}\cosh mx_0 - C_{Ai}}{C_{Al} - C_{Ai}\cosh mx_0} \tag{14}$$

where C_{Al} is the concentration in the main body of liquid. This fraction approaches unity as cosh mx_0 approaches unity or when

$$mx_0 = x_0\sqrt{k/\mathscr{D}_{Al}} < 0.2 \tag{15}$$

This equation then represents the restriction for the case being considered.

Though this is a special case of the treatment by Hatta, the application of the resulting kinetic equations to design is still somewhat complicated.

We do not take up this subject here, however Trambouze et al. (1961) have applied such equations to batch, plug flow, and backmix reactor design.

Chemical reaction controls

Slow reaction in both phases. When reaction is not too slow the movement of material between phases offers resistance to reaction and the two-film model is useful in accounting for this resistance to transfer of material. If reaction is very slow, however, reactant materials have sufficient time to move from phase to phase and to become uniformly distributed within these phases subject to the phase distribution equilibrium. Here, then, the resistance to mass transfer is negligible, the two-film model plays no role, and reaction controls the rate of the over-all process.

Now if both A and B are soluble in appreciable amounts in both phases, as shown in Fig. 4, the reaction will proceed in both phases, the over-all rate of reaction being the sum total of the individual rates of reaction.

If the reaction is

$$\text{A (in gas phase)} + \text{B (in liquid phase)} \rightarrow \text{products}$$

with elementary second-order kinetics in both phases, we have

$$-r_{\text{A,over-all}} = -\frac{1}{V}\frac{dN_\text{A}}{dt} = f_g(-r_{\text{A}g}) + f_l(-r_{\text{A}l})$$
$$= f_g(kp_\text{A}p_\text{B})_{\text{gas}} + f_l(kC_\text{A}C_\text{B})_{\text{liquid}} \tag{16}$$

where f_g and f_l are the volume fractions of gas and liquid. With the phase distribution relationships

$$p_\text{A} = H_\text{A}C_\text{A} \tag{17}$$

$$p_\text{B} = H_\text{B}C_\text{B} \tag{18}$$

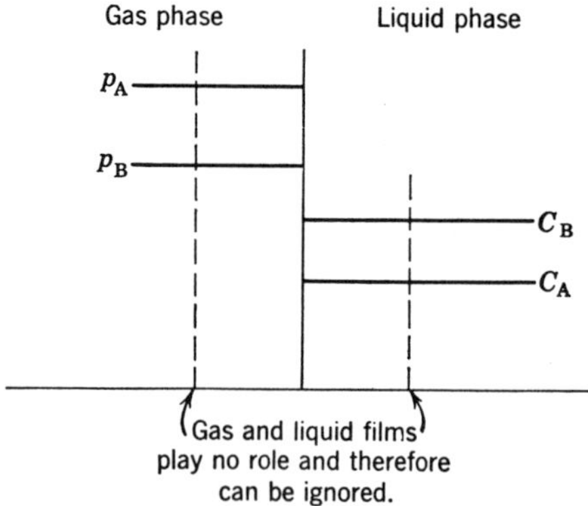

Fig. 4. Concentrations of reactants in the phases when reaction is slow and occurs in both phases.

the over-all rate of reaction in terms of p_A and C_B is

$$-r_{\text{over-all}} = -\frac{1}{V}\frac{dN_A}{dt} = \left[\frac{(fk)_{\text{liquid}}}{H_A} + (fk)_{\text{gas}}H_B\right]p_A C_B \qquad (19)$$

The nitration of aromatics, say

$$C_6H_6 \begin{pmatrix}\text{organic}\\ \text{phase}\end{pmatrix} + HNO_3 \begin{pmatrix}\text{aqueous}\\ \text{phase}\end{pmatrix}$$

$$\rightarrow C_6H_5NO_2 \begin{pmatrix}\text{organic}\\ \text{phase}\end{pmatrix} + H_2O \begin{pmatrix}\text{aqueous}\\ \text{phase}\end{pmatrix}$$

offers examples of this kind of reaction, because even though the reactants and products are each preferentially soluble in one of the two phases as noted above, still the reaction does proceed appreciably in both aqueous and organic phases. Extensions of Eq. 19 to reactions with more involved stoichiometry or kinetics is straightforward.

Slow reaction in one phase. If a reactant is soluble only in one phase, reaction occurs in that phase alone. Thus if B is not soluble in gas $H_B = 0$ and Eq. 19 reduces to

$$-r_A = -\frac{1}{V_{\text{mixture}}}\frac{dN_A}{dt} = \frac{(fk)_{\text{liquid}}}{H_A} p_A C_B \qquad (20)$$

or in terms of the volume of active (or liquid) phase

$$-r_A = -\frac{1}{V_{\text{liquid}}}\frac{dN_A}{dt} = \frac{k_{\text{liquid}}}{H_A} p_A C_B = k_{\text{liquid}} C_A C_B \qquad (21)$$

Alternate approaches to the kinetics of absorption with reaction

Alternate methods of treating absorption with fairly fast reactions can be found elsewhere [Perry and Pigford (1953), Sherwood and Pigford (1952), and van Krevelen and Hoftyzer (1948, 1953)]. In these treatments the mass transfer coefficient k_l is modified to account for the effects of reaction, the combined coefficient being k_l^*. Charts are then prepared giving the ratio

$$\frac{k_l^*}{k_l} = \frac{1}{\mathscr{E}} > 1$$

as a function of the pertinent parameters.

These corrected mass transfer coefficients are then used with modifications of the regular design methods for situations where mass transfer is the rate controlling process.

Empirical forms of the rate equation

In a large number of reactions the theoretical expressions for rate have not been developed because one or the other of the processes is not controlling, because the reaction is not simple and irreversible, or because the values of the required constants k_g, k_l, H, etc., are not known. For these reactions simplified rate expressions are used.

For relatively fast reactions between gas-phase reactant A and liquid-phase reactant B the rate expression used is often of the form

$$-r_A'' = -\frac{1}{S}\frac{dN_A}{dt} = k\Delta = \begin{pmatrix}\text{over-all}\\ \text{transfer}\\ \text{coefficient}\end{pmatrix}\begin{pmatrix}\text{displacement}\\ \text{from}\\ \text{equilibrium}\end{pmatrix} \tag{22}$$

where k accounts for the reaction and mass transfer resistances of both phases and where Δ expresses the amount of reactant still unconverted or, for reversible reactions, the difference between the actual and equilibrium concentrations of the reactants. Rate equations such as these are strictly empirical and are risky to extrapolate.

For relatively slow reactions the form of rate equation often used is one based on unit volume of total mixture or

$$-r_A = -\frac{1}{V_{\text{total}}}\frac{dN_A}{dt} = kC_A{}^aC_B{}^b \tag{23}$$

Example 3 (p. 415) illustrates the use of an equation of this kind.

APPLICATION TO DESIGN

Figure 5 shows the variety of equipment used for fluid-fluid contacting. Note that many of the contacting devices shown, *a* to *e*, employ flow that can be treated as cocurrent or countercurrent plug flow. Other contacting devices such as single agitated vessels, mixer-settlers, and batteries of such units, *f* to *i*, are also widely used.

Design for all such systems will vary, depending on the model for the flow pattern selected, the relative rates of reaction versus mass transfer, and the solubilities of active compounds.

Many factors in the design of equipment for fluid-fluid contacting with reaction and without reaction are the same, such as determining the permissible flow rates for fluids and estimating the diameter of column needed, and selecting the type of contactor. These aspects are covered in the standard texts on the subject [Sherwood and Pigford (1952), Treybal (1955)]. The factors in design that are particular to reacting systems are those influenced by the change in rate produced by reaction. It is these factors, such as height of equipment, which we consider here.

We use the following nomenclature in this section.

a = interfacial contact area per unit volume of tower

f = volume fraction of a phase in which reaction occurs

i = any participant, reactant or product, in the reaction

A, B, R, and S = participants in the reaction

U = carrier or inert component in a phase, hence neither reactant, product nor diffusing component

T = total moles in liquid phase

$\mathbf{Y}_A = p_A/p_U$, moles A/mole inert in the gas

$\mathbf{X}_A = C_A/C_U$, moles A/mole inert in the liquid

$G = G'p_U/\pi$, upward molar flow rate of inerts in the gas phase per square foot of tower cross section

$L = L'C_U/C_T$, downward molar flow rate of inerts in the liquid phase per square foot of tower cross section

G', L' = molar flow rate of all gas and all liquid per square foot of tower cross section

With this nomenclature

$$\begin{aligned} \pi &= p_A + p_B + \cdots + p_U \\ C_T &= C_A + C_B + \cdots + C_U \end{aligned} \tag{24}$$

$$d\mathbf{Y}_A = d\left(\frac{p_A}{p_U}\right) = \frac{p_U\,dp_A - p_A\,dp_U}{p_U^2} \tag{25}$$

and

$$d\mathbf{X}_A = d\left(\frac{C_A}{C_U}\right) = \frac{C_U\,dC_A - C_A\,dC_U}{C_U^2} \tag{26}$$

Let us now consider a number of contacting patterns.

Towers (counter or cocurrent plug flow), mass transfer controls

Straight mass transfer without reaction. To determine the tower height, we must in all cases combine the rate expression with a material balance expression. The former is a function of concentration of reactants, and the latter serves to interrelate the changing concentrations of reactants throughout the tower.

Consider steady-state countercurrent operations. In simple mass transfer without reaction there is only one transferring component; thus a material balance for mutually insoluble inerts in a differential element of volume shows that

$$\begin{pmatrix}\text{A lost}\\ \text{by gas}\end{pmatrix} = \begin{pmatrix}\text{A gained}\\ \text{by liquid}\end{pmatrix} \tag{27a}$$

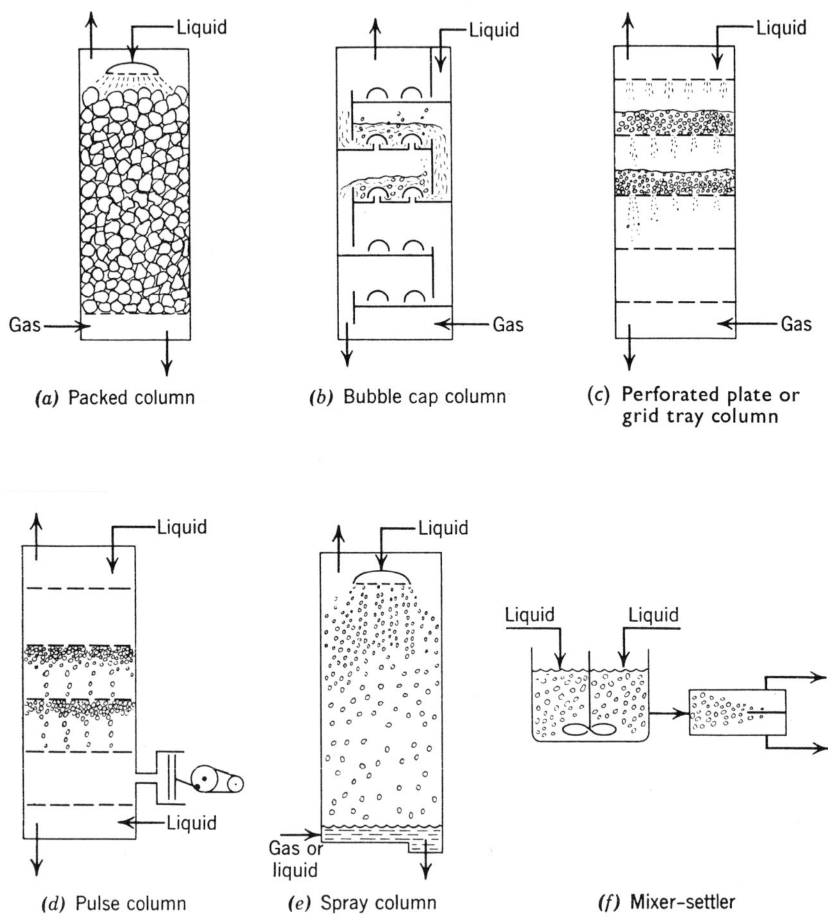

(a) Packed column (b) Bubble cap column (c) Perforated plate or grid tray column

(d) Pulse column (e) Spray column (f) Mixer-settler

Fig. 5. Equipment used in fluid-fluid contacting with reaction. (a–e) Countercurrent flow, (f) backmix flow or single-stage contacting, (g) countercurrent or cocurrent flow, (h) countercurrent flow (settlers used between stages in liquid-liquid systems), (i) cocurrent flow, (j) single-stage contacting, (k) batch system.

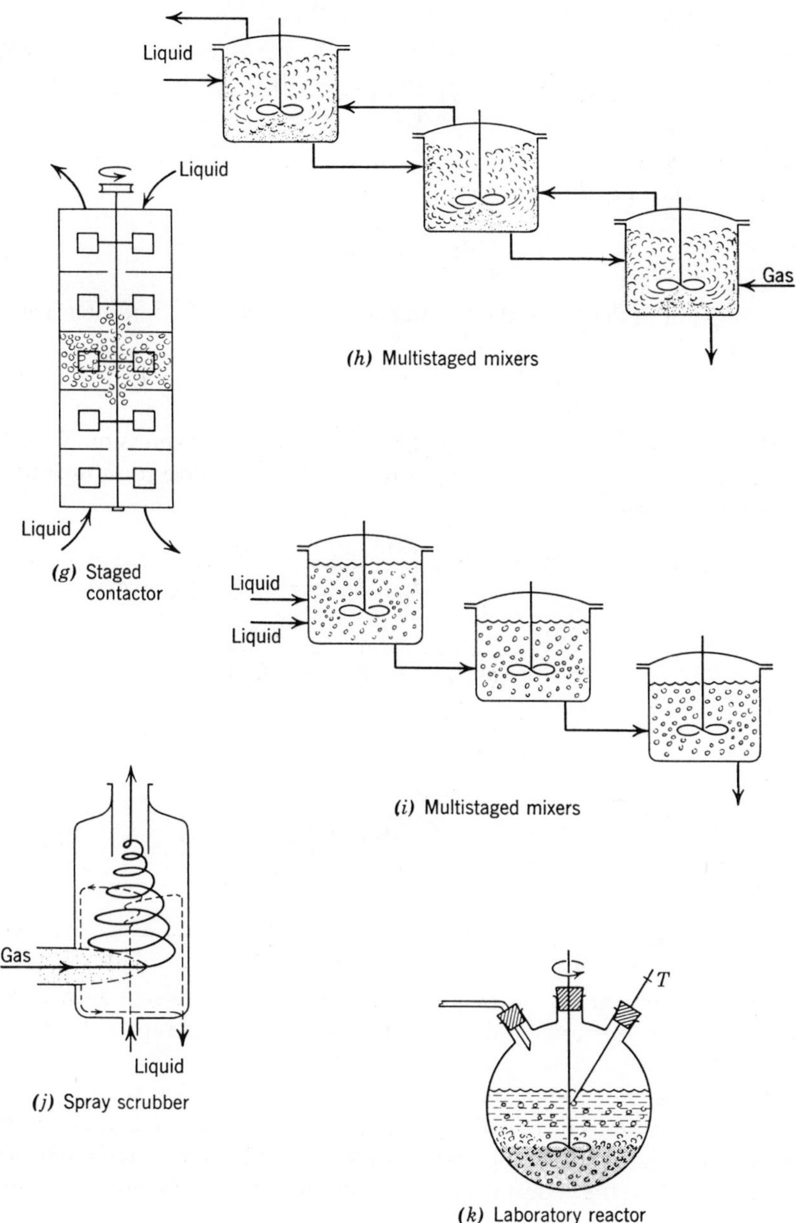

(g) Staged contactor

(h) Multistaged mixers

(i) Multistaged mixers

(j) Spray scrubber

(k) Laboratory reactor

or

$$\begin{aligned} G d\mathbf{Y}_A = L d\mathbf{X}_A &= \frac{G\pi\, dp_A}{(\pi - p_A)^2} = \frac{LC_T\, dC_A}{(C_T - C_A)^2} \\ &= d\left(\frac{G' p_A}{\pi}\right) = d\left(\frac{L' C_A}{C_T}\right) = \frac{G'\, dp_A}{\pi - p_A} = \frac{L'\, dC_A}{C_T - C_A} \end{aligned} \tag{27b}$$

For dilute systems where $C_A \ll C_T$ and $p_A \ll \pi$ we have $L \approx L'$ and $G \approx G'$, hence Eq. 27 simplifies to

$$\frac{G}{\pi}\, dp_A = \frac{L}{C_T}\, dC_A \tag{28}$$

At any point in the tower the transfer of A per unit surface of interface is given by

$$-r_A'' = -\frac{1}{S}\frac{dN_A}{dt} = k_{Ag}(p_A - p_{Ai}) = k_{Al}(C_{Ai} - C_A) \tag{29}$$

Combining the material balance, Eq. 27, and the rate expression, Eq. 29, allows us to determine the height of tower. Thus we have for absorption without reaction

$$\begin{aligned} h &= \frac{G}{a}\int_{\mathbf{Y}_{A1}}^{\mathbf{Y}_{A2}} \frac{d\mathbf{Y}_A}{-r_A''} = G\pi \int_{p_{A1}}^{p_{A2}} \frac{dp_A}{k_{Ag}a(\pi - p_A)^2(p_A - p_{Ai})} \\ &= LC_T \int_{C_{A1}}^{C_{A2}} \frac{dC_A}{k_{Al}a(C_T - C_A)^2(C_{Ai} - C_A)} \\ &= G' \int_{p_{A1}}^{p_{A2}} \frac{dp_A}{k_{Ag}a(\pi - p_A)(p_A - p_{Ai})} \\ &= L' \int_{C_{A1}}^{C_{A2}} \frac{dC_A}{k_{Al}a(C_T - C_A)(C_{Ai} - C_A)} \end{aligned} \tag{30}$$

Again for dilute systems $L \approx L'$ and $G \approx G'$; hence

$$h = \frac{G}{\pi k_{Ag} a} \int_{p_{A1}}^{p_{A2}} \frac{dp_A}{p_A - p_{Ai}} = \frac{L}{C_T k_{Al} a} \int_{C_{A1}}^{C_{A2}} \frac{dC_A}{C_{Ai} - C_A} \tag{31}$$

Figure 6 summarizes the design procedure for countercurrent operations. For cocurrent operations (downward flow of gas) G is replaced by $-G$ throughout.

Mass transfer with reaction. For mass transfer with reaction the rate expressions involve the concentrations of both reactants A and B. Thus in contrast with simple absorption or extraction the material balance must interrelate the concentrations of both these reactants throughout the tower.

The design procedure is best described by referring to the fairly general type of reaction,

$$\text{A (in gas)} + b\text{B (in liquid)} \rightarrow \text{products}$$

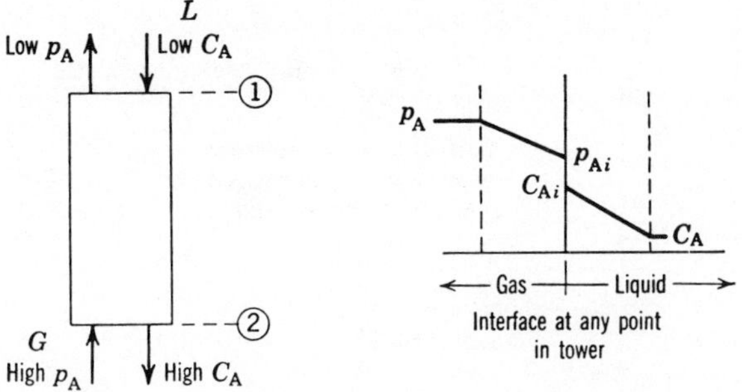

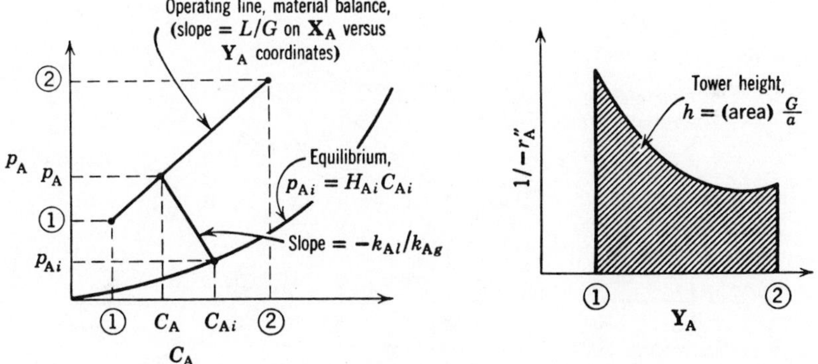

Fig. 6. Design procedure for straight mass transfer without reaction.

with moderately to infinitely fast rate, the phases being in countercurrent plug flow. Since the reaction is limited to the region close to the phase interface, the two-film theory may be used, and the expression describing the rate of disappearance of reactants is given by Eq. 6, 8, or 12.

The material balance for A and B is obtained by noting that of the two reactants, A alone is present in the main body of gas and B alone is present in the main body of liquid. Secondly, for each mole of A reacted b moles of B are consumed. Thus, by referring to Fig. 7, the differential material balance for countercurrent flow is

$$\begin{pmatrix}\text{A lost}\\ \text{by gas}\end{pmatrix} = \frac{1}{b}\begin{pmatrix}\text{B lost}\\ \text{by liquid}\end{pmatrix} \tag{32a}$$

or

$$G\,d\mathbf{Y}_A = -\frac{L\,d\mathbf{X}_B}{b} = G\,d\left(\frac{p_A}{p_U}\right) = -\frac{L}{b}\,d\left(\frac{C_B}{C_U}\right) \tag{32b}$$
$$= d\left(\frac{G'p_A}{\pi}\right) = -\frac{1}{b}\,d\left(\frac{L'C_B}{C_T}\right)$$

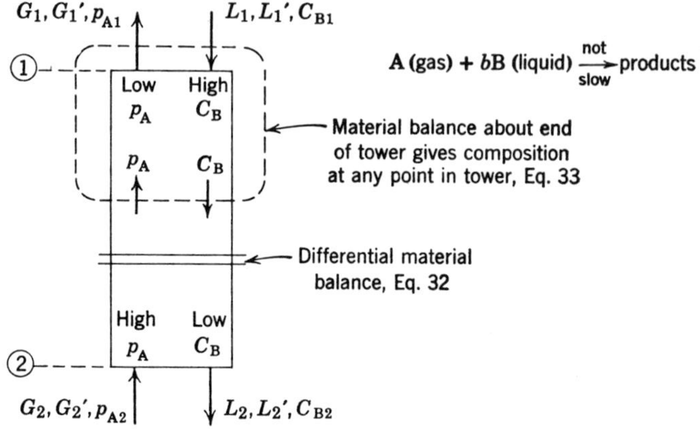

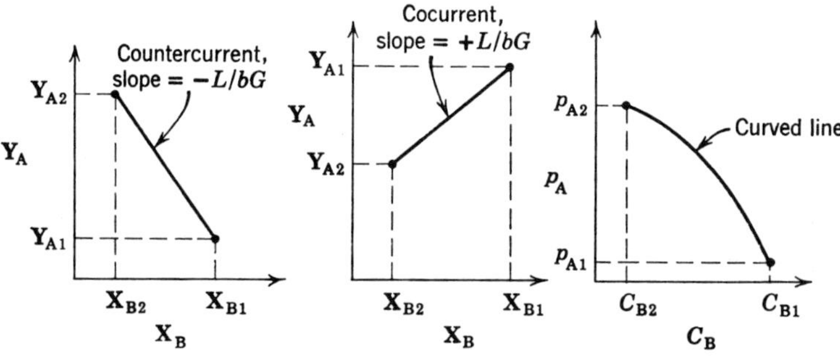

Fig. 7. Development of the material balance for tower operations. A straight line is obtained only with the mole ratio diagram.

For cocurrent operations (downward flow of gas) G is replaced by $-G$ throughout.

The characteristic difference in the material balance between mass transfer with and without reaction is seen by comparing the word equations of Eq. 27 and Eq. 32.

Compositions at any point in the tower are found in terms of the end conditions by integration of Eq. 32; thus

$$\begin{aligned} G(\mathbf{Y}_A - \mathbf{Y}_{A1}) &= -\frac{L(\mathbf{X}_B - \mathbf{X}_{B1})}{b} = G\left(\frac{p_A}{p_U} - \frac{p_{A1}}{p_{U1}}\right) \\ &= -\frac{L}{b}\left(\frac{C_B}{C_U} - \frac{C_{B1}}{C_{U1}}\right) \\ &= \frac{G' p_A}{\pi} - \frac{G_1' p_{A1}}{\pi} = -\frac{1}{b}\left(\frac{L' C_B}{C_T} - \frac{L_1' C_{B1}}{C_{T1}}\right) \end{aligned} \tag{33}$$

These expressions give the composition of reactants A and B in the phases throughout the tower. Again for cocurrent flow G is replaced by $-G$ throughout. Figure 7 shows some of the many possible graphical representations of the material balance. In the general case, however, only one is a straight line.

In special cases Eq. 32 and 33 may be simplified. For example, when all participants in the reaction are dilute $p_U \approx \pi$, $C_U \approx C_T$, and we obtain, for the differential material balance,

$$\frac{G}{\pi}\,dp_A = -\frac{L}{bC_T}\,dC_B \tag{34}$$

and for point conditions

$$\frac{G}{\pi}(p_A - p_{A1}) = -\frac{L}{bC_T}(C_B - C_{B1}) \tag{35}$$

Another special case occurs when no inert or carrier component is present. Thus each phase contains only one pure reactant and whatever products of reaction have accumulated within that phase. For this situation L and G are zero, and the only pertinent forms of the material balance are those involving L' and G'. Example 2 shows one of the many possible forms that the material balance may take in a specific situation.

The height of tower is found by combining the rate equation and material balance for a differential element of tower volume as shown in Fig. 8. Noting that the rate expressions, Eqs. 6, 8, and 12, are all based on

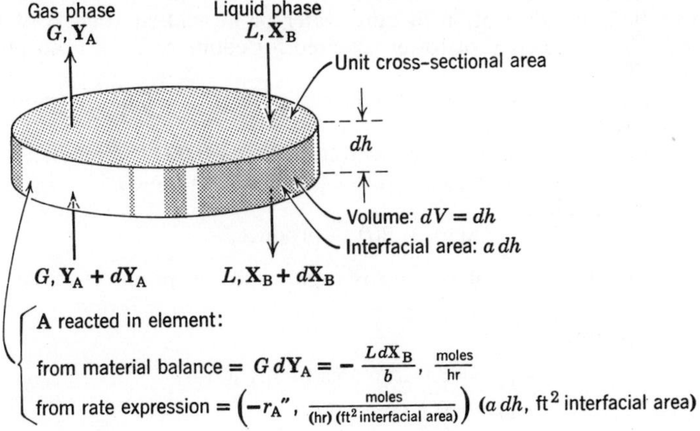

Fig. 8. Development of design equation for tower operations when reaction is restricted to interfacial region between phases.

unit interfacial area, we have for the disappearance of A

$$G\,d\mathbf{Y}_A = -\frac{L\,d\mathbf{X}_B}{b} = \left(\frac{\text{moles A reacted}}{\text{(unit interfacial area) (time)}}\right)\left(\frac{\text{interfacial area}}{\text{unit of volume}}\right)\left(\begin{matrix}\text{height}\\ \text{of}\\ \text{element}\end{matrix}\right)$$

$$= (-r_A'')a\,dh \qquad (36)$$

Rearranging and integrating we obtain in terms of A or B

$$h = G\int_{\mathbf{Y}_{A1}}^{\mathbf{Y}_{A2}} \frac{d\mathbf{Y}_A}{(-r_A'')a} = \frac{L}{b}\int_{\mathbf{X}_{B2}}^{\mathbf{X}_{B1}} \frac{d\mathbf{X}_B}{(-r_A'')a} \qquad (37)$$

where $d\mathbf{Y}_A$ and $d\mathbf{X}_B$ are given by Eqs. 25 and 26. For dilute systems

$$h = \frac{G}{\pi}\int_{p_{A1}}^{p_{A2}} \frac{dp_A}{(-r_A'')a} = \frac{L}{bC_T}\int_{C_{B2}}^{C_{B1}} \frac{dC_B}{(-r_A'')a} \qquad (38)$$

When the rate term in Eq. 37 or 38 is replaced by the appropriate expression, Eq. 6, 8, or 12, the height of tower can then be found. Naturally in most cases the integral must be evaluated either graphically or numerically.

The following example illustrates the use of these equations.

Example 1

The concentration of an undesirable impurity A in air is to be reduced from 0.1% to 0.02% by absorption in pure water or in acid solution B of various strengths. Find the height of tower required for countercurrent absorption:

(*a*) In pure water.

(*b*) In strong acid solution of concentration $C_B = 0.05$ lb mole/ft³, or approximately 0.8*N*.

(*c*) In dilute acid solution of concentration $C_B = 0.002$ lb mole/ft³.

(*d*) In acid solution of concentration $C_B = 0.008$ lb mole/ft³

Data: The reaction

$$A(g) + B(l) \rightarrow \text{products}(l)$$

takes place in the liquid phase and is rapid, and the products remain in the liquid.

For the packing used

$$k_{Ag}a = 2.0 \text{ lb moles/(hr)(ft}^3\text{)(atm)}$$
$$k_{Al}a = 0.1/\text{hr}.$$

The solubility of A in pure water is given by

$$H_A = (2 \text{ atm})(\text{ft}^3)/\text{lb mole}$$

Flow rates of liquid and gas are

$$L' = 140 \text{ lb moles/(hr)(ft}^2)$$
$$G' = 20 \text{ lb moles/(hr)(ft}^2) \text{ at } \pi = 1 \text{ atm}$$

Molar density of liquid is

$$C_T = 3.5 \text{ lb moles/ft}^3$$

Assume that the diffusivities of A and B in water are the same. Hence we may write

$$k_{Al} = k_{Bl} = k_l$$

Solution. Figure E1*a* shows the quantities known at this point. Since we are dealing with dilute solutions, we may use the simplified form of the material balance, Eq. 28. Integrating we obtain

$$p_A - p_{A1} = \frac{L}{G}\frac{\pi}{C_T}(C_A - C_{A1})$$

or
$$p_A - 0.0002 = \frac{(140)(1)}{(20)(3.5)}(C_A - 0)$$

or
$$p_A - 0.0002 = 2C_A$$

and the concentration of A in the outlet liquid is

$$C_{A2} = \frac{0.0010}{2} - 0.0001 = 0.0004 \text{ lb mole/ft}^3$$

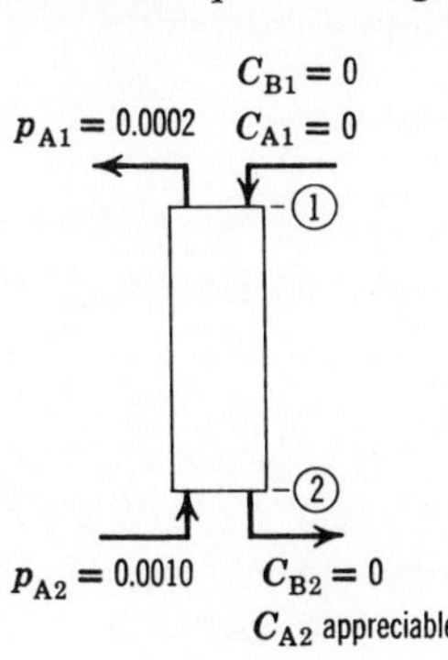

Fig. E1*a*

Select a number of partial pressures of A in the tower, determine the corresponding concentration of A in the liquid, calculate the equilibrium partial pressure of A, p_A^*, corresponding to this concentration in the liquid, and then calculate the over-all driving force for physical absorption. This procedure is shown in Table E1*a*.

Table E1*a*

p_A	C_A	$p_A^* = H_A C_A$	$\Delta p = p_A - p_A^*$
0.0002	0	0	0.0002
0.0006	0.0002	0.0004	0.0002
0.0010	0.0004	0.0008	0.0002

The over-all mass transfer coefficient based on volume of tower is

$$\frac{1}{K_{Ag}a} = \frac{1}{k_{Ag}a} + \frac{H_A}{k_l a}$$
$$= \frac{1}{2} + \frac{2}{0.1} = 20.5$$

Hence
$$K_{Ag}a = 0.0488 \text{ lb mole/(hr)(ft}^3\text{)(atm)}$$

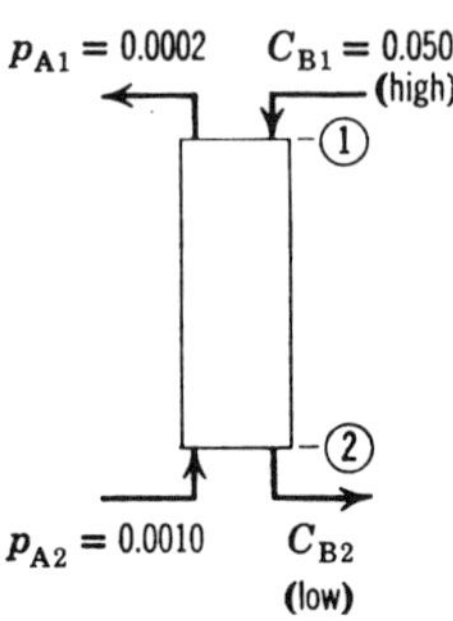

Fig. E1*b*

The height of tower is then given by Eq. 31, or

$$h = \frac{G}{\pi}\int \frac{dp_A}{(-r_A'')a} = \frac{G}{\pi}\int_{p_{A1}}^{p_{A2}} \frac{dp_A}{K_{Ag}a\Delta p_A}$$

$$= 20\int_{0.0002}^{0.0010} \frac{dp_A}{(0.0488)(0.0002)} = 1640 \text{ ft}$$

Comment: Here the liquid film provides over 95% of the resistance to transfer. Hence we can with little error consider this to be a liquid-film-controlling process.

(*b*) This part of the problem is solved as follows (see Fig. E1*b*).

1. Express the material balance and find the concentration of acid in the exit stream.
2. Find which of the two forms of rate equation should be used.
3. Determine the tower height.

1. *Material balance.* For dilute solutions with rapid reaction Eq. 35 gives

$$p_A - p_{A1} = \frac{L\pi}{GbC_T}(C_{B1} - C_B)$$

or

$$p_A - 0.0002 = \frac{(140)(1)}{(20)(1)(3.5)}(0.05 - C_B)$$

or

$$p_A = 0.1002 - 2C_B$$

The concentration of unreacted B leaving the tower is

$$C_{B2} = \frac{0.1002 - 0.0010}{2} = 0.0496 \text{ lb mole/ft}^3$$

2. *Form of rate equation to use.* Check both ends of the tower:

$$\text{at top}\begin{cases} k_{Ag}ap_A = (2.0)(0.0002) = 0.0004 \text{ lb mole/(hr)(ft}^3) \\ k_l aC_B = (0.1)(0.05) = 0.005 \text{ lb mole/(hr)(ft}^3) \end{cases}$$

$$\text{at bottom}\begin{cases} k_{Ag}ap_A = 0.0020 \\ k_l aC_B = 0.00496 \end{cases}$$

At both ends of the tower $k_{Ag}p_A < k_l C_B$; therefore gas-phase resistance controls and Eq. 8 should be used.

3. *Height of tower.* From Eqs. 38 and 8

$$h = \frac{G}{\pi}\int \frac{dp_A}{(-r_A'')a} = \frac{G}{\pi}\int_{p_{A1}}^{p_{A2}} \frac{dp_A}{k_{Ag}ap_A}$$

$$= 20\int_{0.0002}^{0.0010} \frac{dp_A}{2.0p_A} = 16.1 \text{ ft}$$

Comment: Even though liquid phase controls in physical absorption, it does not necessarily follow that it should still control when reaction occurs. In fact, we see here that it is the gas phase alone which influences the rate of the over-all process. Reaction serves merely to eliminate the resistance of the liquid film.

(*c*) 1. *Material balance* (see Fig. E1*c*). As in part *b* we find from Eq. 35

$$p_A = 0.0042 - 2C_B$$

and at the bottom of the tower

$$C_{B2} = \frac{0.0042 - 0.0010}{2} = 0.0016 \text{ lb mole/ft}^3$$

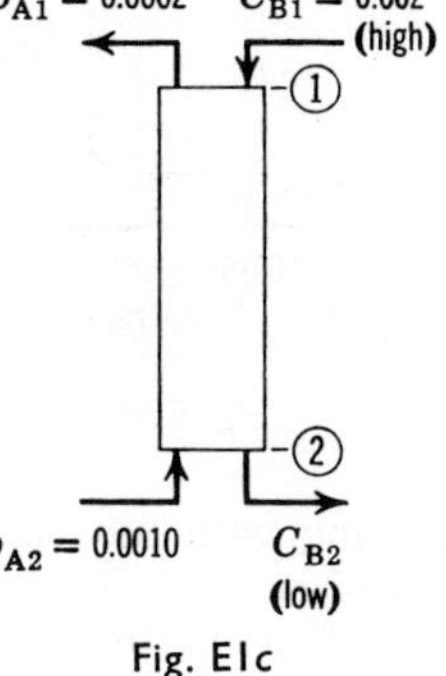

Fig. E1c

2. *Form of rate equation to use.* Check both ends of the tower:

$$\text{at top}\begin{cases} k_{Ag}ap_A = 0.0004 \\ k_l aC_B = 0.0002 \end{cases}$$

$$\text{at bottom}\begin{cases} k_{Ag}ap_A = 0.0020 \\ k_l aC_B = 0.00016 \end{cases}$$

At both ends of the tower $k_{Ag}p_A > k_l C_B$; therefore the reaction takes place within the liquid film, and Eq. 6 must be used, or

$$-r_A'' = \frac{H_A C_B + p_A}{1/k_{Ag} + H_A/k_l}$$

3. *Height of tower.* At a number of locations evaluate $H_A C_B + p_A$ as shown in Table E1*c*.

Table E1*c*

p_A	C_B from Material Balance	$H_A C_B = 2C_B$	$p_A + H_A C_B$
0.0002	0.0020	0.0040	0.0042
0.0006	0.0018	0.0036	0.0042
0.0010	0.0016	0.0032	0.0042

Hence the tower height from Eq. 38 and 6 is

$$h = \frac{G}{\pi}\int \frac{dp_A}{(-r_A'')a} = \frac{G}{\pi}\int_{p_{A1}}^{p_{A2}} \frac{1/k_{Ag}a + H_A/k_l a}{H_A C_B + p_A}\, dp_A$$

$$= 20\int_{0.0002}^{0.0010} \frac{20.5\,dp_A}{0.0042} = 78.1 \text{ ft}$$

(*d*) 1. *Material balance* (see Fig. E1*d*). As with parts *b* and *c* we have at any point in the tower $p_A = 0.0162 - 2C_B$. From this expression we find for the bottom of the tower $C_{B2} = 0.0076$.

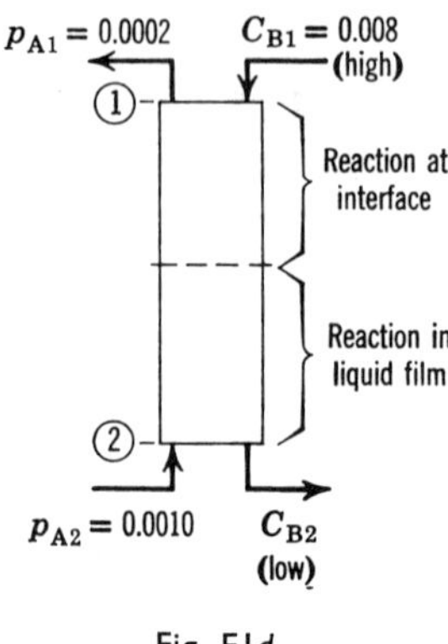

Fig. E1*d*

2. *Form of rate equation to use.* Check both ends of the tower:

$$\text{at top}\begin{cases} k_{Ag}ap_A = 0.0004 \\ k_l aC_B = 0.0008 \end{cases}$$

$$\text{at bottom}\begin{cases} k_{Ag}ap_A = 0.0020 \\ k_l aC_B = 0.00076 \end{cases}$$

At the top $k_{Ag}p_A < k_l C_B$; hence Eq. 8 must be used.

At the bottom $k_{Ag}p_A > k_l C_B$; hence Eq. 6 must be used.

Let us now find the condition at which the reaction zone just reaches the interface and where the form of rate equation changes. This occurs where

$$k_{Ag}p_A = k_l C_B \qquad \text{or} \qquad 20p_A = C_B$$

Solving with the material balance we find that the change occurs at $p_A = 0.000395$.

3. *Height of tower.* The rate is found from Table E1*d*. As may be expected, at $p_A = 0.000395$ the calculated rates from Eqs. 6 and 8 are identical.

Table E1*d*

p_A	C_B	$H_A C_B$	$p_A + H_A C_B$	$K_{Ag}a$ or $\dfrac{1}{\dfrac{1}{k_{Ag}a} + \dfrac{H_A}{k_l a}}$	$(-r_A'')a$	$\dfrac{1}{(-r_A'')a}$
0.0002				2.0	0.0004	2500 } Use
0.000395				2.0	0.00079	1265 } Eq. 8
0.000395	0.0079	0.0158	0.0162	0.0488	0.00079	1265 }
0.0007	0.00775	0.0155	0.0162	0.0488	0.00079	1265 } Use
0.0010	0.0076	0.0152	0.0162	0.0488	0.00079	1265 } Eq. 6

The tower height can be found by graphical integration or analytically as follows:

$$h = h_{\text{upper section}} + h_{\text{lower section}}$$

$$= \frac{G}{\pi}\int_{0.0002}^{0.000395} \frac{dp_A}{k_{Ag}ap_A} + \frac{G}{\pi}\int_{0.000395}^{0.0010} \frac{1/k_{gA}a + H_A/k_l a}{p_A + H_A C_B}\, dp_A$$

$$= \frac{20}{2}\left(\ln\frac{3.95}{2}\right) + 20\,\frac{(20.5)(0.000605)}{(0.0162)}$$

$$= 6.8 + 15.3 = 22.1 \text{ ft.}$$

Figure E1*e* summarizes the method of solution.

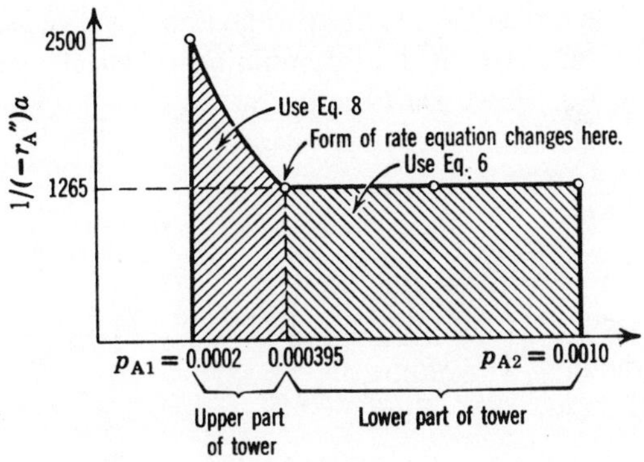

Fig. E1e

Comment: We note that two distinct zones are present. Situations may be encountered where even another zone may be present. For example, if the entering liquid contains insufficient reactant, a point is reached in the tower where all this reactant is consumed. Below this point physical absorption alone takes place in reactant free liquid. The methods of parts *a* and *d*, when used together, deal in a straightforward manner with this three zone situation. Secor and Southworth (1961) develop the explicit expressions for tower height of these three zones based on assumptions which are reasonable for dilute systems.

Comparing solutions for the four parts of this problem shows how reaction increases the effectiveness of the absorption process.

Towers (counter or cocurrent plug flow), reaction controls

When reaction is very slow compared to mass transfer, the two-film theory is not applicable and the rate of reaction is best measured in terms of unit volume of reacting phase rather than unit interfacial surface between phases. We still continue to refer to the phases as gas and liquid; however, two liquids may just as easily be used.

Determination of tower height is generally difficult because of the complexities of the material balance, for reactants can be present in appreciable quantities in both phases—flowing up the tower in one fluid and flowing down the tower in the other fluid. In general the design methods of extraction (triangular diagrams, Janecke diagrams, and so on) must be used. However, let us develop the design equation for the reaction

$$\text{A (in gas)} + b\text{B (in liquid)} \rightarrow \text{products}$$

with the following restrictions on the material balance; B is insoluble in gas, and the amount of unreacted A in the liquid is small compared to the A in the gas phase. With these restrictions unreacted B flows downward in the liquid, unreacted A flows upward in the gas, and the material balance of Eq. 32 is applicable.

Noting that each mole of A reacting in the liquid is replaced by 1 mole of fresh A from the gas stream, and combining material balance with rate equation as with Eq. 36 we get (see Fig. 9)

$$G\,d\mathbf{Y}_A = -\frac{L\,d\mathbf{X}_B}{b}$$

$$= \left(\frac{\text{moles of } A \text{ reacted}}{\text{volume of liquid-time}}\right)\left(\frac{\text{volume of liquid phase}}{\text{volume of fluid}}\right)\left(\begin{matrix}\text{height of}\\ \text{element}\end{matrix}\right) = (-r_A)f\,dh \qquad (39)$$

Because the rate is based on unit volume of fluid, the volume fraction of reacting phase f appears in Eq. 39 instead of the interfacial area per unit volume a as in Eq. 36. On integration we then obtain the desired design equation

$$h = \frac{G}{f}\int_{\mathbf{Y}_{A1}}^{\mathbf{Y}_{A2}} \frac{d\mathbf{Y}_A}{-r_A} = \frac{L}{bf}\int_{\mathbf{X}_{B2}}^{\mathbf{X}_{B1}} \frac{d\mathbf{X}_B}{-r_A} \qquad (40)$$

where $d\mathbf{Y}_A$ and $d\mathbf{X}_B$ are given by Eqs. 25 and 26 and $-r_A$ is the appropriate rate expression in volumetric units, for example Eq. 21.

Equation 40 may take on a variety of special forms when applied to specific physical situations. This is often due to the particular form of the material balance which is applicable.

For example, consider a spray tower with dilute B present in liquid droplets, A present in gas, and reaction given by Eq. 21. If conditions are

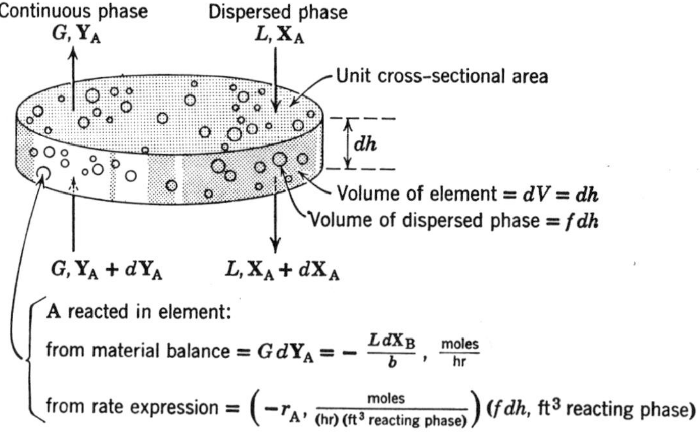

Fig. 9. Development of design equation for tower operations for slow reaction occurring only in dispersed phase. Rate is based on unit volume of fluid.

such that the concentration of A in the gas is approximately constant throughout the tower Eq. 40 becomes

$$h \approx \frac{L}{bf}\int \frac{d(C_B/C_T)}{kC_AC_B} = \frac{L}{bfkC_AC_T}\int_{C_{B2}}^{C_{B1}} \frac{dC_B}{C_B}$$

$$= \frac{LH_A}{bfkp_AC_T}\ln\frac{C_{B1}}{C_{B2}} \tag{41}$$

The following example illustrates still another form of the design equation, again because of the particular form of the material balance which is applicable.

Example 2

Benzene is to be chlorinated by countercurrent contacting with a stream of pure gaseous chlorine in a tower. The reaction

$$C_6H_6\begin{pmatrix}\text{liquid}\\ \text{phase}\end{pmatrix} + Cl_2\begin{pmatrix}\text{gas}\\ \text{phase}\end{pmatrix} \rightarrow C_6H_5Cl\begin{pmatrix}\text{liquid}\\ \text{phase}\end{pmatrix} + HCl\begin{pmatrix}\text{gas}\\ \text{phase}\end{pmatrix}$$

is slow, elementary, and irreversible and occurs in the liquid phase between dissolved chlorine and benzene. With the additional assumptions:

constant molar density of liquid, C_T = constant
constant pressure in gas phase, π = constant
plug flow of both streams
small amount of dissolved and unreacted chlorine in liquid
low solubility of HCl in liquid
H_A constant
the reaction of Cl_2 with C_6H_5Cl able to be neglected

derive the expression for the tower height as a function of the variables of the system.

Solution. Let A = chlorine, B = benzene, R = monochlorobenzene, S = hydrogen chloride.

First of all, the material balance cannot be written in terms of L and G because no inerts are present. But we note that for each mole of chlorine used 1 mole HCl is formed and is returned to the gas phase. Similarly, the total molar flow rate of liquid is unchanged because for each mole of benzene reacted a mole of chlorobenzene is formed. Thus the total molar flow rates of gas and liquid remain unchanged, or L' and G' are constant. Thus the material balance expression, Eq. 32, or

$$d\left(\frac{G'p_A}{\pi}\right) = -\frac{1}{b}\,d\left(\frac{L'C_B}{C_T}\right)$$

becomes

$$\frac{G'}{\pi}\,dp_A = -\frac{L'}{C_T}\,dC_B \tag{i}$$

Combining with the rate expression based on unit volume of reacting or continuous phase

$$-r_A = -r_B = kC_AC_B$$

we obtain

$$\frac{G'}{\pi}\,dp_A = -\frac{L'}{C_T}\,dC_B = kC_AC_Bf\,dh$$

where f is now the volume fraction of liquid or reacting phase. By rearranging and integrating, the height of tower is then

$$h = \frac{G'H_A}{kf\pi}\int_{p_{A1}}^{p_{A2}}\frac{dp_A}{p_AC_B} = \frac{L'H_A}{kfC_T}\int_{C_{B2}}^{C_{B1}}\frac{dC_B}{p_AC_B} \tag{ii}$$

with p_A and C_B related by the material balance. Integrating the differential material balance, Eq. i, we find at any point in the tower,

$$C_B = C_T - \frac{G'C_T}{L'\pi}(p_A - p_{A1}) \tag{iii}$$

Replacing Eq. iii in Eq. ii and integrating analytically gives

$$h = \frac{-G'H_A}{fC_Tk[\pi + (G'/L')p_{A1}]}\ln\frac{p_{A1}[\pi - (G'/L')(\pi - p_{A1})]}{\pi^2}$$

or more conveniently in terms of mole fractions

$$h = \frac{-G'H_A}{f\pi C_Tk[1 + (G'/L')y_{A1}]}\ln y_{A1}\left[1 - \frac{G'}{L'}(1 - y_{A1})\right] \tag{42}$$

where

$$y_A = \frac{p_A}{\pi} \quad \text{and} \quad x_A = \frac{C_A}{C_T}$$

Figure E2 shows that the rate is maximum at some intermediate position within the tower, dropping off at either end where the concentration of one or the other of the components is very low.

Mixer-settlers (backmix flow of both phases)

Mixer-settlers are industrial devices for bringing into intimate contact and then separating immiscible fluids. Each of these units operates as an ideal contactor or backmix reactor. For gas-liquid systems where density differences between phases are great, the settler is not needed. Mixer-settlers are frequently used for systems in which a slow reaction is occurring.

Single-stage contacting is illustrated in Fig. 5*f*. Again consider reactant A present in the gas phase and reactant B present in the liquid phase. Often reactions for which mixer-settlers are selected have rates which, based on unit volume of mixture, can be approximated by

$$-r_A = -\frac{1}{V_{\text{total}}}\frac{dN_A}{dt} = kC_AC_B \tag{43}$$

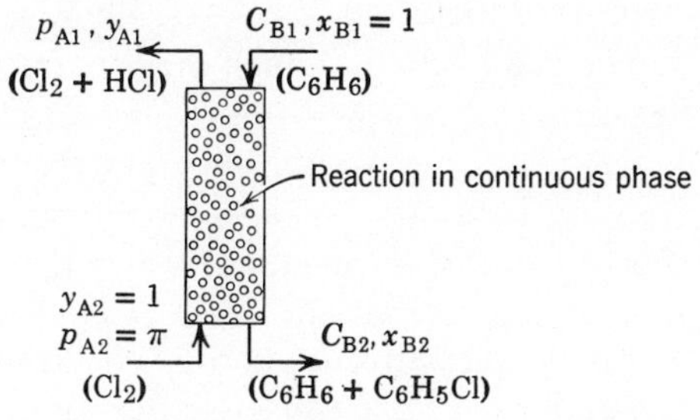

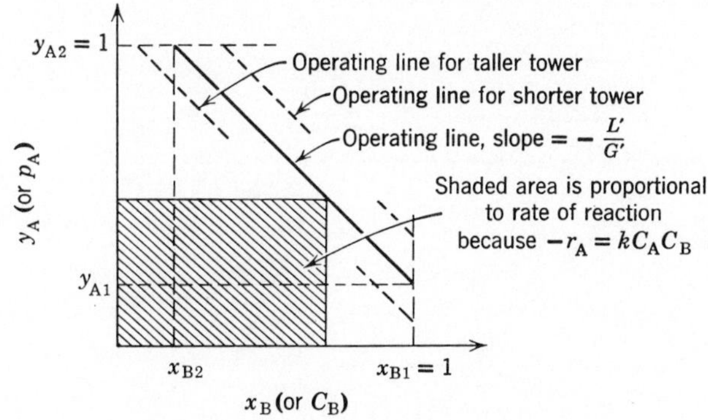

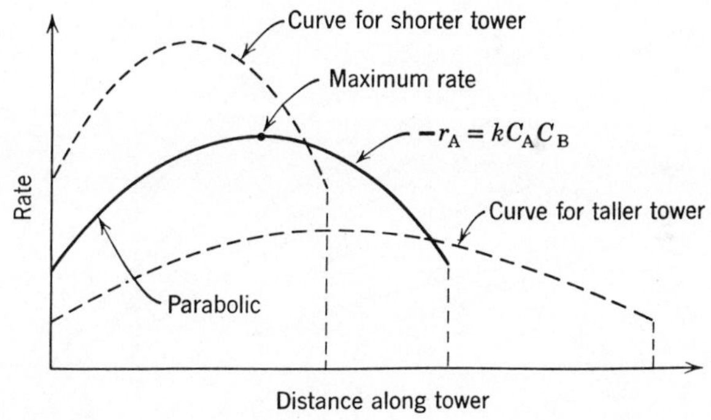

Fig. E2

With the same mean residence time of fluids in the vessel, the mixture may be viewed to be homogeneous and conversions can be calculated by the methods of Chapter 6.

Multistage cocurrent contacting as shown in Fig. 5*i* can similarly be treated by the methods in Chapter 6 for backmix reactors in series.

Multistage countercurrent contacting, shown in Figs. 5*g* and *h*, is one case that cannot be treated by the methods of Chapter 6. This operation is much like countercurrent plug flow of Figs. 5*a* and *e*. Actually Figs. 5*b*, *c*, and *d* are also stagewise or stepwise contacting, though they are frequently treated as continuous operations.

Given a fixed number of contactors, design for such systems always involves a trial and error solution; however, for the simple form of rate given by Eq. 43 charts have been prepared by Jenney (1955), Figs. 10, 11, and 12, to eliminate much of the tedious trial and error calculations required. These charts allow rapid comparisons among cocurrent and countercurrent multistage operations, single mixer-settler operations, countercurrent plug flow operations, and batch operations.

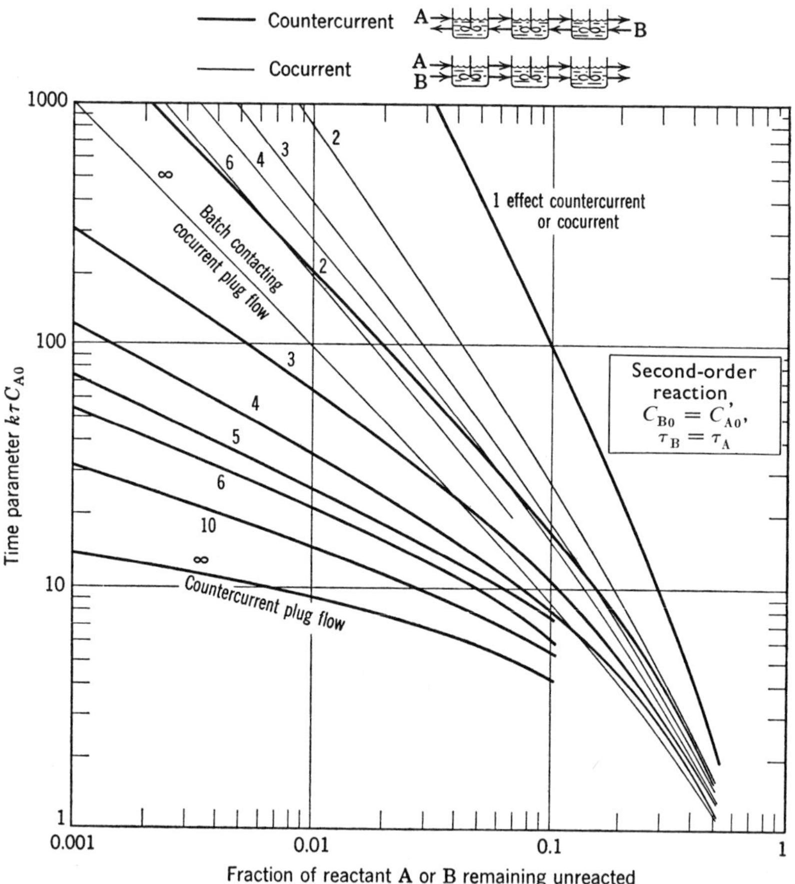

Fig. 10. Over-all conversion versus dimensionless time parameter for the contacting of immiscible phases where the kinetics of reaction is given by Eq. 43. Adapted from Jenney (1955).

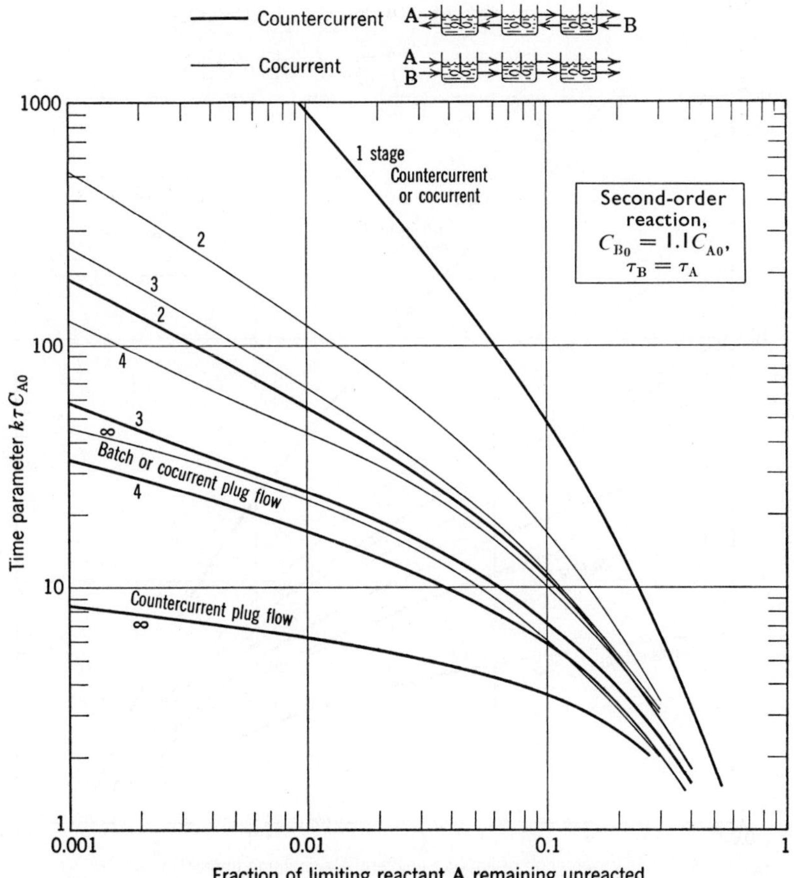

Fig. 11. Over-all conversion versus dimensionless time parameter for the contacting of immiscible phases where the kinetics of reaction is given by Eq. 43. Adapted from Jenney (1955).

Figure 13, also prepared by Jenney (1958), allows us to find intermediate conversions between stages in multistage operations. This information is helpful in estimating intercooler loads when strong heat effects are present or when different temperatures are to be maintained in the backmix units.

The following example illustrates the use of these charts.

Example 3

Reactants A and B are present in separate phases. When these phases are brought into intimate contact in a backmix reactor, the reaction

$$A + B \rightarrow \text{products}$$

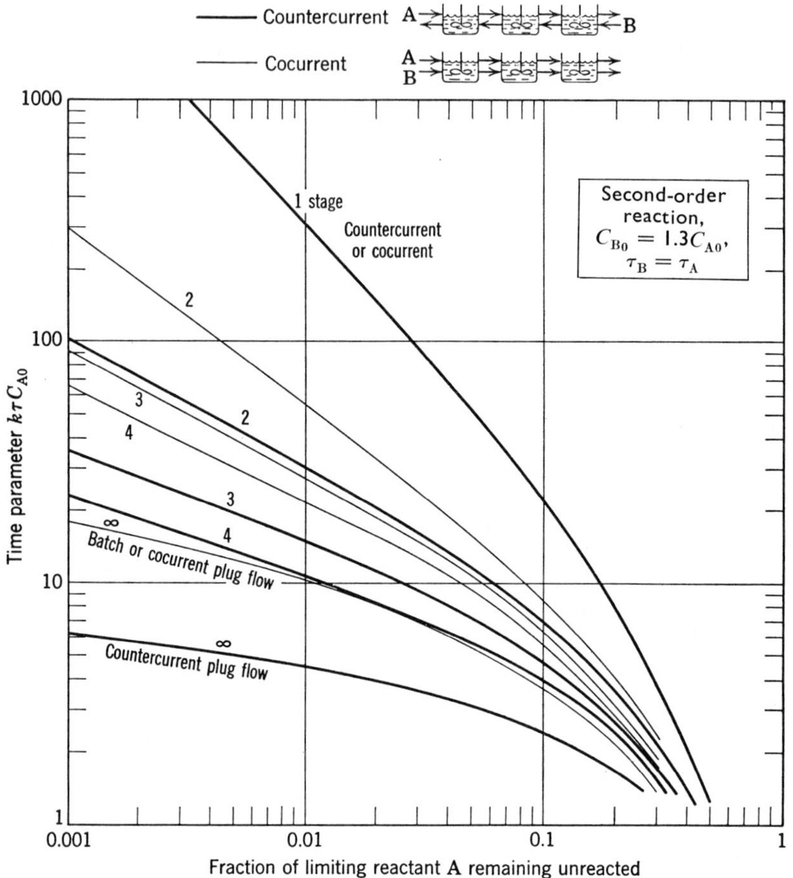

Fig. 12. Over-all conversion versus dimensionless time parameter for the contacting of immiscible phases where the kinetics of reaction is given by Eq. 43. Adapted from Jenney (1955).

proceeds slowly with over-all kinetics:

$$-r_A = -\frac{1}{V_{\text{total}}}\frac{dN_A}{dt} = kC_A C_B$$

For equimolar feed and $C_{A0} = C_{B0}$ conversion is 95 %. We plan to raise the conversion to 99 % using the same feed.

(*a*) Using three backmix reactors, each equal in size to the original unit, with cocurrent flow of fluids through the reactors, find how much production can be raised.

(*b*) Repeat part *a* using countercurrent flow of fluids rather than cocurrent flow.

(*c*) Find the fractional conversion of reactants leaving each of the three backmix reactors of part *b*.

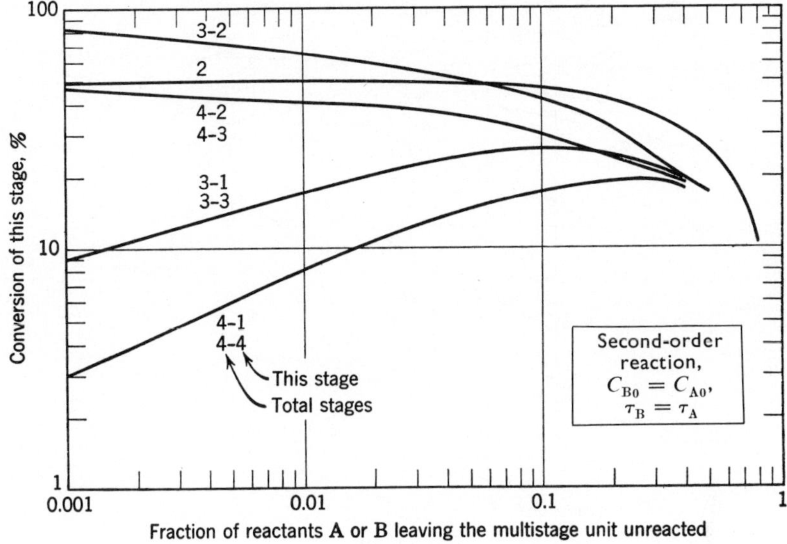
100
10
1
0.001
0.01
0.1
1
Conversion of this stage, %
Fraction of reactants A or B leaving the multistage unit unreacted
3-2
2
4-2
4-3
3-1
3-3
4-1
4-4
This stage
Total stages
Second-order reaction, $C_{B0} = C_{A0}$, $\tau_B = \tau_A$

(a)

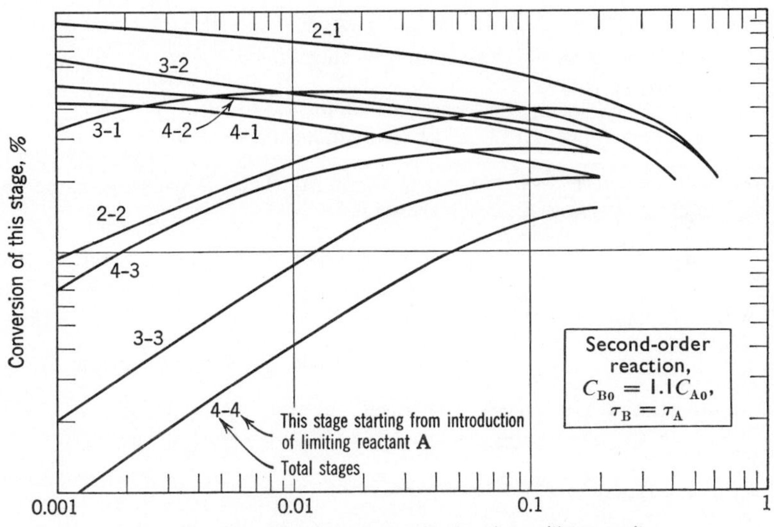
0.001
0.01
0.1
1
Conversion of this stage, %
Fraction of limiting reactant leaving the multistage unit
2-1
3-2
3-1
4-2
4-1
2-2
4-3
3-3
4-4
This stage starting from introduction of limiting reactant A
Total stages
Second-order reaction, $C_{B0} = 1.1C_{A0}$, $\tau_B = \tau_A$

(b)

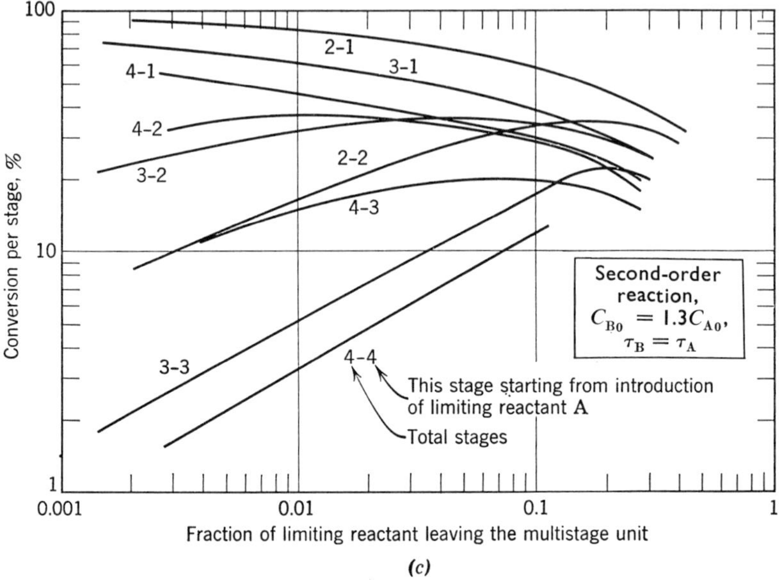

(c)

Fig. 13. Intermediate conversion between stages for the countercurrent contacting of immiscible phases. Adapted from Jenney (1958).

(*d*) Repeat part *a* using countercurrent plug flow in a column equal in size to three backmix reactors.

Assume identical mean residence time of the two phases, ignore expansion, and let the volume fraction of the phases remain unchanged.

Solution. (*a*) *Cocurrent, three stages* (see Fig. E3*a*). From Fig. 10 we have for one backmix reactor at 95% conversion

$$(k\tau C_{A0})_{j=1} = 380$$

For cocurrent flow in three reactors, 99% conversion, the same figure gives

$$(k\tau C_{A0})_{j=3} = 380$$

The holding time is the same in both cases; however, the volume is three times as great in the cocurrent unit. Hence production is three times as high.

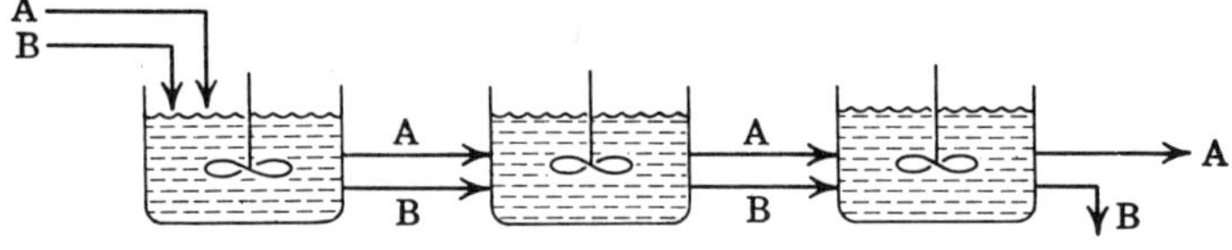

Fig. E3*a*

Comment: All cocurrent flow operations can be handled by the methods and charts of Chapter 6 if we note the analogy between a homogeneous system and a heterogeneous fluid-fluid system in which both fluids move through the equipment in an identical manner. Thus from Fig. 6.7 we also find

$$(k\tau C_{A0})_{j=1} = 380$$

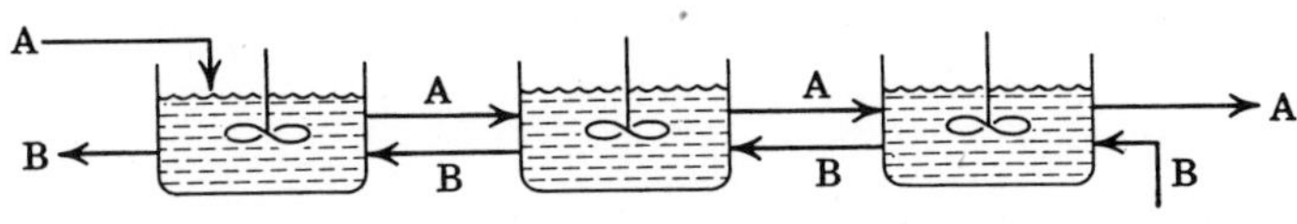

Fig E3*b*

(*b*) *Countercurrent, three stages* (see Fig. E3*b*). From Fig. 10 we again have for 95% conversion

$$(k\tau C_{A0})_{j=1} = 380$$

and for three reactors with countercurrent flow of fluids we find from the same figure

$$(k\tau C_{A0})_{j=3} = 63$$

But

$$\frac{F_{99\%}}{F_{95\%}} = \frac{\tau_{95} V_{99}}{\tau_{99} V_{95}} = \frac{(380)(3)}{(63)(1)} = 18$$

Hence production is 18 times as high if countercurrent flow is used. This is a sixfold improvement over cocurrent flow.

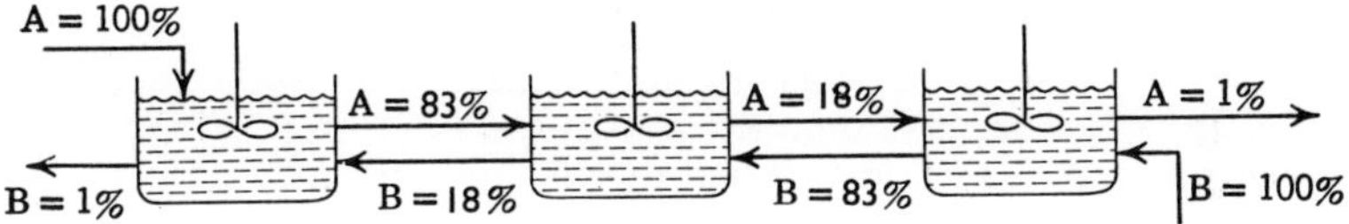

Fig. E3*c*

(*c*) *Conversion between units*. From Fig. 13*a* we find the conversion to be 17% in the extreme units. By subtraction conversion is 65% in the middle unit. Thus we have concentrations as shown in Fig. E3*c*.

(*d*) *Countercurrent plug flow* (see Fig. E3*d*). Figure 10 gives

$$(k\tau C_{A0})_{j=\infty} = 9.2$$

Therefore

$$\frac{F_{99\%}}{F_{95\%}} = \frac{\tau_{95} V_{99}}{\tau_{99} V_{95}} = \frac{(380)(3)}{(9.2)(1)} = 124$$

Hence production is 124 times as high if countercurrent plug flow is used.

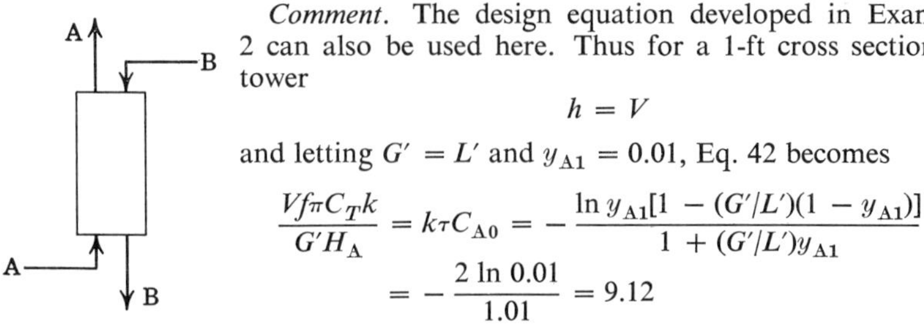

Fig. E3*d*

Comment. The design equation developed in Example 2 can also be used here. Thus for a 1-ft cross section of tower

$$h = V$$

and letting $G' = L'$ and $y_{A1} = 0.01$, Eq. 42 becomes

$$\frac{Vf\pi C_T k}{G'H_A} = k_T C_{A0} = -\frac{\ln y_{A1}[1 - (G'/L')(1 - y_{A1})]}{1 + (G'/L')y_{A1}}$$

$$= -\frac{2 \ln 0.01}{1.01} = 9.12$$

which agrees closely with the value obtained from the charts.

Semibatch contacting patterns

In semibatch operation where one fluid is continuously passed through a vessel containing a second fluid, the contact time for a given extent of reaction between the components of these two fluids may be wanted.

The approach taken again depends on the form of the material balance. Consider for example a gas bubbling through a vessel containing liquid. Reactant A is present in the gas and, in its rapid passage through the vessel, the concentration of A in the gas does not change appreciably. Reactant A is absorbed and reacts slowly with component B of the liquid. Agitation is sufficient to keep compositions throughout the liquid uniform. With the passage of time the concentration of B will fall but the concentration of A will remain unchanged. If the kinetics is first order with respect to both A and B, we then have

$$-r_B = -\frac{1}{V_{\text{liquid}}}\frac{dN_B}{dt} = -\frac{dC_B}{dt} = kC_A C_B$$

Rearranging and integrating, noting that C_A is constant, we obtain

$$-\int_{C_{B0}}^{C_B} \frac{dC_B}{C_B} = kC_A \int_0^t dt$$

or

$$t = \frac{1}{kC_A}\ln\frac{C_{B0}}{C_B} = \frac{-1}{kC_A}\ln(1 - X_B) \tag{44}$$

or

$$\frac{C_B}{C_{B0}} = (1 - X_B) = e^{-C_A kt} = e^{-p_A kt/H_A}$$

Equation 41 and the equation just given are essentially identical expressions, one applied to plug flow, the other to batch contacting of a liquid with a uniform gas environment.

REMARKS

In reviewing design for fluid-fluid systems we may feel disturbed that we have been able to treat so small a number of very restricted situations. Unfortunately, only a few systems can be treated in an elementary manner, showing that there is need for further work in this area.

Though small in number, still the methods presented to cover the range from very fast to very slow reactions and may well be used as limits for situations not satisfying the restrictions of the systems treated. In addition, very often our knowledge of the parameters $k_g a$, $k_l a$, $\mathscr{D}$, and H_i is not precise enough to justify the complexity of the more rigorous treatments.

RELATED READINGS

H. Hofmann, *Chem. Eng. Sci.*, **8,** 113 (1958).

REFERENCES

P. V. Danckwerts, *Trans. Faraday Soc.*, **46,** 300 (1950); *A.I.Ch.E. Journal*, **1,** 456 (1955).
S. Hatta, *Technol. Repts Tôhoku Univ.*, **10,** 119 (1932), from Sherwood and Pigford (1952).
R. Higbie, *Trans. A.I.Ch.E.*, **31,** 365 (1935).
T. M. Jenney, *Chem. Eng.*, **62,** 198 (Dec. 1955).
———, *Chem. Eng.*, **65,** 166 (May 19, 1958).
W. K. Lewis and W. G. Whitman, *Ind. Eng. Chem.*, **16,** 1215 (1924).
R. H. Perry and R. L. Pigford, *Ind. Eng. Chem.*, **45,** 1247 (1953).
R. M. Secor and R. W. Southworth, *A.I.Ch.E. Journal*, **7,** 705 (1961).
T. K. Sherwood and F. A. L. Holloway, *Trans. Am. Inst. Chem. Engrs.*, **36,** 21 (1940).
——— and R. L. Pigford, *Absorption and Extraction*, second edition, McGraw-Hill, New York, 1952.
A. J. Teller, *Chem. Eng.*, **67,** 111 (July 11, 1960).
P. Trambouze, M. T. Trambouze, and E. L. Piret, *A.I.Ch.E. Journal*, **7,** 138 (1961).
R. E. Treybal, *Mass Transfer Operations*, McGraw-Hill, New York, 1955.
D. W. van Krevelen and P. Hoftyzer, *Rec. trav. chim.*, **67,** 563 (1948); *Chem. Eng. Sci.*, **2,** 145 (1953), *Chim. Ind.*, XXIème congrès int. Chim. Ind., 168 (1948*a*).

PROBLEMS

1. CO_2 is to be removed from air by countercurrent contacting with water at 77°F.

(*a*) What are the relative resistances of gas and liquid films for this operation?
(*b*) What simplest form of rate equation would you use for tower design?
(*c*) For this removal operation would you expect reaction with absorption to be helpful? Why?

From the literature we have for CO_2 in air and water

$$k_g a = 5.0 \text{ lb mole/(hr)(ft}^3\text{)(atm)}$$

$$k_l a = 25\text{/hr}$$

$$H = 1640 \text{ atm/mole fraction in solution}$$

2. We plan to use an NaOH solution to hasten the removal of CO_2 from air at 77°F (see data of previous problem).

(*a*) What form of rate equation would be appropriate to use when $p_{CO_2} = 0.01$ atm and the solution is $2N$ in NaOH?

(*b*) How much can absorption be speeded compared to physical absorption with pure water?

(*c*, *d*) Repeat parts *a* and *b* for $p_{CO_2} = 0.2$ atm and a solution $0.2N$ NaOH

3. Consider a highly water-soluble gas such as ammonia for which at about 10°C

$$H \approx 0.5 \text{ atm/mole fraction gas, in dilute solution}$$

Also consider the slightly soluble gases such as carbon monoxide, oxygen, hydrogen, methane, ethane, nitric oxide, and nitrogen for which

$$H \approx 50{,}000 \text{ atm/mole fraction gas, in dilute solution}$$

For pure physical absorption of such highly soluble and slightly soluble gases in water, assuming no reaction:

(*a*) What are the relative resistances of the gas and liquid films?

(*b*) Which resistance if any controls the absorption process?

(*c*) What form of rate equation should be used for design in these two cases?

(*d*) How does the solubility of the slightly soluble gas affect its rate of absorption in water?

(*e*) In which case (slightly or highly soluble gas) would chemical reaction be more helpful in speeding the process and why?

For the estimation purposes of this problem, use the rough order of magnitude estimation of k_l and k_g given in this chapter.

4. Consider the absorption of a base A by water in a packed column. At a location where gas is being absorbed by pure water, the over-all rate based on unit volume of tower may be expressed as

$$-r_A = (-r_A'')a = -\frac{1}{V}\frac{dN_A}{dt} = K_{Ag}ap_A$$

where $K_{Ag}a$ is the over-all coefficient based on unit volume of tower.

Now suppose that an acid B is added to the water to aid the absorption.

(*a*) Assuming rapid reaction, show how $K_{Ag}a$ should vary with acid strength. Show this on a plot of $K_{Ag}a$ versus acid strength. Also show how this plot should allow estimation of the individual mass transfer coefficients for physical absorption.

Sherwood and Holloway (1940) present the following data for the absorption of ammonia in acid solution of various strengths at 25°C.

$K_{Ag}a$, lb moles/(hr)(ft^3)(atm)	18.8	19.5	21	22	24	23
Acid normality	0.4	1.0	1.5	2.0	2.8	4.2

(*b*) From this data show that the gas film contributes 77% of the over-all resistance to mass transfer in physical absorption of ammonia in air.

(*c*) Estimate the fraction of the over-all resistance supplied by the gas film, using literature values for H and the estimates for k_l and k_g given in this chapter. Compare with the experimentally found value of part *b*.

5. Consider the infinitely fast reaction of Example 1. If the acid strength of the absorbing liquid is raised, a point is reached above which further increases will not increase the over-all rate of mass transfer and decrease the tower height. Find this minimum concentration for maximum transfer rate.

6. Repeat parts *a*, *b*, and *d* of Example 1, using cocurrent flow of fluids in the tower.

7. Repeat Example 1 using a dilute acid of concentration

$$C_B = 0.0002 \text{ lb mole/ft}^3$$

8. An impurity A in a gas is to be reduced from 1% to 2 ppm by countercurrent contact with liquid containing a reactant of concentration $C_B =$ 0.0002 lb mole/ft^3

$$\begin{aligned} k_{Ag}a &= 20 \text{ lb moles/(hr)(ft}^3\text{)(atm)} \\ k_{Al}a &= k_{Bl}a = 0.5/\text{hr} \\ L &= 140 \text{ lb moles/(hr)(ft}^2\text{)} \\ G &= 20 \text{ lb moles/(hr)(ft}^2\text{)} \\ H_A &= 18 \text{ (atm)(ft}^3\text{)/lb moles} \\ C_T &= 3.5 \text{ lb moles/ft}^3 \end{aligned}$$

Let the reaction A + B → product be rapid.

(*a*) Find the height of tower needed.

(*b*) What recommendations do you have (about the concentration of liquid-phase reactant) that may help improve the process?

(*c*) What incoming concentration of B would give the minimum height of tower? What is this height?

9. Example 2 views the two fluids as passing countercurrent through an unpacked tower. What is the correct expression corresponding to Eq. 42 for the two fluids passing through a packed column with fraction voids ϵ and with f the fraction of void volume occupied by liquid phase?

10. Suppose that 50% conversion of benzene to monochlorobenzene is attained in countercurrent plug flow operations using pure chlorine and pure benzene feed, $L'/G' = 1$ (see Example 2). How much can conversion be increased if the height of tower is doubled? Assume that no side reactions occur.

11. In actual fact, when chlorine and benzene are contacted the primary and desired product, monochlorobenzene, in the presence of chlorine further decomposes to yield polychlorinated compounds.

With respect to maximizing monochlorobenzene production, evaluate and order the following proposed contacting schemes. Give reasons for the ordering.

Cocurrent and countercurrent plug flow, cocurrent and countercurrent flow through three backmix reactors, batch contacting and continuous contacting in a single backmix reactor.

12. Reactants A and B are present in separate phases. For equimolar feed of A and B countercurrent in three backmix reactors (see Example 3), 99% conversion of A is now attained.

(*a*) A fourth reactor is to be added to the three operating at present. For the same conversion how much can production be raised?

(*b*) Find the conversion occurring in each unit, and with a sketch show the compositions of fluids leaving each unit.

13. Consider the three-reactor systems of the previous problem.

(*a*) If the volumetric flow rate remains unchanged but C_{B0} is raised 30% so that 1.3 moles B/mole A are fed to the unit, how should this affect the production?

(*b*) Find the conversion occurring in each unit, and with a sketch show the compositions of fluids leaving each unit.

14. For a slow reaction between A and B initially present in different phases with second-order kinetics of Eq. 43, is countercurrent or cocurrent plug flow more efficient? Verify this conclusion by comparing reactor volumes for 99% conversion of limiting reactant using (*a*) equimolar feed, (*b*) feed consisting of 1.3 moles B/mole A, and (*c*) a large excess of B.

15. Two fluids are contacted and reacted in a mixer-settler. The continuous phase consists of pure reactant A which is but slightly soluble in phase B′ containing reactant B. The reaction is slow and is confined to the dispersed phase as follows:

$$\mathrm{A} + \mathrm{B} \rightarrow \text{products}; \qquad -\frac{1}{V_{\substack{\text{dispersed}\\ \text{phase}}}}\frac{dN_A}{dt} = kC_AC_B$$

Pure A is continually recycled; products of the reaction remain in the dispersed phase.

(*a*) Assuming backmix flow in the mixer and negligible holding time in the settler, derive an expression for the concentration of B in the stream leaving the mixer-settler in terms of $\bar{t}_B$, k, C_{B0}, and the unchanged concentration of A within the dispersed phase.

(*b*) Find the rate constant for the reaction (gram moles, liters, minutes) from the following experimental information:

Feed rate of phase B′ = 1 cc/5 sec.
Fraction of dispersed phase in the reactor = 24%
Volume of fluid in the reactor = 1500 cc

Concentration of A in dispersed phase $= 2.7 \times 10^{-5}$ gm mole/liter
Concentration of B in the dispersed phase entering reactor $= 0.02$ gm mole/liter
Concentration of B in the dispersed phase leaving reactor $= 0.0125$ gm mole/liter.

16. The two fluids of the previous problem are contacted in a column of height h. Fluid A remains stationary in the column, but fluid B′ is dispersed and falls through the column in the form of fine droplets.

(*a*) Noting that different-sized droplets fall at different rates and are therefore in the reactor for different lengths of time, derive an expression for the extent of reaction of B in terms of the pertinent variables of the system.

Let $F(R)$ be the volumetric feed rate of droplets of size R, and let the velocity of fall of droplets be given by the terminal settling velocity of Stokes law or

$$u_t = \frac{2\Delta\rho}{9\mu} R^2 = MR^2$$

(*b*) Experiments show that the volumetric size distribution of a spray can often be approximated by a normal, error, or Gaussian distribution,

$$y = \frac{1}{\sigma\sqrt{2\pi}} e^{-(R-\bar{R})^2/2\sigma^2}$$

where $y\,dR$ is the volume fraction of dispersed phase of size between R and $R + dR$, $\bar{R}$ is the mean size of droplets, and σ is the standard deviation, a measure of the spread of droplet sizes.

Derive an expression giving the extent of reaction of B in the spray column in terms of this continuous size distribution of droplets.

14

SOLID-CATALYZED FLUID REACTIONS

The rates of a large number of reactions have been observed to be affected by the presence of materials which are neither original reactants nor final products of the reaction. Such materials, called catalysts, may slow down reactions, in which case they are called negative catalysts, or they may speed up reactions, in which case they are called positive catalysts. Catalysts may be solids or fluids. When in fluid form the design is straightforward and is considered in the chapters on fluid systems. In this chapter we treat the reaction in which the catalyst is a solid and the reacting material is a fluid, usually a gas.

Catalytic gas-phase reactions play an important role in many industrial processes, as in the production of methanol, ammonia, sulfuric acid, nitric acid, and various petrochemicals, and usually involve the high-energy rupture, breakdown or synthesis of low-molecular-weight materials. Let us, as an example, consider the reactions which are an indispensable part of modern petroleum technology.

Natural petroleum contains a variety of materials, primarily hydrocarbons, and as the demands of the oil industry for products change, it is obvious that no natural material consisting of a mixture of many compounds can be used effectively unless the molecular structures of the undesirable fractions are drastically modified. Today the philosophy of this industry is one of flexibility, to tailor-make products to meet these rapidly changing demands by the decomposition or breaking down of molecules, by the reforming or rebuilding of molecules, and by the rearrangement of the constituents of molecules to produce new compounds. The reactions which take place can be classified as follows.

1. *Cracking.* The rupture of high-molecular-weight materials at a C—C bond to yield lower-molecular-weight products:

$$\underset{n\text{-butane}}{CH_3{-}CH_2{-}CH_2{-}CH_3} \rightarrow \underset{\text{methane}}{CH_4} + \underset{\text{propene}}{CH_2{=}CH{-}CH_3}$$

2. *Dehydrogenation.* The rupture of a C—H bond to yield hydrogen and olefins:

$$\underset{n\text{-pentane}}{CH_3{-}CH_2{-}CH_2{-}CH_2{-}CH_3} \rightarrow \underset{\text{pentene-1}}{CH_2{=}CH{-}CH_2{-}CH_2{-}CH_3} + H_2$$

Both cracking and dehydrogenation produce olefins, or unsaturated, compounds. These are highly reactive materials which can be used in the rebuilding of new compounds.

3. *Polymerization.* The combining of two olefins to yield a higher-molecular-weight olefin:

$$\underset{\text{butene-1}}{CH_2{=}CH{-}CH_2{-}CH_3} + \underset{\text{propene}}{CH_2{=}CH{-}CH_3} \rightarrow \underset{\text{4-methylhexene-1}}{CH_2{=}CH{-}CH_2{-}\overset{\overset{\large CH_3}{|}}{C}H{-}CH_2{-}CH_3}$$

4. *Alkylation.* The combining of an olefin with a paraffin to yield a higher-molecular-weight paraffin:

$$\underset{\substack{\text{ethene}\\\text{(ethylene)}}}{CH_2{=}CH_2} + \underset{\substack{\text{2 methylpropane}\\\text{(isobutane)}}}{CH_3{-}\overset{\overset{\large CH_3}{|}}{C}H{-}CH_3} \rightarrow \underset{\text{2,2-dimethylbutane}}{CH_3{-}\overset{\overset{\large CH_3}{|}}{\underset{\underset{\large CH_3}{|}}{C}}{-}CH_2{-}CH_3}$$

Alkylation possesses two advantages over polymerization for the controlled rebuilding of higher-molecular-weight material. First, alkylation produces an unreactive paraffin. Polymerization produces reactive olefin which can react further to yield a wide variety of materials. This is undesirable for the controlled rebuilding of compounds. Second, alkylation needs less of the relatively scarce olefinic material, which must be produced by some previous process such as cracking and dehydrogenation.

5. *Isomerization.* The rearrangement of the constituents of molecules without change in molecular weight:

```
        CH2                  CH2    CH3
       /   \                /   \  /
   H2C       CH2       H2C       CH
    |         |    →    |         |
   H2C       CH2       H2C-------CH2
       \   /            methylcyclopentane
        CH2
    cyclohexane
```

6. *Aromatization or cyclization.* The rearrangement of the constituents of a compound accompanied by decomposition or dehydrogenation:

$$\underset{n\text{-heptane}}{CH_3{-}(CH_2)_5{-}CH_3} \rightarrow \underset{\text{toluene}}{C_6H_5{-}CH_3} + 4H_2$$

In any actual industrial process a mixture of compounds is usually treated under fairly extreme conditions; therefore it is not surprising that a variety of changes and reactions occur simultaneously. This produces a spectrum of compounds, some desirable, others undesirable. Although a catalyst can easily speed the rate of reactions a thousandfold or a million-fold, still, when a variety of reactions are encountered, the most important characteristic of a catalyst is its selectivity. By this we mean that it only changes the rates of certain reactions, often a single reaction, leaving the rest unaffected. Thus, in the presence of an appropriate catalyst, products containing predominantly the materials desired can be obtained from a given feed.

The following are some general observations.

1. The selection of a catalyst to promote a specific reaction is not very well understood; therefore in practice extensive trial and error are needed to produce a satisfactory catalyst.

2. Duplication of the chemical constitution of a good catalyst is no guarantee that the material produced will have any catalytic activity.

3. This observation suggests that it is the physical or crystalline structure which somehow imparts catalytic activity to a material. This view is strengthened by the fact that heating a catalyst above a certain critical temperature may cause it to lose its activity, often permanently. Thus present research on catalysts is strongly centered on the surface structure of the material.

4. It is thought that reactant molecules are somehow changed, energized, or affected to form intermediates in the regions close to the catalyst surface, and various theories have been proposed to explain this catalytic activity. In one theory the intermediate is viewed as an association of a reactant molecule with a region of surface; in other words the molecules are somehow attached to the surface. In another theory molecules are thought to move down into the atmosphere close to the surface and be under the influence of the surface forces. In this view the molecules are still mobile but are nevertheless modified by the surface forces. In still a third theory it is thought that an active complex, a free radical, is formed at the surface of the catalyst. This free radical then moves back into the main gas stream, triggering a chain of reactions with fresh molecules before being finally

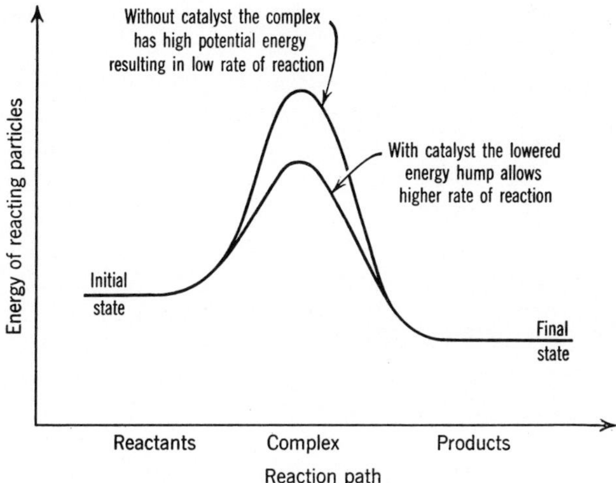

Fig. 1. Representation of action of a catalyst.

destroyed. In contrast with the first two theories, which consider the reaction to occur in the vicinity of the surface, this theory views the catalyst surface simply as a source or generator of free radicals, with the reaction occurring in the main body of the gas far from the surface.

5. In terms of the transition-state theory the catalyst reduces the potential energy barrier over which the reactants must pass to form products. From Chapter 2 we know that this decrease in energy is reflected by a nearly corresponding decrease in activation energy for the reaction which in turn increases the rate of reaction. For example, Table 2.2 shows that if the activation energy for a reaction taking place at 0°C drops from 70 to 40 kcal the rate of reaction rises to about 10^{24} times the original rate. This lowering in energy barrier is shown in Fig. 1.

6. Though a catalyst may speed up a reaction, it never determines the equilibrium or end point of a reaction. This is governed by thermodynamics alone. Thus with or without a catalyst the equilibrium constant for the reaction is always the same. For this reason speeding the forward reaction of an elementary reaction will also speed up the reverse reaction in such a manner that Eq. 2.4 always holds.

7. Since the solid surface is responsible for catalytic activity, a large readily accessible surface in easily handled materials is desirable. By a variety of methods active surface areas the size of football fields can be obtained per cubic centimeter of catalyst.

Though there are many problems related to solid catalysts, we consider only the various aspects of how catalysts act, insofar as these views influence the form and development of the kinetic rate equations needed in design. We simply assume that we have available a given material with certain catalytic properties with which to promote a specific reaction. We wish to evaluate the kinetic behavior of reactants in the presence of this material and then use this information for design.

Thus again, as with noncatalytic heterogeneous reactions, we follow a two-step procedure: to determine the kinetics of the reaction and to use this information for design.

THE RATE EQUATION

The continuous-reaction model

In solid-catalyzed gas-phase reactions, somehow the presence of catalyst surface in the proximity of reactive gas molecules causes the reaction to proceed. With porous catalyst pellets immersed in and permeated with reactive gas, we then have reaction proceeding at all the gas-solid interfaces both at the outside boundaries and within the pellets themselves. For such reactions we select, as the most reasonable representation of reality, a continuous-reaction model which pictures reaction occurring to a lesser or greater extent throughout the catalyst pellets. This is in contrast to the shrinking unreacted-core model with its definite zone of reaction which seemed to be the most reasonable representation of reality in the majority of the noncatalyzed gas-solid reactions of Chapter 12.

In developing rate expressions for the continuous-reaction model, the various processes that may cause resistance to reaction must be taken into account. For a single porous catalyst particle we may visualize these processes as follows.

Gas film resistance. Reactants must diffuse from the main body of the fluid to the exterior surface of the catalyst.

Pore diffusion resistance. Because the interior of the pellet contains so much more area than the exterior of the particle, most of the reaction takes place within the particle itself. Therefore the reactants must in general move into the pellet through the pores.

Surface phenomenon resistance. At some point in their wanderings the reactant molecules are associated with the surface of the catalyst where they react to give products that are released to the fluid phase within the pore.

Pore diffusion resistance for products. Products then diffuse out of the pellet.

Gas film resistance for products. Products then move from the mouth of the catalyst pores into the main gas stream.

Again, as with the heterogeneous systems of Chapters 12 and 13, not all these terms need to be considered at any one time. Frequently the last two

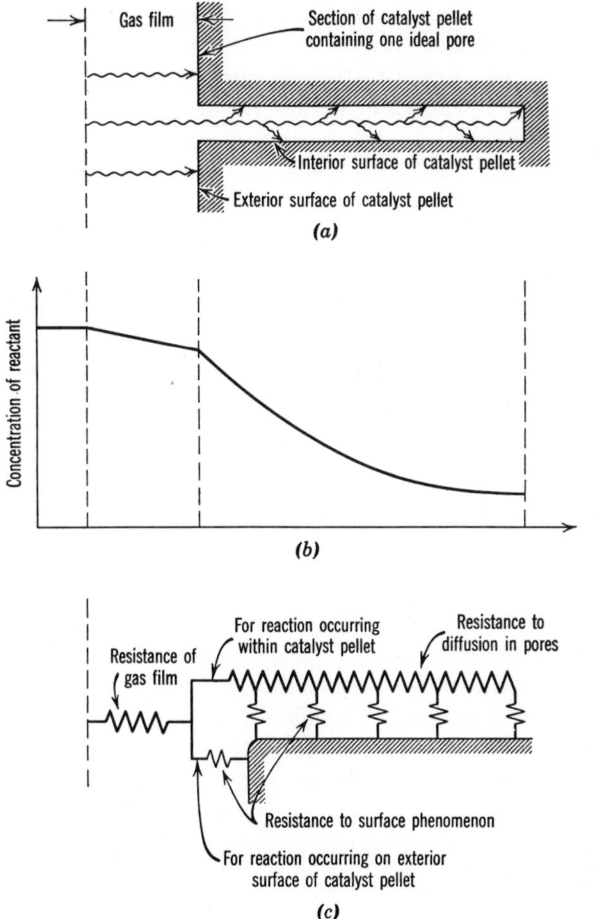

Fig. 2. Continuous-reaction model for porous catalysts: (*a*) sketch of a catalyst pore, (*b*) concentration of reactants within a pore, (*c*) electrical analog of a pore.

steps may be ignored or may be incorporated in the first two terms. For example, where there is no change in the number of moles during reaction the outward diffusion of product can be taken into account simply by considering equimolar counterdiffusion of reactant into the pores rather than diffusion of reactant through a stagnant fluid.

Considering only the movement of reactants through a single idealized catalyst pore, we then have three resistances to account for, as shown in Fig. 2. At first thought these resistance steps may seem to be analogous to the gas film diffusion, ash layer diffusion, and reaction resistance steps of noncatalytic gas-solid reactions which occur in series (Chapter 12). However, Fig. 2 shows that in catalytic reactions these steps do not all occur in series or in parallel: hence the simple methods of combining resistances shown in Chapter 11 cannot be used here. It is true that the gas film and surface reaction steps are in series relationship with each other; however, it is the pore diffusion step which is not related in a simple way to the other steps. Consequently, as we presently show, film and surface reaction resistances can be treated separately in turn, whereas the pore diffusion resistance can never be treated independently.

Let us now consider the various forms of rate equation when one or the other of the resistances to reaction is great.

Film resistance controls

When the gas film resistance is much greater than that of pore diffusion or surface phenomenon, the rate of reaction is limited by the rate of flow of reactant to the surface as given by the mass transfer coefficient k_g between gas and solid. The rate based on unit exterior surface of particle S_{ex} is then

$$-\frac{1}{S_{ex}}\frac{dN_A}{dt} = k_g(C_{Ag} - C_{Ae}) \tag{1}$$

where C_{Ag} is the concentration of reactant A in the gas stream and C_{Ae} is its equilibrium concentration on the surface.

Values for the mass transfer coefficient for various contacting schemes can be found from the available literature, usually as empirical or semi-empirical dimensionless correlations such as Eq. 12.22. The observed over-all reaction rate will be the same for both catalytic and noncatalytic fluid-solid reactions if gas film resistance controls.

Surface phenomenon controls

Because of the great industrial importance of catalytic reactions, considerable effort has been put into developing theories that would form rational bases for the development of kinetic equations for reaction. Very detailed mechanisms have been proposed. The most useful for our purposes supposes that the reaction takes place on an active site on the surface of the catalyst. Thus three steps are viewed to occur successively at the surface.

Step 1. A molecule is adsorbed onto the surface and is attached to an active site.

Step 2. It then reacts either with another molecule on an adjacent site (dual-site mechanism), or with one coming from the main gas stream (single-site mechanism), or it simply decomposes while on the site (single-site mechanism).

Step 3. Products are desorbed from the surface, which gives the site further opportunity to adsorb fresh reactants.

In addition, an equilibrium is considered to exist between all species of molecules, free reactants and free products as well as site-attached reactants, intermediates, and products taking part in these three processes.

Rate expressions derived from various postulated mechanisms are all of the form:

$$\text{Rate of reaction} = \frac{\left(\text{kinetic term}\right)\left(\begin{array}{c}\text{driving force or displace-}\\ \text{ment from equilibrium}\end{array}\right)}{(\text{resistance term})} \tag{2}$$

For example, for the reaction

$$A + B \rightleftharpoons R + S, \qquad K$$

occurring in the presence of inert carrier material U, the rate expression when adsorption of A controls is

$$-r_A'' = \frac{k(p_A - p_R p_S / K p_B)}{1 + K_{RS} p_R p_S + K_B p_B + K_R p_R + K_S p_S + K_U p_U}$$

When reaction between adjacent site-attached molecules of A and B controls, the rate expression is

$$-r_A'' = \frac{k(p_A p_B - p_R p_S / K)}{(1 + K_A p_A + K_B p_B + K_R p_R + K_S p_S + K_U p_U)^2}$$

whereas for desorption of R controlling it becomes

$$-r_A'' = \frac{k(p_A p_B / p_S - p_R / K)}{1 + K_A p_A + K_B p_B + K_R p_A p_B / p_S + K_S p_S + K_U p_U}$$

Each detailed mechanism of reaction with its controlling factor has its corresponding rate equation, involving anywhere from three to seven arbitrary constants, the K values. For reasons to be made clear, we do not intend to use equations such as these. Consequently we do not go into their derivations. These are given by Hougen and Watson (1947), Corrigan (1954, 1955), and elsewhere.

Now in terms of the contact time or space time, most catalytic conversion data can be fitted adequately by relatively simple first- or nth-order rate expressions; see Prater and Lago (1956). Since this is so, we are justified in asking why we have to concern ourselves with selecting one of a host of rather complicated rate expressions suggested by theoretical mechanisms. Why not select the simplest empirical rate expression which satisfactorily fits the data?

The following points summarize the arguments for and against the use of simple empirical kinetic equations.

Truth and predictability. The strongest argument in favor of searching for the actual mechanism is that if we find one which reasonably represents what truly occurs, extrapolation to new and more favorable operating conditions is much more safely done. This is a powerful argument. Other arguments, such as augmenting knowledge of the mechanism of catalysis with the final goal of producing better catalysts in the future, do not concern a design engineer who has a specific catalyst at hand.

Problems of finding the mechanism. We must show that the family of curves representing the rate equation type of the favored mechanism fits the data so much better than the other families that the others can be rejected. With the large number of parameters (three to seven) that can be chosen arbitrarily for each rate-controlling mechanism, a very extensive experimental program is required, using very precise and reproducible data, which in itself is quite a problem. We should bear in mind that it is not good enough to select the mechanism that best fits the data. Differences in fit may be so slight as to be explainable entirely in terms of experimental error. In statistical terms these differences may not be "significant." Unfortunately, if a number of alternative mechanisms fit the data equally well, we must recognize that the equation selected is simply one of good fit, not one that represents reality. With this admitted, there is no reason why we should not use the simplest and easiest-to-handle equation of satisfactory fit. In fact, unless there are good positive reasons for using the more complicated of two equations, we should always select the simpler of the two if both fit the data equally well. The statistical analyses and comments by Chou (1958) on the codimer example in Hougen and Watson (1947) in which 18 mechanisms were examined illustrate the difficulty in finding the correct mechanism from kinetic data, and show that even in the most carefully conducted programs of experimentation the magnitude of the experimental error will very likely overshadow any of the differences predicted by the various mechanisms.

Thus it is hardly ever possible to determine with reasonable confidence which is the correct mechanism.

Dangers in extrapolation. Let us suppose that we have found the correct mechanisms. Extrapolating to unexplored regions is still dangerous because other resistances may become important, in which case the form of the over–all rate equation changes. But, such an equation does serve as a guide to expected favorable operating conditions.

Problems of combining resistances. Again let us suppose that we have found the correct mechanism and resultant rate equation for the surface phenomenon. Combining this step with any of the other resistance steps, such as pore or film diffusion, becomes rather impractical. When this has to be done, it is best to replace the three to seven constant equation by an equivalent first-order rate expression, which can then be combined with other reaction steps to yield an over-all rate expression.

From this discussion we conclude that it is good enough to use the simplest available correlating rate expression which satisfactorily represents the data.

For additional comments questioning the validity of the active-site approach, suggesting forms of kinetic equations to be used in reactor design, and suggesting what is the real utility of the active site theory see Weller (1956) and Boudart (1956).

Form of rate equation to be used when surface phenomenon controls. For design purposes we usually can fit the data satisfactorily by a first-order irreversible or reversible rate equation,

$$-r_A = kC_A \qquad \text{or} \qquad -r_A = k(C_A - C_{Ae})$$

by an nth order irreversible rate equation,

$$-r_A = kC_A{}^n$$

or by simplified expressions suggested by the active-site theory

$$-r_A = \frac{kC_A}{1 + k_1C_A} \qquad \text{or} \qquad -r_A = \frac{k(C_A - C_{Ae})}{1 + k_1C_A}$$

and

$$-r_A = \frac{kC_A}{(1 + k_1C_A)^2} \qquad \text{or} \qquad -r_A = \frac{k(C_A - C_{Ae})}{(1 + k_1C_A)^2}$$

and similar equations when more than one reactant is involved. Rate expression such as this will be used to represent situations in which surface phenomena control.

Qualitative predictions from active-site theory. For design the real value of the active-site theory is that it gives a qualitative idea of what may happen on extrapolation to new operating conditions. Imagine molecules adsorbing, reacting, and desorbing from the surface. From findings in adsorption we know that a rise in pressure results in an increase in amount of material adsorbed. Hence if adsorption is rate controlling, an increase in reactant concentration will result in an increase in rate of reaction.

Suppose desorption controls. Desorption, being an equilibrium process between site-attached and free product molecules, is unaffected by an increase in concentration of reactants. Hence we get no increase in rate with a rise in reactant concentration.

When the chemical reaction controls, we visualize that all the active sites are constantly and continually in use. Many cases may be considered here. For example, consider a single-site mechanism such as in the decomposition of site-attached reactant A with no other material present. Increasing the concentration of reactant in the gas atmosphere above the surface will not speed up this reaction because the surface is assumed to be already saturated with A, since the surface decomposition is rate controlling. Again consider the dual-site mechanism for the reaction A + B → products. This mechanism visualizes that a molecule of A on a site reacts by attacking a molecule of B on a neighboring site. Now if A is in excess on the surface, the reaction rate is mainly a function of the concentration of B on the surface. Increasing C_B or decreasing C_A will both allow more B molecules on the surface and therefore increase the rate of reaction. Increasing C_A will simply swamp the surface with A, crowding out B and

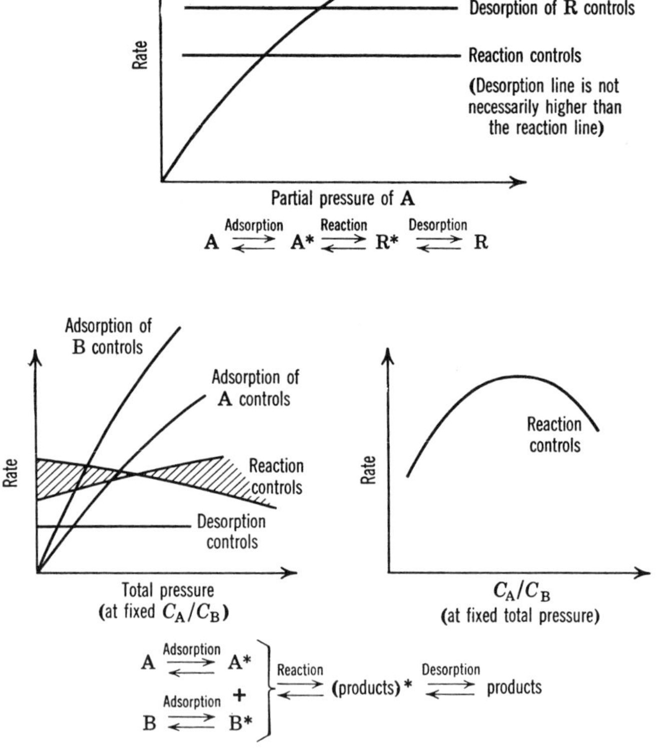

Fig. 3. Variation of reaction rate with reactant ratio and total pressure for the various controlling mechanisms.

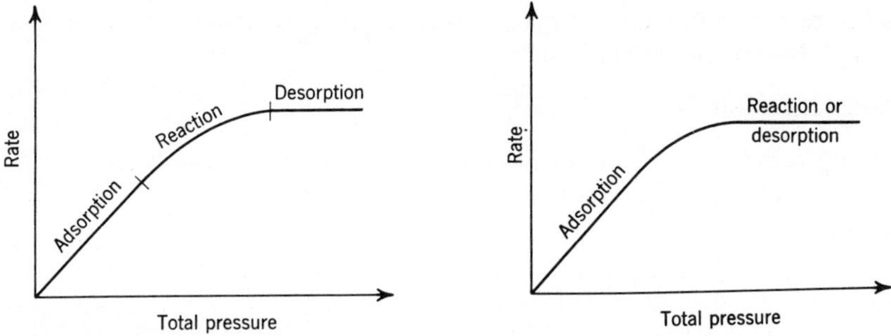

Fig. 4. Change in controlling mechanism as a function of reactant concentration or total pressure for reaction of two reactants with single-site mechanism,

$$\left.\begin{matrix} A \underset{}{\overset{\text{adsorption}}{\rightleftharpoons}} A^* \\ + \\ B \end{matrix}\right\} \overset{\text{reaction}}{\rightleftharpoons} (\text{products})^* \overset{\text{desorption}}{\rightleftharpoons} \text{products}$$

and with fixed reactant ratio, or for reaction of single reactants.

further slowing down the rate of reaction. Figure 3 summarizes these conclusions. Other cases can similarly be considered.

Effect of change in operating pressures. The active-site theory allows us to predict what may happen to the rate when we extrapolate to higher or lower operating pressures. In general, at very low pressures with adsorption controlling we have essentially a first-order reaction. At higher pressures the surface will become increasingly saturated with molecules. If these do not react rapidly enough, surface reaction becomes controlling, causing the rate to level off or even drop. If the reactants on the surface react rapidly but the products do not desorb rapidly enough, the surface will become saturated with product molecules and desorption will control, in which case the reaction rate will again level off.

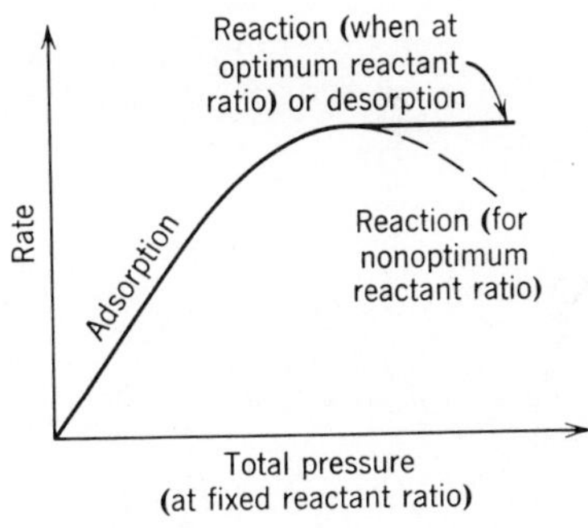

Fig. 5. Change in controlling mechanism for the dual-site mechanism:

$$\left.\begin{matrix} A \overset{\text{adsorption}}{\rightleftharpoons} A^* \\ + \\ B \overset{\text{adsorption}}{\rightleftharpoons} B^* \end{matrix}\right\} \overset{\text{reaction}}{\rightleftharpoons} (\text{products})^* \overset{\text{desorption}}{\rightleftharpoons} \text{products}$$

The effect of pressure on rate of reaction as predicted by the active-site theory is given in Figs. 4 and 5 and shows that at low pressure all reactions are approximated by a first-order rate. At higher pressures the rate levels off, becoming zero order, or may even drop. A more detailed presentation using initial rate data is given by Yang and Hougen (1950).

Pore diffusion resistance important

Single cylindrical pore, first-order reaction. Consider at first a single cylindrical pore, with reactant A diffusing into the pore, a first-order reaction

$$\mathrm{A} \rightarrow \text{product} \qquad \text{and} \qquad -\frac{1}{S}\frac{dN_{\mathrm{A}}}{dt} = k_s C_{\mathrm{A}}$$

taking place at the walls of the pore, and product diffusing out of the pore, as shown in Fig. 6. This simple model will later be extended.

The flow of materials into and out of any section of pore is shown in detail in Fig. 7. At steady state a material balance for reactant A for this elementary section gives

$$\text{output} - \text{input} + \text{disappearance by reaction} = 0 \tag{4.1}$$

or with the quantities shown in Fig. 7,

$$-\pi r^2 \mathscr{D}\left(\frac{dC_{\mathrm{A}}}{dx}\right)_{\text{out}} + \pi r^2 \mathscr{D}\left(\frac{dC_{\mathrm{A}}}{dx}\right)_{\text{in}} + k_s C_{\mathrm{A}}(2\pi r\,\Delta x) = 0$$

Rearranging

$$\frac{\left(\dfrac{dC_{\mathrm{A}}}{dx}\right)_{\text{out}} - \left(\dfrac{dC_{\mathrm{A}}}{dx}\right)_{\text{in}}}{\Delta x} - \frac{2k_s}{\mathscr{D}r}C_{\mathrm{A}} = 0$$

and taking the limit as Δx approaches zero (see the equation above Eq. 9.31), we obtain

$$\frac{d^2C_{\mathrm{A}}}{dx^2} - \frac{2k_s}{\mathscr{D}r}C_{\mathrm{A}} = 0 \tag{3}$$

Note that the first-order chemical reaction is expressed in terms of unit surface area of catalyst pore; hence k_s has units of length per time. In general, the interrelation between rate constants on different bases is given by

$$\left(k, \frac{1}{\text{hr}}\right)\left(\begin{matrix}\text{volume,}\\ \text{ft}^3\end{matrix}\right) = \left(k_m, \frac{\text{ft}^3}{(\text{hr})(\text{lb})}\right)\left(\begin{matrix}\text{mass of}\\ \text{catalyst, lb}\end{matrix}\right) = \left(k_s, \frac{\text{ft}}{\text{hr}}\right)\left(\begin{matrix}\text{surface of}\\ \text{catalyst, ft}^2\end{matrix}\right)$$

or

$$kV = k_m W = k_s S \tag{4}$$

Hence for the cylindrical catalyst pore

$$k = k_s\left(\frac{\text{surface}}{\text{volume}}\right) = k_s\left(\frac{2\pi r L}{\pi r^2 L}\right) = \frac{2k_s}{r} \tag{5}$$

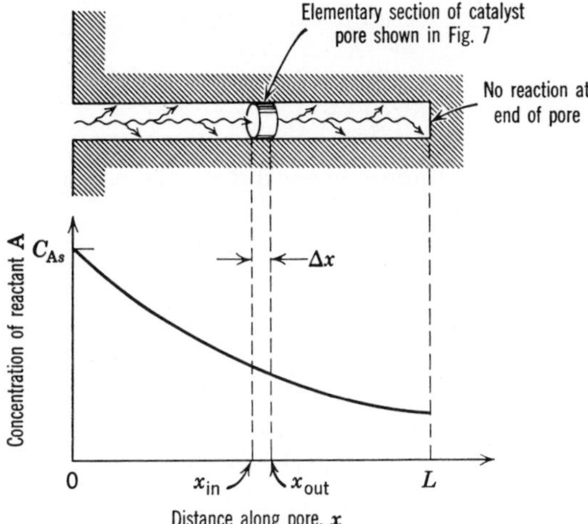

Fig. 6. Representation of a cylindrical catalyst pore.

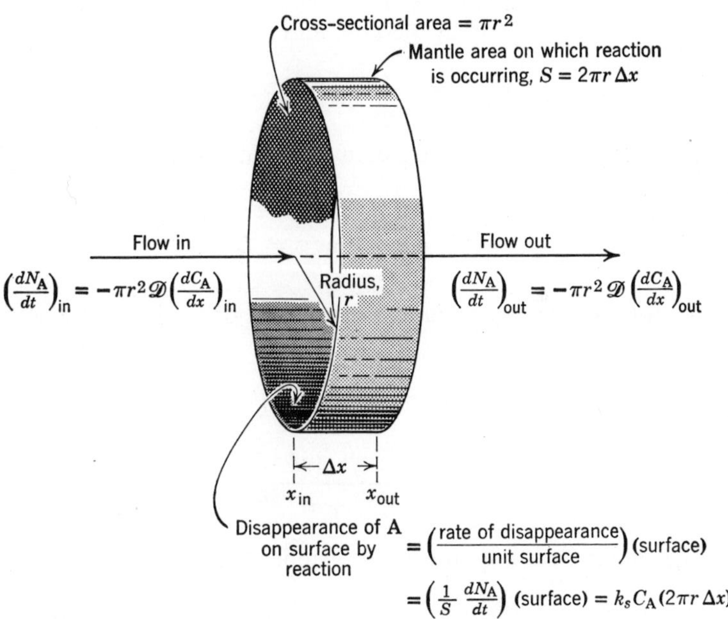

Fig. 7. Setting up the material balance for the elementary slice of catalyst pore.

Thus in terms of volumetric units Eq. 3 becomes

$$\frac{d^2C_A}{dx^2} - \frac{k}{\mathscr{D}} C_A = 0 \tag{6}$$

This is a frequently encountered linear differential equation whose general solution is

$$C_A = M_1 e^{mx} + M_2 e^{-mx}$$

where (7)

$$m = \sqrt{k/\mathscr{D}} = \sqrt{2k_s/\mathscr{D}r}$$

and where M_1 and M_2 are constants. It is in the evaluation of these constants that we restrict the solution to this system alone by specifying what is particular about the model selected, a procedure which requires a clear physical picture of this model. These specifications are called the boundary conditions of the problem. Since two constants are to be evaluated, we must find and specify two boundary conditions. Examining the physical limits of the conceptual pore, we find that the following statements can always be made. First, at the pore entrance, or at the surface of the catalyst pellet,

$$C_A = C_{As} \qquad \text{at} \qquad x = 0 \tag{8a}$$

Second, because there is no flux or movement of material through the interior end of the pore

$$\frac{dC_A}{dx} = 0, \qquad \text{at } x = L \tag{8b}$$

With the appropriate mathematical operations of Eqs. 7 and 8 we then obtain

$$M_1 = \frac{C_{As}e^{-mL}}{e^{mL} + e^{-mL}}$$

$$M_2 = \frac{C_{As}e^{mL}}{e^{mL} + e^{-mL}} \tag{9}$$

Hence the concentration gradient of reactant within the pore is

$$\frac{C_A}{C_{As}} = \frac{e^{m(L-x)} + e^{-m(L-x)}}{e^{mL} + e^{-mL}} = \frac{\cosh m(L-x)}{\cosh mL} \tag{10}$$

Since the rate is proportional to concentration in a first-order reaction, the mean concentration within the pore $\bar{C}_A$ compared to the maximum possible concentration C_{As} should be a measure of how much the reaction

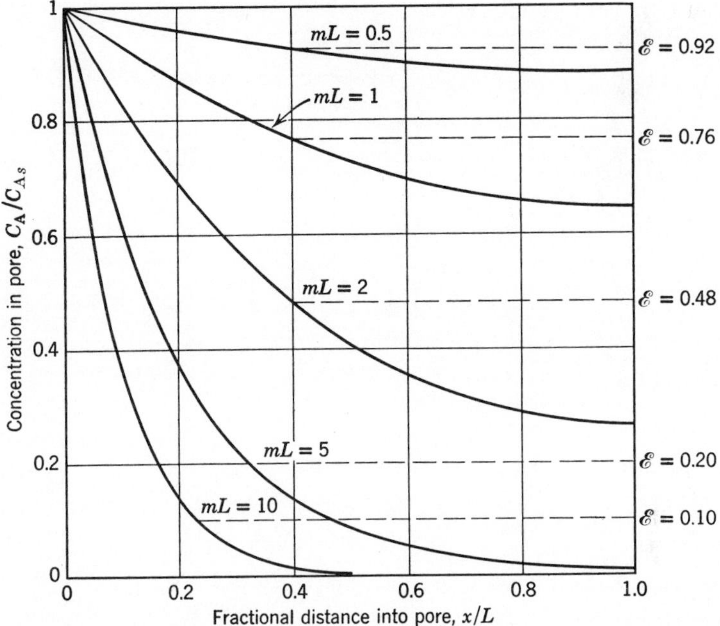

Fig. 8. Distribution and average value of reactant concentration within a catalyst pore as a function of the parameter *mL*.

rate is lowered by pore diffusion. This ratio $\bar{C}_A/C_{As}$ is defined as the effectiveness factor $\mathscr{E}$. With Eq. 10 we can find

$$\mathscr{E} = \frac{\begin{pmatrix}\text{average reaction} \\ \text{rate within pore}\end{pmatrix}}{\begin{pmatrix}\text{maximum reaction rate} \\ \text{if pore diffusion is absent}\end{pmatrix}} = \frac{\bar{C}_A}{C_{As}} = \frac{\tanh mL}{mL} \tag{11}$$

Figure 8 shows how C_A varies within a pore in terms of the dimensionless parameter mL and also shows the value of $\mathscr{E}$ for the curves drawn. The relation between mL and $\mathscr{E}$, given by Eq. 11, is shown more clearly in Fig. 9.

From these figures or Eq. 11 we find

$$\mathscr{E} \approx 1, \qquad \text{when} \qquad mL < 0.5$$

In this range of low mL values the concentration of reactant does not drop appreciably within the pore: thus pore diffusion offers negligible resistance to reaction. This can also be verified by noting that a small value for $mL = L\sqrt{k/\mathscr{D}}$ means either a short pore, slow reaction or rapid diffusion, all three factors tending to make diffusion unimportant.

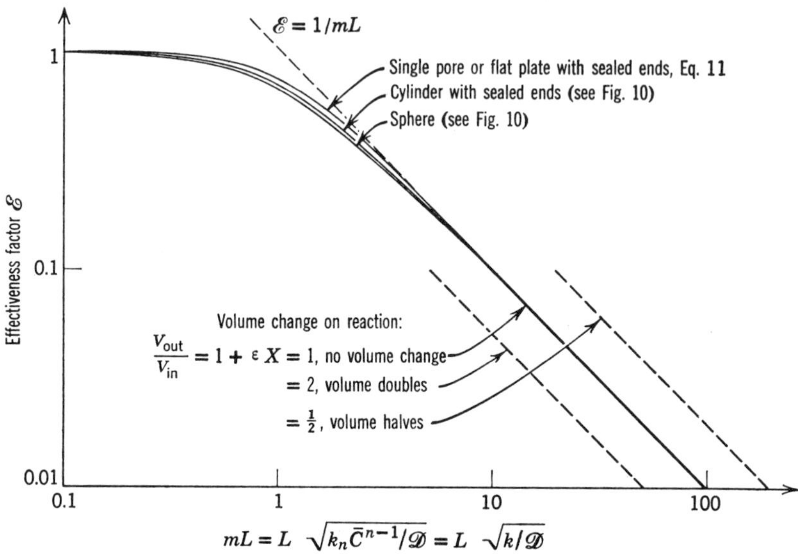

Fig. 9. The effectiveness factor as a function of the parameter mL for various catalyst shapes and for volume change during reaction. Prepared from Aris (1957) and Thiele (1939).

In the other extreme

$$\mathscr{E} \approx \frac{1}{mL} \qquad \text{when} \qquad mL > 5$$

In this range of high mL values the reactant concentration drops rapidly on moving into the pore; hence diffusion becomes important and plays a major role in determining rate of reaction. Note that the effectiveness factor defined here is identical to that used in Eq. 13.13.

The average rate of reaction within the whole pore is then

$$-\frac{1}{S}\frac{dN_A}{dt} = k_s\bar{C}_A = k_s C_{As}\mathscr{E}$$

or

$$-\frac{1}{(\text{pore volume})}\frac{dN_A}{dt} = k\bar{C}_A = kC_{As}\mathscr{E} \tag{12}$$

which shows that in terms of the only concentration we can measure, that in the main gas stream C_{As}, pore diffusion can be accounted for by the effectiveness factor. Thus the effectiveness factor can properly be considered to be an efficiency term.

From the discussion related to Fig. 2 we found that pore diffusion resistance does not act in series with surface reaction resistance and hence cannot be treated independent of it. Equation 12 seems at first sight to indicate that pore diffusion can be accounted for by a separate, multiplicative correction-type term $\mathscr{E}$. This is true, however, this factor $\mathscr{E}$ involves not only a diffusion term but a surface reaction term as well in the form of the rate constant. Thus pore diffusion can never become controlling in the sense that it alone will determine the rate of reaction.

We have gone into considerable detail to develop the expressions for the simple case of diffusion into a single cylindrical pore for a first-order irreversible reaction because it shows how the nonadditive pore resistance effect is to be treated. Relaxing the various restrictions of this treatment leads us to a variety of useful extensions and generalizations. These follow.

Catalyst pellets of regular geometry. Aris (1957) showed that if we use as a measure of catalyst pore length

$$L = \frac{\text{(volume of pellet)}}{\begin{pmatrix}\text{exterior surface of pellet} \\ \text{available for reactant pene-} \\ \text{tration and diffusion}\end{pmatrix}} \tag{13}$$

the effectiveness factor can be related to the dimensionless parameter mL. Figures 9 and 10 summarize these results for flat plates with sealed ends, cylinders with sealed ends, and spheres. The $\mathscr{E}$ versus mL curves for these various types of pellets conveniently coincide everywhere except in the intermediate region. However, in no case is the difference in $\mathscr{E}$ at given mL greater than 18%.

Particles of irregular shape. The close matching of the curves of Fig. 9 for particles of various regular shapes gives confidence that the length parameter L defined in Eq. 13 is the correct one to use for particles of any shape. Thus for particles of irregular shape the mean value of the three curves of Fig. 9 cán be used to estimate $\mathscr{E}$ with an error probably smaller than 10%.

Mixture of particles of various shapes and sizes. For a catalyst bed consisting of a mixture of particles of various shapes and sizes Aris (1957) showed that the correct mean effectiveness factor is

$$\mathscr{E} = \mathscr{E}_1 f_1 + \mathscr{E}_2 f_2 + \cdots \tag{14}$$

where $f_1, f_2, \ldots$ are the volume fractions of particles of sizes 1, 2, . . . in the mixture.

Molar volume change. With decrease in fluid density (expansion) during reaction, or $V_{out}/V_{in} = 1 + \varepsilon x > 1$, the increased outflow of molecules from the pores makes it harder for reactants to diffuse into the

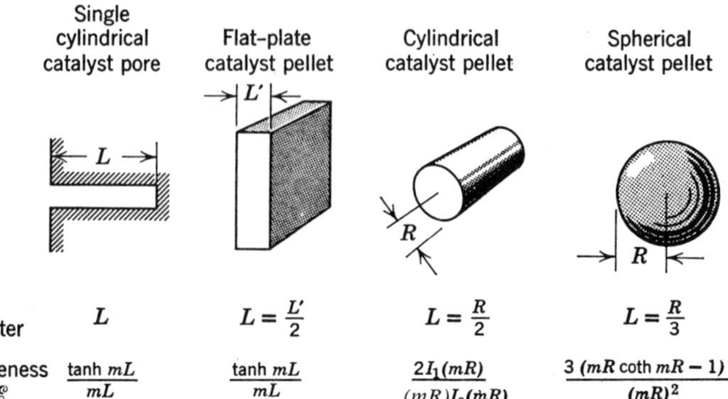

	Single cylindrical catalyst pore	Flat-plate catalyst pellet	Cylindrical catalyst pellet	Spherical catalyst pellet
Length parameter	L	$L=\frac{L'}{2}$	$L=\frac{R}{2}$	$L=\frac{R}{3}$
Effectiveness factor $\mathscr{E}$	$\frac{\tanh mL}{mL}$	$\frac{\tanh mL}{mL}$	$\frac{2I_1(mR)}{(mR)I_0(mR)}$	$\frac{3\,(mR\coth mR-1)}{(mR)^2}$

Fig. 10. Summary of effectiveness factor and length parameters used for various shapes of catalyst pellets

where $m = \sqrt{k_n\bar{C}_A^{n-1}/\mathscr{D}} = \sqrt{k/\mathscr{D}}$

$\mathscr{D}$ = effective volumetric diffusion coefficient in catalyst, area/time

k = first-order or pseudo first-order $(= k_nC_A^{n-1})$ reaction rate constant on volumetric basis, per time

$I_0(\ )$ = modified Bessel function of zero order

$I_1(\ )$ = modified Bessel function of first order

n = order of reaction

k_n = reaction rate constant on a volumetric basis for an nth-order reaction, $(\text{conc})^{1-n}$/time

$\bar{C}_A$ = mean concentration of A within pore, moles/volume

Prepared from Aris (1957).

catalyst, increasing the diffusional resistance and lowering $\mathscr{E}$. On the other hand, volumetric contraction, $V_{out}/V_{in} < 1$, results in a net molar flow into the catalyst and hence an increase in $\mathscr{E}$. Thiele (1939) found that the over-all effect of this flow is a translation of the $\mathscr{E}$ versus mL curve along the abscissa as shown in Fig. 9.

Reactions of any order. In Chapter 11 we showed that treating a linear effect (diffusion) with a nonlinear effect (reaction with order different from unity) leads to complications. In such situations we usually fall back on approximate methods of solution. Here the nonlinear effect of an nth-order reaction is best handled by approximating it with a first-order rate expression with pseudo first-order rate constant k. Thus

$$m = \sqrt{k_n\bar{C}_A^{n-1}/\mathscr{D}} \approx \sqrt{k/\mathscr{D}}$$

where

$$k = k_n\bar{C}_A^{n-1} \tag{15}$$

Because C_A varies within the porous material, k and m are not constant, so we can only approximate $\mathscr{E}$ by using a mean value $\bar{C}_A$ for the changing concentration of reactant.

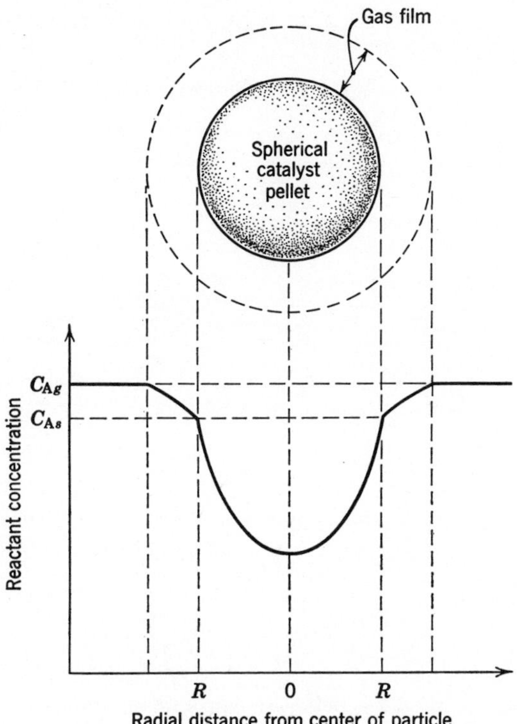

Fig. 11. Concentration profile for a spherical catalyst pellet.

Heat effects during reaction. Strong heat effects accompanying reaction may result in appreciable temperature variations within the individual catalyst particles. For example, if the reaction is highly exothermic the interior of the particles will be at a higher temperature than the exterior surface. Consequently, based on the temperature measured in the gas space between particles, reaction is faster than expected, the over-all effect being an increase in effectiveness factor. For endothermic reactions the opposite is true. Carberry (1961) has extended Fig. 9 to account for these nonisothermal situations.

Combination of resistances

By the methods outlined in the illustrative example of Chapter 11, the over-all effect of gas film resistance and the combination of pore resistances and first-order chemical reaction can readily be combined since these are linear processes. Thus, referring to Fig. 11, we have for the gas film

$$-\frac{1}{S_{\text{ex}}}\frac{dN_A}{dt} = k_g(C_{Ag} - C_{As})$$

whereas for diffusion and reaction within the interior of the particle we have, based on particle volume V_p, and neglecting the slight contribution to reaction by the exterior surface of the particle,

$$-\frac{1}{V_p}\frac{dN_A}{dt} = kC_{As}\mathscr{E} \tag{12}$$

Combining these two expressions, eliminating the unknown surface concentration, gives

$$-\frac{1}{S_{ex}}\frac{dN_A}{dt} = \frac{1}{S_{ex}/k\mathscr{E}V_p + 1/k_g} C_{Ag}$$

or

$$-\frac{1}{V_p}\frac{dN_A}{dt} = \frac{1}{1/k\mathscr{E} + V_p/k_g S_{ex}} C_{Ag} \tag{16}$$

which for spherical particles of radius R becomes

$$-\frac{1}{S_{ex}}\frac{dN_A}{dt} = \frac{1}{3/k\mathscr{E}R + 1/k_g} C_{Ag}$$

or

$$-\frac{1}{V_p}\frac{dN_A}{dt} = \frac{1}{1/k\mathscr{E} + R/3k_g} C_{Ag} \tag{17}$$

Note that in Eqs. 16 and 17 k is the first-order rate constant based on unit volume of particle, whereas k_g is the mass transfer coefficient based on unit exterior surface of particle. With rates defined on other bases, care must be taken to make the appropriate conversion of units.

Exterior and interior surface. Until now, because of its relatively small surface area, we have assumed the contribution to reaction by the exterior surface of a catalyst particle to be negligible. But when reaction is so rapid that the reactant has little chance to penetrate the catalyst particle, this assumption does not hold, and the over-all rate must account for reaction both in the interior and on the outside of the particle. Referring to Fig. 2, we find the over-all effect of all these resistances to be

$$-\frac{1}{S_{ex}}\frac{dN_A}{dt} = \frac{1}{\dfrac{1}{k_g} + \dfrac{1}{k\mathscr{E}(V_p/S_{ex})[S_{in}/(S_{ex}+S_{in})] + k_s}} C_{Ag}$$

or

$$-\frac{1}{V_p}\frac{dN_A}{dt} = \frac{1}{\dfrac{V_p}{k_g S_{ex}} + \dfrac{1}{k\mathscr{E}[S_{in}/(S_{in}+S_{ex})] + k_s(S_{ex}/V_p)}} C_{Ag} \tag{18}$$

Resistance of: gas film; reaction in interior; reaction on exterior where

$$k_s(S_{\text{in}} + S_{\text{ex}}) = kV_p$$

Now when

$$\mathscr{E}\frac{S_{\text{in}}}{S_{\text{ex}}} \ll 1$$

reaction on the exterior surface of the catalyst predominates over reaction within the pores, and Eq. 18 reduces to

$$-\frac{1}{S_{\text{ex}}}\frac{dN_A}{dt} = \frac{1}{1/k_g + 1/k_s}C_{Ag} \tag{19}$$

Equation 19 is the expression for reaction on nonporous catalyst particles.

Equation 18 also reduces, under appropriate limiting conditions, to all the previously derived expressions with individual resistances controlling or important.

Experimental methods for finding rates

Any type of reactor, batch, backmix, or plug flow, may be used to explore the kinetics of catalytic reactions. Since only one fluid phase is present in these reactions, the rates can be found as with homogeneous reactions. The only special precaution we must observe is to make sure that the equation used is dimensionally correct and that the various terms are carefully and precisely defined. The reason for this precaution is the wide variety of bases (void or bulk volume, surface area or mass of catalyst) that may be used to express rates of reaction. To illustrate, for batch constant volume systems Eq. 5.3 in its various forms becomes

$$\underline{\frac{t}{C_{A0}}} = \int\frac{dX_A}{-r_A} = \underline{\frac{V}{V_r}\int\frac{dX_A}{-r_A'}} = \frac{V}{S}\int\frac{dX_A}{-r_A''} = \frac{V}{W}\int\frac{dX_A}{-r_A'''} \tag{20a}$$

For steady state plug flow systems Eq. 5.11 in its various forms becomes

$$\underline{F_{A0}\,dX_A} = -r_A\,dV = \underline{-r_A'\,dV_r} = -r_A''\,dS = -r_A'''\,dW \tag{20b}$$

and for backmix operations similar expressions result.

The V_r, $-r_A'$ system of units indicated by the underlined terms of Eq. 20 is usually the most convenient to use in catalytic systems. By comparing these underlined equations we see that we need to know the fraction voids

$\epsilon = V/V_r$, both between pellets and within pellets if porous, if we wish to interrelate batch and flow system data.

In the rest of the text of this chapter V and $-r_A$ units are used, however all the equations hold equally well if these measures are replaced by V_r and $-r_A'$. The illustrative examples at the end of the chapter use the latter set.

Differential reactor. We have a differential reactor when we choose to consider the rate to be constant at some average value throughout the reactor. Since reaction rates are concentration-dependent, the assumption of constant rate is reasonable when composition changes in the experimental reactor are small. A differential reactor is usually visualized to be small, as the name implies; however, this is not necessary because if the rate is slow the reactant composition change is small, even in a large reactor. In addition, when we have a zero-order reaction we can always consider the reactor to be a differential reactor, no matter how great is the composition change at isothermal conditions.

Rates of reaction in differential reactors are found in a straightforward manner since integration of the plug flow design equation becomes trivial. Thus we have

$$\frac{V}{F_{A0}} = \int_{X_{A,in}}^{X_{A,out}} \frac{dX_A}{-r_A} = \frac{1}{(-r_A)_{av}} \int_{X_{A,in}}^{X_{A,out}} dX_A = \frac{X_{A,out} - X_{A,in}}{(-r_A)_{av}}$$

or

$$(-r_A)_{av} = \frac{F_{A0}(X_{A,out} - X_{A,in})}{V} \tag{21}$$

The procedure is as follows.

1. Make a series of kinetic runs using different concentrations of reactants for each run.
2. Select the highest reactant concentration as the basis for calculating conversions and call this concentration C_{A0}. It is convenient, though not necessary, to do this. Other bases such as feed concentration for each run may be used if preferred. Then F_{A0} is calculated for each run.
3. Determine for each kinetic run $X_{A,in}$, $X_{A,out}$, F_{A0}, and V.
4. Calculate from Eq. 21 the rate of reaction $-r_A$ for each kinetic run.
5. We now have a series of rate versus average reactant concentration data. Applying the differential methods of analysis of Chapter 3, a rate equation can be found from this information.

Figure 12 briefly summarizes this procedure, and Example 1 illustrates the use of the differential reactor for finding a rate equation and for scale-up.

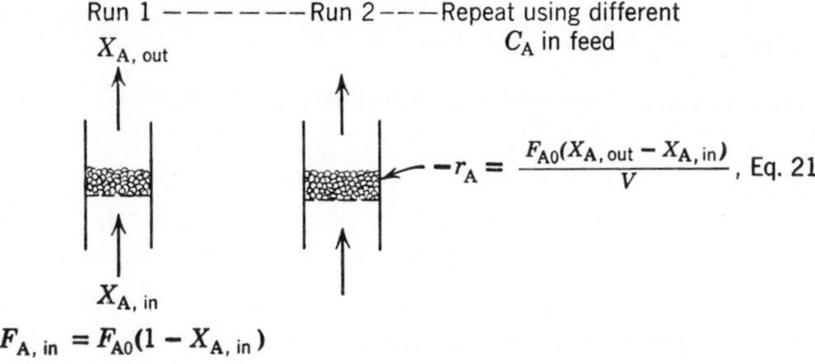

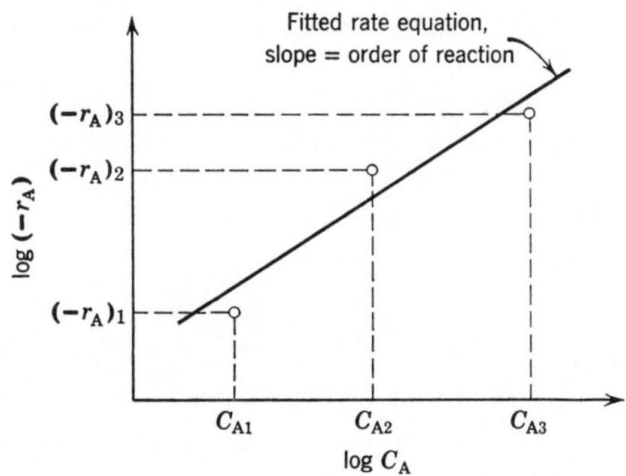

Fig. 12. Summary of the method for finding the reaction rate and rate equation by the use of a differential reactor. For convenience one basis C_{A0} should be used to calculate conversions for all runs.

Integral reactor. When the variation in reaction rate within a reactor is so large that we choose to consider these variations in the method of analysis, we have an integral reactor. Since rates are concentration-dependent, such large variations in rate may be expected to occur when the composition of reactant fluid changes significantly in passing through the reactor. We may follow one of two procedures in searching for a satisfactory rate expression.

Integral analysis. Here a specific mechanism with its corresponding rate equation is put to the test by integrating the rate equation for the reactor flow conditions. The procedure is as follows.

1. Make a series of runs varying V and/or F_{A0} in such a manner that a wide range of conversions X_A is obtained.

2. Select a rate equation to be tested. Integrating the plug flow design equation, we obtain

$$\frac{V}{F_{A0}} = \int_0^{X_A} \frac{dX_A}{-r_A} \tag{5.12}$$

Since $-r_A$ is the rate expression to be tested, a numerical value for the right-hand side of this expression can be obtained for each experimental run.

3. A linearity test can then be performed to test the rate equation.

Equations 5.16 to 5.19 are the integrated forms of Eq. 5.12 for simple kinetic equations, and Example 2*b* illustrates the general procedure.

Differential analysis. Integral analysis provides a straightforward rapid procedure for testing some of the simpler rate expressions. But the integrated forms of these expressions become unwieldy with more complicated rate expressions. In these situations, the differential method of analysis becomes more convenient when searching for a rate equation. Rearranging Eq. 5.11, we obtain the expression that allows us to find rates of reaction in integral reactors. Thus, we have

$$-r_A = \frac{dX_A}{dV/F_{A0}} = \frac{dX_A}{d(\dot{V}/F_{A0})} \tag{22}$$

The procedure is as follows.

1. Make a series of runs using feed of the same composition C_{A0} but varying the feed rate F_{A0} or reactor volume V to obtain a series of different V/F_{A0} values.

2. Calculate for each kinetic run $X_{A,\text{out}}$ and V. In all runs F_{A0}, $C_{A,\text{in}} = C_{A0}$ and $X_{A,\text{in}} = 0$ are fixed.

3. Plot $X_{A,\text{out}}$ versus V/F_{A0} for all runs.

4. Fit the best curve to the $X_{A,\text{out}}$ versus V/F_{A0} data, making it pass through the origin.

5. Equation 22 shows that the rate of reaction at any value of X_A is simply the slope of this curve; hence at a number of X_A values find the slope of this curve (or rate of reaction) as well as the corresponding concentration of reactant C_A.

6. We now have a series of rates versus concentrations which can be correlated by the methods of Chapter 3 to obtain a rate equation.

Figure 13 briefly summarizes this procedure, and Example 2 illustrates the use of differential analysis of integral reactor data in scale-up and in determining a rate expression for a particular reaction.

Comparison of differential and integral reactors. Differential reactors present a number of attractive features. First of all, each run

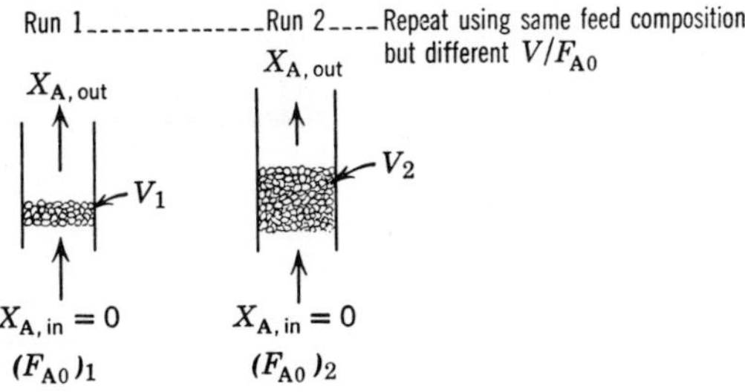

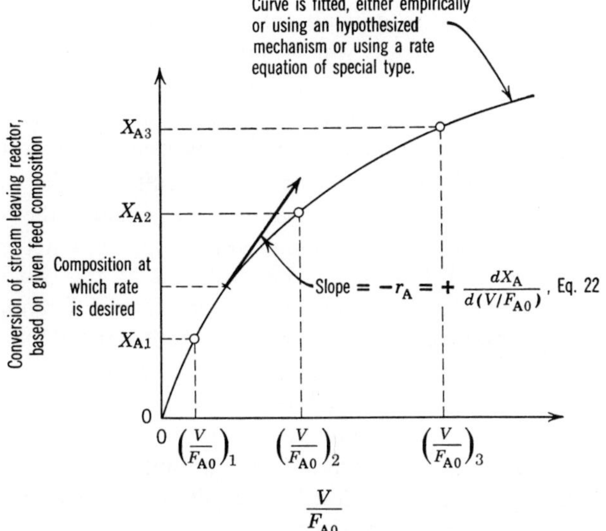

Fig. 13. Summary of the method of finding the reaction rate by the use of an integral reactor.

gives directly a value for the rate of reaction. This is not so with the integral reactor where a series of runs must first be made, followed either by the testing of a preselected rate equation or by curve fitting and taking of slopes. An additional point in favor of differential reactors is that they are easier to keep isothermal because of the low conversion of materials.

To counter these attractive features, differential reactors require more accurate methods of analysis of stream compositions to yield results of comparable accuracy to integral reactors because in differential reactors the rate is found by measuring concentration differences which are usually small. Another drawback of the differential reactors is in the study of

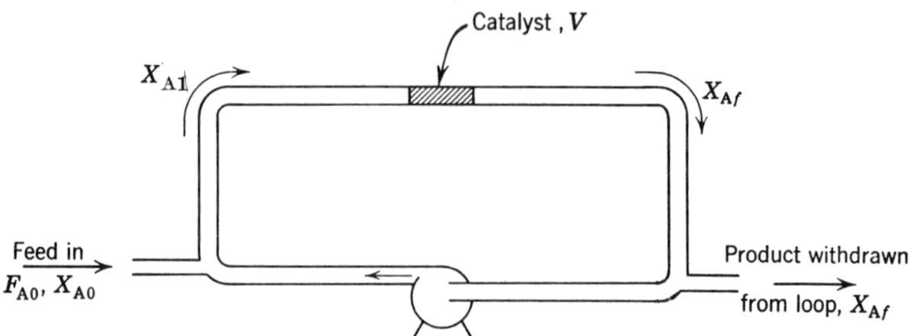

Fig. 14. Sketch of the recycle reactor. At high recycle ratios this setup behaves as a backmix reactor.

complex reactions where it is difficult, often impossible, to prepare a synthetic feed for the various runs which matches the composition of the actual fluid in its various stages of conversion.

Which reactor to use in experimentation can only be decided after weighing the advantages and disadvantages for the specific reaction under study. In general, the differential reactor is more suited to the study of pore diffusion and chemical reaction resistance steps, whereas the integral reactor is probably more convenient to study film diffusion kinetics.

Recycle (or backmix) reactor. The problems at the end of this chapter suggest various modifications of the ordinary differential and integral reactors that may be devised to obtain kinetic data. One experimental scheme deserves special mention since it combines most of the good features of both integral and differential reactors and avoids their shortcomings. This is a steady-state flow system, shown in Fig. 14, consisting of a recycle loop containing a fixed amount of catalyst.

Let us feed a reactant stream at a fixed composition and flow rate to the reactor loop, and let the conversion of the selected reactant A in the various streams be as shown in Fig. 14. In addition, let us choose always to consider the rate of reaction to be the same at all points in the catalyst bed in any specific run. Thus we choose to consider this to be a differential reactor.

With recycle absent $X_{A1} = X_{A0}$ and we have

$$(-r_A)_{av} = \frac{X_{Af} - X_{A0}}{V/F_{A0}} \tag{23}$$

where $(-r_A)_{av}$ is measured at some average conversion of the streams entering and leaving the catalytic bed. Thus

$$X_{Af} > X_{A,av} > X_{A1} \tag{24}$$

Since $X_{Af} - X_{A1}$ may be large, choosing to use an average rate may lead to serious error.

Now suppose that a part of the product stream is recycled. As the recycle flow rate is raised, the incoming feed is mixed with increased amounts of product stream causing X_{A1} to approach X_{Af}. From Eq. 24 we see that this makes the error in the assumption of constant rate decrease accordingly. Thus at high recycle ratios we have

$$(-r_A)_f = \frac{X_{Af} - X_{A0}}{V/F_{A0}} \tag{25}$$

where the rate is measured at the exit stream conditions and is based on the measure of catalyst volume V selected. This type of reactor is called a *recycle or recirculation reactor* but may properly be considered to be a *backmix reactor*. Perkins and Rase (1958) discuss the many aspects of this reactor.

The attractive features of the recycle reactor which recommend its use in many situations are as follows.

1. A direct measure of reaction rate is obtained with each experimental run.
2. The large changes in reactant concentration across the whole loop minimizes the effects of errors in analysis of feed and product stream compositions, giving accurate and precise rate measurements.
3. Heat effects are minimized, and good temperature control is possible. Actually, all the catalyst need not be at one location but may be distributed throughout the loop.

Determining controlling resistances and the rate equation

Interpretation of experiments becomes difficult when more than one resistance affects the rate. To avoid this problem we should like, with preliminary runs, to find first the limits of operations where the various resistances become important. This will allow us to select conditions of operations in which the resistances can be studied separately.

Film resistance. First of all, it is best to see whether film resistance needs to be considered. This can be done in one of many ways. Where experimental rate data are available, the mean first-order rate constant for these runs can be compared with the predicted mass transfer coefficient for that type of flow system, such as Eq. 12.22. In all cases we should find that the mass transfer coefficient is the upper limit to the reaction rate or

$$kV_p \leqslant k_g S_{ex} \tag{26}$$

If the two terms in this equation are of the same order of magnitude, we may reasonably suspect that the gas film is playing a role in determining

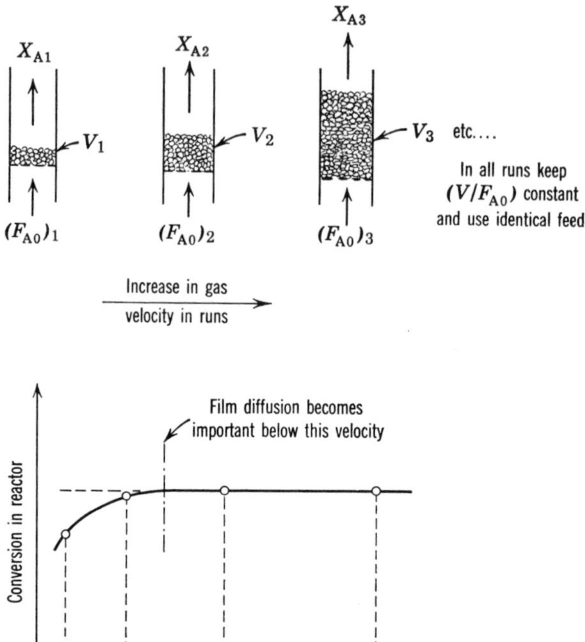

Fig. 15. Summary of a method to determine whether gas film resistance influences the rate of reaction.

the reaction rate. On the other hand, if kV_p is much smaller than k_gS_{ex}, we may conclude that some other step is providing the major resistance to reaction; therefore gas film resistance can be ignored.

By experiment we can determine the limits of operations where the resistance of the gas film plays a role by noting conversions in plug flow reactors when using varying flow rates of identical feed.

Figure 15 shows an experimental procedure for exploring gas film resistance. A number of experimental runs are made at constant V/F_{A0}, but at varying flow rates of identical feed. Where gas film resistance is important, conversion will vary with changing gas flow rate. Where gas film resistance does not influence the rate of reaction, conversion should remain the same at all gas flow rates. The limits of operations where gas film resistance just begins to make itself felt is then the point where conversion just begins to drop.

Figure 16 illustrates a second procedure for studying gas film resistance. Again, conversions are compared at given V/F_{A0} but different F_{A0}. A

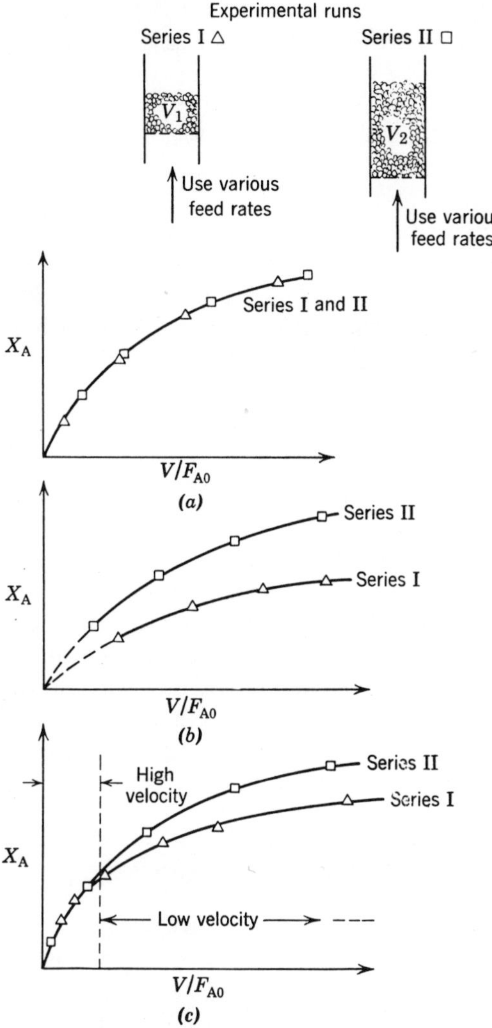

Fig. 16. Summary of a method for determining whether gas film resistance affects the rate of reaction. (*a*) Runs overlap; hence film diffusion is unimportant. (*b*) Film diffusion is important throughout the range of velocities covered. (*c*) Film diffusion affects rate at low velocities but plays no role at high velocities.

decrease in conversion is evidence of gas film resistance causing a drop in reaction rate.

Of the two experimental procedures, the first is to be preferred because it can cover a wider range of conditions and can allow easier detection of the onset of film diffusion.

In using either of these methods, we should always select operating conditions where bed backmixing is negligible or plays the same role throughout; otherwise we may ascribe incorrect causes for observed drops in conversion.

Pore resistance. Assuming that we have examined for the effect of film diffusion, know in what range of experimental conditions it may become important, and are operating in the region where film diffusion can be ignored, we may study the effect of pore diffusion. From what we have mentioned earlier, pore diffusion can never be studied alone since it is not in a series relationship with the chemical reaction step. Pore diffusion is accounted for by the effectiveness factor in the rate equation, using concentrations in the main gas stream, or

$$-r_A = -\frac{1}{V}\frac{dN_A}{dt} = k\mathscr{E}C_A \tag{12}$$

where $\mathscr{E}$ is a function of mL as given by Fig. 9 or Eq. 11. To find the effect of pore diffusion, we should like to see how $\mathscr{E}$ varies with mL. If $\mathscr{E}$ remains unchanged as mL is varied, we are in the region where pore diffusion is unimportant, or $mL < 0.5$. If $\mathscr{E}$ varies reciprocally with mL, we are in the region of strong pore diffusion, $mL > 10$ (see after Eq. 11). This then is how we find the range of conditions where pore diffusion plays a role. Thus the procedure is to make kinetic runs with catalyst particles of the same kind but of different size, hence different mL values, and observe how the rate of reaction is affected. For example, with particles of size R_1 and R_2, and with the same concentration of reactant in both runs, we have

$$\text{with } R_1 \qquad (-r_A)_1 = k\mathscr{E}_1 C_A$$
$$\text{with } R_2 \qquad (-r_A)_2 = k\mathscr{E}_2 C_A$$

If the resistance to pore diffusion is negligible, $\mathscr{E} = 1$ and the rate of reaction should be the same for both sizes of particles, or

$$\frac{r_1}{r_2} = \frac{k\mathscr{E}_1 C_A}{k_2\mathscr{E}_2 C_A} = \frac{\mathscr{E}_1}{\mathscr{E}_2} = 1 \tag{27}$$

If we are operating in the region of strong pore diffusion, $\mathscr{E} = 1/mL$, and we should find

$$\frac{r_1}{r_2} = \frac{\mathscr{E}_1}{\mathscr{E}_2} = \frac{mL_2}{mL_1} = \frac{R_2}{R_1} \tag{28}$$

Thus the rate of reaction varies inversely with particle size.

How do we find the transition between these two regions? If the original runs with different-sized particles showed identical rates, thus negligible resistance to pore diffusion, then further runs should be made under conditions in which diffusional resistance becomes increasingly important relative to the resistance to chemical reaction. In other words, progressively larger-sized particles or higher-temperature levels should be selected until the rate of reaction starts to drop. On the other hand, if we originally were in the region of strong diffusional resistance, succeeding runs should be made with smaller particles or at lower temperatures. Thus the $\mathscr{E}$ versus mL curve can be found and fitted.

It is interesting to note the behavior of nth-order reactions $-r = k_n C^n$ in the region of strong pore diffusion where $\mathscr{E} = 1/mL$. The first-order reaction becomes

$$-r = kC\mathscr{E} = \frac{kC}{mL} = \frac{(k\mathscr{D})^{1/2}}{L} C \tag{29}$$

But with an nth order reaction where $k = k_n C^{n-1}$ we obtain

$$-r = \frac{(k_n\mathscr{D})^{1/2}}{L} C^{(n+1)/2} \tag{30}$$

Thus an nth-order reaction behaves like a reaction of order $(n + 1)/2$ or

0 order becomes $\frac{1}{2}$ order
1st order remains 1st order
2nd order becomes 1.5 order
3rd order becomes 2nd order

In addition, the observed rate constant now becomes proportional to $\sqrt{k_n}$. Thus with an Arrhenius-type temperature dependency, $k = k_0 e^{-E/RT}$, we then have for any reaction order

$$k^{1/2} \propto k_0^{1/2} e^{-E/2RT}$$

or

$$E_{\text{observed}} = \frac{E_{\text{true}}}{2} \tag{31}$$

Thus the observed or measured activation energy under strong diffusional resistance is only one-half the true activation energy.

Chemical reaction. Kinetic equations based on the various active-site models may be obtained by the methods outlined by Yang and Hougen (1950) or Corrigan (1955). However, since these require an extensive research program to explore, and must be replaced by the corresponding linear rate expressions anyway if the diffusional resistances are to be considered, we consider only the simpler empirical forms of rate equations to represent the kinetics when surface phenomena control. With film diffusion absent, the rate of surface reaction can then be found in a straightforward manner with pore diffusional effects either present or absent.

PRODUCT DISTRIBUTION IN MULTIPLE REACTIONS

More often than not solid-catalyzed reactions are multiple reactions; reactions occur side by side, and the products of these decompose further. Of the variety of products formed, usually only one is desired, and it is the yield of this material which is to be maximized. In cases such as these the question of product distribution is of primary importance.

Now the general rules for maximizing a given product in homogeneous reactions apply equally well to solid-catalyzed reactions. These rules were developed in Chapter 7 and dealt with the type of flow patterns to be used in the reactor. Briefly then, for reactions in parallel the key to optimizing yields is to maintain the proper high or low concentration levels of reactants within the reactor, whereas for reactions in series the key is to avoid the mixing of fluids of different compositions. These considerations hold for the over-all or gross flow pattern of fluid through any reactor.

In catalytic reactions the fluid in the interior of catalyst pellets may differ in properties from the neighboring main body of fluid. These many local nonhomogeneities caused by lowered reactant concentration within the catalyst pellets may result in a product distribution different from what would be observed were this nonhomogeneity absent. Here we consider the difference between the true (at the reacting surface of the catalyst) and observed (material entering the main gas stream from the catalyst) product distribution. Knowing the reasons for this difference will suggest how to control the operating conditions so as to obtain the most favorable over-all yield of desired product.

In terms of fractional yields we may say that the over-all fractional yield Φ is found from the observed instantaneous fractional yields φ_{obs}, whereas the latter is related to the true instantaneous fractional yield φ_{true}. Thus

$$\varphi_{\text{true}} \xrightarrow[\text{reaction kinetics}]{\text{catalyst properties,}} \varphi_{\text{obs}} \xrightarrow[\text{Ch. 7}]{\text{methods of,}} \Phi$$

Here we examine the relation between φ_{true} and φ_{obs}. We leave to Chapter 7 the finding of Φ from φ_{obs}.

Reactions in parallel

Here we treat two reactions which characterize the types of parallel-path reaction found in solid-catalyzed reactions. We relate φ_{true} with φ_{obs} for these reactions when pore diffusion is strong, when surface reaction controls, and when film diffusion controls.

Decomposition of a single reactant by two paths. Consider the parallel-path decomposition

$$\begin{array}{ll} & \text{R (desired)}, \qquad r_R = k_1 C_A{}^{a_1} \\ & {}^{k_1}\nearrow \\ \text{A} & \\ & {}^{k_2}\searrow \\ & \text{S (unwanted)}, \qquad r_S = k_2 C_A{}^{a_2} \end{array} \tag{32}$$

which has an instantaneous fractional yield

$$\varphi_{\text{true}}\left(\frac{\text{R}}{\text{R}+\text{S}}\right) = \frac{1}{1 + (k_2/k_1)C_A^{a_2-a_1}} \tag{33}$$

Surface reaction controls. When surface reaction is rate controlling, the concentration of reactant within the pellets and in the main gas stream are the same, and Eq. 33 represents both the observed and true instantaneous fractional yield.

Film resistance controls. When diffusional resistance across the gas film about the particles controls, then C_A at the reaction surface will be lower than in the main gas stream. From Eq. 33 we see that this lowered reactant concentration will favor the reaction of lower order. Hence if the desired reaction is of lower order, operating under conditions where film diffusion influences the rate will be advantageous and will raise the observed fractional yield above the true fractional yield. If the desired reaction is of higher order, the opposite occurs. The extent of actual shift in φ is not easy to determine.

When both reactions are of the same order, or $a_1 = a_2$, Eq. 33 becomes

$$\varphi_{\text{true}} = \frac{1}{1 + k_2/k_1}$$

Strong pore diffusion. Under conditions of strong pore diffusion use of Eq. 30 yields

$$\varphi_{\text{obs}} = \frac{1}{1 + \left(\dfrac{k_2}{k_1}\right)^{1/2} C_A^{(a_2-a_1)/2}} \tag{34}$$

Side-by-side decomposition of two reactants. Consider a feed consisting of two components, both of which react when in contact with a solid catalyst, for example

$$\begin{aligned} &\text{A} \xrightarrow{k_1} \text{R} \quad \text{(desired)}, \qquad r_R = k_1 C_A{}^a \\ &\text{B} \xrightarrow{k_2} \text{S} \quad \text{(unwanted)}, \qquad r_S = k_2 C_B{}^b \end{aligned} \tag{35}$$

where the rates indicated are the true rates of reaction on the solid surface.

Then the instantaneous fractional yield of desired product is

$$\varphi_{\text{true}}\left(\frac{\text{R}}{\text{R}+\text{S}}\right) = \frac{1}{1 + k_2 C_{\text{B}}{}^{b}/k_1 C_{\text{A}}{}^{a}} \tag{36}$$

Film resistance controls. When mass transfer of reactants through the gas film surrounding the particles controls the over-all rates, then C_A and $C_B \rightarrow 0$ on the exterior surface of the particles, and the over-all rates of reaction of A and B in terms of main stream concentrations become

$$r_{\text{R}} = k_{\text{A}g}(C_{\text{A}} - 0) = k_{\text{A}g} C_{\text{A}}$$

$$r_{\text{S}} = k_{\text{B}g}(C_{\text{B}} - 0) = k_{\text{B}g} C_{\text{B}}$$

Thus the observed fractional yield is

$$\varphi_{\text{obs}}\left(\frac{\text{R}}{\text{R}+\text{S}}\right) = \frac{1}{1 + k_{\text{B}g} C_{\text{B}}/k_{\text{A}g} C_{\text{A}}} \approx \frac{1}{1 + C_{\text{B}}/C_{\text{A}}} \tag{37}$$

irrespective of reaction kinetics.

Strong pore diffusion. In this region the observed rates of reaction, as given by Eq. 30, are

$$r_{\text{R}} = \frac{(k_1 \mathscr{D}_{\text{A}})^{1/2}}{L} C_{\text{A}}^{(a+1)/2}$$

$$r_{\text{S}} = \frac{(k_2 \mathscr{D}_{\text{B}})^{1/2}}{L} C_{\text{B}}^{(b+1)/2}$$

hence the observed fractional yield

$$\varphi_{\text{obs}}\left(\frac{\text{R}}{\text{R}+\text{S}}\right) = \frac{1}{1 + \left(\dfrac{k_2 \mathscr{D}_{\text{B}} C_{\text{B}}^{b+1}}{k_1 \mathscr{D}_{\text{A}} C_{\text{A}}^{a+1}}\right)^{1/2}} \tag{38}$$

For first-order reactions this becomes simply

$$\varphi_{\text{obs}}\left(\frac{\text{R}}{\text{R}+\text{S}}\right) = \frac{1}{1 + \left(\dfrac{k_2 \mathscr{D}_{\text{B}}}{k_1 \mathscr{D}_{\text{A}}}\right)^{1/2} \dfrac{C_{\text{B}}}{C_{\text{A}}}} \approx \frac{1}{1 + \left(\dfrac{k_2}{k_1}\right)^{1/2} \dfrac{C_{\text{B}}}{C_{\text{A}}}} \tag{39}$$

Surface reaction controls. Since C_A and C_B are the same at the surface and in the main gas stream $\varphi_{\text{obs}} = \varphi_{\text{true}}$ and Eq. 36 holds. For first-order reactions this becomes simply

$$\varphi_{\text{obs}} = \varphi_{\text{true}} = \frac{1}{1 + k_2 C_{\text{B}}/k_1 C_{\text{A}}} \tag{40}$$

Reactions in series

As characteristic in behavior of reactions in which the desired product can decompose further, let us consider the successive first-order decompositions

$$A \xrightarrow{k_1} R \xrightarrow{k_2} S$$

Film diffusion controls. Consider the physical picture when film diffusion controls. The individual molecules of A in the main gas stream wander in random fashion through the gas film to the surface of the particle. Since this diffusive process offers the total resistance to the over-all process, the molecules of reactant reaching the exterior surface of the particle decompose in a relatively short time to form R. There is no need for the interior surface of the particles to be used. The exterior surface does all the work, and the particle can just as well be nonporous.

To be recovered the R molecules formed at the surface must diffuse outward through the gas film. However, if during these random wanderings the molecules of R collide with the surface a few times, the chances are that they will decompose into S.

Though no neat expression has yet been developed to give the yield of R for this situation, still, by analogy to the extremely fast reaction between two fluids treated in Chapter 10, we can expect that the greater the mass transfer resistance with respect to reaction, the lower the $C_{R,max}$. In the extreme for infinitely fast reactions the probability of R escaping from the surface without reaction becomes negligible. Thus for film diffusion controlling

$$C_{R,max} \rightarrow 0$$

or

$$\varphi_{obs}\left(\frac{R}{R+S}\right) \rightarrow 0 \tag{41}$$

Strong pore diffusion. An analysis similar to that on page 438 using the appropriate kinetic rate expressions gives the concentration ratio of materials in the main gas stream (or pore mouths) at any point in the reactor. Thus the differential expression, see Wheeler (1951) for details and compare with Eq. 7.32, is

$$\frac{dC_R}{dC_A} = -\frac{1}{1+\gamma} + \gamma\frac{C_R}{C_A}, \qquad \gamma = \left(\frac{k_2}{k_1}\right)^{1/2} \tag{42}$$

For a backmix reactor integration with $C_{R0} = 0$ gives

$$\frac{C_R}{C_{A0}} = \frac{1}{1+\gamma}\cdot\frac{C_A(C_{A0}-C_A)}{C_A+\gamma(C_{A0}-C_A)} \tag{43}$$

For a plug flow reactor integration with $C_{R0} = 0$ gives

$$\frac{C_R}{C_{A0}} = \frac{1}{1+\gamma} \cdot \frac{1}{1-\gamma}\left[\left(\frac{C_A}{C_{A0}}\right)^{\gamma} - \frac{C_A}{C_{A0}}\right] \tag{44}$$

Comparing Eqs. 43 and 44 with the corresponding expressions for no resistance in pores, Eqs. 7.36 and 7.33, shows that here the distribution of A and R is given by a reaction having the square root of the true k ratio, with the added modification that C_R is divided by $1 + \gamma$. The maximum yield of R is likewise affected. Thus for plug flow Eq. 3.45 becomes

$$\frac{C_{R,\max}}{C_{A0}} = \frac{\gamma^{\gamma/\gamma-1}}{1+\gamma}, \qquad \gamma = \left(\frac{k_2}{k_1}\right)^{1/2} \tag{45}$$

and for backmix flow Eq. 7.25 is modified to give

$$\frac{C_{R,\max}}{C_{A0}} = \frac{1}{(1+\gamma)(\gamma^{1/2}+1)^2} \tag{46}$$

Table I. The role of diffusion in pores for first order reactions in series

	$\frac{C_{R,\max}}{C_{A0}}$ for plug flow			$\frac{C_{R,\max}}{C_{A0}}$ for backmix flow		
$\frac{k_2}{k_1}$	No Resistance	Strong Resistance	Percent Decrease	No Resistance	Strong Resistance	Percent Decrease
1/64	0.936	0.650	30.6	0.790	0.486	38.5
1/16	0.831	0.504	39.3	0.640	0.356	44.5
1/4	0.630	0.333	47.6	0.444	0.229	48.5
1	0.368	0.184	50	0.250	0.125	50
4	0.157	0.083	47.2	0.111	0.057	48.5
16	0.051	0.031	38.2	0.040	0.022	44.5

This analysis and table shows that the yield of R is about halved with strong resistance to diffusion in the pores.

Surface reaction controls. When surface reaction is the rate-controlling step, then C_A does not drop in the interior of catalyst particles. Thus true rates are observed and

$$\varphi_{\text{obs}}\left(\frac{\text{R}}{\text{R}+\text{S}}\right) = \varphi_{\text{true}}\left(\frac{\text{R}}{\text{R}+\text{S}}\right) \tag{47}$$

Summary

Table 2 shows, for reactions with elementary kinetics, the relation between the true and the observed ratio of k values.

For more on this subject see Wheeler (1951).

Table 2. The observed k ratio in terms of the true k ratio

	$A \xrightarrow{k_1} S$, $A \xrightarrow{k_2} R$	$A \xrightarrow{k_1} R$, $B \xrightarrow{k_2} S$	$A \xrightarrow{k_1} R \xrightarrow{k_2} S$
Film diffusion controls	$\left(\dfrac{k_1}{k_2}\right)_{obs} = \dfrac{k_1}{k_2}$	$= \dfrac{k_{Ag}}{k_{Bg}} \approx 1$	$\to 0$
Strong pore diffusion	$= \left(\dfrac{k_1}{k_2}\right)^{1/2}$	$\approx \left(\dfrac{k_1}{k_2}\right)^{1/2}$	
Surface reaction controls	$= \dfrac{k_1}{k_2}$	$= \dfrac{k_1}{k_2}$	$= \dfrac{k_1}{k_2}$

Extensions to real catalysts

Consider a pore structure consisting of numerous small pores (micropores) branching from relatively few larger pores (macropores). If we assume that the surface area of micropores is relatively large, reaction can be assumed to take place in these pores only. Based on this model Carberry (1962*b*) showed that in the region of strong pore diffusion

$$\left(\frac{k_1}{k_2}\right)_{obs} = \left(\frac{k_1}{k_2}\right)^{1/4}$$

This result suggests that for a real catalyst particle

$$\left(\frac{k_1}{k_2}\right)_{obs} = \left(\frac{k_1}{k_2}\right)^{\alpha}, \qquad \alpha < 1$$

where α is now dependent on the pore structure geometry. Thus with α unknown, the only reliable estimate of the true k ratio would be from experiments under conditions where pore diffusion is unimportant. On the other hand finding the ratio of k values under strong and negligible pore resistance should yield the value of α. This in turn should shed light on the pore structure geometry of the catalyst.

This shift of α from one-half may also affect the treatment of strong pore diffusion kinetics which leads to Eqs. 11 and 31 and to the slope of -1 in Fig. 9.

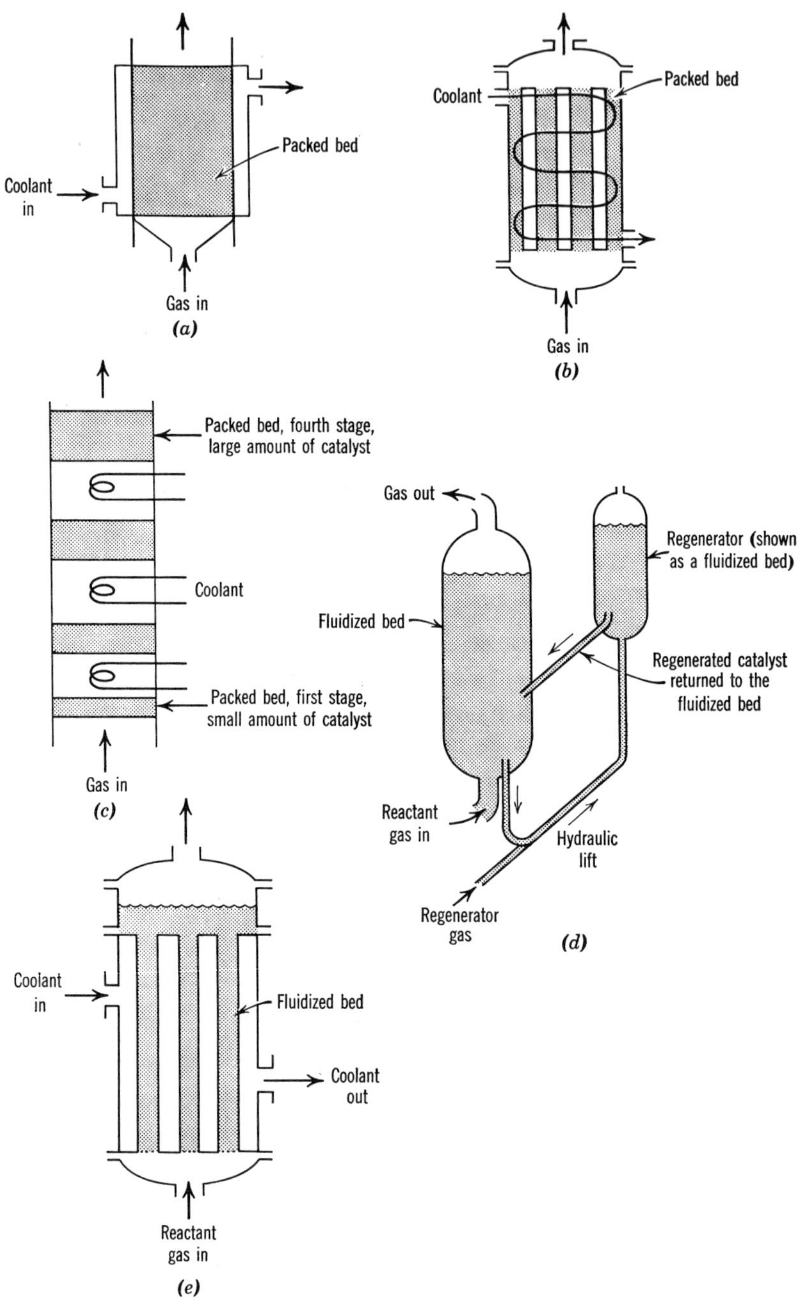
Packed bed
Coolant in
Gas in
(a)
Coolant
Packed bed
Gas in
(b)
Packed bed, fourth stage, large amount of catalyst
Coolant
Packed bed, first stage, small amount of catalyst
Gas in
(c)
Gas out
Regenerator (shown as a fluidized bed)
Fluidized bed
Regenerated catalyst returned to the fluidized bed
Reactant gas in
Hydraulic lift
Regenerator gas
(d)
Coolant in
Fluidized bed
Coolant out
Reactant gas in
(e)

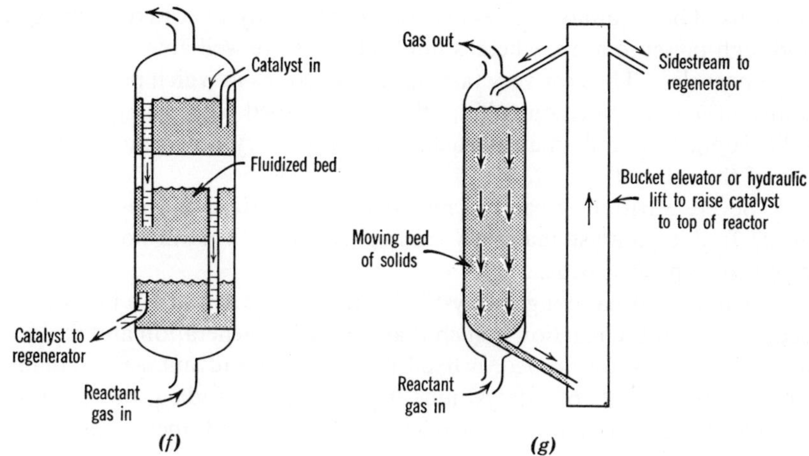

Fig. 17. Various types of catalytic reactors.

APPLICATION TO DESIGN

Contacting of reactant gas with solid catalyst can be effected in many ways. Each offers specific advantages and disadvantages, and economic considerations should determine the pattern selected. Figure 17 illustrates a number of catalytic reactors. These may be divided into two broad types, the fixed-bed reactors of Figs. 17*a*, *b*, and *c* and the fluidized-bed reactors of Figs. 17*d*, *e*, and *f*. The moving-bed reactor of Fig. 10*g* is an intermediate case which embodies some of the advantages and some of the disadvantages of fixed- and fluidized-bed reactors. In comparing the merits of these broad types of reactors, we see the following.

1. Gases in tubular fixed bed reactors approximate plug flow; in fluidized beds they behave in a manner as yet unknown but intermediate between plug and backmix flow with some extent of bypassing. Hence at high conversion fluidized beds must be much larger than fixed beds for the same treatment rates. In addition, if multiple reactions occur, the amount of intermediate formed in fluidized beds is not as great as in packed beds. This fact follows from Chapter 7.

2. Temperature control in fixed beds is difficult. Nonisothermal conditions exist within the reactor, requiring varying heat loads, and the hot spots that occur may well ruin a catalyst. Fluidized beds are much more uniform in temperature. In small-scale laboratory operations the problem of heat removal is usually not severe; however, the larger the unit, the more important becomes this problem.

3. Fixed beds cannot use very small sizes of catalyst because of plugging and high-pressure drop, whereas fluidized beds are well able to use small-sized particles. Thus for very fast surface reactions in which pore and film diffusion may be rate controlling, the fluidized bed with its vigorous gas-solid contacting and small particles will allow very much more efficient use of the catalyst.

4. Severe attrition of catalyst may occur in fluidized and moving beds; hence friable catalyst materials cannot be used. This is not a serious problem in packed beds.

5. The cost of handling catalyst is higher in fixed beds than in fluidized beds; hence if the reaction is such that frequent regeneration and replacement of catalyst are needed, a fixed bed is at a disadvantage. Actually, when large amounts of catalyst must frequently be handled, this becomes the overriding consideration for rejecting the fixed-bed operations.

With these points in mind, let us proceed to Fig. 17. Figure 17*a* is a typical packed bed embodying all its advantages and disadvantages. Figure 17*b* shows how the problem of hot spots can be substantially reduced by increasing the cooling surface. Figure 17*c* shows how inter-cooling can still further reduce the unwanted overheating. Note that in the first stage where reaction is fastest, conversion is kept low by having less catalyst present than in the other stages. Units such as these can all be incorporated in a single shell or can be kept separate with heat exchangers between stages.

Figure 17*d* shows a typical fluidized bed with attendant regenerator which operates by continuously removing and regenerating a portion of the catalyst in the reactor. Such a reactor embodies both shortcomings of fluidized-bed reactors. Figure 17*e* shows one procedure for reducing gas backmixing in fluidized beds and for increasing heat transfer from such beds. Figure 17*f* shows a three-stage countercurrent unit which is very efficient in overcoming the shortcomings of fluidized beds with regard to backmixing. Figure 17*g* shows a moving-bed reactor. Such units share with fixed beds the advantages of plug flow and disadvantages of large particle size, but they also share with fluidized beds the advantages of low catalyst-handling costs.

These factors must all be weighed to obtain optimum design. It may happen that the best design is one that uses two different reactor types in series. For example, for high conversion and a very exothermic reaction we may well look into the use of a fluidized bed followed by a fixed bed.

Proper interpretation of data and reliable scale-up predictions for catalytic reactions are complicated by a number of factors which cannot be treated in a simple manner. These factors, which we do not consider here, are:

1. The nonisothermal conditions so frequently found within a packed-bed reactor combined with the deviations from plug flow lead to problems requiring simultaneous consideration of heat and mass dispersion in both axial and radial directions. When we realize that, in addition, we may have temperature gradients within individual catalyst pellets and different rate-controlling steps existing at different locations in the reactor, we see the magnitude of the problem of obtaining reliable predictions of conversion. See Carberry (1962*a*) for a recent attack on some aspects of this problem.

2. More important still is the effect of all these temperature and concentrations variations on product distribution. This problem is practically untouched to date.

3. Changes in catalyst behavior may be difficult to predict. Often a rapid initial drop in activity of fresh catalyst is followed by a slow continuous decrease in activity. This whole phenomenon can be called aging of catalyst and may be due to temporary or permanent poisoning of the material. In addition, a change in operating conditions may result in a slow, delayed creeping of catalyst activity upward or downward to new levels. These hysteresis effects indicate that often the past history of the catalyst may influence its present behavior.

When faced with an actual design problem, we inevitably ask which factors should be considered and incorporated in our model and which should be ignored. Only good engineering judgment can answer this. A wise decision clearly requires an awareness of the degree of predictive accuracy needed (preliminary feasability study? detailed design recommendation?) and the reliability of the data being used (it makes little sense to employ elegant and high-powered analyses based on crude order of magnitude data), both of these factors considered and weighed within the framework of resources available. Often the simple model for ideal flow is quite satisfactory. In this case, with the complete kinetics of the reaction known, design is straightforward using the methods given in Chapter 5.

Finally, how much laboratory data should be taken and how far can we extrapolate this data and still assure an adequate design? This is a difficult question to answer. Only with game theory strategy, where we maximize our expectation of profit, can we properly balance the cost of additional experimentation against the possible gain that may accrue in operating at new extrapolated conditions. Usually it pays to obtain the additional experimental information. This is one of the primary uses of a pilot plant, to obtain kinetic data at a variety of operating conditions which will then be used to select the optimum in operating conditions for the chemical plant.

Example I. Differential Reactor

The catalytic reaction

$$A \rightarrow 4R$$

is run at 3.2 atm and 117°C in a plug flow reactor which contains 10-cc bulk volume of catalyst and uses a feed consisting of the partially converted product of 20 liters/hr of pure unreacted A. Table E1*a* summarizes the results.

Table E1*a*

Run	1	2	3	4
$C_{A,in}$, gm moles/liter	0.100	0.080	0.060	0.040
$C_{A,out}$, gm moles/liter	0.084	0.070	0.055	0.038

(*a*) What is the rate equation for this reaction?

(*b*) Using the rate equation, find the size of plug flow reactor (liters) which would yield 35% conversion of A to R for a feed rate of 2000 gm moles A/hr at 3.2 atm and 117°C.

(*c*) Repeat part *b* without using the rate equation but by graphical integration of the design equation.

Solution. (*a*) Since the maximum variation about the mean concentration is 8% (run 1), we may consider this to be a differential reactor; therefore we may apply Eq. 22 to find the reaction rate.

Basing conversion for all runs on pure A at 3.2 atm and 117°C, we have

$$C_{A0} = \frac{N_{A0}}{V_{\text{fluid}}} = \frac{p_{A0}}{RT} = \frac{3.2 \text{ atm}}{\left(0.082 \frac{(\text{liters fluid})(\text{atm})}{(\text{gm mole})(°\text{K})}\right)(390°\text{K})} = 0.1 \frac{\text{gm moles A}}{\text{liter fluid}}$$

and

$$F_{A0} = C_{A0}v = \left(0.1 \frac{\text{gm moles A}}{\text{liter}}\right)\left(20 \frac{\text{liters}}{\text{hr}}\right) = 2 \frac{\text{gm moles A}}{\text{hr}}$$

With density change during reaction, concentrations and conversions are related by

$$\frac{C_A}{C_{A0}} = \frac{1 - X_A}{1 + \varepsilon_A X_A} \qquad \text{or} \qquad X_A = \frac{1 - C_A/C_{A0}}{1 + \varepsilon_A(C_A/C_{A0})}$$

where $\varepsilon_A = 3$ for the basis selected (pure A).

Table E1*b* shows the details of the calculations. Plotting $-r_A$ versus C_A as shown in Fig. E1*a* gives a straight line through the origin, indicating a first-order decomposition. The rate in terms of moles A reacted/(hr)(liter catalyst) is then found from Fig. E1*a* to be

$$-r_A' = \frac{1}{V_r}\frac{dN_A}{dt} = \left(96 \frac{\text{liters fluid}}{(\text{hr})(\text{liter catalyst})}\right)\left(C_A, \frac{\text{gm moles A}}{\text{liter fluid}}\right)$$

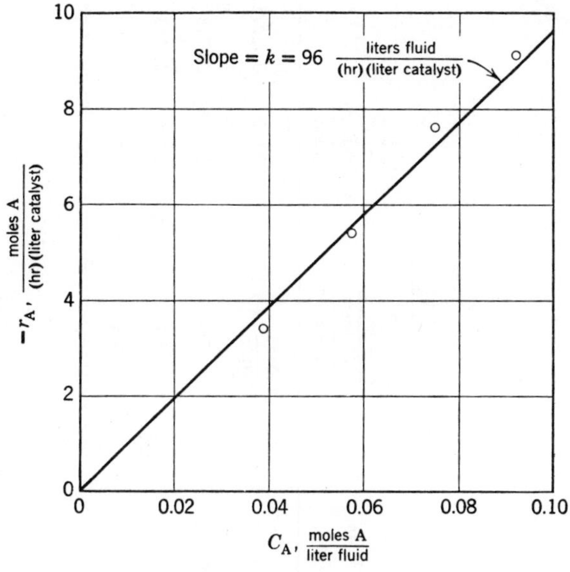

Fig. E1*a*

(*b*) The volume of catalyst required is given by the design equation for plug flow reactors. Showing all units and being careful to distinguish between the various volume terms used, we have

$$\frac{V_r,\ \text{liters catalyst}}{F_{A0},\ \dfrac{\text{moles A}}{\text{hr}}} = \int_{X_A=0}^{X_A=0.35} \frac{dX_A,\ \dfrac{\text{moles A reacted}}{\text{mole A}}}{-r_A',\ \dfrac{\text{moles A reacted}}{(\text{hr})(\text{liter catalyst})}}$$

With a first-order rate equation we obtain

$$V_r = F_{A0}\int_0^{X_A}\frac{dX_A}{kC_A} = \frac{F_{A0}}{kC_{A0}}\int_0^{0.35}\frac{1+\varepsilon_A X_A}{1-X_A}\,dX_A$$

By using Eq. 5.17 to evaluate the integral, this becomes

$$V_r = \frac{F_{A0}}{kC_{A0}}\left[(1+\varepsilon_A)\ln\frac{1}{1-X_A} - \varepsilon_A X_A\right]_0^{0.35}$$

By replacing all the known values into this expression,

$$V_r = \frac{2000\ \dfrac{\text{moles A}}{\text{hr}}}{\left(96\ \dfrac{\text{liters fluid}}{(\text{hr})(\text{liter catalyst})}\right)\left(0.1\ \dfrac{\text{moles A}}{\text{liter fluid}}\right)}\left(4\ln\frac{1}{0.65} - 1.05\right)$$

$$= 140 \text{ liters catalyst.}$$

Table E1b

$\frac{C_{A,in}}{C_{A0}}$	$\frac{C_{A,out}}{C_{A0}}$	$C_{A,av}$ moles/liter	$X_{A,in} = \frac{1 - \frac{C_{A,in}}{C_{A0}}}{1 + \varepsilon_A \frac{C_{A,in}}{C_{A0}}}$	$X_{A,out} = \frac{1 - \frac{C_{A,out}}{C_{A0}}}{1 + \varepsilon_A \frac{C_{A,out}}{C_{A0}}}$	$\Delta X_A = X_{A,out} - X_{A,in}$	$-r_A' = \frac{\Delta X_A}{V_r/F_{A_0}} = \frac{\Delta X_A}{\frac{0.01 \text{ liters}}{2 \text{ moles/hr}}}$	$\frac{1}{-r_A'}$, $\frac{\text{(hr)(liter)}}{\text{moles}}$	$X_{A,av}$
1	0.84	0.092	$\frac{1-1}{1+3} = 0$	$\frac{1 - 0.84}{1 + 3(0.84)} = 0.0455$	0.0455	$\frac{0.0455}{0.01/2} = 9.1$	0.110	0.02275
0.8	0.70	0.075	0.0588	0.0968	0.0380	7.6	0.1316	0.0778
0.6	0.55	0.0575	0.1429	0.1698	0.0269	5.4	0.186	0.1563
0.4	0.38	0.039	0.2727	0.2897	0.0170	3.4	0.294	0.2812

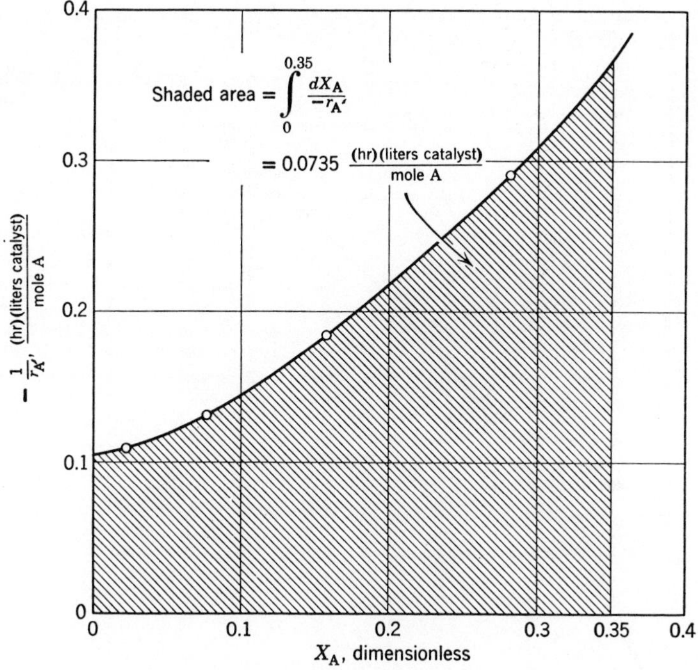

Fig. E1*b*

(*c*) To find the volume directly, graphically integrate the design equation of part *b*, using the tabulated $1/(-r_A')$ versus X_A data. From Fig. E1*b*

$$\int_0^{0.35} \frac{dX_A}{-r_A'} = 0.0735$$

Hence

$$V_r = \left(2000 \frac{\text{moles A}}{\text{hr}}\right)\left(0.0735 \frac{(\text{hr})(\text{liters catalyst})}{\text{mole A}}\right) = 147 \text{ liters catalyst}$$

Example 2. Integral Reactor

The catalytic reaction

$$A \rightarrow 4R$$

is studied in a plug flow reactor using various amounts of catalyst and 20 liters/hr of pure A feed at 3.2 atm and 117°C. The concentrations of A in the effluent stream is recorded for the various runs as shown in Table E2*a*.

Table E2*a*

Runs	1	2	3	4	5
Volume of catalyst used, cc	20	40	80	120	160
$C_{A,out}$, gm moles/liter	0.074	0.060	0.044	0.035	0.029

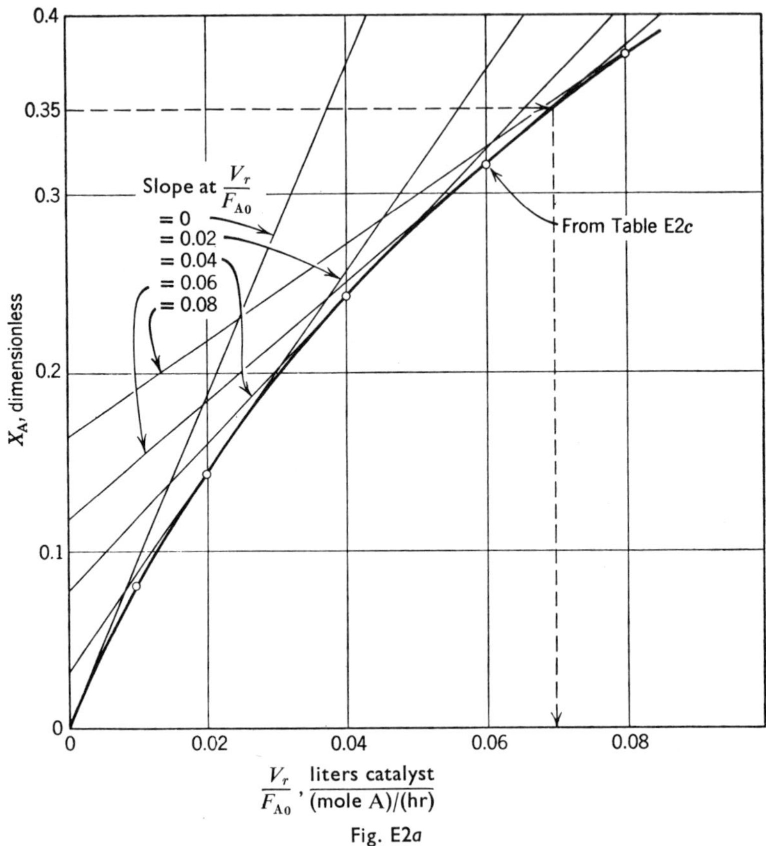

Fig. E2*a*

(*a*) Find the size of plug flow reactor (liters) which would yield 35% conversion of A to R for a feed rate of 2000 gm moles A/hr at 3.2 atm and 117°C.

(*b*) Find the rate equation for this reaction, using the integral method of analysis.

(*c*) Repeat part *b*, using the differential method of analysis.

Solution. (*a*) From Example 1 we have for all experimental runs

$$C_{A0} = 0.1 \text{ moles A/liter fluid}$$
$$F_{A0} = 2 \text{ moles A/hr}$$
$$\varepsilon_A = 3$$

Since the concentration varies significantly during the runs, the experimental reactor should be considered to be an integral reactor.

The size of reactor needed can be found directly from an X_A versus V_r/F_{A0} plot. From the first four columns of Table E2*c* and Fig. E2*a* we find at 35% conversion

$$\frac{V_r}{F_{A0}} = 0.07 \frac{\text{(liters catalyst)(hr)}}{\text{mole A}}$$

and for a feed rate of 2000 moles A/hr,

$$V_r = \left(0.07 \frac{\text{(liters catalyst)(hr)}}{\text{mole A}}\right)\left(2000 \frac{\text{moles A}}{\text{hr}}\right)$$

$$= 140 \text{ liters catalyst.}$$

(*b*) *Integral analysis.* Try a first-order rate expression. If this is not satisfactory, try some other simple forms of rate equation. Using the same units as in Example 1*b*, we then have

$$\frac{V_r}{F_{A0}} = \int_0^{X_A} \frac{dX_A}{-r_A'} = \int_0^{X_A} \frac{dX_A}{kC_A} = \frac{1}{kC_{A0}} \int_0^{X_A} \frac{1 + \varepsilon_A X_A}{1 - X_A} dX_A$$

Using Eq. 5.17 to evaluate the integral, we have

$$k \frac{C_{A0} V_r}{F_{A0}} = (1 + \varepsilon_A) \ln \frac{1}{1 - X_A} - \varepsilon_A X_A$$

and with ε_A, C_{A0}, and F_{A0} replaced this becomes

$$\left(4 \ln \frac{1}{1 - X_A} - 3X_A\right) = k\left(\frac{V_r}{20}\right)$$

A plot of the terms in the two parentheses should yield a proportionality relationship with k as the constant of proportionality. Evaluating these terms in Table E2*b* for the data points and plotting as in Fig. E2*b*, we see that there is no reason to suspect that we do not have a linear relationship. Hence we may conclude that the first-order rate equation satisfactorily fits the data. With k evaluated from Fig. E2*b*, we then have

$$-r_A', \frac{\text{moles A}}{\text{(hr)(liter catalyst)}} = \left(95 \frac{\text{liters fluid}}{\text{(hr)(liter catalyst)}}\right)\left(C_A, \frac{\text{moles A}}{\text{liter fluid}}\right)$$

Table E2*b*

X_A [from Table E2c]	$4 \ln \frac{1}{1 - X_A}$	$3X_A$	$\left(4 \ln \frac{1}{1 - X_A} - 3X_A\right)$	V_r, liters catalyst	$\frac{V_r}{20}$
0.0808	0.3372	0.2424	0.0748	0.02	0.001
0.1429	0.6160	0.4287	0.1873	0.04	0.002
0.2415	1.1080	0.7245	0.3835	0.08	0.004
0.317	1.5268	0.951	0.5758	0.12	0.006
0.379	1.908	1.137	0.771	0.16	0.008

(*c*) *Differential analysis.* Equation 22 shows that the rate of reaction is given by the slope of the X_A versus V_r/F_{A0} curve. The tabulation (Table E2*c*) based on Fig. E2*a* shows how the rate of reaction is found at various C_A. The linear relation between $-r_A'$ and C_A in Fig. E2*c* then gives for the rate equation:

$$-r_A' = -\frac{1}{V_r}\frac{dN_A}{dt} = \left(93 \frac{\text{liters fluid}}{\text{(hr)(liter catalyst)}}\right)\left(C_A, \frac{\text{moles A}}{\text{liter fluid}}\right)$$

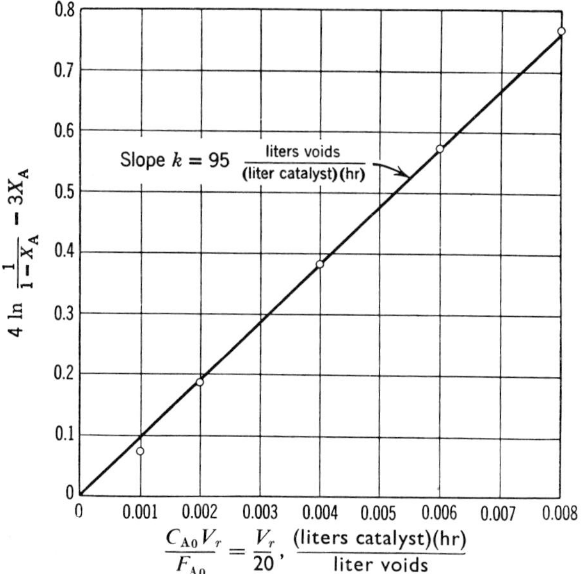

Fig. E2*b*

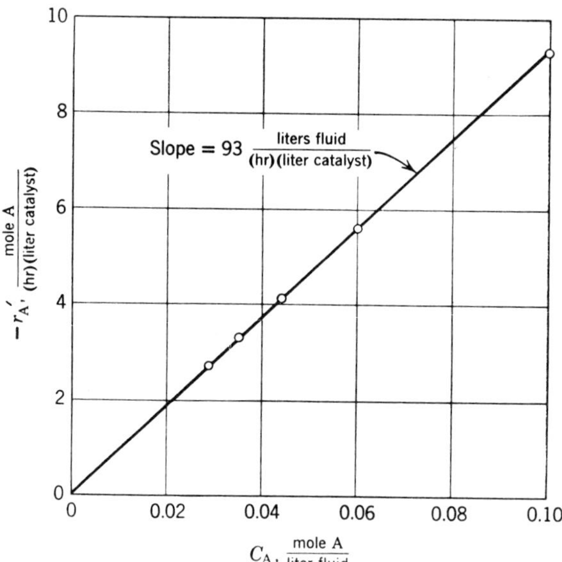

Fig. E2*c*

Table E2c

V_r, liters catalyst	$\frac{V_r}{F_{A0}}$, $\frac{\text{(liters catalyst)(hr)}}{\text{mole A}}$	$\frac{C_{A,\text{out}}}{C_{A0}}$	$X_A = \dfrac{1 - \frac{C_A}{C_{A0}}}{1 + \varepsilon_A \frac{C_A}{C_{A0}}}$	From Fig. E2*a* $-r_A' = \dfrac{dX_A}{d\left(\frac{V_r}{F_{A0}}\right)}$, $\frac{\text{moles A}}{\text{(hr)(liter catalyst)}}$
0	0	1	0	$\frac{0.4}{0.043} = 9.3$
0.02	0.01	0.74	0.0808	—
0.04	0.02	0.60	0.1429	5.62
0.08	0.04	0.44	0.2415	4.13
0.12	0.06	0.35	0.317	3.34
0.16	0.08	0.29	0.379	2.715

RELATED READINGS

T. E. Corrigan, Refresher Series, Parts 5 and 6, *Chem. Eng.* (Nov. 1954–July 1955).
——— and W. C. Mills, Refresher Series, Parts 9 and 10, *Chem. Eng.*, (April 1956–Oct. 1956).
G. F. Froment, *Ind. chim. belge*, **25,** 245 (1960).
O. A. Hougen and K. M. Watson, *Chemical Process Principles*, Part III, John Wiley and Sons, New York, 1947.
J. M. Smith, *Chemical Engineering Kinetics*, McGraw-Hill, New York, 1956.
P. B. Weisz and C. D. Prater, *Advances in Catalysis*, **6,** 143 (1954).
A. Wheeler, *Advances in Catalysis*, **3,** 250 (1951).

REFERENCES

R. Aris, *Chem. Eng, Sci.*, **6,** 262 (1957).
M. Boudart, *A.I.Ch.E. Journal*, **2,** 62 (1956).
J. B. Butt, H. Bliss, and C. A. Walker, *A.I.Ch.E. Journal*, **8,** 42 (1962).
J. J. Carberry, *A.I.Ch.E. Journal*, **7,** 350 (1961).
———, *A.I.Ch.E. Journal*, **8,** 557 (1962*a*).
———, *Chem. Eng. Sci.*, **17,** 675 (1962*b*).
Chan-Hui Chou, *Ind. Eng. Chem.*, **50,** 799 (1958).
T. E. Corrigan, *Chem. Eng.*, **61,** 236 (Nov. 1954); **61,** 198 (Dec. 1954); **62,** 199 (Jan. 1955); **62,** 195 (Feb. 1955).
———, *Chem. Eng.*, **62, 203** (May 1955); **62,** 227 (July 1955).
O. A. Hougen and K. M. Watson, *Chemical Process Principles*, Part III, John Wiley and Sons, New York, 1947.
H. Kubota, M. Ishizawa, and M. Shindo, *Sulphuric Acid* (*Japan*), **23,** 284 (1959); from H. Kubota T. Akehata, and M. Shindo, *Can. J. Chem. Eng.*, **39,** 64 (April 1961).
T. K. Perkins and H. F. Rase, *A.I.Ch.E. Journal*, **4,** 351 (1958).
C. D. Prater and R. M. Lago, *Advances in Catalysis*, **8,** 293 (1956).
W. Resnick, *Ind. Eng. Chem.*, **52,** 865 (1960).
E. W. Thiele, *Ind. Eng. Chem.*, **31,** 916 (1939).
S. Weller, *A.I.Ch.E. Journal*, **2,** 59 (1956).
A. Wheeler, *Advances in Catalysis*, **3,** 250 (1951).
K. H. Yang and O. A. Hougen, *Chem. Eng. Progr.*, **46,** 146 (1950).

PROBLEMS

1. Derive the expression

$$\mathscr{E} = \frac{\tanh mL}{mL} \tag{11}$$

by the following two methods.

(*a*) The effectiveness factor may be viewed as

$$\mathscr{E} = \frac{\begin{pmatrix}\text{average reactant}\\ \text{concentration in pore}\end{pmatrix}}{\begin{pmatrix}\text{maximum possible}\\ \text{reactant concentration}\end{pmatrix}} = \frac{\bar{C}_A}{C_{As}}$$

Evaluate $\bar{C}_A$ by integration of Eq. 10 along the length of pore; then solve for $\mathscr{E}$.

(*b*) The effectiveness factor may also be looked upon as

$$\mathscr{E} = \frac{\begin{pmatrix}\text{actual rate of}\\ \text{disappearance of}\\ \text{reactant in pore}\end{pmatrix}}{\begin{pmatrix}\text{maximum possible}\\ \text{rate of}\\ \text{disappearance}\end{pmatrix}} = \frac{\begin{pmatrix}\text{actual flow rate of reactant}\\ \text{into pore}\end{pmatrix}}{\begin{pmatrix}\text{flow rate into pore if reaction}\\ \text{proceeds at rate correspond-}\\ \text{ing to } C_{As} \text{ everywhere within}\\ \text{pore, or maximum rate}\end{pmatrix}}$$

$$= \frac{\left(\dfrac{dN_A}{dt}\right)_{\text{pore entrance}}}{\begin{pmatrix}\text{interior}\\ \text{surface}\\ \text{of pore}\end{pmatrix}\begin{pmatrix}\text{maximum}\\ \text{reaction}\\ \text{rate}\end{pmatrix}}$$

Evaluate these terms and then find $\mathscr{E}$. Note the analogy with the equations for heat flow from fins.

2. When the smallest size of particle in a bed of mixed catalyst particles exhibits strong diffusional effects, show that a mean characteristic length $\bar{L}$ can be used to determine the effectiveness factor $\mathscr{E}$ for the bed. Derive the expression for $\bar{L}$ in terms of the amounts of the various sizes of particles making up the mixed bed.

3.(*a*) What fraction of the over-all resistance to mass transfer and reaction is provided by the gas film in a catalytic decomposition if the observed rate based on volume of catalyst bed is

$$k = 4/\text{time}$$

and if the gas film resistance as estimated by the dimensionless correlations of mass transfer is

$$k_g = 0.008 \text{ ft/time}$$

(*b*) If gas film resistance were negligible, what would be the observed rate of reaction expressed on a mass basis?

Data: Bed porosity $= 0.33$
Diameter of spherical catalyst pellets $= \frac{1}{16}$ in.
Bulk density of bed $= 120 \text{ lb/ft}^3$

4. Derive Eqs. 16 and 17 either by combining the appropriate rate equations or by using the electrical resistance analog.

5. Derive Eq. 18 either by combining the appropriate rate equations or by using the electrical resistance analog.

6. While being shown around Lumphead Laboratories, you stop to view a packed-bed reactor used to obtain kinetic data. It consists of a glass column packed with 2 in. inert material, 1 in. active catalyst, then another 2 in. inert material. Should this be considered a differential or integral reactor?

7. What is the most reasonable interpretation of the data in Table P7*a* in terms of controlling resistances if (*a*) the catalyst is nonporous, (*b*) the catalyst is porous.

Table P7*a*

Run	Quantity of Catalyst	Feed Rate of Given Feed Material	Fractional Conversion of Reactant	Catalyst Diameter
1	10	10	0.06	1
2	30	30	0.06	1
3	30	30	0.02	3

(*c*) What can you tell about the controlling resistances and about catalyst porosity from the set of data in Table P7*b*?

Table P7*b*

Run	Quantity of Catalyst	Feed Rate of Given Feed Material	Fractional Conversion of Reactant	Catalyst Diameter
4	10	0.5	0.08	2
5	80	4	0.08	2
6	20	1	0.06	4
7	100	5	0.06	4

8. What can you tell about the controlling resistances and activation energy for the reaction from the data in Table P8? Is the catalyst porous?

Table P8

Run	Quantity of Catalyst	Feed Rate of Given Feed Material	Fractional Conversion of Reactant	Catalyst Diameter	Temperature, °C
1	10	5	0.08	1	344
2	9	3	0.06	2	344
3	12	6	0.08	2	372
4	18	9	0.08	2	372

9. A nonporous material which we suspect to be common gravel is claimed to accelerate the rate of reaction of A with B which normally proceeds homogeneously as follows: $A + B \rightarrow R$. To test this claim, two sets of runs are made in a tubular reactor using identical operating conditions of temperature, pressure, and feed composition (equimolar mixture of A, B, and inert). From the data in Table P9 is the claim justified and to what extent approximately does the claimed catalyst influence the rate of reaction?

Table P9

Run	Volumetric Feed Rate, cc/sec	Mole Fraction of R in Product Stream	
1	26	0.26	Empty reactor; void volume = 50 cc
2	57	0.14	
3	142	0.055	
4	20	0.21	Reactor packed with claimed catalyst; bed porosity = 0.36
5	38	0.12	
6	89	0.057	

10. Determine the order of reaction and size of reactor required for 35% conversion for the reaction of Example 1 with one modification. Take the stoichiometry to be $A \rightarrow R$.

Note: This is equivalent to ignoring density changes when analyzing the data of Example 1. Comparison of answers will show whether this simplified treatment significantly changes the answer.

11. Determine the approximate order of reaction and the size of reactor for 35% conversion for the reaction of Example 2 with one modification. Take the stoichiometry to be $A \rightarrow R$.

12. Because the catalytic reaction $A \rightleftharpoons R$ is highly exothermic with rate highly temperature-dependent, a long tubular flow reactor immersed in a trough

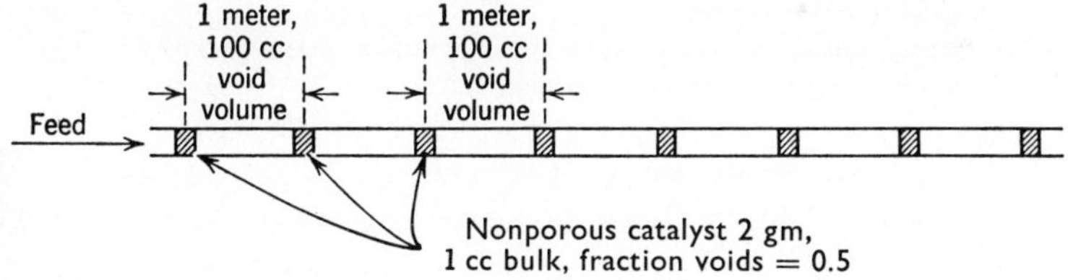

Fig. P12

of water, as shown in Fig. P12, is used to obtain essentially isothermal kinetic data. Pure A at 0°C and 1 atm flows through this tube at 10 cc/sec, and the stream composition is analyzed at various locations.

Distance from feed input, meters	0	12	24	36	48	60	72	84	∞
Partial pressure of A, mm Hg	760	600	475	390	320	275	240	215	150

(*a*) Determine the size of plug flow reactor operating at 0°C and 1 atm required to effect a 50% conversion of A to R for a feed rate of 200 lb moles A/hr.

(*b*) Suppose that this data had been obtained for a reaction whose stoichiometry is $A \rightleftharpoons 2.5R$.

Find the volume of reactor required for the same feed rate and conversion as given in part *a*.

13. A closed-loop experimental flow system as shown in Fig. P13 is used to study the kinetics of a catalytic flow reaction $A \rightleftharpoons R$. Pure A is introduced into

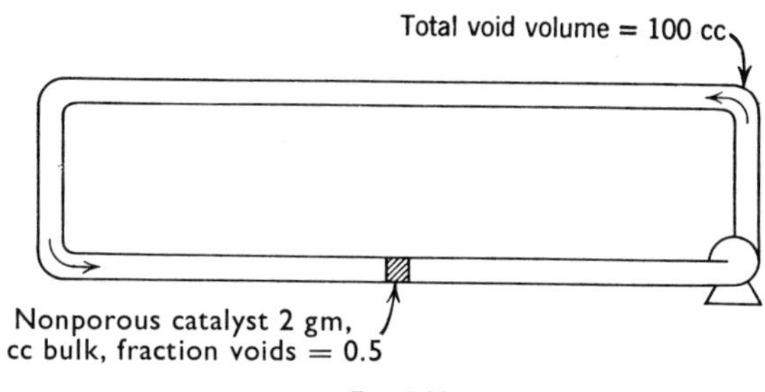

Fig. P13

the system and is circulated at 0°C and 1 atm at 10 cc/sec. The stream is analyzed from time to time with the following results:

Time, min	0	2	4	6	8	10	12	14	∞
Partial pressure of A, mm Hg	760	600	475	390	320	275	240	215	150

Assume plug flow throughout.

(*a*) Determine the size of a plug flow reactor operating at 0°C and 1 atm required to effect a 50% conversion of A to R for a feed rate of 200 lb moles pure A/hr.

(*b*) Repeat part *a* with the modification that an inert at a partial pressure of 1 atm is present in the closed loop so that the total pressure at the start is 2 atm.

See Butt et al. (1962) for an example of the use of this type of reactor.

14. Let the data of the previous problem be for a reaction with stoichiometry $A \rightleftharpoons 2.5R$, assuming plug flow throughout.

(*a*) Find the rate equation for the reaction based on both void volume and bulk volume of catalyst, using seconds for time.

(*b*) What would be the partial pressure of A in a very, very long plug flow reactor using feed of pure A at 0°C and 1 atm?

(*c*) Find the size of a plug flow reactor operating at 0°C and 1 atm required to effect a 50% conversion of A to R for a feed rate of 200 lb moles pure A/hr.

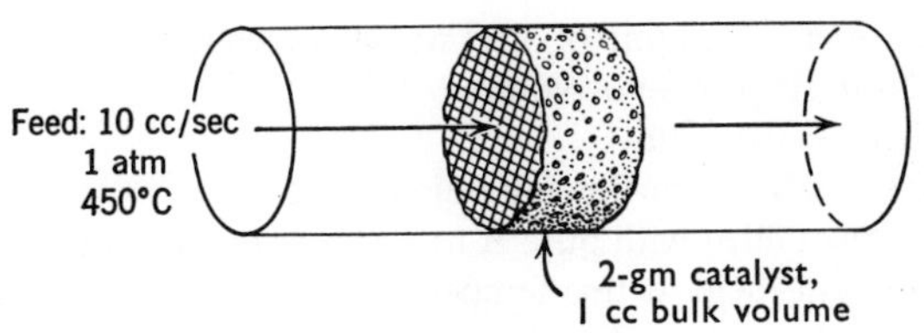

Fig. P15

15. An experimental setup as shown in Fig. P15 is used to study the kinetics of the gas-phase reaction $A \rightarrow R$. Feed at different stages of conversion is passed through the experimental setup, and the concentration of A is accurately determined upstream and downstream from the catalyst, with the results given in Table P15.

Table P15

p_A (upstream)	p_A (downstream)
760	754.2
650	645.8
600	596.4
500	497.5
450	448.0
400	398.4
350	348.8
300	299.1
200	199.6
100	99.9

(*a*) What is the rate equation (in concentration units and based on bulk volume of catalyst) for this reaction?

(*b*) Using the rate equation, find the size of plug flow reactor (ft^3) that would yield a 50% conversion of A for a feed rate of 200 lb moles A/hr.

(*c*) Repeat part *b* without using the rate equation but by direct graphical integration of the design equation.

16. The solid-catalyzed decomposition of gaseous A proceeds as follow :

$$A \rightarrow R + S, \qquad -r_A = kC_A^2$$

A tubular pilot plant reactor packed with 5 ft^3 of catalyst is fed 500 ft^3/hr of pure A at 300°C and 20 atm. Conversion of reactant is 65%.

In a larger plant it is desired to treat 8000 ft^3/hr of feed gases at 40 atm absolute pressure and 300°C containing 60% A and 40% diluents to obtain 85% conversion of A. Compute the internal volume of the reactor required.

17. The reaction $A \rightarrow R + S$ takes place only in the presence of a special catalyst and produces no side products. To study this reaction, an experimental reactor with an internal volume of 3 ft^3 was completely filled with this catalyst:

density = 130 lb/ft^3 of reactor volume
specific surface = 650 ft^2/lb
fraction voids available for flowing fluids = 0.57

The reactor was then filled with pure A to 2 atm pressure at 40°C. It was heated quickly to 400°C and held at this temperature, after which the pressure of the gas within the bomb was noted at 4 min intervals with the following results.

Time, min	4	8	12	16	20
Pressure, atm	4.75	5.50	6.28	7.00	7.72

(*a*) If a reactor with 400 ft^3 available for catalyst is fed pure A continuously at 20 atm absolute pressure and is operated at 400°C, compute the volume of A per minute that can be fed to the reactor at the reactor operating conditions if a 40% conversion is to be obtained.

(*b*) If a conversion of 80% is required, find the feed rate of A.

(*c*) How should the pressure be varied to increase the production rate of R and S.

Assume that plug flow conditions prevail in the flow reactor and that the same rate mechanism and rate laws hold in the batch and flow reactor.

(*d*) Discuss the adequacy and reasonableness of these assumptions.

18. Assume that the reaction

$$\underset{\text{butene}}{CH_2{=}CH{-}CH_2{-}CH_3} \rightarrow \underset{\text{butadiene}}{CH_2{=}CH{-}CH{=}CH_2} + H_2$$

is first order in the presence of a special catalyst and does not produce any side products.

An experimental reactor with an internal volume of 3 ft^3 is packed with this catalyst:

density = 70 lb/ft^3 of reactor volume
specific surface = 23 ft^2/lb
fraction voids available for flowing fluids = 0.57

and is then flushed out and filled with pure butene to 2 atm pressure at 40°C. The bomb is then heated quickly, essentially instantaneously, to 400°C and held at this temperature. After 8 min at 400°C the pressure in the bomb has risen to 6.01 atm absolute.

(*a*) If a reactor with 400 ft^3 available for catalyst is fed pure butene continuously at 20 atm absolute pressure and is operated at 400°C, compute the volume of butene that can be fed to the reactor at the reactor operating conditions if a 40% conversion is to be obtained.

(*b*) If a conversion of 80% is required, find the butene feed rate. Assume that plug flow conditions prevail in the flow reactor and that the same rate mechanism and rate laws hold in both batch and flow reactor.

(*c*) Discuss the adequacy and reasonableness of these assumptions.

19. The kinetics of the catalytically controlled gas-phase reaction $2A \rightarrow R$ is studied in a constant-volume batch reactor as follows. A small experimental reactor is filled with catalyst, the resulting void space being 48%. Pure A is introduced until the total pressure in the reactor is 2.5 atm at 40°C (p_{A0} = 1.5 atm). The reactor is then heated rapidly to 400°C and held at this temperature. The pressure of the gas in the bomb is recorded at definite time intervals, with the results shown in Table P19.

Table P19

Time, min	Total Pressure, atm
1	5.26
2	5.01
3	4.76
4	4.51
5	4.30
6	4.13
7	4.01
8	3.93
9	3.88
10	3.84
11	3.81

(*a*) For a feed rate of 150 lb moles A/hr, 25% inerts, at 40 atm pressure and 400°C, what size of plug flow reactor would give 90% conversion?
(*b*) Have you any suggestions on how to improve operations?
(*c*) How much smaller would the reactor need to be if the feed were pretreated so that the inerts constitute only 5% of the feed stream?
Assume that the ideal gas law holds and the fixed operating temperature is 400°C.

20. Table P20 summarizes the results of three series of runs in a packed-bed reactor on the solid-catalyzed first-order decomposition $A \rightarrow R \rightarrow S$.

Table P20

Size of Porous Catalyst, in.	Temperature of Run, °C	V/F_{A0}	$C_{R,max}/C_{A0} = C_{R,max}$
$\frac{1}{8}$	300	27	0.50
$\frac{1}{4}$	300	54	0.50
$\frac{1}{4}$	320	21	0.50

Further experiments anywhere between 200 and 340°C are planned to search for the conditions under which production of R is maximized. What operating conditions (catalyst size and temperature) should we explore, and what fractional yield or R may we expect to find?

21. Sulfur dioxide is converted into sulfur trioxide by the reaction

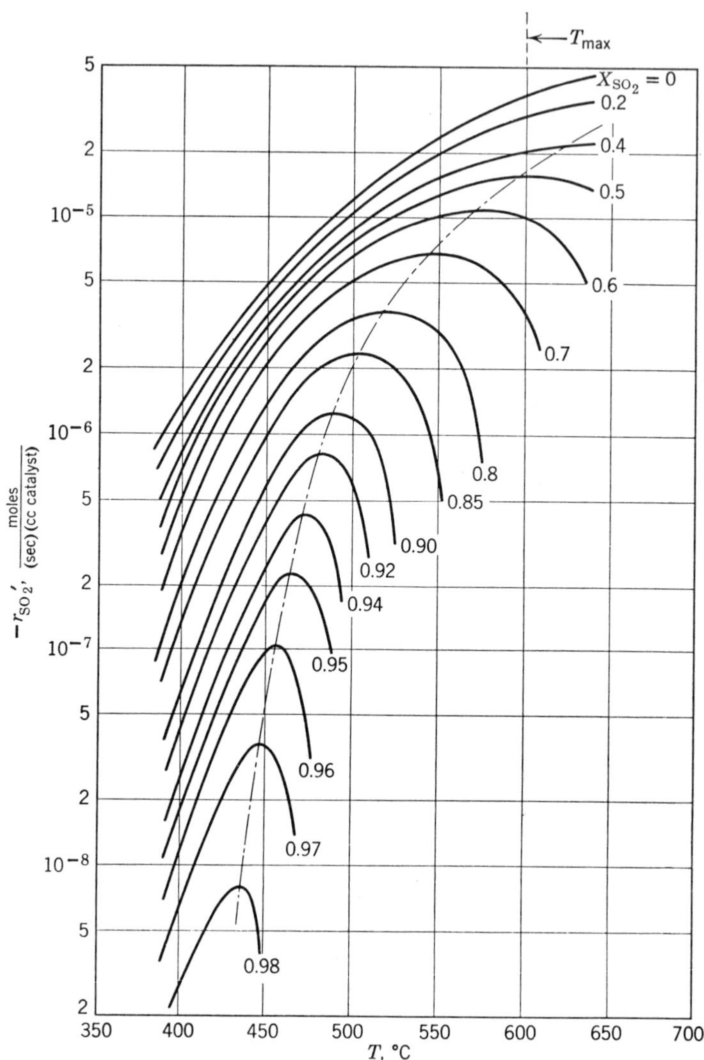

Fig. P21. From Kubota et al. (1961).

$2SO_2 + O_2 \rightarrow 2SO_3$. The kinetics of this reaction, using an industrial vanadium catalyst, has been studied by Kubota et al. (1959) for a feed consisting of 8% SO_2, 12% O_2, and 80% N_2 at an average pressure of 800 mm Hg. The rate of reaction as a function of temperature and fractional conversion of limiting reactant, SO_2, is summarized in Fig. P21.

We wish to compare the catalyst requirements of single and multistage fluidized-bed reactors and packed-bed reactors to effect 98% conversion of SO_2, limiting the maximum allowable operating temperature to 600°C. Assume plug flow in the packed bed and backmix flow in each of the fluidized beds.

Based on weight of catalyst required in a tubular reactor in which the optimum temperature progression through the reactor is used:

(*a*) Find the weight of catalyst required in a fluidized-bed reactor. At what temperature should this reactor be operated?

(*b*) Repeat part *a* using a two-stage (equal-sized) fluidized-bed reactor, each stage maintained at its optimum temperature. What are these temperatures?

(*c*) Repeat, using a two-stage fluidized-bed reactor, each stage of such size that the total amount of catalyst required is minimized. What should be the temperatures of the two stages?

22. A gaseous material decomposes according to the elementary reaction $2A \rightarrow R + S$ when in contact with a solid catalyst.

The kinetics of this reaction is investigated in a packed-bed reactor using $\frac{1}{8}$ in. spherical beads in the following manner. A 2-in. layer of noncatalytically active beads is laid down on a support. This is then followed by a $\frac{1}{2}$-in. layer of catalyst beads and in turn is followed by another 2-in. layer of nonactive beads. The 2-in. fore and after sections are to eliminate entrance and exit flow pattern disturbances. For a gas flow rate corresponding to a particle Reynolds number of 23, the reactant is 99% decomposed. Find the error in the calculated second-order rate constant which would result if plug flow is assumed. Assume isothermal conditions throughout.

23. On graduation you choose a position with the Clumsy Chemical Corporation, and you are immediately assigned to a small group (project leader and two technicians) which has just started work on the characteristics of a certain catalyst. The catalyst is manufactured only in the form of spherical pellets $\frac{1}{16}$, $\frac{1}{8}$, and $\frac{1}{4}$ in. in diameter.

The day you arrive you find yourself in charge of the group, since the group leader has come down with the flu. Data, taken in the experimental reactor the previous week, are brought to you for evaluation.

(*a*) From the data given in Table P23, what can you find out about the catalyst? Variables that may have to be considered include porosity of catalyst, bed backmixing, film and pore diffusion, adsorption, desorption, and surface reaction.

(*b*) The technicians will soon be here for instructions. What are your suggestions for the next set of experimental runs?

Data:

The reaction is of the type $A \rightarrow R$.

The temperature of all runs is 291°C.

The experimental section of the reactor is $1\frac{1}{2}$-in. i.d. and over 1 ft long.

No other units are given; however, you may consider that the tabulated values are all consistent. W = weight of catalyst.

You cannot tell on inspection whether the catalyst is porous or not.

Your stock of $\frac{1}{16}$-in. catalyst is exhausted.

Table P23

$W = 10$, $d_p = \frac{1}{4}$ in.

Run	F_{A0}	X_A
1	10	0.20
2	7	0.28
3	5	0.37
4	4	0.44
5	2.5	0.59
6	2	0.66
7	1.5	0.72

$W = 10$, $d_p = \frac{1}{8}$ in.

Run	F_{A0}	X_A
8	10	0.37
9	7	0.48
10	5	0.60
11	4	0.68
12	3	0.78
13	2	0.88
14	1.5	0.92

$W = 20$, $d_p = \frac{1}{4}$ in.

Run	F_{A0}	X_A
15	20	0.20
16	15	0.26
17	10	0.37
18	8	0.44
19	6	0.54
20	4	0.68
21	3	0.76

$W = 20$, $d_p = \frac{1}{8}$ in.

Run	F_{A0}	X_A
22	20	0.37
23	15	0.46
24	10	0.60
25	8	0.68
26	6	0.78
27	4	0.90
28	3	0.95

$W = 3$, $d_p = \frac{1}{16}$ in.

Run	F_{A0}	X_A
29	6	0.29
30	3	0.50
31	1.5	0.75
32	1	0.85

24. The solid-catalyzed first-order decomposition A $\rightarrow$ R $\rightarrow$ S is studied in a recycle reactor in which the recycle rate of fluid is at least 50 times the throughput rate. The results are summarized in Table P24.

Table P24

Size of Porous Catalyst, in.	Temperature or Runs, °C	τ, sec	$C_{R,max}/C_{A0}$
$\frac{1}{8}$	300	30	0.17
$\frac{1}{4}$	300	60	0.17
$\frac{1}{4}$	320	30	0.17

From these data an installation is planned to produce as much R as possible from a feed identical to that used in the experiments.

(*a*) Choose between a packed-bed or fluidized-bed reactor.
(*b*) Choose between $\frac{1}{4}$-in. and $\frac{1}{8}$-in. catalyst.
(*c*) In the range between 280 and 320°C select the operating temperature.
(*d*) Determine the space time.
(*e*) Predict $C_{R,max}/C_{A0}$.

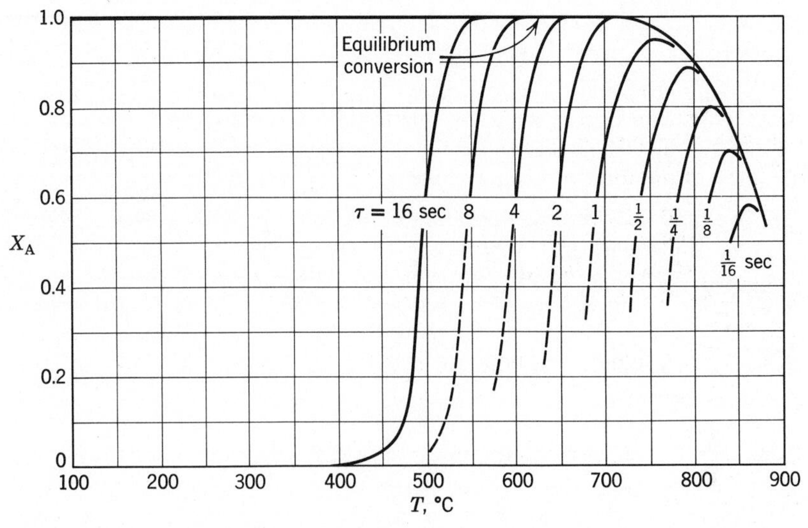

Fig. P25

25. Catalysts lose their effectiveness with use. This is the result of slow progressive poisoning and is manifested by a drop in rate constant for the reaction. Poisoning may be temporary, in which case regeneration will restore the catalyst's original activity, or it may be permanent, in which case a point is reached at which a given batch of catalyst must be replaced. Let us consider permanent poisoning in this problem.

A fluidized-bed reactor is being planned to effect a catalytic reaction, the fluidized solid being the catalyst.

Data: A is the limiting reactant, feed temperature is 160°F:

$$F_{A0} = 100 \text{ lb moles A/hr}$$
$$C_{A0} = 0.001 \text{ lb mole A/ft}^3$$
$$\tau = 16 \text{ sec, based on entering feed conditions}$$
$$\Delta H_r = -24{,}000 \text{ Btu/lb mole A (independent of temperature)}$$
$$C_{p,\text{mixture}} = 48 \text{ Btu/(lb mole A fed)(°F)}$$

The material balance curves for the kinetics of fresh catalyst are given in Fig. P25.

Experiments show that the reaction rate constant halves every two weeks because of poisoning.

When the conversion of A drops to 70%, the catalyst is replaced.

(*a*) How long can the process operate before the catalyst must be replaced?

(*b*) The maximum hourly heat load must be known for the proper design of the heat transfer coils. Determine this.

(*c*) Tabulate or plot the heat load and conversion at two-week intervals.
(*d*) What is the mean conversion of reactant A on a long-time basis?
For more on how to treat time-varying catalyst activity see Resnick (1960).

26. With cross flow absent, determine the conversion for catalytic first-order reactions occurring in the fluidized beds of models M1 to M5 and M8 of Table 9.1.

27. Where cross flow is absent, determine the conversion for homogeneous first-order reactions occurring in the fluidized beds of models M1, M2, . . . , M5 of Table 9.1. Let V' be the void volume in a phase, noting that this quantity is a function of the total volume of phase and volume of solids in a phase.

28. (*a*) Table P28 records data for the solid-catalyzed reaction $A \to R \to S$ occurring isothermally in an experimental recycle reactor. Under what conditions (what controlling resistance, packed or fluidized-bed operations) will the concentration of intermediate be maximized? What is the expected value of $C_{R,max}/C_{A0}$?
Note: It is not known whether the catalyst is porous or not.

Table P28

Size of Catalyst, in.	V/F_{A0}	$C_{R,max}/C_{A0}$
$\frac{1}{8}$	27	0.5
$\frac{1}{4}$	54	0.5

(*b*) Repeat part *a* if for both runs $V/F_{A0} = 27$ and $C_{R,max}/C_{A0} = 0.17$.

29. Find the mean activity of catalyst $\bar{k}$ in terms of the activity of fresh catalyst k_0, both in a single-stage reactor and in an equal-sized two-stage fluidized-bed reactor. Let $\bar{t}$ be the holding time of catalyst in the reactor, let t' be the time required for the activity of a particle of catalyst to drop halfway to its final value, and let the activity
(*a*) drop linearly with time,
(*b*) decay exponentially to zero,
(*c*) decay exponentially to a final activity k_e
Note: The first-order rate constant for the conversion of gas-phase reactant is a direct measure of the activity of the catalyst.

30. The catalytic gas-phase decomposition of A yields a variety of products which for the sake of simplicity can be designated as R (desired product) and S (undesired product). Under optimum conditions of maximum R yield, the stoichiometric relationship characterizing the over-all reaction is $A \to 0.8R + 3.2S$. This occurs in the presence of cadmium-impregnated WW pumice catalyst (porosity = 0.375) at 635°F.

Experimental studies in a constant-volume bomb at 635°F using a 50% A, 50% inert mixture give the following results:

Time, sec	0	30	60	90	120	150
Total pressure, atm	4.00	5.17	6.43	7.60	8.79	9.97

Six moles R/hr are to be produced from a feed of pure A ($4.00/mole) in a packed tubular reactor. Any pressure from atmospheric up to 20 atm absolute may be used. Naturally, the cost of reactor and supporting equipment will depend not only on its size but also on the pressure selected. This cost on an hourly basis is

$$\$2.00 + (\$0.03/\text{ft}^3)(\text{pressure in atm})^{0.6}, \qquad \pi \geqslant 1 \text{ atm}$$

and includes cost of catalyst replacement because of poisoning, etc.

(*a*) For optimum conditions assuming isothermal plug flow operations, find the operating pressure, the fractional conversion A, the size of reactor, and the unit cost of producing R.

(*b*) Feed consisting of 25% inerts instead of pure A can be purchased at $3.20/mole A. How would a change to this new feed affect the operations?

(*c*) If the stoichiometric equation were $A \rightarrow 0.8R + 0.2S$ and the rate equation were that of part *a*, in what way would this affect the answer to part *a*?

(*d*) If tracer experiments indicate that the flow pattern in the flow reactor can be approximated by simply assuming that one-sixth of the fluid bypasses the reactor completely, the rest passing through the catalyst in ordinary dispersed plug flow, how would this affect the answer to part *a*? Take particle Reynolds number = 350, particle size = 0.25 in., reactor diameter = 4 ft.

NAME INDEX

SUBJECT INDEX